OF
TIME
AND
PLACE

The Fountainhead Series

JAMES E. MILLER, JR.
Department Chairman and Professor of English, University of Chicago.
Fulbright Lecturer in American Literature: Oriental Institute, Naples, and the
University of Rome, 1958-1959; University of Kyoto and Doshisha University,
Kyoto, Japan, 1968. President of the National Council of Teachers of English,
1970. Awarded a Guggenheim Fellowship, 1969-70. Author of *F. Scott
Fitzgerald: His Art and His Techniques, Quests Surd and Absurd: Essays in
American Literature,* and *Word, Self, Reality: The Rhetoric of Imagination.*

ROBERT O'NEAL
Humanities Coordinator for the Indiana Humanities Project. Former Pro-
fessor and Chairman, English, Journalism, and Humanities, at San Antonio
College, and at Berry College, Georgia. Lecturer, Georgia Institute of Higher
Education. Author of *Teachers' Guide to World Literature for the High
School,* (N.C.T.E.), and co-author and photographer of *English for You.*

HELEN M.McDONNELL
English Supervisor, Ocean Township Junior and Senior High Schools,
Oakhurst, New Jersey. Immediate past chairman, Committee on Comparative
and World Literature, National Council of Teachers of English. Contributor of
articles to *Scholastic Teacher, New Educational Materials,* and other
professional magazines.

OF TIME
AND PLACE

Comparative World Literature In Translation

Introduction: W. H. AUDEN

Scott, Foresman and Company

Editorial Offices: Glenview, Illinois

Regional Sales Offices: Palo Alto, California ·
Tucker, Georgia · Glenview, Illinois ·
Oakland, New Jersey · Dallas, Texas

The authors and editors of *Of Time and Place* wish
to express their appreciation to the following teachers. Acting as
reader-consultants, they chose from the many selections submitted to
them those that they believed were more relevant to the interests and
needs of today's youth. They tested their opinions against classroom
use and contributed ideas that evolved during the give-and-take of
class discussion.

SISTER EUGENE FOX, S.C.
Denver, Colorado

MR. THOMAS GAGE
Arcata, California

MRS. JEANNE LUCKETT
Jackson, Mississippi

MRS. ELIZABETH DRUM McDOWELL
Nashville, Tennessee

MR. RONALD MIDKIFF
Rome, Georgia

MR. ELMER E. MOORE, JR.
Dobbs Ferry, New York

MR. ROBERT ROMANO
Wilmington, Massachusetts

Cover: MODERN TECHNIQUES IN
THE SERVICE OF MAN, a tapestry by
Maurice Andres. Courtesy of Edita S.A., Lausanne.

ISBN: 0-673-10435-4
1987 Impression.
Copyright ⟨ 1976 Scott, Foresman and Company.
Previous edition copyright ⟨ 1970 Scott, Foresman and Company
under the title *Man in Literature Comparative World
Studies in Translation.*
All Rights Reserved.
Printed in the United States of America.

910-VHP-9190898887

CONTENTS

Translation
An Essay by W. H. Auden

To translate means to serve two masters—something nobody can do. Hence, as is true of all things that in theory no one can do—it becomes in practice everybody's job. Everyone must translate and everyone does translate.

FRANZ ROSENZWEIG

I remember saying to Anatole France that translation was an impossible thing. He replied: "Precisely, my friend; the recognition of that truth is a necessary preliminary to success in the art."

J. LEWIS MAY

COMMUNICATION CODES AND PERSONAL SPEECH

Each of us is at one and the same time both an individual, a member of the human race and of a certain society, and also a unique person. The term individual is both a biological description—*a* man, *a* woman, *a* child—and a social-cultural one—*an* American, *an* Englishman, *a* lawyer, *a* doctor. As individuals we are the result of natural selection, sexual reproduction and social conditioning. The society or societies to which we belong, however, must be called corporate persons. On the other hand no two individuals are identical. Each of us is also a unique person who can say "I," choose to do this rather than that, and accept the responsibility for the consequences, whatever they may turn out to be. As persons we are called into being, not by any biological process, but by other persons—our parents, our siblings, our friends, our enemies.

Human beings, therefore, use words for two purposes which, though they often overlap, are quite different. As individuals we use words to request and supply information which it is essential for us to know if we are to survive and function properly. Many, perhaps most, animals have such a code—auditory or visual or olfactory signals by which they communicate vital information about food, sex, territory, the presence of enemies. Our use of words as a code is best illustrated by phrase books for tourists abroad, giving the equivalents in other languages for such remarks as:

> Where is the railroad station?
> What time is it?
> I want a double-room with bath.
> How much is that?

Provided that the way of living and the social needs of two linguistic groups are more or less the same, exact translation from one language into another is possible. Provided a culture is technologically advanced enough to have a railroad, it will have

---

Winner of a Pulitzer Prize in Poetry, W. H. Auden is also noted as critic, translator, and dramatist. Among his numerous publications are: The Age of Anxiety *(poetry),* The Shield of Achilles *(poetry),* The Collected Poetry of W. H. Auden, *and* The Dyer's Hand *(critical essays).*

a word meaning *station*; provided it has a money economy, it will be possible to translate the value of one currency into the other.

But, as we have seen, every society is a corporate person; that is to say every society holds certain general ideas about the nature of man, the world, good and evil, which its individual members take for granted, but which may and, to some degree, always do differ from those of other societies. Here problems of translation begin to arise.

During World War II Roosevelt and Churchill announced as their peace aims the Four Freedoms—Freedom of Speech, Freedom from Fear, etc.—but in scarcely any other language except English can the concept of freedom *from* be exactly translated. Then, anyone whose mother tongue is English and who starts to learn another language very soon discovers words for which we have no exact equivalent so that, when we attempt to translate them, we must either use different English words according to the context, or, in despair, use the foreign word. How, for example, is one to translate the Greek word *polis* or the French word *esprit* or the German word *Schadenfreude*?

As persons we are capable, as the other animals are not, of personal speech. In speech one unique person addresses another unique person by choice—he could have remained silent. We speak as persons because we desire to disclose ourselves to each other and to share our experiences, not because we must, but because we enjoy sharing them. When we genuinely speak, we do not have the words ready to do our bidding; we have to find them, we do not know exactly what we are going to say until we have said it, and we say something new that has never been said in exactly the same way before.

This means that, even if speaker and listener use the same language, they both have to translate, for no two persons speak their mother-tongue in exactly the same way. Suppose, for example, a friend tells me that he has fallen in love. In order to understand him, I have to ask myself two questions. Firstly: "Have I had an experience similar to the one he is describing?" Secondly: "If so, is it the experience I myself would describe as falling in love?" Furthermore, if I am fully to understand either his experience or my own, I must know something about the history of the concept of "falling in love" as it has developed in Western culture, and try to imagine what sense of our experiences people would make who belong to cultures where the concept is unknown.

LANGUAGE AND TIME

The author of a literary work writes, consciously at any rate, for an audience who not only speak the same tongue but are also his contemporaries. His translator does the same, only now both the tongue and the times are different. How is the translator to find words in his own language which will convey to his contemporaries the same meaning and emotional overtones which the original had for the author's? Any answer will be guesswork.

Take, for example, the two biblical words *ecclesia* and *presbuteros*, usually translated as *church* and *priest*. In Tyndale's translation of the Bible they become *congregation* and *elder*. Tyndale felt that, in the sixteenth century, the conventional terms would be taken to mean what they meant to Roman Catholics. As a Protestant, he was convinced that the Roman Church had perverted the true Christian faith, that the Apostles and the Early Christians would have been horrified by what the Roman Church and its hierarchy had become. Others, not all of them Catholics, preferred the old terms. Who can say for certain which was right?

Again, take this phrase from Vergil: "Rosea cervice refulsit." Dryden translates it as:
    She turned and made appear
    Her neck refulgent.

Here I think one may say with certainty that Dryden has made a mistake. To be sure, the English word *refulgent* is etymologically derived from the Latin, but it has a neo-classical tone which *refulsit* cannot have had for Vergil's contemporaries. To them, I believe, the effect must have been much nearer that conveyed by Gavin Douglas' translation:

> Her nek schane like unto the rois in May

even though no month is mentioned in the original.

One translator of Homer, in an attempt to enable the monolingual reader "to smack the sound, if not the full sense of the Greek," even went so far as to write *hydropot* for "water-drinker."

THE GOAL OF THE TRANSLATOR

A translation in the proper sense is not a "trot." A trot is like a pair of spectacles for the weak-sighted; a translation is like a book in Braille for the blind. The translator, that is to say, has to assume that his readers cannot and probably never will be able to read the original.

As a general rule, I believe that translation should be a work of collaboration. The person responsible for the final version into English, let us say, must not only possess English as his mother-tongue; he must also be a master of it, alive to its subtlest nuances. But very few writers who are masters of their own tongue have equal mastery over another. As his collaborator, therefore, he needs a person who knows some English but whose mother-tongue is the original, or, in the case of dead languages like Greek and Latin, a first-rate philological scholar.

Once, either by himself, or with the help of a collaborator, the translator has learned exactly *what* his author says, his real task begins, the task of capturing in his own tongue the author's tone of voice. Let us say he is translating Goethe. The question he must ask and try as far as possible to answer is: "What, without ceasing to be himself, would Goethe have written, had he thought and written in English?"

In poetry form and content, sound and sense are as inseparable a unity as body and soul, so that any verse translation is to some degree an "imitation" rather than a translation. A poet's imagery can usually be accurately translated because it is derived from sensory perceptions common to all men, whatever language they speak. But effects which depend upon language, like rhymes and puns, are not reproducible. For instance, in no other tongue but English can one make this joke of Hilaire Belloc's:

> When I am dead, I hope it may be said:
> His sins were scarlet, but his books were read.

Then there are the problems of prosody and meter. Even when two languages possess the same metrical form—sonnets have been written in nearly all European languages—exact copying is very difficult. German and Italian, for example, are polysyllabic and highly inflected; English contains many more monosyllabic words and has very few inflections. In the case of languages like Greek and Latin, whose prosodies are based, not as ours upon stressed and unstressed syllables, but upon long and short syllables, the wise translator will forget all about the original meter.

However closely the verse translator may strive to reproduce what the original says, his first obligation is to produce a good English poem. In trying to do so, he cannot escape from the aesthetic presuppositions of his age as to what is truly "poetic" in form and diction. Thus Dryden translated Vergil and Pope translated Homer into heroic couplets, and it would never have occurred to them to do anything else since, in their time, the heroic couplet was considered the only possible medium for a long serious poem. Again, until this century the only kind of unrhymed verse which was considered to be poetry was the five-foot iambic line of blank verse. It is only since poets have started to write English poems of their own in looser unrhymed forms, that, as translators, they have been able to make similar experiments.

It follows from all this that there cannot be a definitive translation of any important poem which will do for all time. Every generation has to make its own version.

The concluding stanza of Horace's Ode 7, Book IV, runs thus:

> Infernis neque enim tenebris Diana pudicum
> liberat Hippolytum,
> nec Letheae valet Theseus abrumpere caro
> vincula Piritheo.

The meter here consists of a dactylic hexameter followed by the second half-line of a pentameter. For it, the Loeb "trot" runs:

> For Diana releases not the chaste Hippolytus from the nether darkness, nor
> has Theseus power to break the Lethean chains of his dear Pirithous.

Here are three versions, one from the eighteenth century, one from the late nineteenth, and the third from the last decade.

> Hippolytus, unjustly slain,
> Diana calls to life in vain;
> Nor can the might of Theseus rend
> The chains of hell that hold his friend.
> SAMUEL JOHNSON

> Night holds Hippolytus the pure of stain,
> Diana steads him nothing, he must stay;
> And Theseus leaves Pirithous in the chain
> The love of comrades cannot take away.
> A. E. HOUSMAN

> Great is the power of Diana and chaste was Hippolytus, yet still
> Prisoned in darkness he lies.
> Passionate Theseus was, yet could not shatter the chains
> Forged for his Pirithous.
> JAMES MICHIE

None of these versions is without merit. It may be noted that the contemporary acceptance of free verse has allowed Mr. Michie to approximate to the original meter. It is rather curious, too, that the version which departs most widely from the Latin is Housman's, who was the greatest Latin scholar of his day. This is not necessarily a criticism. Some English poems which have most successfully captured the *spirit* of poets like Horace and Juvenal have been imitations *after* Horace or Juvenal which made no attempt to reproduce the original exactly. Not only can there be no definitive verse translation, but also each translator has to follow his own taste in poetry. As Arthur Waley has written: "The translator must use the tools he knows best how to handle. What matters is that a translator should have been excited by the work he translates, should be haunted day and night by the feeling that he must put it into his own language."

PICTURE RELIEF WITH PUPPETS by Aika Brown. Courtesy of the Israel Museum, Jerusalem.

The Righteous

The Trap

IGNAZIO SILONE[1]/ Italy
(1900–1978)

translated from the Italian by Samuel Putnam

Daniel was still out at the pig-sty, looking after the sow who was having young ones, when someone called to him from the house thirty yards away. He had much to do yet, and had told them once that he did not care to be disturbed; so he did not answer. It was Daniel's wife, Filomena; she had called him two or three times.

"Daniel! Oh, Daniel! There's someone wants to talk to you." When she received no reply, she was silent.

Daniel had done all he could to see that the sow had an easy time of it; but that is the sort of thing you can never be sure about. The night before, he had put the animal on a strict diet and, by way of further precaution, had given her a strenuous castor-oil enema. What he feared more than anything else was that she would become constipated, which might result in a paralysis of the lower regions and the drying up of her milk. He had summoned to help him one Agostino, a native of Bergamo,[2] who had lived at Ticino[3] for a number of years. Agostino was a mason by trade, but in the off-season he was a man of all work.

Things had started off well. Three pigs had already made their appearance, looking like three enormous rats emerging from a bloody flask. Agostino's chief concern was with finding a suitable name for each. The fourth one was slow in coming, and while Agostino held its snout, Daniel had to draw the young one out, leaving the way open for the others.

"We ought to call this one Benito,"[4] suggested Agostino.

"Nothing doing!" replied Daniel. "These pigs have already been sold to an Italian firm."

"You haven't the nerve!" said the man from Bergamo.

At this point, the voice of Daniel's younger daughter, Luisa, was heard.

"Daddy! There's someone wants to talk to you!"

Daniel meanwhile went on with the umbilical dressings of the young pigs, which was to avoid infection. Had he not already told them at the house that he did not want to be bothered by anything but his work? Again he made no reply. He put the young animals in a large wooden crate lined with straw and covered them over with a woolen blanket, while Agostino saw to the cleaning of the pig-sty and the removing of the evidences of the obstetrical operation. Silvia, Daniel's elder daughter, now called from the path which ran down to the pig-sty.

"Daddy! There's someone here who wants to speak to you!"

"The Trap" by Ignazio Silone, translated by Samuel Putnam from SHORT FICTION OF THE MASTERS, edited by Leo Hamalian and Frederick R. Karl. Copyright © 1963 by G. P. Putnam's Sons.
1. *Silone* (si lō′ nē). **2.** *Bergamo* (ber′ gä mô), a town twenty-five miles northeast of Milan, Italy. **3.** *Ticino* (tē chē′ nô), a canton in Switzerland including the towns of Ascona and Bellinzona. Unless otherwise indicated, all of the towns mentioned in the story are in Switzerland. **4.** *Benito*, a reference to Benito Mussolini, leader of the Fascist movement, who governed Italy as Prime Minister from 1922 to 1943, but who was in fact dictator from 1925 until his death.

Silvia was accompanied by Caterina, the seamstress, an old lady from the province of Florence, who had been a dressmaker at Minusio for years, but who earned the better part of her living by going around from house to house and doing mending. When Daniel saw Caterina, he was annoyed.

"Is that why you've been yelling at me for the last hour?" he demanded. For Caterina was not exactly what you would call a person of few words.

"Caterina wants to talk to you," Silvia went on, taking no notice of her father's reproof. Agostino and Silvia went off toward the house, and Caterina was left alone with Daniel.

"You know very well," Caterina began, "that I have always attended strictly to my own business—"

"That's no business of mine," said Daniel; his tone was anything but encouraging.

"Well, you know, don't you, that all the years I've lived at Ticino I've never meddled with other people's affairs?"

"That doesn't concern me," said Daniel as he made for the house.

When she saw that he had no intention of listening to her, Caterina abandoned all preliminaries and got down to facts.

"An Italian gentleman has just been to see me," she said; "he made me a proposition; he wants me to play the spy!"

Daniel stopped short. Caterina caught her breath and then went on to tell about the call she had received from this gentleman, whom she had met once by chance in an office at Locarno.

"'You've lived here at Ticino for a good many years,' he said to me, 'you ought to know everybody. Your business takes you everywhere, into any number of homes; you listen to any number of conversations. You're an old woman and alone in the world; no one is afraid to talk in front of you—' I told him that everybody certainly did respect me, because I've always minded my own business. He kept on talking that way, and then at last he said:

'If you've a mind to get certain information for me concerning the activities of some of the anti-Fascist Italians here in Ticino, between Ascona and Bellinzona, you can earn a little something that will make it easier for you in your old age—'"

Daniel had recovered from his surprise and was watching Caterina closely as, trembling and sighing, she went on with her story.

"Why did you come to me?" he wanted to know.

"Why did I come to you?" Caterina echoed.

"I am a native of Ticino," said Daniel, "and the affairs of these Italians don't interest me; that's the reason I'd like to know why you came to me. Who sent you?"

The old lady was taken aback.

"What do you mean?" she stammered. "You've known me for thirty years. You know that I've always been a hard worker and have always minded my own business."

"What I want to know," Daniel broke in on her, raising his voice, "what I want to know is, who sent you here?"

"Nobody!" Caterina insisted. "I'm sorry to have bothered you; I'll be going."

Caterina took the foot-path which skirted Daniel's house and which came out on the Gordola-Minusio highway. Daniel followed her and, after a bit, resumed the discussion.

"If no one sent you, then why did you come?"

"I wanted some advice," said Caterina, and she kept on walking.

"What kind of advice?"

"Whether or not I should accept the gentleman's offer." The old lady came to a stop. "I don't know what to do. I never was in such a predicament in all my life. If I accept, I'll earn something substantial, but by doing harm to those who have never harmed me. If I refuse, they're sure to look on me as an anti-Fascist and persecute me every way they can. You've known me for thirty years. You know that

I'm neither a Fascist nor an anti-Fascist. You know that I've always been a hard worker and minded my business."

Daniel was lost in thought for a moment. Caterina started to walk away again, sighing resignedly. Once more he followed her. At the end of the path, Agostino was waiting.

"I'll tell you what," Daniel suddenly said to her, "you needn't be afraid. So long as you're honest you have nothing to fear. Tell Agostino what you've just told me and do as he says."

He watched the pair as they went down the road in the direction of Gordola; then he turned back to the pig-sty, to look after the sow.

It was one morning while Daniel was at work with his daughter Silvia on the vines in the arbor that Agostino went past again for the first time. The vines were being eaten by an insect which had bored its way through the bark, and Daniel had wanted to take advantage of a free morning to get at them. He would run a metal scraper over the ailing stalks in such a manner as to remove the bark and lay bare the hidden chrysalises, and Silvia would come after him to sprinkle the shoots with boiling water. It was at this time that Agostino went by upon a truckload of brick and shouted to Daniel:

"Did you hear about it? That business is coming along!"

"What business?" Daniel answered him, although he understood well enough what Agostino meant.

"You know, that business we were talking about!" And Agostino gave a wave of his hand as the truck disappeared down the road. Daniel shook his head.

"Those Italians are all right," he remarked, turning to his daughter. "Bighearted, impulsive, never think of danger—but they talk too much!"

"Listen, Daddy," said Silvia, plucking up courage at this point to voice a wish she had been cherishing for a long time, "I know that, though you don't say anything about it, you are doing a great deal to help free Italy, and I too would like so much to help!"

"Silvia," was her father's reply, "I wish you would pick up the pieces of bark which I have chipped off the vines, and which are lying around on the ground here, and burn them. That is all you have to do just now!"

His daughter obeyed. Daniel watched her as she went about the arbor, bending down at the foot of each vine and gathering up in her apron the tiny pieces of bark. Silvia had been twenty last November. And there was pride and trepidation in her father's glance as it rested on her. She was the dearest thing in his life, and the one over which hung the greatest threat.

Some days afterward Agostino came past a second time, one Sunday morning. Daniel and Filomena were talking with a woman who was telling them how, at Cadenazzo and at Robasacco, the night before, a number of hen-houses had been raided by foxes.

"They found fifty hens with their throats slit and their blood sucked!" The woman was precise regarding details.

"If that's the case," Daniel disagreed, "then it's not a fox but a polecat."

At this point, a chauffeur from Cadenazzo came past and they put the question up to him.

"It's a fox," declared the chauffeur, "and maybe more than one. In one henhouse, all they found left was a bunch of wing-feathers."

"We'll have to be looking after our hens," said Filomena to Daniel. "Last year they were sick, and this year, of course, it would have to be foxes!"

"The thing to do," suggested Daniel, "is to set a trap."

Agostino now arrived on the scene.

"It's coming to a head," he said to Daniel, calling him over to one side. "Caterina did what I told her to, and that fellow from the police has swallowed the hook. We'll have to be on the watch now!"

"What are you thinking about doing?" inquired Daniel.

"The thing to do is to set a trap," Agostino answered.

Daniel burst out laughing when he heard the word trap, and Filomena, who had caught nothing more than the word, now took a hand in the conversation.

"A trap's not always enough," she observed, turning to Agostino. "The fox is too wise for that. Almost always, before nibbling at the bait, he feels all around it, and he doesn't take it in his mouth right away but joggles it about and draws it over to him with his paw. It's all right to set a trap, but it's a good thing to put a little poisoned food around the hen-house at the same time."

Agostino did not get the drift at first.

"But you can't be sure of poison, even," said Daniel to his wife; "a fox has to be pretty hungry if, when he's near a hen-house, he wastes any time in picking up what's lying around on the ground. And even if he eats a piece of poisoned meat or a few chestnuts soaked in strychnine, you can't be sure then. No one has ever yet found just the right dose of strychnine to give a fox, when you don't know what kind of a fox it is. If he's big and strong, and there isn't much strychnine, all he gets is a little belly-ache, which doesn't keep him from eating the hens; but if it's a strong dose, he'll vomit it up right away, get it off his stomach, and have all the keener an appetite for chickens."

"It seems, then, there's no chance of catching a fox!" Agostino had finally realized what it was they had been talking about before he came.

"There is a chance," said Daniel, "but it's not easy. And anyway," he added, "no fox ever yet was caught by talking about it."

Filomena now went back into the house, for Luisa, the younger daughter, had called her; and the two men went out into the garden back of the house to continue their conversation.

"Caterina," Agostino was saying, "after many qualms and no end of holding back, has finally taken the job of spying on the work that we are doing here in Locarno. That fellow from the Italian police came to see her again yesterday and left her an address in Pallanza to which she is to write in case she has any information to give him."

"He didn't tell Caterina who the persons are she is supposed to spy on?" asked Daniel.

"It seems not, for the present," said Agostino, "but he told her in a general way that she was to get the names of all those Italian migratory workers who are all the time crossing the border into Switzerland and who there are in touch with revolutionary circles. He told her also that she could make a nice little sum of money if she would help him track down those who are responsible for smuggling revolutionary books and publications into Italy."

"He didn't say who it was he suspected of doing that?"

"Apparently not," said Agostino, "from the story that Caterina gave me." And then he went on: "I had to promise Caterina that, in case of any trouble, we'd see to it that she got out all right; I told her we'd provide her with the means to go to Zurich and live. For the thirty years she's been here in Ticino, as you know, that's all she's dreamed of, to be able to live in Zurich."

"Does Caterina suspect that I have any connection with the Italian revolutionists?"

"You can put that out of your head," Agostino assured him. "Every time she's talked to me—you know Caterina, with a sigh after every other word—she's told me how she has always minded her own affairs and always means to, and how Mr. Daniel, fine man that he is, is one Ticinese who has never meddled in politics, she can swear to that—"

Silvia, from the window of her room, had caught sight of her father and Agostino at the far end of the garden.

"May I come down?" she called to her father.

"Of course!" the two men replied.

The girl left the house and came down the garden path. As she reached them, the pair changed the conversation and began talking about the weather.

Every night Daniel set a trap at the entrance to the hen-house and put some poisoned food about, but no fox came. And Agostino's fox seemingly was in no more of a hurry to set foot in the man from Bergamo's trap, for Daniel had heard no more about it.

"A farmer's life," he would say, "is one continual war with the weather and with animal parasites, but the hardest war of all is the one against the fox."

The work of scraping the vines had been finished, and he now began on the fruit trees. He would clean the trunks of their dried branches, dead bark, and moss, by way of uncovering the parasites' nests. Wherever there was a hole surrounded by a little streak of red, Silvia would then insert an iron wire to kill the wood-worm hidden at the bottom. When the cleaning was finished, Filomena came with a pail of lime, and each trunk was given a white-washing to the height of a man's head.

"The trees," observed Daniel, "are now protected on the earth side, but who is going to protect them from the heavens?"

Agostino, exchanging pleasantries with Luisa, was waiting for Daniel at the door of the house.

"What's new?" was Daniel's question.

"The trap is ready!" the man from Bergamo replied.

"And the fox, what about him?"

"He'll be there tonight!"

"If only we could finish off all the foxes at once!" Daniel exclaimed.

Agostino then proceeded to inform Daniel of the way in which the provocateur was to be trapped.

"Caterina has written him that she has important information to give him, and she's made an appointment for nine o'clock tonight, at Rivapiana, down by the lake, opposite the old chapel of San Quirico. Caterina will be there, and I mean to be there too, with a couple of others."

"But don't you think," said Daniel, "that it might be well to notify the police?"

"That wouldn't be wise at all," said Agostino, "The consulate might get wind of it right away, and the fox wouldn't show up."

Daniel could not very well offer an objection to this, seeing that a number of subordinates among the police were suspected of being disloyal. The thing that worried him more than anything else was the possible trouble that might be caused the Italian emigrants.

"It ought to be done by Ticinesi!" said Daniel; but Agostino was not of this opinion.

"Too many people would be in on it then; and what's more, an Italian fox—an Italian trap!"

That evening Daniel took the train for Locarno; and along about ten o'clock he started strolling along the lake toward Saleggi, as he waited for Agostino, who was to let him know how the thing had turned out. About half-past ten, in place of Agostino, there appeared one Lucca, an Italian carpenter who lived at Minusio.

"Agostino," he told Daniel, "has been slightly wounded in one hand, and so he did not come, because he did not want to attract attention by going around with a bandaged hand."

"And what about the other man?"

"We left him lying on the ground! He came to keep the appointment with a couple of others, who went off and left him alone with Caterina, saying they would be back in an hour. We were in behind San Quirico, and we waited until they were a good distance away—they left in the direction of Navigia. In the meantime, Caterina, with her usual tears and sighs, was filling the informer with all sorts of foolishness, telling him over and over again how she had never in all her life meddled with anyone's business but her own and never would, but how all the same she had discovered, beyond any doubt, that revolutionary books and magazines to be taken into Italy were being deposited in the Franciscan Convent at Madonna del Sasso, up above Locarno."

Daniel had a good laugh at this.

"Agostino went up alone at first," Lucca went on, "leaving us there behind the church. It had been agreed that he was to make use of his revolver only in case the fellow tried to take him. He acted as if he just happened to be passing. As it was dark, he lighted a cigarette, and pretended to recognize the stranger by the glow of the match. 'Ha!' he called out, and then the rumpus began. We came out of our hiding place, while Caterina took to her heels."

"Did you have a hand in it, too?"

"Oh, there wasn't any need of that. All we did was keep a watch to see that nobody came. Agostino soon enough had the best of him. He threw him to the ground and held him with his knee and then started pounding his face as if he were crushing stone. We knew how strong Agostino was, but we never knew how much hate he had in him—"

"You mustn't forget," Daniel reminded Lucca, "that the Fascists killed Agostino's brother! You say he was wounded in the hand?"

"Yes, the spy bit him. He got Agostino's hand between his teeth and wouldn't let go. With his free hand Agostino was pounding the fellow on the jaw like a madman, but the spy held on with his teeth. Then Agostino took him by the throat and choked him just about to death."

"Did he finish him?" Daniel was alarmed.

"I think he did."

"Then Agostino in all probability will have to clear out of the country," Daniel said. "He may have to go to France—"

In view of the unforeseen turn which events had taken, Daniel made up his mind to spend the night at Locarno and to go to Bellinzona the following morning. In order that his family might not be worried about him, he went into a café and telephoned to Silvia.

"It's a lucky thing you called," his daughter said. "I've been trying for an hour to reach you, everywhere in Locarno where you're known—"

"Why, what's happened?" Daniel asked in some alarm.

"Nothing at our house," Silvia hastened to reassure him. "But not far away, on the Gordola road, there's been an automobile collision and one man was seriously injured. They got a doctor as quick as they could, and the doctor said his injuries were so serious that it would be dangerous to move him very far. They inquired in a number of houses whether they could take him in; but you know very well that, here in our neighborhood, there are nothing but hovels, like stables. And so the neighbors assured them that our house was the only possible one. Mother, to tell the truth, was rather put out about it; she said that, you being away from home, we couldn't very well take in a stranger, but I told her that I knew you would approve of it—"

"Certainly!" Daniel interrupted her. "Where did you put him?"

"In my room, on the second floor," said Silvia. "I'll sleep with Luisa; she'll be only too glad to have me."

"Is he in danger of death?"

"The doctor wouldn't say as to that. He said that he would send a nurse in this very night, although I told him that I could do everything that was necessary without any help."

"Where is he from? What's his name?" Daniel questioned her further.

"The poor fellow can't talk yet," his daughter explained. "He must come from a well-to-do family, though, for the doctor insisted that mother accept something as a deposit, to cover any expense that we might be put to."

"I'm really very sorry," said Daniel in conclusion, "that I can't come home tonight; but I'm staying over in Locarno, and tomorrow morning I'm going to Bellinzona, on some business that can't be put off. I leave everything to you; be a good girl and do whatever the doctor tells you to."

Daniel telephoned from Bellinzona the next day to find out if the injured man was still alive. It was Luisa who answered the phone, as Silvia had gone out to make a few purchases.

"He's a little better," said the young girl. "A nurse came in an automobile last night, but Silvia insisted on staying up anyway—and now the doctor's here again."

The doctor came to the telephone.

"Doctor, I want you to make yourself perfectly at home in my house," Daniel said to him. "I regret very much having to be so far from home at a time like this."

"I think the patient may be considered out of danger," the physician replied. "He's had rather a severe cerebral shake-up, but I don't look for any complications. So far as your family is concerned, I will take care of everything."

"Who is he?" inquired Daniel. "Where are his people?"

"He is Umberto Stella, an Italian engineer from Bologna. You may have heard the name. He came to Switzerland to make a study of certain hydroelectric plants."

"Whoever he may be," said Daniel, "I want you to feel that my house and my family are at your disposal."

At Bellinzona Daniel at once set about endeavoring to find out just what course the authorities might have taken in their investigation of the semi-homicidal affair at Rivapiana. He prudently refrained from bringing up the subject himself, leaving to others to speak of it first. With such an object in view, he called on his lawyer and went with him to the courthouse, by way of settling certain formalities which, as it happened, were not at all pressing. He stopped everyone he knew on the street. He bought a couple of morning newspapers but found in them not the slightest allusion to what had occurred the evening before. It was evident that nothing whatever was known of the affair at Bellinzona. Upon finding himself alone with his lawyer, he finally ventured a hint.

"I hear," he began, "that there was some kind of a political fracas among the Italians, not far from Locarno, last night—"

"Nobody's heard anything of it around here," replied the lawyer. "It must have been one that didn't get anywhere. If it had been anything serious, they would have known of it here at once. The tension between the two parties is very high in this town!"

This answer confirmed Daniel in a suspicion he already had, to the effect that Lucca's imagination had been working overtime and had dramatized a comparatively unimportant incident.

"Those Italians," said Daniel, by way of bringing the conversation to a close, "are fine fellows, big-hearted and impulsive, but they don't know when to stop talking."

"It's better the way it is," he thought to himself, "or otherwise, Agostino and Caterina would have had to leave Switzerland." Nevertheless, the fact that he had spent a night away from home and lost a day on account of such an affair annoyed him more than a little. On the train going back, he found himself in the company of a number of farmers who were talking of the fox and how it was massacring the chickens at Magadino.

"That fox is pretty clever," one of them was saying; "he's too clever for any trap!"

"But there's a new kind of trap," a second one put in, "an Italian invention—"

"It makes a lot of noise, but it doesn't catch anything!" was the first speaker's rejoinder.

"That's true enough," said Daniel, joining in the discussion, "it does make a lot of noise, and it doesn't catch a thing. All you have is a fracas that doesn't get anywhere."

Upon reaching home, Daniel went up at once to the second floor to see the patient. But on the threshold of the room Silvia barred his way, putting a finger to her lips for him to be silent.

"He has need of complete rest," the daughter whispered in her father's ear; "no visitors, no formalities, nothing that can disturb him mentally, the doctor says."

"Then there's nothing that I can do?" Daniel was a bit crestfallen.

"Before you go back downstairs, you can take your shoes off so as not to make so much noise," Silvia advised him in a hushed tone.

Daniel took off his shoes and went back down the stairs and out into the garden. He entered the toolshed and started sharpening stakes with a hedge-knife. He had no sooner begun than Silvia came running out in her slippered feet.

"Are you crazy?" she said. "Here we have a sick man in the house, and you're making all this noise."

Daniel put down the hedge-knife.

"I suppose I may at least eat?" he plaintively inquired.

Silvia nodded and ran back upstairs. Daniel took the spade and began digging up a corner of the garden. In a little while he saw Silvia leave the house with a market-basket. He then went back into the house, took off his shoes, and hastily crept up to the second floor. At the door he met the nurse, who told him that he might enter, "but only for a moment."

There in Silvia's little white bed, Daniel had a glimpse of an enormous head all bandaged in white. Although he was not naturally of a humorous turn of mind, he could not help thinking of the head of St. Nicholas of the Snows.[5] In that huge expanse of white, there was a tiny hole for an eye, and another one a little larger which probably represented a mouth.

"There, that will do," the nurse said, ushering Daniel to the door. Going downstairs, shoes in hand, the latter met Silvia coming back.

"Where have *you* been?" Silvia demanded in a tone of reproof.

"Is that any way to speak to your father?" said Daniel, and he went back to digging in the garden. As he was digging away, Filomena came out to him.

"Silvia's lost her head!" Filomena complained to her husband. "Ever since yes-

terday, she hasn't shut an eye nor touched a morsel of food."

"Silvia has found her head!" Daniel answered; "she is one girl who has a heart."

"Too much of a one!" responded Silvia's mother.

"Too much of a one? You can never have too much heart," said Daniel. He was well satisfied with his daughter. His glance, always, as he gazed at her was one filled with pride and trepidation.

At the foot of the garden wall there were a few cowslips growing. Silvia came out and plucked them all, for the patient's room.

"But he can't see them! He has his eyes bandaged!" Filomena objected.

"Mother," said Silvia, "you know very well that you can see flowers with your eyes shut."

Daniel spent a good part of the following day in a vineyard which he had on the hillside. Upon coming home in the evening, he inquired after the patient's condition and learned from Silvia that their guest was improving rapidly. They had let the nurse go, and Silvia had taken the care of the patient upon herself. Daniel had a glimpse of the man only two or three times, and the impression he received was an altogether favorable one. He had, moreover, a good many other things on his mind, and so failed to notice the profound change that was taking place in the girl.

"You might give a little less thought to others and a little more to your own daughter!" his wife reproved him one evening.

"Silvia is not a child any longer, and she has a good head on her," was Daniel's curt response.

"She has a head all right, but no experience," replied his wife, who had resolved to unburden herself of what had been on her mind for a number of days past. Daniel reflected.

---

5. *St. Nicholas of the Snows,* one of the most popular saints in the Greek and Latin Churches, the patron saint of sailors, children, and Russia.

"You think I ought to speak to her?" he asked.

"I think you had better before it is too late!"

The next day Daniel had to go to bring a bag of seedling peas to a friend of his who lived at Comuna, in Val Verzasca, and Silvia went with him. At Comuna it did not take him long to get through with what little business he had, and he refused all invitations to go to the café.

"I prefer a little walk with my daughter," he explained to his acquaintances; "she's getting a trifle pale lately and needs the exercise."

Father and daughter then set out in silence along the road to Gordola. The wagon-road at this point ran at a considerable elevation above the stream, which could be heard tumbling down before them.

"Couldn't we walk along it?" Silvia asked.

"I don't believe so," said Daniel; but with the desire of giving in to any whim his daughter might have, he added: "We have plenty of time, though; we might go down to the river."

They found a small foot path, steep as a stair, and after many windings and turnings, they came to where the torrent was foaming against a wall of rock. The water was clear-running, and they could see every stone at the bottom. Up to this time father and daughter had exchanged only the briefest and most insignificant of words. This more than anything else gave Daniel a sense of the change which had taken place in their relations.

"Oh, look!" cried Silvia, pointing down at her feet to a strip of sand a dozen inches or so underwater, "how pretty!"

"That is spawn," her father informed her. "At the end of September the trout leave the lower part of the river and come up toward the source, and the females, full of eggs, start looking for a well-protected sandy spot. With the aid of their tails they displace the gravel and drop their eggs, which are mixed with the sand."

"And is that the way trout are born?"

"The fertilizing is done by the males, which come along after the females and sprinkle over the spot where the eggs have been deposited a thick white milky fluid. The eggs ought to be hatching about now."

Silvia looked in wonderment at the strip of sand where this mystery was accomplished.

"How beautiful," she said, "and how simple!"

"Trout, my dear girl, don't go to church!"

That was all that was said between them during this jaunt.

"Did you speak to her?" Daniel's wife asked him when they came home.

"Yes."

"What did you say?"

"Nothing."

The engineer had left his room for the first time one day and was lying stretched out on a reclining chair in the garden, when Caterina arrived from Gordola at the same time as Daniel.

"Miss Silvia!" the engineer was calling.

Caterina stopped instantly. Going up to the hedge which hid the garden from the street, she strove to see who it was that had called.

"Mr. Daniel," she said trembling all over, "that man whom you've taken in is the spy who came to Rivapiana that evening!"

"You're out of your senses!" Daniel exclaimed; and he went on to tell Caterina how it was, in his absence, the stranger had come to be brought there. Caterina went up to the hedge again and studied the convalescent intently, as he sat in the garden jesting with Silvia.

"That's the one!" she repeated; "I'm going away before he sees me."

"Very well," said Daniel, who had turned pale. "Tell Agostino to come here tomorrow at this same time; tell him, I'll make sure that no one sees him."

Silvia came running up to meet her father.

"Now that our patient is better," she

said, "I think it would be nice of you to have a little talk with him. You will see what a really fine person it is that chance has thrown our way."

"Yes, I should be very much interested in having a talk with him," said Daniel, who was doing his best to keep from showing how disturbed he was; "we can have lunch together today."

At the table, however, as he saw the man sitting there between Silvia and Luisa, the situation became unbearable to Daniel, and, pretending that he was feeling slightly ill, he excused himself and went outside. The others joined him in the garden.

"What's new in the papers?" the self-styled engineer inquired of Daniel. "It's been weeks since I've seen a newspaper."

"There's a fresh tragedy every day," replied Daniel. "Yesterday it was a big railroad wreck in France, with hundreds of dead."

"Every day a tragedy," said the alleged engineer, "but the most tragic thing of all is the way in which men go to meet their tragedies. Think of all those hundreds of persons killed in that railroad disaster. In the same train were farmers and merchants, doctors and lawyers, students, army officers, fashionable modistes, what not. They were all on the same train, and they were not on the same train. The farmer was thinking of the prices he would get from the merchant, the lawyer was thinking of the Cross of the Legion of Honor,[6] the army officer was thinking of his wealthy fiancée, the doctor was engaged in a mental lawsuit with the mayor of his village, and the student, out of the corner of his eye, was admiring his new necktie. Each was thus traveling in his own train. And each of us has his own train in society, until, of a sudden, we all find that we are on the same train, the train of death. The student's necktie ends up under the countryman's clogs, the officer's sword is run through the traveling salesman's belly, and the modiste's latest model goes up in smoke. For all were on the same train, and they did not know it."

"But the railroad company soon enough saw to that," said Daniel; "they soon saw to it that the unity which had been re-established by death was broken, by putting the fur-coated corpses on one side and those in plain workmen's blouses on the other."

"Can it be," said Silvia, "that human beings are condemned to be set over against one another like that, even after death?"

"There is a vast gulf," replied the convalescent, "between man's nature, his destiny, and the thing that society makes of him. During these past days, when I was fighting off death, that subject became an obsession with me. Each of us is traveling on his own train, and we are all on the same train!"

"Present-day society," said Daniel, "is based upon keeping men divided and set against one another. The vast majority of them are separated from and set against the fruit of their own labor. For no sooner does it leave their hands than the product of men ceases to belong to those who have made it but becomes instead their enemy; the thing produced is set over against the human beings who produced it, the inanimate object becomes the fetish before which living man must bow."

"But must it always be like that?" persisted Silvia.

"When I was young," the invalid went on, "I too hoped for a society that would be different from the one we have."

Daniel rose and went back to his spading. Spring was coming on, and it was time that the work was getting under way. It was with an unwonted vigor that he sank the spade in the earth, throwing the entire weight of his body upon his right foot and tossing the clods into the air. Behind him came Filomena, breaking

---

6. *Cross of the Legion of Honor,* a military and civil order of merit which was founded by Napoleon in 1802.

up the clods with a three-pronged rake. A pleasing odor of moist earth hung over the garden. The sweat was trickling down Daniel's face; internally, he was very much upset. The invalid remained in the garden, stretched out in the armchair, until the first evening stars appeared from behind Monte Ceneri.

"It's been so long," he said, half to himself, "it's been so many, many years since I've had a glimpse of the sky."

Silvia rose and returned shortly with a book.

"There is a similar case here," she told him, "in this first volume of Tolstoy's *War and Peace*. Prince Andrei, in November, 1805, had fallen wounded in the outskirts of Pratzen, in a battle between the Russian troops and those of Napoleon.[7] Here is what Tolstoy has to say about it:

"'Then he opened his eyes, to see what the outcome of the struggle between the two Frenchmen and the artilleryman had been, whether the red-haired artilleryman had been slain or not; he also wanted to know whether the cannon had been saved or captured. But all he could see was the high heavens up above him, no longer filled with light, but immeasurably far above, and covered over with tranquil-gliding gray clouds. 'How calm and still and restful it all is,' thinks Prince Andrei. 'All that has no resemblance whatsoever to this running, shrieking and fighting of ours; the tranquil gliding of those clouds over the high unending heavens has nothing in common with this struggle of the Frenchmen and the artilleryman, as with grim, distorted faces they strive for the possession of a cannon swob. How does it happen that I have never seen these heavens before? How happy I am to have seen them at last. Yes all is as naught, it is all a mistake and a lie, all except that endless expanse of blue. There is nothing, nothing beyond that. Yet even it does not exist; there is nothing but stillness and peace. And God be thanked for it!'"

The moon came up, flooding the Magadino plain with an eerie light.

"The moon," Luisa observed, "has eyes and a nose like us."

"Those things," Silvia explained to her younger sister, "are seas and mountains."

Their guest took it upon himself to round out the explanation.

"If the inhabitants of the moon," he said, "happen to be looking down at the earth at this moment, we probably look much the same to them as the moon does to us. Seen from up there, what are the great cities of the earth? Italy must look like a comma and Switzerland like a period."

"And how does Mussolini look from up there?" Luisa wanted to know.

"You'd better watch out," said Daniel, "or you'll be straining your eyes."

A general laugh went round at this.

The next day, when Daniel saw Agostino coming, he went out to meet him and brought him into the house from the side opposite the garden, where the engineer was seated out in the sun. The two men went up to Luisa's room, and there, from behind the Venetian shutters, Agostino was able to take a good look at the man without being seen.

"That is the one!" he said softly; and rubbing his hands, he added: "This time he's not going to get away from us!"

"What do you mean?" said Daniel with a frown.

"I mean just that, that he's not going to get away from us this time."

"You're joking." The tone of Daniel's voice took his friend from Bergamo by surprise.

"The fox is in the trap," said the latter; "do you mean to say, you're going to let him go? We've got in our hands at last, without his knowing it, one of those who in Italy have been massacring our people, in prison and on the deportation islands; and should we let him get away?" Agostino was wrought up about the matter.

---

7. *a battle between the Russian troops and those of Napoleon,* a reference to the battle of Austerlitz, which crushed the Russian army.

"That man is a guest in my house," Daniel calmly announced.

"He's a spy!" said Agostino.

"He was a spy," answered Daniel, in the same calm voice, "but now he's a guest. He came to my house at the point of death and sought hospitality, and he has been cured in my house."

It was all Agostino could do to believe his ears.

"I can't understand such scruples as that," he said. "You know as well as I do the methods that the Fascists use against us; you know, don't you, there are no moral scruples where they are concerned?"

"I know it," was Daniel's response; "that's why I'm not a Fascist."

"And that's why we're always beaten!"

"That's why we'll win out in the end!" This was Daniel's last word. Agostino could only shake his head, in the face of such stubbornness as this.

"How long is he going to be here yet?"

"Another week, perhaps; he's not very strong yet."

"Then we'll have time to talk it over before he has a chance to get away."

Daniel decided to say nothing about it to the other members of the family, so as not to alarm them or arouse their guest's suspicions. It was at this time that one of Filomena's sisters who lived at Vira had a child, and Daniel with his wife and Silvia went to pay her a visit, leaving Luisa at home with the invalid.

"You've been here all these weeks," said the little girl, "and you haven't yet seen our house."

"That's because I've been in bed all the time," said the engineer.

Luisa then proceeded to show him the storeroom, where they kept the potatoes, the onions, their fruit, and the garden tools. On the second floor she showed him her own room, which her sister Silvia shared with her for the time being. The guest's attention was attracted by a photograph fastened up on the wall with a tissue paper flower on either side.

"Who is that?" he asked.

"That's Matteotti,"[8] Luisa informed him.

The engineer dropped down on a chair.

"Who is Matteotti?" was his next question.

"He was the man who stuck up for the poor people, and for that reason he was killed by Mussolini."

"Are you an anti-Fascist?"

"I most certainly am!"

"And Silvia, what about her?"

"She's more of a one than I am."

"And your father?"

"More than any of us—not in what he says, but in what he does."

Luisa then showed the guest the third floor.

"This is my parent's room," she said.

"And what's this?" The engineer pointed to a small room adjoining.

"Oh, you mustn't go in there; Daddy doesn't allow it. He has a lot of papers in there, and he doesn't want us to muss them up."

Luisa and the guest went back to the garden. The invalid began striding up and down the path and kept it up for a good half hour. Then, as if he had made up his mind to something, he came up to Luisa.

"Would you mind running down with a telegram for me?" And when he had given the little girl the wording of the telegram and a few pennies, he added: "I'm tired; I am going to bed at once."

It was in vain that Silvia knocked at their guest's door the next morning, when she came to bring him his breakfast. Her repeated knocking brought not the slightest response. The door was locked. Feeling certain that something dreadful had happened, Silvia began calling at the top of her voice, and the whole family came running up. When Daniel had taken the door off its hinges, it was found that the guest was not in his room. The bed had

---

8. *Matteotti* (mät′ te ôt′ tē), Italian socialist leader murdered for his opposition to the Fascist regime (1885-1925).

not been slept in. His suitcases had disappeared.

"He's gone!" Silvia cried.

"He left without saying good-by!" wailed Luisa.

"He's been gone ever since yesterday," Filomena declared, pointing to the bed.

In a couple of bounds, Daniel was on the third floor, and a moment later, the other members of the family were terror-struck by his furious outcries:

"Thief! Crook! Traitor! He's taken all my papers with him! He's taken away all my papers!"

It was like a mortal blow to Daniel. When the women came up, their eyes fell on the disordered room; all the drawers had been overturned on the floor. At this point, Agostino came in. He did not know what had happened yet, but he was very pale and he seemed excited.

"Yesterday evening," Daniel explained to him, "the spy left the house while I was away and took all my papers with him, among others, those about the smuggling. Quick! There's not a minute to lose; we must let the ones concerned know."

"This morning," said Agostino, "at Luino, a score of seasonal laborers, who are in the habit of coming over to work in Switzerland during the daytime and going back into Italy at night, were arrested."

Silvia stood staring at her father and Agostino, as if all this were some kind of play which they were putting on for her benefit.

"No! no!" she moaned, "it's not true! It's all a joke! Agostino, for heaven's sake, tell me it's not true!"

Daniel was on his feet.

"We've got to think of saving the others, before that spy gets his hands on them!"

And he and Agostino were off in a hurry.

It was late in the evening when Daniel came home. Filomena and Luisa were seated by the hearth, while Silvia sat on a chest, over in one corner of the dark kitchen.

"The smugglers," announced Daniel from the kitchen door, "were arrested early this morning. A consignment of books at Brissago was seized at noon today. The police have been to Caterina's house. I hear that Agostino has been arrested, and that he will probably be expelled from the country. Haven't they been here yet?"

"No," said Filomena.

Daniel dropped down on the doorsill. The night wore slowly on, with the slow procession of the stars. The cock crowed for the first time, but no one so much as thought of going to bed, no one thought of going up to the second floor where *that man* had lived until yesterday. The cock crowed a second time. Mother and daughter still sat by the hearth, the elder daughter on a chest over in a corner of the kitchen, and the father there on the doorsill. It was like a wake for the dead. The cock crowed a third time.

Then came an animal's shrill cry, like the yelp of a dog in pain, and the squawking of hens broke in upon the silence of the night. Daniel leaped to his feet and ran across the garden to the hen-house. In front of it he saw a fox with one paw in the trap; planting its remaining feet upon the ground and arching its back, the animal was doing its utmost to free the prisoned member. When it saw the man approaching, it began leaping furiously from side to side, tugging on the chain by which the trap was securely fastened.

"At last!" said Daniel in a ferocious tone of voice. And snatching up an ax which lay beside the hen-house, as if he were hewing at an oak, he began raining terrible blows upon the animal's head, its back, its belly, its legs—blow after blow, the blows of a madman, death-dealing blows continued to rain down, even after the little beast had been hacked to tiny bits and reduced to nothing more than a puddle of blood-soaked mush.

THE END

Development

INTERPRETATION

1. Use the following questions as the basis for a discussion of Daniel's interior conflict: *(a)* What traits does Daniel share with his daughter Silvia? *(b)* In what way is her likeness to him a cause of concern to him? *(c)* How do Daniel and Agostino differ in their basic attitudes toward anti-Fascism? *(d)* Summarize the way in which Silvia and Agostino reflect two opposing forces at work in Daniel's mind.

2. Daniel and the engineer have one rather lengthy conversation which centers on the symbol of the train. *(a)* What does the guest mean by the sentence, "Each of us is traveling on his own train, and we are all on the same train"? *(b)* Considering the event which immediately precedes this conversation, explain Daniel's state of mind as implied in his answer: "Present-day society . . . is based upon keeping men divided and set against one another" (page 23, column 2, paragraph 4). *(c)* How does this metaphor, of a train carrying separate compartments and headed toward a single end, apply to the relationship between Daniel and his guest; and how does it function as a device of foreshadowing?

3. *(a)* What reason does Daniel give for not following Agostino's entreaties to seize the spy? *(b)* Considering the story as a whole, does this choice of the code of hospitality appear more or less admirable than the code of expediency urged by Agostino? Defend your judgment.

4. *(a)* What earlier action in the story constitutes a direct parallel to Daniel's bludgeoning the fox at the end? *(b)* Which one of the following best describes your final impression of him as a result of this action? Defend your choice.

(1) Daniel has learned to be more realistic in his approach to life.

(2) Daniel has abandoned his ideals and has yielded to his primitive, emotional nature.

(3) Daniel has not "learned" anything nor has he changed in any basic way.

(4) Daniel is more aware at the end than he was at the beginning that freedom of choice is strictly limited if one wishes to survive in this world.

5. There are many traps suggested in the texture of this story. How might the following elements of the story be related to the central idea of the trap? *(a)* Daniel's continual war with the weather and with animal parasites. *(b)* Silvia's infatuation with the engineer-spy. *(c)* Daniel's choice of the code of hospitality. *(d)* The element of coincidence that brought the spy to Daniel's home.

TECHNIQUE

1. Daniel's involvement in the anti-Fascist movement is revealed very gradually: *(a)* What is the first real clue? *(b)* What further hints are revealed in his attitude toward Caterina's announcement?

2. The author includes several "farm scenes," which appear at first to have little relevance to the main plot of the story. *(a)* With what other scenes in the story do these contrast? *(b)* What connection exists between such scenes and the basic conflict acted out in the main plot?

EXTENSIONS

1. Silone's story portrays the time-honored Western tradition of hospitality as a "trap" which leads to the hero's destruction. To what extent are such traditions traps, and to what extent are they useful and valuable patterns to follow? Consider traditions of language as well as those of ethics and etiquette.

The Last Judgment

KAREL ČAPEK[1] / Czechoslovakia
(1890–1938)

translated from the Czech by Norma Jeanne McFadden and Leopold Pospisil

The notorious multiple-killer Kugler, pursued by several warrants and a whole army of policemen and detectives, swore that he'd never be taken. He wasn't, either—at least not alive. The last of his nine murderous deeds was shooting a policeman who tried to arrest him. The policeman indeed died, but not before putting a total of seven bullets into Kugler. Of these seven, three were fatal. Kugler's death came so quickly that he felt no pain. And so it seemed Kugler had escaped earthly justice.

When his soul left his body, it should have been surprised at the sight of the next world—a world beyond space, grey, and infinitely desolate—but it wasn't. A man who has been jailed on two continents looks upon the next life merely as new surroundings. Kugler expected to struggle through, equipped only with a bit of courage, as he had in the last world.

At length the inevitable Last Judgment got around to Kugler.

Heaven being eternally in a state of emergency, Kugler was brought before a special court of three judges and not, as his previous conduct would ordinarily merit, before a jury. The courtroom was furnished simply, almost like courtrooms on earth, with this one exception: there was no provision for swearing in witnesses. In time, however, the reason for this will become apparent.

The judges were old and worthy councillors with austere, bored faces. Kugler complied with the usual tedious formalities: Ferdinand Kugler, unemployed, born on such and such a date, died . . . at this point it was shown Kugler didn't know the date of his own death. Immediately he realized this was a damaging omission in the eyes of the judges; his spirit of helpfulness faded.

"Do you plead guilty or not guilty?" asked the presiding judge.

"Not guilty," said Kugler obdurately.

"Bring in the first witness," the judge sighed.

Opposite Kugler appeared an extraordinary gentleman, stately, bearded, and clothed in a blue robe strewn with golden stars.

At his entrance the judges arose. Even Kugler stood up, reluctant but fascinated. Only when the old gentleman took a seat did the judges again sit down.

"Witness," began the presiding judge, "Omniscient God, this court has summoned You in order to hear Your testimony in the case against Kugler, Ferdinand. As You are the Supreme Truth, You need not take the oath. In the interest of the proceedings, however, we ask You to keep to the subject at hand rather than branch out into particulars—unless they have a bearing on this case.

"And you, Kugler, don't interrupt the Witness. He knows everything, so there's no use denying anything.

"And now, Witness, if you would please begin."

That said, the presiding judge took off his spectacles and leaned comfortably on

1. *Čapek* (chä′pek).

the bench before him, evidently in preparation for a long speech by the Witness. The oldest of the three judges nestled down in sleep. The recording angel opened the Book of Life.

God, the Witness, coughed lightly and began:

"Yes. Kugler, Ferdinand. Ferdinand Kugler, son of a factory worker, was a bad, unmanageable child from his earliest days. He loved his mother dearly, but was unable to show it; this made him unruly and defiant. Young man, you irked everyone! Do you remember how you bit your father on the thumb when he tried to spank you? You had stolen a rose from the notary's garden."

"The rose was for Irma, the tax collector's daughter," Kugler said.

"I know," said God. "Irma was seven years old at that time. Did you ever hear what happened to her?"

"No, I didn't."

"She married Oscar, the son of the factory owner. But she contracted a venereal disease from him and died of a miscarriage. You remember Rudy Zaruba?"

"What happened to him?"

"Why, he joined the navy and died accidentally in Bombay. You two were the worst boys in the whole town. Kugler, Ferdinand, was a thief before his tenth year and an inveterate liar. He kept bad company, too: old Gribble, for instance, a drunkard and an idler, living on handouts. Nevertheless, Kugler shared many of his own meals with Gribble."

The presiding judge motioned with his hand, as if much of this was perhaps unnecessary, but Kugler himself asked hesitantly, "And . . . what happened to his daughter?"

"Mary?" asked God. "She lowered herself considerably. In her fourteenth year she married. In her twentieth year she died, remembering you in the agony of her death. By your fourteenth year you were nearly a drunkard yourself, and you often ran away from home. Your father's death came about from grief and worry; your

mother's eyes faded from crying. You brought dishonor to your home, and your sister, your pretty sister Martha, never married. No young man would come calling at the home of a thief. She's still living alone and in poverty, sewing until late each night. Scrimping has exhausted her, and patronizing customers hurt her pride."

"What's she doing right now?"

"This very minute she's buying thread at Wolfe's. Do you remember that shop? Once, when you were six years old, you bought a colored glass marble there. On that very same day you lost it and never, never found it. Do you remember how you cried with rage?"

"Whatever happened to it?" Kugler asked eagerly.

"Well, it rolled into the drain and under the gutterspout. As a matter of fact, it's still there, after thirty years. Right now it's raining on earth and your marble is shivering in the gush of cold water."

Kugler bent his head, overcome by this revelation.

But the presiding judge fitted his spectacles back on his nose and said mildly, "Witness, we are obliged to get on with the case. Has the accused committed murder?"

Here the Witness nodded his head.

"He murdered nine people. The first one he killed in a brawl, and it was during his prison term for this crime that he became completely corrupted. The second victim was his unfaithful sweetheart. For that he was sentenced to death, but he escaped. The third was an old man whom he robbed. The fourth was a night watchman."

"Then he died?" Kugler asked.

"He died after three days in terrible pain," God said. "And he left six children behind him. The fifth and sixth victims were an old married couple. He killed them with an axe and found only sixteen dollars, although they had twenty thousand hidden away."

Kugler jumped up.

"Where?"

"In the straw mattress," God said. "In a linen sack inside the mattress. That's where they hid all the money they acquired from greed and penny-pinching. The seventh man he killed in America; a countryman of his, a bewildered, friendless immigrant."

"So it was in the mattress," whispered Kugler in amazement.

"Yes," continued God. "The eighth man was merely a passerby who happened to be in Kugler's way when Kugler was trying to outrun the police. At that time Kugler had periostitis and was delirious from the pain. Young man, you were suffering terribly. The ninth and last was the policeman who killed Kugler exactly when Kugler shot him."

"And why did the accused commit murder?" asked the presiding judge.

"For the same reasons others have," answered God. "Out of anger or desire for money; both deliberately and accidentally—some with pleasure, others from necessity. However, he was generous and often helpful. He was kind to women, gentle with animals, and he kept his word. Am I to mention his good deeds?"

"Thank You," said the presiding judge, "but it isn't necessary. Does the accused have anything to say in his own defense?"

"No," Kugler replied with honest indifference.

"The judges of this court will now take this matter under advisement," declared the presiding judge, and the three of them withdrew.

Only God and Kugler remained in the courtroom.

"Who are they?" asked Kugler, indicating with his head the men who had just left.

"People like you," answered God. "They were judges on earth, so they're judges here as well."

Kugler nibbled his fingertips. "I expected . . . I mean, I never really thought about it. But I figured You would judge, since—"

"Since I'm God," finished the Stately Gentleman. "But that's just it, don't you see? Because I know everything, I can't possibly judge. That wouldn't do at all. By the way, do you know who turned you in this time?"

"No, I don't," said Kugler, surprised.

"Lucky, the waitress. She did it out of jealousy."

"Excuse me," Kugler ventured, "but You forgot about that good-for-nothing Teddy I shot in Chicago."

"Not at all," God said. "He recovered and is alive this very minute. I know he's an informer, but otherwise he's a very good man and terribly fond of children. You shouldn't think of any person as being completely worthless."

"But I still don't understand why You aren't the judge," Kugler said thoughtfully.

"Because my knowledge is infinite. If judges knew everything, absolutely everything, then they would also understand everything. Their hearts would ache. They couldn't sit in judgment—and neither can I. As it is, they know only about your crimes. I know all about you. The entire Kugler. And that's why I cannot judge."

"But why are they judging . . . the same people who were judges on earth?"

"Because man belongs to man. As you see, I'm only the witness. But the verdict is determined by man, even in heaven. Believe me, Kugler, this is the way it should be. Man isn't worthy of divine judgment. He deserves to be judged only by other men."

At that moment the three returned from their deliberation.

In heavy tones the presiding judge announced, "For repeated crimes of first degree murder, manslaughter, robbery, disrespect for the law, illegally carrying weapons, and for the theft of a rose: Kugler, Ferdinand, is sentenced to lifelong punishment in hell. The sentence is to begin immediately.

"Next case, please: Torrance, Frank.

"Is the accused present in court?"

THE END

Development

INTERPRETATION

1. When God is sworn in as a witness, He is admonished to "keep to the subject at hand." *(a)* What is there in the attitude of the court which leads us to suspect that He will not do this? *(b)* How is God characterized so as to make His seeming garrulousness appear believable on a literal level?

2. *(a)* In what ways does your attitude toward Kugler differ from what it would probably be had you read a newspaper account of his life and death? *(b)* What, in particular, is the effect of the stolen rose, the lost marble, and the hidden money on your attitude toward him? *(c)* Discuss the extent to which your attitude supports God's statement, "You shouldn't think of any person as being completely worthless."

3. The following are some possible ways to describe God's attitude toward Kugler: *(a)* remote and objective; *(b)* patronizing; *(c)* affectionate and protective; *(d)* friendly but detached; *(e)* gently scolding. Defend your choice as to the most accurate description.

4. Here are two interpretations of "The Last Judgment":

(a) Čapek's vision of the last judgment is a gloomy one, for his painful awareness of human failings leads him to insist that men "get what they deserve"—and no one "deserves" mercy. His God is an ineffectual being who sees and understands, but, because He understands, cannot act.

(b) Čapek's intense awareness of human complexity has led him to construct a story around the flabby humanitarianism expressed in the phrase, "To understand all is to forgive all." While the narrow-minded human judges (clearly unsympathetic characters) damn Kugler to hell for, among other things, stealing a rose, merciful God finds extenuating circumstances for the very worst of his—and everyone else's—offenses.

Point out the strength and the weaknesses of these two interpretations as you understand them in terms of the story.

5. God's last remark to Kugler is "Man isn't worthy of divine judgment. He deserves to be judged only by other men." The statement seems to go beyond what the story had previously implied: that God is kept from judging by his omniscience. *(a)* What is the difference between saying that God cannot judge and saying that man is unworthy of His judgment? *(b)* Is God's remark consistent with his character as Čapek has established it? *(c)* Is the theme of the story more concerned with the nature of God or with the nature of man? Discuss.

TECHNIQUE

1. The topic (eternal judgment) and the setting (the heavenly court) of "The Last Judgment" lead the reader to expect a certain appropriate seriousness in tone from the author. *(a)* Describe the tone of the first few paragraphs of the story. *(b)* What effect does Čapek's tone have on the reader's attitude toward the topic and setting of the story?

2. Note that the last sentence of paragraph one reads, "And so it seemed Kugler had escaped earthly justice." As you continue reading, this sentence takes on an ironic twist. Explain the irony, supporting your explanation with details from the text.

EXTENSIONS

1. Would you like to be "judged" as Kugler is? Why or why not?

The Outlaws

SELMA LAGERLÖF / Sweden
(1858 — 1940)

translated from the Swedish by Pauline Bancroft Flach

A peasant had killed a monk and fled to the woods. He became an outlaw, upon whose head a price was set. In the forest he met another fugitive, a young fisherman from one of the outermost islands, who had been accused of the theft of a herring net. The two became companions, cut themselves a home in a cave, laid their nets together, cooked their food, made their arrows, and held watch one for the other. The peasant could never leave the forest. But the fisherman, whose crime was less serious, would now and then take upon his back the game they had killed, and would creep down to the more isolated houses on the outskirts of the village. In return for milk, butter, arrowheads, and clothing he would sell his game, the black mountain cock, the moor hen, with her shining feathers, the toothsome doe, and the long-eared hare.

The cave which was their home cut down deep into a mountain-side. The entrance was guarded by wide slabs of stone and ragged thornbushes. High up on the hillside there stood a giant pine, and the chimney of the fireplace nestled among its coiled roots. Thus the smoke could draw up through the heavy hanging branches and fade unseen into the air. To reach their cave the men had to wade through the stream that sprang out from the hill slope. No pursuer thought of seeking their trail in this merry brooklet. At first they were hunted as wild animals are. The peasants of the district gathered to pursue them as if for baiting a wolf or bear. The bowmen surrounded the wood while the spear carriers entered and left no thicket or ravine unsearched. The two outlaws cowered in their gloomy cave, panting in terror and listening breathlessly as the hunt passed on with noise and shouting over the mountain ranges.

For one long day the young fisherman lay motionless, but the murderer could stand it no longer, and went out into the open where he could see his enemy. They discovered him and set after him, but this was far more to his liking than lying quiet in impotent terror. He fled before his pursuers, leaped the streams, slid down the precipices, climbed up perpendicular walls of rock. All his remarkable strength and skill awoke to energy under the spur of danger. His body became as elastic as a steel spring, his foot held firm, his hand grasped sure, his eye and ear were doubly sharp. He knew the meaning of every murmur in the foliage; he could understand the warning in an upturned stone.

When he had clambered up the side of a precipice he would stop to look down on his pursuers, greeting them with loud songs of scorn. When their spears sang above him in the air, he would catch them and hurl them back. As he crashed his way through tangled underbrush something within him seemed to sing a wild song of rejoicing. A gaunt, bare hilltop stretched itself through the forest, and all alone upon its crest there stood a towering pine. The red brown trunk was bare, in

"The Outlaws" by Selma Lagerlöf, translated by Pauline Bancroft Flach from INVISIBLE LINKS. Reprinted by permission of The American-Scandinavian Foundation.

the thick grown boughs at the top a hawk's nest rocked in the breeze. So daring had the fugitive grown that on another day he climbed to the nest while his pursuers sought him in the woody slopes below. He sat there and twisted the necks of the young hawks as the hunt raged far beneath him. The old birds flew screaming about him in anger. They swooped past his face, they struck at his eyes with their beaks, beat at him with their powerful wings, and clawed great scratches in his weather-hardened skin. He battled with them, laughing. He stood up in the rocking nest as he lunged at the birds with his knife, and he lost all thought of danger and pursuit in the joy of battle. When recollection came again and he turned to look for his enemies, the hunt had gone off in another direction. Not one of the pursuers had thought of raising his eyes to the clouds to see the prey hanging there, doing schoolboy deeds of recklessness while his life hung in the balance. But the man trembled from head to foot when he saw that he was safe. He caught for a support with his shaking hands; he looked down giddily from the height to which he had climbed. Groaning in fear of a fall, afraid of the birds, afraid of the possibility of being seen, weakened through terror of everything and anything, he slid back down the tree trunk. He laid himself flat upon the earth and crawled over the loose stones until he reached the underbrush. There he hid among the tangled branches of the young pines, sinking down, weak and helpless, upon the soft moss. A single man might have captured him.

Tord was the name of the fisherman. He was but sixteen years old, but was strong and brave. He had now lived for a whole year in the wood.

The peasant's name was Berg, and they had called him "The Giant." He was handsome and well-built, the tallest and strongest man in the entire county. He was broad-shouldered and yet slender. His hands were delicate in shape, as if they had never known hard work, his hair was

brown, his face soft-coloured. When he had lived for some time in the forest his look of strength was awe-inspiring. His eyes grew piercing under bushy brows wrinkled by great muscles over the forehead. His lips were more firmly set than before, his face more haggard, with deepened hollows at the temples, and his strongly marked cheek-bones stood out plainly. All the softer curves of his body disappeared, but the muscles grew strong as steel. His hair turned grey rapidly.

Tord had never seen any one so magnificent and so mighty before. In his imagination, his companion towered high as the forest, strong as the raging surf. He served him humbly, as he would have served a master, he revered him as he would have revered a god. It seemed quite natural that Tord should carry the hunting spear, that he should drag the game home, draw the water, and build the fire. Berg, the Giant, accepted all these services, but scarce threw the boy a friendly word. He looked upon him with contempt, as a common thief.

The outlaws did not live by pillage, but supported themselves by hunting and fishing. Had not Berg killed a holy man, the peasants would soon have tired of the pursuit and left them to themselves in the mountains. But they feared disaster for the villages if he who had laid hands upon a servant of God should go unpunished. When Tord took his game down into the valley they would offer him money and a pardon for himself if he would lead them to the cave of the Giant, that they might catch the latter in his sleep. But the boy refused, and if they followed him he would lead them astray until they gave up the pursuit.

Once Berg asked him whether the peasants had ever tried to persuade him to betrayal. When he learned what reward they had promised he said scornfully that Tord was a fool not to accept such offers. Tord looked at him with something in his eyes that Berg, the Giant, had never seen before. No beautiful woman whom he had loved in the days of his youth had ever looked at him like that; not even in the eyes of his own children, or of his wife, had he seen such affection. "You are my God, the ruler I have chosen of my own free will." This was what the eyes said. "You may scorn me, or beat me, if you will, but I shall still remain faithful."

After this, Berg gave more heed to the boy and saw that he was brave in action but shy in speech. Death seemed to have no terrors for him. He would deliberately choose for his path the fresh formed ice on the mountain pools, the treacherous surface of the morass in springtime. He seemed to delight in danger. It gave him some compensation for the wild ocean storms he could no longer go out to meet. He would tremble in the night darkness of the wood, however, and even by day the gloom of a thicket or a deeper shadow could frighten him. When Berg asked him about this he was silent in embarrassment.

Tord did not sleep in the bed by the hearth at the back of the cave, but every night, when Berg was asleep the boy would creep to the entrance and lie there on one of the broad stones. Berg discovered this, and although he guessed the reason he asked the boy about it. Tord would not answer. To avoid further questions he slept in the bed for two nights, then returned to his post at the door.

One night, when a snow-storm raged in the treetops, piling up drifts even in the heart of the thickets, the flakes swirled into the cave of the outlaws. Tord, lying by the entrance, awoke in the morning to find himself wrapped in a blanket of melting snow. A day or two later he fell ill. Sharp pains pierced his lungs when he tried to draw breath. He endured the pain as long as his strength would stand it, but one evening, when he stooped to blow up the fire, he fell down and could not rise again. Berg came to his side and told him to lie in the warm bed. Tord groaned in agony, but could not move. Berg put his arm under the boy's body and carried him to the bed. He had a feeling while doing it as if he were touching a clammy snake; he had a taste in his mouth as if he had eaten unclean horseflesh, so repulsive was it to him to touch the person of this common thief. Berg covered the sick boy with his own warm bear-skin rug and gave him water. This was all he could do, but the illness was not dangerous, and Tord recovered quickly. But now that Berg had had to do his companion's work for a few days, and had had to care for him, they seemed to have come nearer to one another. Tord dared to speak to Berg sometimes as they sat together by the fire cutting their arrows.

"You come of good people, Berg," Tord said one evening. "Your relatives are the richest peasants in the valley. The men of your name have served kings and fought in their castles."

"They have more often fought with the rebels and done damage to the king's property," answered Berg.

"Your forefathers held great banquets at Christmas time. And you held banquets too, when you were at home in your house. Hundreds of men and women could find place on the benches in your great hall, the hall that was built in the days before St. Olaf[1] came here to Viken for christening. Great silver urns were there, and mighty horns, filled with mead, went the rounds of your table."

Berg looked at the boy again. He sat on the edge of the bed with his head in his hands, pushing back the heavy tangled hair that hung over his eyes. His face had become pale and refined through his illness. His eyes still sparkled in fever. He smiled to himself at the pictures called up by his fancy—pictures of the great hall and of the silver urns, of the richly clad guests, and of Berg, the Giant, lording it in the place of honor. The peasant knew that even in the days of his glory no one had ever looked at him with eyes so shin-

---

1. *St. Olaf*, patron saint of Norway and King of Norway from 1016 to 1029. He was converted to Christianity while in England fighting the Danes.

ing in admiration, so glowing in reverence, as this boy did now, as he sat by the fire in his worn leather jacket. He was touched, and yet displeased. This common thief had no right to admire him.

"Were there no banquets in your home?" he asked.

Tord laughed: "Out there on the rocks where father and mother live? Father plunders the wrecks and mother is a witch. When the weather is stormy she rides out to meet the ships on a seal's back, and those who are washed overboard from the wrecks belong to her."

"What does she do with them?" asked Berg.

"Oh, a witch always needs corpses. She makes salves of them, or perhaps she eats them. On moonlit nights she sits out in the wildest surf and looks for the eyes and fingers of drowned children."

"That is horrible!" said Berg.

The boy answered with calm confidence: "It would be for others, but not for a witch. She can't help it."

This was an altogether new manner of looking at life for Berg.

"Then thieves have to steal, as witches have to make magic?" he questioned sharply.

"Why, yes," answered the boy. "Every one has to do the thing he was born for." But a smile of shy cunning curled his lips, as he added: "There are thieves who have never stolen."

"What do you mean by that?" spoke Berg.

The boy still smiled his mysterious smile and seemed happy to have given his companion a riddle. "There are birds that do not fly; and there are thieves who have not stolen," he said.

Berg feigned stupidity, in order to trick the other's meaning: "How can any one be called a thief who has never stolen?" he said.

The boy's lips closed tight as if to hold back the words. "But if one has a father who steals—" he threw out after a short pause.

"A man may inherit house and money, but the name thief is given only to him who earns it."

Tord laughed gently. "But when one has a mother—and that mother comes and cries, and begs one to take upon one's self the father's crime—and then one can laugh at the hangman and run away into the woods. A man may be outlawed for the sake of a fish net he has never seen."

Berg beat his fist upon the stone table, in great anger. Here this strong, beautiful boy had thrown away his whole life for another. Neither love, nor riches, nor the respect of his fellow men could ever be his again. The sordid care for food and clothing was all that remained to him in life. And this fool had let him, Berg, despise an innocent man. He scolded sternly, but Tord was not frightened any more than a sick child is frightened at the scolding of his anxious mother.

High up on one of the broad wooded hills there lay a black swampy lake. It was square in shape, and its banks were as straight, and their corners as sharp as if it had been the work of human hands. On three sides steep walls of rock rose up, with hardy mountain pines clinging to the stones, their roots as thick as a man's arm. At the surface of the lake, where the few strips of grass had been washed away, these naked roots twisted and coiled, rising out of the water like myriad snakes that had tried to escape from the waves, but had been turned to stone in their struggle. Or was it more like a mass of blackened skeletons of long-drowned giants which the lake was trying to throw off? The arms and legs were twisted in wild contortions, the long fingers grasped deep into the rocks, the mighty ribs formed arches that upheld ancient trees. But now and again these iron-hard arms, these steel fingers with which the climbing pines supported themselves, would loosen their hold, and then the strong north wind would hurl the tree from the ridge far out into the swamp. There it would lie, its crown burrowing deep in the muddy water. The fishes found good hiding places amid its twigs, while the roots rose up over the water like the arms of some hideous monster, giving the little lake a repulsive appearance.

The mountains sloped down on the fourth side of the little lake. A tiny rivulet foamed out here; but before the stream could find its path it twisted and turned among boulders and mounds of earth, forming a whole colony of islands, some of which scarce offered foothold, while others carried as many as twenty trees on their back.

Here, where the rocks were not high enough to shut out the sun, the lighter foliaged trees could grow. Here were the timid, grey-green alders, and the willows with their smooth leaves. Birches were here, as they always are wherever there is a chance to shut out the evergreens, and there were mountain ash and elder bushes, giving charm and fragrance to the place.

At the entrance to the lake there was a forest of rushes as high as a man's head, through which the sunlight fell as green upon the water as it falls on the moss in the true forest. There were little clearings among the reeds, little round ponds where the water lilies slumbered. The tall rushes looked down with gentle gravity upon these sensitive beauties, who closed their white leaves and their yellow hearts so quickly in their leather outer dress as soon as the sun withdrew his rays.

One sunny day the outlaws came to one of these little ponds to fish. They waded through the reeds to two high stones, and sat there throwing out their bait for the big green, gleaming pike that slumbered just below the surface of the water. These men, whose life was now passed entirely among the mountains and the woods, had come to be as completely under the control of the powers of nature as were the plants or the animals. When the sun shone they were open-hearted and merry, at evening they became silent, and the night,

which seemed to them so all-powerful, robbed them of their strength. And now the green light that fell through the reeds and drew out from the water stripes of gold, brown, and black-green, smoothed them into a sort of magic mood. They were completely shut out from the outer world. The reeds swayed gently in the soft wind, the rushes murmured, and the long, ribbon-like leaves struck them lightly in the face. They sat on the grey stones in their grey leather garments, and the shaded tones of the leather melted into the shade of the stones. Each saw his comrade sitting opposite him as quietly as a stone statue. And among the reeds they saw giant fish swimming, gleaming and glittering in all colours of the rainbow. When the men threw out their lines and watched the rings on the water widen amid the reeds, it seemed to them that the motion grew and grew until they saw it was not they themselves alone that had occasioned it. A Nixie,[2] half human, half fish, lay sleeping deep down in the water. She lay on her back, and the waves clung so closely to her body that the men had not seen her before. It was her breath that stirred the surface. But it did not seem to the watchers that there was anything strange in the fact that she lay there. And when she had disappeared in the next moment they did not know whether her appearance had been an illusion or not.

The green light pierced through their eyes into their brains like a mild intoxication. They saw visions among the reeds, visions which they would not tell even to each other. There was not much fishing done. The day was given up to dreams and visions.

A sound of oars came from among the reeds, and they started up out of their dreaming. In a few moments a heavy boat, hewn out of a tree trunk, came into sight, set in motion by oars not much broader than walking sticks. The oars were in the

2. *Nixie*, a female water spirit, or mermaid. Her appearance was considered to be an omen of drowning.

hands of a young girl who had been gathering water-lilies. She had long, dark brown braids of hair, and great dark eyes, but she was strangely pale, a pallor that was not grey, but softly pink tinted. Her cheeks were no deeper in colour than the rest of her face; her lips were scarce redder. She wore a bodice of white linen and a leather belt with a golden clasp. Her skirt was of blue with a broad red hem. She rowed past close by the outlaws without seeing them. They sat absolutely quiet, less from fear of discovery than from the desire to look at her undisturbed. When she had gone, the stone statues became men again and smiled:

"She was as white as the water-lilies," said one. "And her eyes were as dark as the water back there under the roots of the pines."

They were both so merry that they felt like laughing, like really laughing as they had never laughed in this swamp before, a laugh that would echo back from the wall of rock and loosen the roots of the pines.

"Did you think her beautiful?" asked the Giant.

"I do not know, she passed so quickly. Perhaps she was beautiful."

"You probably did not dare to look at her. Did you think she was the Nixie?"

And again they felt a strange desire to laugh.

While a child, Tord had once seen a drowned man. He had found the corpse on the beach in broad daylight, and it had not frightened him, but at night his dreams were terrifying. He had seemed to be looking out over an ocean, every wave of which threw a dead body at his feet. He saw all the rocks and islands covered with corpses of the drowned, the drowned that were dead and belonged to the sea, but that could move, and speak, and threaten him with their white stiffened fingers.

And so it was again. The girl whom he had seen in the reeds appeared to him in his dreams. He met her again down at the bottom of the swamp lake, where the light was greener even than in the reeds, and there he had time enough to see that she was beautiful. He dreamed that he sat on one of the great pine roots in the midst of the lake while the tree rocked up and down, now under, now over the surface of the water. Then he saw her on one of the smallest islands. She stood under the red mountain ash and laughed at him. In his very last dream it had gone so far that she had kissed him. But then it was morning, and he heard Berg rising, but he kept his eyes stubbornly closed that he might continue to dream. When he did awake he was dazed and giddy from what he had seen during the night. He thought much more about the girl than he had done the day before. Toward evening it occurred to him to ask Berg if he knew her name.

Berg looked at him sharply. "It is better for you to know it at once," he said. "It was Unn. We are related to each other."

And then Tord knew that it was this pale maiden who was the cause of Berg's wild hunted life in forest and mountain. He tried to search his memory for what he had heard about her.

Unn was the daughter of a free peasant.[3] Her mother was dead, and she ruled in her father's household. This was to her taste, for she was independent by nature, and had no inclination to give herself to any husband. Unn and Berg were cousins, and the rumor had long gone about that Berg liked better to sit with Unn and her maids than to work at home in his own house. One Christmas, when the great banquet was to be given in Berg's hall, his wife had invited a monk from Draksmark, who, she hoped, would show Berg how wrong it was that he should neglect her for another. Berg and others besides him hated this monk because of his appearance. He was very stout and absolutely white. The ring of hair around his bald head, the brows above his moist eyes, the color of his skin, of his hands, and of his

3. *free peasant,* a peasant who was not bound to serve a feudal lord.

garments, were all white. Many found him very repulsive to look at.

But the monk was fearless, and as he believed that his words would have greater weight if many heard them, he rose at the table before all the guests, and said: "Men call the cuckoo the vilest of birds because he brings up his young in the nest of others. But here sits a man who takes no care for his house and his children, and who seeks his pleasure with a strange woman. Him I will call the vilest of men." Unn rose in her place. "Berg, this is said to you and to me," she cried. "Never have I been so shamed, but my father is not here to protect me." She turned to go, but Berg hurried after her. "Stay where you are," she said. "I do not wish to see you again." He stopped her in the corridor, and asked her what he should do that she might stay with him. Her eyes glowed as she answered that he himself should know best what he must do. Then Berg went into the hall again and slew the monk.

Berg and Tord thought on awhile with the same thoughts, then Berg said: "You should have seen her when the white monk fell. My wife drew the children about her and cursed Unn. She turned the faces of the children toward her, that they might always remember the woman for whose sake their father had become a murderer. But Unn stood there so quiet and so beautiful that the men who saw her trembled. She thanked me for the deed, and prayed me to flee to the woods at once. She told me never to become a robber, and to use my knife only in some cause equally just."

"Your deed had ennobled her," said Tord.

And again Berg found himself astonished at the same thing that had before now surprised him in the boy. Tord was a heathen, or worse than a heathen; he never condemned that which was wrong. He seemed to know no sense of responsibility. What had to come, came. He knew of God, of Christ, and the Saints, but he knew them only by name, as one knows the names of the gods of other nations. The ghosts of the Scheeren Islands were his gods. His mother, learned in magic, had taught him to believe in the spirits of the dead. And then it was that Berg undertook a task which was as foolish as if he had woven a rope for his own neck. He opened the eyes of this ignorant boy to the power of God, the Lord of all justice, the avenger of wrong who condemned sinners to the pangs of hell everlasting. And he taught him to love Christ and His Mother, and all the saintly men and women who sit before the throne of God praying that His anger may be turned away from sinners. He taught him all that mankind has learned to do to soften the wrath of God. He told him of the long trains of pilgrims journeying to the holy places; he told him of those who scourged themselves in their remorse; and he told him of the pious monks who flee the joys of this world.

The longer he spoke the paler grew the boy and the keener his attention as his eyes widened at the visions. Berg would have stopped, but the torrent of his own thoughts carried him away. Night sank down upon them, the black forest night, where the scream of the owl shrills ghostly through the stillness. God came so near to them that the brightness of His throne dimmed the stars, and the angels of vengeance descended upon the mountain heights. And below them the flames of the underworld fluttered up to the outer curve of the earth and licked greedily at this last refuge of a race crushed by sin and woe.

Autumn came, and with it came storm. Tord went out alone into the woods to tend the traps and snares, while Berg remained at home to mend his clothes. The boy's path led him up a wooded height along which the falling leaves danced in circles in the gust. Again and again the feeling came to him that some one was walking behind him. He turned several times, then went on again when he had seen that it was only the wind and the leaves. He threatened the rustling circles with his fist, and kept on his way. But he had not silenced the sounds of his vision. At first it was the little dancing feet of elfin children; then it was the hissing of a great snake moving up behind him. Beside the snake there came a wolf, a tall, grey creature, waiting for the moment when the adder should strike at his feet to spring upon his back. Tord hastened his steps, but the visions hastened with him. When they seemed but two steps behind him, ready for the spring, he turned. There was nothing there, as he had known all the time. He sat down upon a stone to rest. The dried leaves played about his feet. The leaves of all the forest trees were there: the little yellow birch leaves, the red-tinged mountain ash leaves, the dried, black-brown foliage of the elm, the bright red aspen leaves, and the yellow-green fringes of the willows. Faded and crumpled, broken and scarred, they were but little like the soft, tender shoots of green that had unrolled from the buds a few months ago.

"Ye are sinners," said the boy. "All of us are sinners. Nothing is pure in the eyes of God. Ye have already been shrivelled up in the flame of His wrath."

Then he went on again, while the forest beneath him waved like a sea in storm, although it was still and calm on the path around him. But he heard something he had never heard before. The wood was full of voices. Now it was like a whispering, now a gentle plaint, now a loud threat, or a roaring curse. It laughed, and it moaned. It was as the voice of hundreds. This unknown something that threatened and excited, that whistled and hissed, a something that seemed to be, and yet was not, almost drove him mad. He shivered in deadly terror, as he had shivered before, the day that he lay on the floor of his cave, and heard his pursuers rage over him through the forest. He seemed to hear again the crashing of the branches, the heavy footsteps of the men, the clanking of their arms, and their wild, bloodthirsty shouts.

It was not alone the storm that roared about him. There was something else in it, something yet more terrible; there were voices he could not understand, sounds as of a strange speech. He had heard many a mightier storm than this roar through the rigging. But he had never heard the wind playing on a harp of so many strings. Every tree seemed to have its own voice, every ravine had another song, the loud echo from the rocky wall shouted back in its own voice. He knew all these tones, but there were other stranger noises with them. And it was these that awoke a storm of voices within his own brain.

He had always been afraid when alone in the darkness of the wood. He loved the open sea and the naked cliffs. Ghosts and spirits lurked here in the shadows of the trees.

Then suddenly he knew who was speaking to him in the storm. It was God, the Great Avenger, the Lord of all Justice. God pursued him because of his comrade. God demanded that he should give up the murderer of the monk to vengeance.

Tord began to speak aloud amid the storm. He told God what he wanted to do, but that he could not do it. He had wanted to speak to the Giant and to beg him make his peace with God. But he could not find the words; embarrassment tied his tongue.

"When I learned that the world is ruled by a God of Justice," he cried, "I knew that he was a lost man. I have wept through the night for my friend. I know that God will find him no matter where he may hide. But I could not speak to him; I could not find the words because of my love for him. Do not ask that I shall speak to him. Do not ask that the ocean shall rise to the height of the mountains."

He was silent again, and the deep voice of the storm, which he knew for God's voice, was silent also. There was a sudden pause in the wind, a burst of sunshine, a sound as of oars, and the gentle rustling of stiff reeds. These soft tones brought up the memory of Unn.

Then the storm began again, and he heard steps behind him, and a breathless panting. He did not dare to turn this time, for he knew that it was the white monk. He came from the banquet in Berg's great hall, covered with blood, and with an open axe cut in his forehead. And he whispered: "Betray him. Give him up, that you may save his soul."

Tord began to run. All this terror grew and grew in him, and he tried to flee from it. But as he ran he heard behind him the deep, mighty voice, which he knew was the voice of God. It was God Himself pursuing him, demanding that he should give up the murderer. Berg's crime seemed more horrible to him than ever it had seemed before. A weaponless man had been murdered, a servant of God cut down by the steel. And the murderer still dared to live. He dared to enjoy the light of the sun and the fruits of the earth. Tord halted, clinched his fists, and shrieked a threat. Then, like a madman, he ran from the forest, the realm of terror, down into the valley.

When Tord entered the cave the outlaw sat upon the bench of stone, sewing. The fire gave but a pale light, and the work did not seem to progress satisfactorily. The boy's heart swelled in pity. This superb Giant seemed all at once so poor and so unhappy.

"What is the matter?" asked Berg. "Are you ill? Have you been afraid?"

Then for the first time Tord spoke of his fear. "It was so strange in the forest. I heard the voices of spirits and I saw ghosts. I saw white monks."

"Boy!"

"They sang to me all the way up the slope to the hilltop. I ran from them, but they ran after me, singing. Can I not lay the spirits? What have I to do with them? There are others to whom their appearance is more necessary."

"Are you crazy tonight, Tord?"

Tord spoke without knowing what words he was using. His shyness had left him all at once, speech seemed to flow from his lips. "They were white monks, as pale as corpses. And their clothes are spotted with blood. They draw their hoods down over their foreheads, but I can see the wound shining there. The great, yawning, red wound from the axe."

"Tord," said the Giant, pale and deeply grave, "the Saints alone know why you see wounds of axe thrusts. I slew the monk with a knife."

Tord stood before Berg trembling and wringing his hands. "They demand you of me. They would compel me to betray you."

"Who? The monks?"

"Yes, yes, the monks. They show me visions. They show me Unn. They show me the open, sunny ocean. They show me the camps of the fishermen, where there is dancing and merriment. I close my eyes, and yet I can see it all. 'Leave me,' I say to them. 'My friend has committed a murder, but he is not bad. Leave me alone, and I will talk to him, that he may repent and atone. He will see the wrong he has done, and he will make a pilgrimage to the Holy Grave.' "

"And what do the monks answer?" asked Berg. "They do not want to pardon me. They want to torture me and to burn me at the stake."

" 'Shall I betray my best friend?' I ask them. He is all that I have in the world. He saved me from the bear when its claws were already at my throat. We have suffered hunger and cold together. He covered me with his own garments while I was ill. I have brought him wood and water, I have watched over his sleep, and led his enemies off the trail. Why should they think me a man who betrays his friend? My friend will go to the priest himself, and will confess to him, and then together we will seek absolution."

Berg listened gravely, his keen eyes searching in Tord's face. "Go to the priest yourself, and tell him the truth. You must go back again among mankind."

"What does it help if I go alone? The spirits of the dead follow me because of your sin. Do you not see how I tremble before you? You have lifted your hand against God himself. What crime is like unto yours? Why did you tell me about the just God? It is you yourself who compel me to betray you. Spare me this sin. Go to the priest yourself." He sank down on his knees before Berg.

The murderer laid his hand on his head and looked at him. He measured his sin by the terror of his comrade, and it grew and grew to a monstrous size. He saw himself in conflict with the Will that rules the world. Remorse entered his heart.

"Woe unto me that I did what I did," he said. "And is not this miserable life, this life we lead here in terror, and in deprivation, is it not atonement enough? Have I not lost home and fortune? Have I not lost friends, and all the joys that make the life of a man? What more?"

As he heard him speak thus, Tord sprang up in wild terror. "You can repent!" he cried. "My words move your heart? Oh, come with me, come at once. Come, let us go while yet there is time."

Berg the Giant sprang up also. "You—did it—?"

"Yes, yes, yes. I have betrayed you. But come quickly. Come now, now that you can repent. We must escape. We will escape."

The murderer stooped to the ground where the battle-ax of his fathers lay at his feet. "Son of a thief," he hissed. "I trusted you—I loved you."

But when Tord saw him stoop for the axe, he knew that it was his own life that was in peril now. He tore his own axe from his girdle, and thrust at Berg before the latter could rise. The Giant fell headlong to the floor, the blood spurting out over the cave. Between the tangled masses of hair Tord saw the great, yawning, red wound of an axe thrust.

Then the peasants stormed into the cave. They praised his deed and told him that he should receive full pardon.

Tord looked down at his hands, as if he saw there the fetters that had drawn him on to kill the man he loved. Like the chains of the Fenrir wolf,[4] they were woven out of empty air. They were woven out of the green light amid the reeds, out of the play of shadows in the woods, out of the song of the storm, out of the rustling of the leaves, out of the magic vision of dreams. And he said aloud: "God is great."

He crouched beside the body, spoke amid his tears to the dead, and begged him to awake. The villagers made a litter of their spears, on which to carry the body of the free peasant to his home. The dead man aroused awe in their souls, they softened their voices in his presence. When they raised him on to the bier, Tord stood up, shook the hair from his eyes, and spoke in a voice that trembled:

"Tell Unn, for whose sake Berg the Giant became a murderer, that Tord the fisherman, whose father plunders wrecks, and whose mother is a witch—tell her that Tord slew Berg because Berg had taught him that justice is the cornerstone of the world."

THE END

---

4. *Fenrir wolf,* in Norse mythology, a monster wolf who could only be restrained by a magic chain forged by dwarfs.

Development

INTERPRETATION

1. (a) Why should Tord's crime of stealing a herring net appear as especially despicable in the eyes of Berg? (b) How does Tord react to Berg, initially? (c) Does your attitude toward them differ from their attitudes toward one another? Why or why not?

2. Explain the irony of these situations in the story: (a) Berg is an outlaw because he murdered a monk. Tord is an outlaw because he pretended to be a thief in order to protect his father. Berg holds Tord in contempt. (b) Tord approves of Berg's murdering the monk; Berg disapproves of Tord's approval.

3. Tord's response to Berg's stirring tale of the monk's murder and Unn's pride in it is to say, "Your deed had ennobled her." (a) What does this mean? (b) How does the statement affect Berg?

4. After hearing Berg's explanation of religion, Tord becomes afraid and is beset by visions which he finally concludes to be "the voice of God." (a) What other instances of Tord's fear have we seen before this one? (b) What is there in Tord's character that makes him regard the forest as a "realm of terror"?

5. When Tord realizes the horror he has committed in slaying Berg, he "looked down at his hands, as if he saw there the fetters that had drawn him on to kill the man he loved." (a) What do these fetters represent? (b) In what sense had they drawn Tord on to kill a man he loved?

6. Tord's reaction to the sight of his fettered hands is to exclaim, "God is great." (a) What about the preceding events has led him to make this statement? (b) What is Tord's understanding of the "greatness" of God? (c) Discuss the irony of this statement in the context of the story.

TECHNIQUE

1. (a) Cite the details which suggest the approximate time period of the story. (b) Describe the setting and characterize its atmosphere. (c) How is the implied time appropriate to the setting?

2. Near the beginning of the story, Lagerlöf describes an incident which is central to an understanding of the character of the peasant outlaw Berg and to the story itself: his battle with the hawks while his pursuers look for him below (page 33, column 1, lines 2-39). (a) What character traits does Berg reveal in the incident? (b) Where does a pine tree recur in the story? (c) What characteristics of Berg's are reflected in the pine? (d) What parallels are there between this incident and the main plot of the story?

3. (a) Cite some of the numerous supernatural elements in the story. (b) Discuss the way in which these details forebode the final scene and increase its impact. (c) Reread the paragraph describing the "black swampy lake" (page 35, column 2, paragraph 4), and discuss the possible symbolic meanings of the lake, the blackened roots, and the rocky slopes.

4. One of the visions which Tord sees is a monk with an open axe-cut in his head, although Berg later tells him that he slew the monk with a knife. (a) What does Tord's vision foreshadow? (b) What does it indicate about the tendency of his thoughts at the time?

EXTENSIONS

1. Man has continually been faced with the irony of nations and individuals who kill and destroy in the name of a religion of peace and charity. (a) How can such an inconsistency be explained? (b) Can it ever be justified? Discuss.

Comparison

1. (a) Identify the judge and the judged in each story. (b) Summarize the conflict between two views of justice expressed in each. (c) Which judge appears to make the best decision? Defend your own judgment.

2. (a) What makes Daniel's decision more difficult than that of the human judges in Čapek's story and thus closer to the stalemate-situation of Čapek's God? (b) What differences are there in the two situations which make it impossible for Daniel, like God, to refrain from judging?

3. Compare and contrast the idea of God as it appears in Čapek's "The Last Judgment" and in Lagerlöf's "The Outlaws." Consider the following points: (a) His power; (b) His love; (c) His demands on mankind; (d) His wrath.

4. Discuss the following, and point out and explain any flaws of interpretation which you find:

(a) Čapek's "The Last Judgment" and Lagerlöf's "The Outlaws" express basically the same point about human nature: that men prefer to ignore the voice of God and to condemn their fellow-creatures without understanding or charity.

(b) Silone's "The Trap" represents vicious anti-idealism. Here the virtuous hero is reduced to hysterical despair as the result of doing a noble deed. "The Trap" is to be contrasted to a highly moral work like Lagerlöf's "The Outlaws" wherein Tord, the instrument of God's justice, triumphs and exults in his triumph.

(c) Daniel's tragic error in "The Trap" comes as a result of ignorance. But, ironically, had he possessed the knowledge of Čapek's God ("The Last Judgment") he would have been forced to commit the same error—too much knowledge about human nature makes one as ineffectual as too little.

5. Read the following paragraph:

"The Trap" is realistic topical fiction, whose central purpose is propaganda, in this case anti-Fascist propaganda. "The Outlaws" is a fantasy, whose purpose is to suggest truths about the subconscious, in this case about the fears and weaknesses buried there. "The Last Judgment" is a parable, whose purpose is to portray an abstract idea, in this case an idea about man's unworthiness and God's separation from him.

(a) Are the categories—realistic topical fiction, fantasy, parable—distinct and clear enough to be useful? Discuss. (b) Do the three stories fit any other categories of technique besides those suggested here? (c) Is there any overlapping of technique that the passage ignores?

6. All three of these stories are concerned with revealing the difficulties of justice: they show "good" human beings doing what they sincerely feel to be the just thing and yet failing—either in their own eyes or in the eyes of the reader. The following lines from Shakespeare's *Merchant of Venice* take a more positive approach to justice:

> But mercy is above this sceptered sway,
> It is enthroned in the hearts of kings,
> It is an attribute to God himself,
> And earthly power doth then show likest
>   God's
> When mercy seasons justice. (Act 4, Scene
>   I, lines 193-197)

(a) How might the choices of the judges in the three stories have differed had they assumed this attitude toward justice? (b) Would the decisions of the judges have appeared more honorable to us had they acted on this view? (c) Does the introduction of "mercy" into the description help solve any of the problems which the stories bring up? If so, in what way?

BLACK WITH RED STRIPE by Antonio Tapies. Courtesy of the Martha Jackson Gallery, New York.

The Lonely People

THE DARLING / ANTON CHEKHOV / RUSSIA

IRENE HOLM / HERMAN JOACHIM BANG / DENMARK

A SIMPLE HEART / GUSTAVE FLAUBERT / FRANCE

The Darling

ANTON CHEKHOV / Russia
(1860 – 1904)
translated from the Russian by Ann Dunnigan

Olenka, the daughter of the retired collegiate assessor Plemyannikov, was sitting on the little porch that faced the courtyard, lost in thought. It was hot, the flies were annoyingly persistent, and it was pleasant to think that it would soon be evening. Dark rain clouds were gathering from the east, bringing with them an occasional breath of moisture.

Kukin, a theater manager who ran an amusement garden known as the Tivoli, and who lodged in the wing of the house, was standing in the middle of the courtyard staring up at the sky.

"Again!" he said in despair. "It's going to rain again! Every day it rains; every day, as if to spite me! I might just as well put a noose around my neck! It's ruin! Every day terrible losses!"

He clasped his hands, turned to Olenka and went on, "That's our life for you, Olga Semyonovna. It's enough to make you weep! You work, you do your very best, you worry and lose sleep, always thinking how to make it better—and what happens? On the one hand, the public is ignorant, barbarous. I give them the very best operetta, a pantomime, magnificent vaudeville artists—but do you think that's what they want? Do you think they understand it? What they want is slapstick! Give them trash! And then, look at the weather! Rain almost every evening. It started the tenth of May and it's been raining incessantly ever since—all May and June. Simply dreadful! The public doesn't come, but I still have to pay the rent, don't I—and the artists?"

The next day toward evening the clouds again appeared, and, laughing hysterically, Kukin said, "Well, go on, rain! Flood the whole park, drown me! Bad luck to me in this world and the next! Let the artists sue me! Let them send me to prison—to Siberia—to the scaffold! Ha! Ha! Ha!"

And the third day it was the same. . . .

Olenka listened to Kukin gravely, silently, and sometimes tears would come into her eyes. She was so moved by his misfortunes that she ended by falling in love with him. He was an emaciated little man with a yellow face and hair combed down over his temples; he spoke in a thin tenor voice, twisting his mouth to one side, and despair was permanently engraved on his face; nevertheless, he aroused a deep and genuine feeling in her. She was always in love with someone and could not live otherwise. First it had been her papa, who was now ill and sat in an armchair in a darkened room, breathing with difficulty; then it had been her aunt, who used to come from Bryansk every other year; and before that, when she was at school, she had been in love with her French teacher. She was a quiet, good-natured, compassionate girl with meek, gentle eyes and very good health. At the sight of her full, rosy cheeks, her soft, white neck with a dark little mole on it, and the kind, ingenuous smile that came over her face when she listened to anything pleasant, men thought, "Yes, not bad!'' and smiled too, while the ladies present could not refrain from suddenly seizing her hand in the middle of a conversation and exclaiming in an outburst of delight, "You darling!"

The house she had lived in since birth, and which, according to her father's will, was to be hers, was located on the outskirts of the city on Gypsy Road, not far from the Tivoli. In the evenings and at night when she heard the band playing and skyrockets exploding, it seemed to her that it was Kukin at war with his fate, assaulting his chief enemy, the apathetic public; then her heart melted, she had no desire to sleep, and when he returned home at daybreak she would tap softly at her bedroom window and, letting him see only her face and one shoulder through the curtain, would smile tenderly at him. . . .

He proposed to her and they were married. And when he had a good look at her neck and her plump, fine shoulders, he clapped his hands together and exclaimed, "Darling!"

He was happy, but as it rained both the day and the night of the wedding, his expression of despair remained unchanged.

They got on well together. She presided over the box office, looked after things in the garden, kept the accounts and paid the salaries; and her rosy cheeks, her sweet, artless smile, shone now in the box-office window, now in the wings of the theater, now at the buffet. She began telling her friends that the most remarkable, the most important and essential thing in the whole world was the theater—that only through the theater could one derive true pleasure and become a cultivated and humane person.

"But do you suppose the public understands that?" she would ask. "What it wants is slapstick! Yesterday we gave *Faust Inside Out*, and almost every box was empty, but if Vanichka and I had put on some kind of trash, then, believe me, the theater would have been packed. Tomorrow Vanichka and I are putting on *Orpheus in Hell*.[1] Do come."

Whatever Kukin said about the theater and the actors she repeated. Like him she despised the public for its ignorance and indifference to art; she took a hand in the rehearsals, correcting the actors, kept an eye on the conduct of the musicians, and when there was an unfavorable notice in the local newspaper, shed tears, and then went to the editor for an explanation.

The actors loved her and called her "Vanichka and I" and "the darling." She was sorry for them and used to lend them small sums of money, and if they deceived her she wept in secret but did not complain to her husband.

They got on well in the winter too. They leased the municipal theater for the season and sublet it for short periods to a Ukrainian troupe, a magician, or a local dramatic club. Olenka grew plumper and was always beaming with satisfaction, while Kukin grew thinner and yellower and complained of terrible losses, although business was not bad during the winter. He coughed at night and she would give him an infusion of raspberries and linden blossoms, rub him with eau de Cologne, and wrap him in her soft shawls.

"What a sweet precious you are!" she would say with perfect sincerity, as she stroked his hair. "My handsome pet!"

At Lent he went to Moscow to gather a new troupe, and without him she could not sleep, but sat all night at the window looking at the stars. She likened herself to the hens, which also stay awake all night and are uneasy when the cock is not in the henhouse. Kukin was detained in Moscow, wrote that he would return by Easter, and in his letters sent instructions regarding the Tivoli. But on the Monday of Passion Week, late in the evening, there was a sudden ominous knocking at the gate; someone was hammering at the wicket as if it were a barrel—boom! boom! boom! The sleepy cook, splashing through

---

1. *Faust Inside Out . . . Orpheus in Hell*. These are probably fictitious plays, but the titles are meant to suggest "high-brow" entertainment.

the puddles in her bare feet, ran to open the gate.

"Open, please!" said someone on the other side of the gate in a deep bass voice. "There is a telegram for you!"

Olenka had received telegrams from her husband before, but this time for some reason she felt numb with fright. She opened the telegram with trembling hands and read:

IVAN PETROVICH DIED SUDDENLY TODAY AWAITING THISD INSTRUC-TIONS FUFUNERAL TUESDAY.

That was exactly the way the telegram had it: "fufuneral" and the incomprehensible word "thisd"; it was signed by the director of the operetta company.

"My precious!" Olenka sobbed. "Vanichka, my precious, my dearest! Why did we ever meet? Why did I know you and love you? Whom can your poor forsaken Olenka turn to now?"

Kukin was buried on Tuesday in the Vagankovo cemetery in Moscow. Olenka returned home on Wednesday, and as soon as she reached her room she sank onto the bed and sobbed so loudly that she could be heard in the street and in the neighboring courtyards.

"The darling!" said the neighbors, crossing themselves. "Darling Olga Semyonovna! Poor soul, how she grieves!"

Three months later Olenka was returning from mass one day, in deep mourning and very sad. It happened that one of her neighbors, Vasily Andreich Pustovalov, the manager of Babakayev's lumberyard, was also returning from church and walked with her. He wore a straw hat, a white waistcoat with a gold watch chain, and looked more like a landowner than a merchant.

"Everything happens as it is ordained, Olga Semyonovna," he said gravely, with a note of sympathy in his voice, "and if one of our dear ones passes on, we must take ourselves in hand and bear it submissively."

Having seen Olenka to her gate, he said good-bye and went on. All day long she seemed to hear his grave voice, and as soon as she closed her eyes she dreamed of his dark beard. She liked him very much. And apparently she had made an impression on him too, because not long afterwards an elderly lady whom she scarcely knew came to have coffee with her, and as soon as she was seated at the table began to talk of Pustovalov, saying that he was a fine steady man and that any marriageable woman would be happy to marry him. Three days later Pustovalov himself paid her a visit. He did not stay long, not more than ten minutes, and said little, but Olenka fell in love with him—she was so much in love that she lay awake all night, inflamed as with a fever, and in the morning she sent for the elderly lady. The betrothal was arranged, and the wedding followed soon afterwards.

After they were married Pustovalov and Olenka got on very well together. As a rule he was in the lumberyard till dinnertime, then he went out on business and Olenka took his place and sat in the office till evening, making out bills and dispatching orders.

"Every year the price of lumber rises twenty per cent," she would say to customers and acquaintances. "Why, we used to deal in local timber, but now Vasichka has to travel to the province of Mogilev every year for wood. And the freight!" she would add, covering her cheeks with her hands in horror. "The freight!"

It seemed to her that she had been in the lumber business for ages and ages, that lumber was the most important and essential thing in life, and she found something touching, dear to her, in such words as *girder, beam, plank, batten, boxboard, lath, scantling, slab.* . . . At night she would dream of whole mountains of boards and planks, long endless caravans of wagons carrying lumber to some distant place; she dreamed of a whole regiment of eight-inch beams twenty-eight feet long standing on end, marching on the lumberyard, beams, girders, slabs, striking against one another with the hollow sound of dry wood, all falling, then rising, piling themselves one upon another. . . . When she cried out in her sleep Pustovalov would speak to her tenderly, saying, "Olenka, what's the matter, darling? Cross yourself!"

Whatever ideas her husband had became her own. If he thought the room was hot or business was slow, she thought so too. Her husband did not care for entertainment of any kind, and on holidays stayed at home, and so did she.

"You are always at home or in the office," her friends said to her. "You ought to go to the theater, darling, or to the circus."

"Vasichka and I have no time for the theater," she would reply sedately. "We are working people, we're not interested in such foolishness. What's the good of those theaters?"

On Saturday evenings they would go to vespers, on holidays to early mass, and as they walked home side by side their faces reflected the emotion of the service. There was an agreeable aroma about them both, and her silk dress rustled pleasantly. At home they had tea and buns with various kinds of jam, and afterwards a pie. Every day at noon, in the yard and beyond the gate in the street, there was a delicious smell of borsch and roast lamb or duck and, on fast days, fish; no one could pass their gate without feeling hungry. In the office the samovar was always boiling and the customers were treated to tea and cracknels. Once a week they went to the baths and returned side by side, both very red.

"Yes, everything goes well with us, thank God," Olenka would say to her friends. "I wish everyone were as happy as Vasichka and I."

When Pustovalov went to the province of Mogilev to buy timber, she missed him dreadfully, and lay awake nights crying. Sometimes in the evening Smirnin, a young army veterinarian to whom they rented the wing of the house, came to see her. They chatted or played cards, and this diverted her. She was especially interested in what he told her of his domestic life. He was married and had a son, but was separated from his wife because she had been unfaithful to him, and now he hated her; he sent her forty rubles a month for the support of the child. Listening to all this, Olenka sighed, shook her head, and was sorry for him.

"Well, God keep you," she would say, accompanying him to the stairs with a candle. "Thank you for passing the time with me, and may the Queen of Heaven give you health."

She always expressed herself in this grave, circumspect manner in imitation of her husband. Just as the veterinarian was about to disappear behind the door below, she would call to him and say, "You know, Vladimir Platonych, you ought to make it up with your wife. For your son's sake, you should forgive her! The little fellow probably understands everything."

When Pustovalov returned she would tell him in a low voice all about the veterinarian and his unhappy life, and they both would sigh, shake their heads, and talk about the little boy, who very likely missed his father. Then, by some strange association of ideas, they both stood before the ikons, bowed to the ground, and prayed that God would send them children.

Thus the Pustovalovs lived quietly and peaceably, in love and complete harmony for six years. Then one winter day, after drinking hot tea in the office, Vasily Andreich went out without his cap to dispatch some lumber, caught cold, and was taken ill. He was treated by the best doctors, but the illness had its way with him, and after four months he died. And again Olenka was a widow.

"Whom can I turn to, my darling?" she sobbed, after burying her husband. "How can I live without you, miserable and unhappy as I am? Good people, pity me!"

She went about in a black dress with weepers, gave up wearing a hat and gloves for good, seldom went out of the house except to go to church or to visit her husband's grave, and at home she lived like a nun. Only after six months did she take off her widow's weeds and open the shutters of her windows. Occasionally she was seen in the mornings, going with her cook to the market, but how she lived and what went on in her house could only be surmised. People based their conjectures on the fact that she was seen drinking tea in her garden with the veterinarian, that he read the newspaper aloud to her, and that, on meeting an acquaintance in the post office, she said, "There is no proper veterinary inspection in our city, and that's why there is so much sickness around. You often hear of people getting ill from milk or catching infections from horses and cows. The health of domestic animals ought to be just as well looked after as the health of human beings."

She repeated the ideas of the veterinarian, and now was of the same opinion as he about everything. It was clear that she could not live even a year without some attachment, and had found new happiness in the wing of her own house. Another woman would have been censured for this, but no one could think ill of Olenka; everything about her was so natural. Neither she nor the veterinarian spoke to anyone of the change in their relations, and tried, indeed, to conceal it, but they did not succeed because Olenka could not keep a secret. When his regimental colleagues visited him, while she poured tea for them or served supper she would talk of the cattle plague, the pearl disease, the municipal slaughterhouses. He would be dreadfully embarrassed, and when the guests had gone, would seize her by the arm and hiss angrily, "I've asked you before not to talk about things you don't understand! When we veterinarians are talking among ourselves, please don't interfere! It's really annoying!"

She would look at him in amazement and anxiously inquire, "But, Volodochka, what am I to talk about?" Then, with tears in her eyes, she would embrace him, begging him not to be angry, and they were both happy.

This happiness did not last long. The veterinarian went away with his regiment, went away forever, as the regiment was transferred to some distant place—it may even have been Siberia. And Olenka was left alone.

Now she was quite alone. Her father had died long ago; his armchair lay in the attic, covered with dust and with one leg missing. She grew thin and plain, and when people met her in the street they did not glance at her and smile as they used to; clearly, her best years were over and behind her, and now a new, uncertain life was beginning, one that did not bear thinking of. In the evening, as she sat on her porch, Olenka could hear the band playing and skyrockets going off at the Tivoli, but this no longer called up anything to her mind. She gazed indifferently into her empty courtyard, thought of nothing, wished for nothing, and later, when darkness fell, she went to bed and dreamed of the empty courtyard. She ate and drank as though involuntarily.

Above all—and worst of all—she no longer had any opinions whatever. She saw objects about her, understood what was going on, but could not form an opinion about anything and did not know what to talk about. And how awful it is to have no opinions! You see a bottle, for instance, or rain, or a peasant driving a cart, but what the bottle, the rain, or the peasant may be for, what the significance of them is, you cannot say, and could not even for a thousand rubles. When Kukin was with her, or Pustovalov, or later, the veterinarian, Olenka could explain everything, could express an opinion on anything you like, but now there was the same emptiness in her mind and heart as in her courtyard. It was painful, and bitter as wormwood in the mouth.

Little by little the town was spreading in all directions; Gypsy Road was now a street, and where the gardens of the Tivoli and the lumberyards had been, houses sprang up and lanes formed. How swiftly time passes! Olenka's house grew shabby, the roof was rusty, the shed sloped, and the whole yard was overgrown with tall grass and prickly nettles. Olenka herself had aged and grown plain; in the summer she sat on the porch, and her soul was empty, bleak, and bitter; in the winter she sat at the window and stared at the snow. There were times when a breath of spring or the sound of church bells brought to her on the wind would suddenly provoke a rush of memories; then her heart melted, her eyes brimmed with tears, but this lasted only a moment, and there was again emptiness and uncertainty as to the purpose of life. Bryska, the black kitten, rubbed against her, purring softly, but Olenka was not affected by these feline caresses. Was that what she needed? She wanted a love that would take possession of her whole soul, her mind, that would give her ideas, a direction in life, that would warm her old blood. She shook the black kitten off her lap and said irritably, "Get away! Go on! There's nothing for you here!"

And so it was, day after day, year after year, no joy whatsoever, no opinions of any sort. Whatever Mavra the cook said, she accepted.

One hot July day, toward evening, when the cattle were being driven home and the whole yard was filled with clouds of dust, someone unexpectedly knocked at the gate. Olenka went to open it herself and was astounded at what she saw: there stood Smirnin, the veterinarian, his hair gray, and in civilian dress. All at once she remembered everything and, unable to control herself, burst into tears, dropping her head onto his breast without a word. She was so moved that she scarcely was aware of going into the house and sitting down to tea with him.

"My dear!" she murmured, trembling with joy. "Vladimir Platonych! What brings you here?"

"I have come here for good," he said. "I've retired from the army and I want to settle down and try my luck on my own. And besides, it's time for my son to go to high school. He's growing up. I am reconciled with my wife, you know."

"Where is she?" asked Olenka.

"She's at the hotel with the boy, and I'm out looking for lodgings."

"Good heavens, my dear, take my house! Lodgings! Goodness, I wouldn't take any rent for it," cried Olenka, growing excited and weeping again. "You live here, and the wing will do for me. Heavens, how glad I am!"

The next day they began painting the roof and white-washing the walls, and Olenka, with her arms akimbo, walked about the yard giving orders. Her face beamed with her old smile, and she was animated and fresh, as though she had waked from a long sleep. The veterinarian's wife arrived, thin and homely, with short hair and a capricious expression. With her came the little boy, Sasha, small for his age (he was going on ten), chubby, with bright blue eyes and dimples in his cheeks. No sooner had he entered the courtyard than he began chasing the cat, and immediately his gay and joyous laughter could be heard.

"Auntie, is that your cat?" he asked Olenka. "When she has little ones, please give us one of her kittens. Mama is terribly afraid of mice."

Olenka talked to him, gave him tea, and her heart grew suddenly warm and there was a sweet ache in her bosom, as if this little boy were her own son. In the evening when he sat in the dining room doing his homework, she gazed at him with tenderness and pity as she whispered, "My darling, my pretty one. . . . How clever you are, my little one, and so fair!"

"An island," he read aloud from the book, "is a body of land entirely surrounded by water."

"An island is a body of land . . ." she repeated, and this was the first opinion she had uttered with conviction after years of silence and emptiness of mind.

She now had opinions of her own, and at supper she talked to Sasha's parents about how difficult the lessons were for children in the high school, but that, nevertheless, a classical education was better than a technical course, because it opened all avenues—you could be a doctor . . . an engineer. . . .

Sasha started going to high school. His mother went to Kharkov to visit her sister and did not come back; his father used to go away every day to inspect herds, and he sometimes was away for three days together. It seemed to Olenka that Sasha was quite forsaken, that he was unwanted, that he was being starved to death, and she moved him into the wing with her and settled him in a little room there.

For six months now Sasha has been living in her wing. Every morning Olenka goes into his room where he lies fast asleep, his hand under his cheek, breathing quietly. She is always sorry to wake him.

"Sashenka," she says sadly, "get up, darling. It's time for school."

He gets up, dresses, says his prayers, and sits down to breakfast; he drinks three glasses of tea, eats two large cracknels and half a buttered roll. He is still not quite awake and consequently ill-humored.

"Now, Sashenka, you have not learned your fable very well," Olenka says, gazing at him as if she were seeing him off on a long journey. "You are such a worry to me! You must do your best, darling; you must study. . . . Pay attention to your teachers."

"Oh, leave me alone, please!" he says.

Then he walks down the street to school, a little figure in a big cap, with a knapsack on his back. Olenka silently follows him.

"Sashenka-a!" she calls. And when he looks round she thrusts a date or a caramel into his hand. When they turn in to the school lane he feels ashamed of being followed by a tall, stout lady; he looks back and says, "You'd better go home, Auntie. I can go alone now."

She stops, but does not take her eyes off him until he has disappeared into the school entrance. Ah, how she loves him! Not one of her former attachments had been so deep; never before had her soul surrendered itself so devotedly and with such joy as now, when her maternal feelings have been quickened. For this little boy who is not her own, for the dimples in his cheeks, for his cap, she would give her whole life, would give it with joy and tears of tenderness. Why? But who knows why?

Having seen Sasha off to school she goes quietly home, contented, serene, full of love; her face, grown younger in the last six months, beams with joy; people meeting her look at her with pleasure and say, "Good morning, Olga Semyonovna, darling. How are you, darling?"

"The lessons in school are so difficult nowadays," she says, as she goes about her marketing. "It's no joke. Yesterday in the first class they gave him a fable to learn by heart, a Latin translation, and a problem. . . . You know, it's too much for the little fellow."

And she begins talking about the teachers, the lessons, the textbooks— saying just what Sasha says about them.

At three o'clock they have dinner together; in the evening they do the homework together, and cry. When she puts him to bed she takes a long time making the sign of the cross over him and whispering a prayer. Then she goes to bed and dreams of that faraway, misty future when Sasha, having finished his studies, will become a doctor or an engineer, will have a large house of his own, horses, a carriage, when he will marry and have children of his own. . . . She falls asleep, still thinking of the same thing, and the tears run down her cheeks from under closed eyelids, while the black cat lies beside her purring: mrr . . . mrr . . . mrr. . . .

Suddenly there is a loud knock at the gate and Olenka wakes up, breathless with fear, her heart pounding. Half a minute later there is another knock.

"It's a telegram from Kharkov," she thinks, her whole body trembling. "Sasha's mother is sending for him. . . . Oh, Lord!"

She is in despair, her head, hands, and feet are cold, and it seems to her that she is the most unfortunate woman in the whole world. But another moment passes, she hears voices: it is the veterinarian coming home from the club.

"Well, thank God!" she thinks. Gradually the weight on her heart lifts, and she feels relieved; she goes back to bed and thinks of Sasha, who is fast asleep in the next room, sometimes crying out in his sleep, "I'll give it to you! Go on! No fighting!"

THE END

Development

INTERPRETATION

1. (a) How do the other characters in the story react to Olenka? (b) Why do they react as they do? (c) Is your attitude toward her the same as theirs? If not, how would you account for the difference?

2. The English word *darling* and the Russian word *dusheckha* (the original title) are both used as terms of endearment. However, the English word is less specific than the Russian, which means "dear little soul." How is this additional meaning, which is lost in translation, relevant to the character?

3. When Olenka falls in love with the veterinary surgeon, Chekhov remarks that she had nothing to fear from public opinion. His explanation of this is left rather vague: ". . . no one could think ill of Olenka; everything about her was so natural." (a) What does this explanation imply about the reasons people think ill of others? (b) What does Chekhov mean by the word *natural*? (c) Describe the tone of Chekhov's explanation.

4. Leo Tolstoy felt that although Chekhov tried to be objective, subconsciously he could not refrain from judging Olenka. As a result, according to Tolstoy, a hint of mockery pervades the story. Do you agree? Cite evidence to either defend or refute Tolstoy's theory.

5. The last line of the story is a cry which Sasha utters in a dream: "I'll give it to you! Go on! No fighting!" (a) Although we have no way of knowing what this "it" actually refers to, how is the reader likely to interpret it? (b) How are Olenka's feelings at this time in contrast to Sasha's? (c) Who is the more sympathetic character at this point, Sasha or Olenka? (d) Have your feelings about Olenka undergone any change from the beginning to the end of the story? If so, how would you describe this change, and why did it take place?

TECHNIQUE

1. (a) What differences are there in the occupations, temperaments, and appearances of Olenka's two husbands? (b) What does the contrast between them contribute to the characterization of Olenka? (c) What specific instances of irony come into play when Olenka's opinions during the second marriage are compared with her opinions during the first?

2. (a) How does Olenka's attachment to Sasha differ from her previous relationships? (b) How does describing this attachment in the present tense affect our reaction to it? (c) What might this tense change suggest about Olenka's future?

Irene Holm

HERMAN JOACHIM BANG / Denmark

(1857—1912)

translated from the Danish by Jacob Wittmer Hartmann

It was announced by the constable's son from the church steps after the services one Sunday that Miss Irene Holm, danseuse[1] at the Royal Theatre, would begin her courses in etiquette, dancing, and gesture, in the inn, on the first of November, for children as well as for those more advanced—ladies and gentlemen—provided a sufficient number of applications be made. Price, five crowns[2] for each child; reduction for several from the same family.

Seven applied, Jens Larsen furnishing the three, at the reduced rate. Miss Irene Holm considered the number sufficient. She arrived at the inn one evening toward the end of October, her baggage an old champagne basket tied with a rope. She was small and worn, with a forty-year-old baby face under her fur cap, and old handkerchiefs tied about her wrists as a protection against rheumatism. She enunciated very distinctly and said, "Thank you so much—but I can do it myself," whenever any one offered to do anything for her and she looked quite helpless. She would have nothing but a cup of tea and then crept into her bed in the little chamber behind the public room, her teeth chattering whenever she thought of the possibility of ghosts.

The next day she appeared with her hair curled, and wearing a close-fitting coat edged with fur, on which the tooth of time had left a visible impress. She had to pay visits to her honored patrons, the parents of her pupils, she said. And might she ask the way? Mrs. Hendriksen went to the doorway and pointed over the flat fields. Miss Holm curtsied her thanks to the three doorsteps.

"Old thing," said Mrs. Hendriksen. She remained standing in the doorway and looked after Miss Holm, who was taking a roundabout way to Jens Larsen's house on the dike, to spare her footgear. Miss Holm was shod in goatskin boots and wore ribbed stockings.

When she had visited the parents—Jens Larsen paid nine crowns for his three—Miss Holm looked about for a room. She got a little whitewashed chamber at the smith's, looking out upon the flat fields, and furnished with a bureau, a bed, and a chair. In the corner, between the bureau and the window, the champagne basket was set down. Miss Holm moved in. The morning was spent in making applications of curling pins, cold tea and warm slate pencils. When the curls were in order, she tidied the room, and in the afternoon she crocheted. She sat on the champagne basket in the corner and took advantage of the last vestige of daylight. The smith's wife came in and sat down on the wooden chair and talked, while Miss Holm listened, smiling graciously and nodding her curled head.

The woman spun out the story in the

"Irene Holm" by Herman Joachim Bang from *The American-Scandinavian Review,* (May, 1916). Reprinted by permission of The American-Scandinavian Foundation.

1. *danseuse* (dän süs′), the French term for a female ballet dancer. 2. *five crowns.* The crown is the standard monetary unit of Denmark. Currently worth about fourteen cents, its value at the time of the story is difficult to determine.

dark for an hour, until it was time for supper, but Miss Holm scarcely knew what she had said. Outside of dancing and gesture, and calculations as to her daily bread—a tedious, eternal calculation —the things of this world had much difficulty in forcing their way into Miss Holm's consciousness. She sat still on her basket with her hands in her lap and only looked fixedly at the line of light under the smith's door. She never went out, for she became homesick as soon as she saw the desolate flat fields, and she was afraid of bulls and of runaway horses. Later in the evening, she would boil water in the tiled oven and eat supper. Then she would put up her curls in papers, and when she had undressed as far as her petticoats, she would practice her steps at the bed-post, moving her legs until it made her perspire.

The smith and his wife did not budge from the keyhole. They had a rear view of the leaps of the ballet; the curling-papers stood out from her head like quills upon the fretful porcupine. Miss Holm was so engrossed that she began to hum aloud as she moved up, down, up, down, in her exercises. The smith and his wife and the children were glued to the keyhole.

When Miss Holm had practiced the prescribed number of minutes, she crept into bed. After practicing she always thought of the time "when she was a student at the ballet-school," and suddenly she would laugh aloud, a carefree laugh, just as she lay there. She fell asleep, still thinking of the time—the happy time —the rehearsals, when they stuck each other's legs with pins . . . and screamed . . . the evenings in the dressing-rooms . . . what a bustle, all the voices . . . and the director's bell. . . . Miss Holm would still wake up at night, if she dreamt of having missed an entrance.

"Now—one—two—" Miss Holm raised her skirt and put out her foot . . . "toes out—one—two—three."

The seven had their toes turned inward—with their fingers in their mouths as they hopped about.

"Little Jens—toes out—one—two— three—make a bow—one—two—three— once more . . ."

Jens Larsen's three children made the bow with their tongues sticking rigidly out of their mouths.

"Little Marie to the right—one—two— three—." Marie went to the left. . . . "Do it over—one—two—three—"

Miss Holm jumped about as a kid, so that a goodly portion of her stockings was visible. The course was in full progress. They danced three times a week in the inn-room with two lamps that hung from the beams. The ancient dust arose in the old room under their stamping. The seven were as completely at sea as a school of fish. Miss Holm straightened their backs and curved their arms.

"One—two—three—clap hands."

"One—two—three—clap hands." The seven staggered as they did so and nearly lost their balance.

Miss Holm got dust in her throat through shouting. They were to dance a waltz, two by two, held each other at arm's length, awkwardly and nervously, as though turning in their sleep. Miss Holm talked and swung them around.

"Good—turn—four—five—good—turn —little Jette."

Miss Holm followed up Jens Larsen's middle child and little Jette and swung them around like a top.

"Good—good—little Jette."

Her eyes smarted with the dust. The seven continued hopping in the middle of the floor in the twilight.

When Miss Holm came home after the dancing lessons, she would tie a hand-kerchief around her curly head. She went about with a perpetual catarrh, and in unoccupied hours she sat with her nose over a bowl of boiling water to relieve it.

They had music for their lessons: Mr. Brodersen's violin. Miss Holm got two new pupils, advanced ones. They all kept moving to Tailor Brodersen's instrument and the dust rose in clouds and the tiled stove danced on its lion's claws. The number of visitors also increased; from the manse came the pastor's daughter and the young curate.

Miss Holm demonstrated under the two oil-lamps with her chest thrown out and her foot extended: "Move your legs, little children, move your legs, that's it . . ."

Miss Holm moved her legs and raised her skirt a little, for there were spectators.

Every week Miss Holm would send her crocheting to Copenhagen. The mail was delivered to the schoolmaster. Invariably she had either sealed or addressed improperly, and the schoolmaster had to do it over, while she stood by and looked on with the humility of a sixteen-year-old.

The newspapers, which the mail had brought, lay ready for distribution on one of the school desks, and one day she begged to be permitted to look at *Berling's*. She had looked at the pile for a week before she had picked up the courage to ask. After that she came every day, in the noon period—the teacher knew her soft knock, with one knuckle. "Come in, Miss; it is open," he would say.

She went into the schoolroom and took *Berling's* from the pile. She read the announcements of the theatres, the repertoire and the criticisms, of which she understood nothing, but it was about the people "down there." It took her a long time to get through a column, while her index finger followed gracefully along the lines. When she had finished reading, she crossed the passage and knocked as before.

"Well," said the teacher, "anything new in town?"

"At least it's about the people down there," she said. "The old conditions, you know."

"The poor little thing," said the teacher, looking out of the window after her. Miss Holm went home to her crocheting.

"The poor little thing, she's crazy about her dancing-master," he said.

A ballet by a new ballet-master was to

be performed at the theatre. Miss Holm knew the list of characters by heart and also the names of all the solo dancers. "You see, we were at school together," she said, "all of us."

On the evening of the ballet she was feverish, as if it were she that was to dance. She lighted the two candles, gray with age, that stood on the dresser, one on each side of the plaster cast of Thorwaldsen's[3] Christ, and she sat on her champagne basket and looked into the flame. But she could not bear being alone. All the old unrest of the theatre came over her. She went into the smith's rooms, where they were at supper, and sat down on a chair by the side of the huge old clock. She talked more in those few hours than all the rest of the year. It was all about theatres and premières, the great soloists, and the master-steps. She hummed and swayed with the upper part of her body as she sat. The smith enjoyed it so much that he began to growl out an ancient cavalry ditty, and he said:

"Mother, we'll drink a punch on that—a real arrack!"

The punch was brewed, and the two candles from the bureau were put on the table and they drank and talked away, but in the midst of the merriment, Miss Holm suddenly grew still, great tears came into her eyes, and she rose and went to her room. In there she settled down on her basket, burst into tears, and sat for a long time before she undressed and went to bed. She went through no "steps" that night.

She was thinking of one thing: He had been at school with her. She lay still in her bed. Now and then she sighed in the dark, and her head moved uneasily on the pillow. In her ears sounded the voice of the ballet-master at school, angry and derisive, "Holm has no go. Holm has no go." He shouted it, and it echoed through the hall. How clearly she heard it—how

3. *Thorwaldsen*, a Danish sculptor of the early nineteenth century who was noted for his neoclassical style.

clearly she saw the hall! The figurantes practiced in long rows, one step at a time. Tired, she leaned against the wall a moment and again the sharp voice of the ballet-master: "Holm, haven't you any ambition at all?"

She saw their room at home, her mother, sitting in the armchair complaining, and her sister working the busy sewing-machine near the lamp, and she heard her mother say in her asthmatic voice: "Did Anna Stein dance the solo?"

"Yes, mother."

"I suppose she had 'La Grande Napolitaine'?"[4]

"Yes, mother."

"And you two entered school at the same time," said her mother, looking over at her from behind the lamp.

"Yes, mother."

And she beheld Anna Stein in the embroidered skirt—with ribbons fluttering in her tambourine, a living and rejoicing vision in the radiance of the footlights, in her great solo. Suddenly she laid her head down in the pillows and sobbed, desperately and ceaselessly in her impotence and despair. It was morning before she fell asleep.

The ballet had been a success. Miss Holm read the criticism at the school. While she was reading, a few small old woman's tears fell on the copy of *Berling's*.

From her sister came letters. Letters of notes due and telling of sore distress. On those days Miss Holm forgot about her crocheting and would sit pressing her temples, the open letter in her lap. Finally she would make the rounds of "her" parents, and blushing and paling would beg half her pay in advance, and what she got she would send home.

The days passed. Miss Irene Holm went to her lessons and returned. She obtained new pupils, half a dozen young farm hands who had united for the purpose of dancing three evenings a week in Peter Madsen's big room near the woods. Miss Holm walked two miles through the winter darkness, as frightened as a hare, pursued by all the old ghost stories that had been current at the ballet school. She had to pass a pond surrounded by willows, stretching their great arms up in the darkness. She felt her heart as a cold stone in her breast.

They danced for three hours, and she gave the commands, swung them about and danced with the gentlemen pupils until her cheeks were a hectic red. When she had to go home, Peter Madsen's gate was locked, and the farmhand went out with her, carrying a light to open the gate. He held the lantern high in his hand for a moment as she walked out into the darkness, hearing his "good night" behind her, and the gate as it scraped over the stones and was locked. The first part of the way there were hedges with bushes that waved and nodded.

Spring was coming and Miss Irene Holm's course was drawing to a close. The party at Peter Madsen's wanted to have a final dance at the inn.

The affair was very fine with "Welcome" in transparencies over the door, and cold supper at two crowns per cover, and the curate and the pastor's daughter to grace the table. Miss Holm was dressed in barège[5] with trimmings and Roman ribbons about her hair. Her fingers were covered with rings exchanged with her friends at the school. Between the dances she sprayed lavender water on the floor and threatened the ladies with the bottle. Miss Holm looked quite young again.

First they danced a quadrille. The parents and the old folks stood along the walls and in the doorways, each one looking after his own offspring, with an appearance of great awe. The young people whirled around in the quadrille with faces like masks, as cautious in their steps as if they were dancing on eggs. Miss

4. *La Grande Napolitaine*, (The Great Neopolitan.) This probably refers to the female lead in the Danish ballet *Napoli (The Fisherman and His Bride)*.
5. *barège*, a sheer fabric of open weave usually made of wool and silk or cotton.

Holm was all encouraging smiles and French endearments under her breath. The band consisted of Mr. Brodersen and his son. Mr. Brodersen, junior, was working the piano which the pastor had lent for the occasion.

When the round dance began, the tone of those present became less constrained. The men applied themselves to the punch in the middle room, and the gentlemen pupils asked Miss Holm to dance. She moved with her head on one side raising herself on her toes with her belated sixteen-year-old gracefulness. The other couples stopped dancing, and Miss Holm and her partner held the floor alone. The men came into the doorway of the little room and all were plunged in profound admiration of Miss Holm, who advanced her feet further beyond her petticoat and swayed with her hips. The pastor's daughter was so amused that she pinched the curate in the arm. After a mazurka, the schoolmaster shouted "Bravo" and all clapped their hands. Miss Holm made the ballet bow with two fingers on her heart. It was time for supper, and she arranged a Polonaise. All were in it; the women nudged each other with embarrassment and delight; the men said: "Well, old woman, I guess we'll try."

A couple began singing "The Country Soldier" and beating time to accompany the song. Miss Irene Holm sat with the schoolmaster under the bust of His Majesty the King. The general tone once more became solemn, after they had seated themselves, and only Miss Holm continued speaking, in the parlor manner, as the players do in a Scribe comedy.[6] Gradually things became more gay. The men began to drink each other's health and to clink glasses across the table.

There was boisterous merriment at the table occupied by the young people, and it was some time before it was quiet enough for the schoolmaster to speak. He spoke of Miss Holm and of the nine muses.[7] He spoke at length, while all along the table the others sat and looked down into their plates. Their faces assumed a solemn and tense expression, as when the parish clerk appeared in the choir-door at church, and they played with little pieces of bread. The speaker was approaching the subject of Freya[8] and her two cats, and proposed a toast for the "Priestess of Art, Miss Irene Holm." Nine long hurrahs were shouted, and everyone wanted to drink with Miss Holm.

Miss Holm had not understood the speech and was much flattered. She rose and saluted with her glass, held aloft by her curved arm. The festive powder had all disappeared in the heat and the exertion, and she had dark red spots in her cheeks.

There was a great hullabaloo: the young people sang, the older folks drank to each other in private and rose from their places, slapped each other on the back and poked each other in the stomach, out on the floor. The women were becoming anxious lest their better halves should take too much. In the midst of the merry-making, Miss Holm, who had become very cheerful, could be heard laughing carelessly, as she had laughed thirty years before, at the dancing school.

Then the schoolmaster said: "Miss Holm really ought to dance." But she *had* danced!

"Yes, but for them all—a solo—that was the thing!"

Miss Holm had understood at once, and a bold wish flamed up within her: they would let her *dance.* But she began to laugh and said to Peter Madsen's wife: "The organist wants me to dance,"—as if that were the most ridiculous thing in the world.

---

6. *Scribe comedy.* Scribe was a nineteenth-century French dramatist who was noted for well-plotted plays with rather weak characters. He wrote many of the librettos for the operas of the French composer Auber. 7. *nine muses,* the daughters of Zeus and Mnemosyne (Memory) in Greek mythology. Each muse represents a particular artistic or intellectual subject; for example, drama, poetry, etc. 8. *Freya,* the goddess of love and beauty in Norse mythology.

Those standing near heard it, and there was a general cry: "Yes—you must dance!"

Miss Holm was flushed up to her hair and said that "the festive atmosphere was almost too exalted."

"And besides there was no music."

"And you couldn't dance in long skirts."

A man shouted across the hall: "They can be raised!" and all laughed aloud and went on begging her.

"Yes, if the pastor's young lady will play a tarantella."

The pastor's young lady was surrounded. She was willing and would try. The schoolmaster rose and struck his glass. "Ladies and gentlemen," he said, "Miss Holm will honor us by dancing." They cried "Hurrah!" and began to get up from the tables. The curate was black and blue, so hard had the pastor's daughter pinched him.

Miss Holm and the latter went in to try the music. Miss Holm was feverish and went back and forth, stretching her limbs. She pointed to the board floor, with its hills and valleys, and said: "But one is not accustomed to dance in a circus!"

At last she said: "All right. The show can begin." She was quite hoarse with emotion. "I shall come in after the first ten beats," she said. "I'll give a signal." She went into the side-room to wait.

Her public entered and stood around in a semi-circle, whispering and curious. The schoolmaster took the candles from the table and set them up in the window-frame, as if for an illumination. Then a knock came at the side-room door.

The pastor's daughter began to play, and all looked toward the door. After the tenth beat it opened, and all clapped their hands. Miss Holm was dancing with her skirt tied up in a Roman scarf. It was "La Grande Napolitaine." She walked on her toes and made turns. The spectators looked at her feet and marveled, for their motion was as that of two drumsticks, and when she stood on one leg, the people clapped again.

She said "Faster!"—and began to whirl around. She smiled and beckoned and fanned and fanned. The upper part of her body, her arms, seemed to have more to do every moment; it became rather a mimic performance than a dance. She looked closely into the faces of the onlookers—her mouth opened—smiled— showed all its teeth (some were awful) —she beckoned, acted—she knew and felt nothing but her "solo." At last she was having her solo! This was no longer "La Napolitaine." It was Fenella,[9] the kneeling Fenella, the beseeching Fenella, the tragic Fenella.

She knew not how she had got up nor how she had got out. She had only heard the music stop suddenly—and the *laughter*—laughter, while she suddenly noticed all the faces. She rose, extended her arms once more, through force of habit—and made her curtsy, while they shouted. Within, in the side-room, she stood at the table a moment, it was dark to her, so absolutely void. Then slowly, and with very stiff hands, she loosened the sash, and smoothed out the skirt, and went in quietly to where the clapping was still going on.

She curtsied, standing close to the piano, but did not raise her eyes from the floor. They were in a hurry to begin dancing. Miss Holm went around quietly saying "Good-bye," and the pupils pressed the money, wrapped in paper, into her hands. Peter Madsen's wife helped her on with her things and at the last moment the pastor's daughter and the curate came and asked to be allowed to accompany her.

They walked along silently. The pastor's daughter was absolutely unhappy, and wanted to make some apology, but did

9. *Fenella*, deaf-and-dumb heroine of Auber's opera *La Muette de Portice*, the text for which was written by Scribe. Fenella's tragic story involves her seduction by a cruel duke, the murder of her fisherman brother, and, finally, her own suicide. Since both the ballet *Napoli* and the opera *La Muette de Portice* involve a fisherman and contain a tarantella, the transition which Miss Holm makes is at least a credible one.

not know what to say, and the little danseuse continued walking with them, silent and pale.

Finally the curate spoke, tortured by the silence: "You see, Miss, those people have no appreciation of the tragic."

Miss Holm remained silent. They had arrived at the smith's house, and she curtsied as she gave them her hand. The pastor's daughter put her arms around her and kissed her: "Good-night, Miss," she said, and her voice was unsteady. The curate and she waited in the road until they had seen the light in the danseuse's room.

Miss Holm took off the barège skirt and folded it up. Then she unwrapped her money and counted it and sewed it up in a little pocket in her petticoat. She managed the needle very awkwardly as she sat thus by candle-light.

The next morning, her champagne basket was lifted into the mail-coach. It was a rainy day, and Miss Holm crept in under a leaky umbrella; she drew up her legs under her, so that she presented a very Turkish appearance on her basket. When they were ready to drive off, with the postman walking by the side of the coach—one passenger being all the poor nag could draw—the pastor's daughter came down from the parsonage, bareheaded. She brought a white chip basket with her, saying: "You can't go off without provisions!"

She bent down under the umbrella and, taking Miss Holm's head in her hands, she kissed her twice. The old danseuse burst into tears, caught the girl's hand and kissed it. The pastor's daughter remained standing in the road and looked after the old umbrella, as long as she could still see it.

Miss Irene Holm had announced a spring course in "Modern Society Dancing" in a neighbouring town. Six pupils had applied. Thither she went—to continue what we are in the habit of calling Life.

THE END

Development

INTERPRETATION

1. Although the title of this story is "Irene Holm," the main character is referred to as "Miss Holm" throughout. *(a)* What does the formality of this second appellation suggest about the human relationships in the character's life? *(b)* The name *Irene* derives from the Greek word for peace. What significance might this meaning have to the characterization of Irene Holm?

2. When Miss Holm is toasted as the "Priestess of Art," she does not understand the speech and is much flattered. What irony do you find in this reaction?

3. Miss Holm's audience sees her "tragic Fenella" as a comic figure (see footnotes 4 and 9). *(a)* What might account for the change in the character which emerges as she dances? *(b)* What symbolism is suggested by this change in character? *(c)* Is the reaction of the audience justifiable, or contemptible?

TECHNIQUE

1. *(a)* Two details associated with Miss Holm—the champagne basket and the curled hair—are mentioned intermittently throughout the story. What facet of her life do they symbolize? *(b)* Twice in the story, Miss Holm makes the gesture of raising her skirts slightly when she dances before spectators. What does this gesture suggest?

2. *(a)* What does Miss Holm wear to the party at Peter Madsen's? What does this costume recall? What does it foreshadow? *(b)* Early in the party Miss Holm gains the "profound admiration" of the men, but "the pastor's daughter was so amused that she pinched the curate in the arm" (page 58, column 1, paragraph 1). What does this action foreshadow?

A Simple Heart

GUSTAVE FLAUBERT / France

(1821 – 1880)

translated from the French by the St. Dunstan Society

For half a century the housewives of Pont-l'Évêque[1] had envied Madame Aubain her servant Félicité.

For a hundred francs a year, she cooked and did the housework, washed, ironed, mended, harnessed the horse, fattened the poultry, made the butter and remained faithful to her mistress—although the latter was by no means an agreeable person.

Madame Aubain had married a comely youth without any money, who died in the beginning of 1809, leaving her with two young children and a number of debts. She sold all her property excepting the farm of Toucques and the farm of Geffosses, the income of which barely amounted to five thousand francs; then she left her house in Saint-Melaine, and moved into a less pretentious one which had belonged to her ancestors and stood back of the market-place. This house, with its slate-covered roof, was built between a passageway and a narrow street that led to the river. The interior was so unevenly graded that it caused people to stumble. A narrow hall separated the kitchen from the parlor, where Madame Aubain sat all day in a straw armchair near the window. Eight mahogany chairs stood in a row against the white wainscoting. An old piano, standing beneath a barometer, was covered with a pyramid of old books and boxes. On either side of the yellow marble mantelpiece, in Louis XV style, stood a tapestry armchair. The clock represented a temple of Vesta[2]; and the whole room smelled musty, as it was on a lower level than the garden.

On the first floor[3] was Madame's bedchamber, a large room papered in a flowered design and containing the portrait of Monsieur dressed in the costume of a dandy. It communicated with a smaller room, in which there were two little cribs, without any mattresses. Next came the parlor (always closed), filled with furniture covered with sheets. Then a hall, which led to the study, where books and papers were piled on the shelves of a bookcase that enclosed three quarters of the big black desk. Two panels were entirely hidden under the pen-and-ink sketches, Gouache landscapes and Audran[4] engravings, relics of better times and vanished luxury. On the second floor, a garret-window lighted Félicité's room, which looked out upon the meadows.

She arose at daybreak, in order to attend mass, and she worked without interruption until night; then, when dinner was over, the dishes cleared away and the door securely locked, she would bury the log under the ashes and fall asleep in front of the hearth with a rosary in her hand. Nobody could bargain with greater obstinacy, and as for cleanliness, the luster on her brass saucepans was the envy and despair of other servants. She was most econom-

"A Simple Heart." Translated and published by the St. Dunstan Society, Akron, Ohio, 1904.
1. *Pont-l'Évêque* (pōn lə vek⁄), a tiny village in the province of Normandy. Unless otherwise noted, all other towns mentioned in the story are also located in Normandy. **2.** *Vesta,* the goddess of chastity in Roman mythology. **3.** *first floor,* in Europe the level above the ground floor. **4.** *Gouache . . . Audran.* A Gouache is a painting in opaque watercolors. The Audrans were a famous French family of painters and engravers who lived during the seventeenth and eighteenth centuries.

ical, and when she ate she would gather up crumbs with the tip of her finger, so that nothing should be wasted of the loaf of bread weighing twelve pounds which was baked especially for her and lasted three weeks.

Summer and winter she wore a dimity kerchief fastened in the back with a pin, a cap which concealed her hair, a red skirt, gray stockings, and an apron with a bib like those worn by hospital nurses.

Her face was thin and her voice shrill. When she was twenty-five, she looked forty. After she had passed fifty, nobody could tell her age; erect and silent always, she resembled a wooden figure working automatically.

Like every other woman, she had had an affair of the heart. Her father, who had been a mason, was killed by falling from a scaffolding. Then her mother died and her sisters went their different ways; a farmer took her in, and while she was quite small, let her keep cows in the fields. She was clad in miserable rags, beaten for the slightest offence, and finally dismissed for a theft of thirty sous[5] which she did not commit. She took service on another farm, where she tended the poultry; and as she was well thought of by her master, her fellow-workers soon grew jealous.

One evening in August (she was then eighteen years old), they persuaded her to accompany them to the fair at Colleville. She was immediately dazzled by the noise, the lights in the trees, the brightness of the dresses, the laces and gold crosses, and the crowd of people all hopping at the same time. She was standing modestly at a distance, when presently a young man of well-to-do appearance, who had been leaning on the pole of a wagon and smoking his pipe, approached her, and asked her for a dance. He treated her to cider and cake, bought her a silk shawl, and then, thinking she had guessed his purpose, offered to see her home. When they came to the end of a field, he threw her down brutally. But she grew frightened and screamed, and he walked off.

One evening, on the road leading to Beaumont, she came upon a wagon loaded with hay, and when she overtook it, she recognized Théodore. He greeted her calmly, and asked her to forget what had happened between them, as it "was all the fault of the drink."

She did not know what to reply and wished to run away.

Presently he began to speak of the harvest and of the notables of the village; his father had left Colleville and bought the farm of Les Écots, so that now they would be neighbors. "Ah!" she exclaimed. He then added that his parents were looking around for a wife for him, but that he, himself, was not so anxious and preferred to wait for a girl who suited him. She hung her head. He then asked her whether she had ever thought of marrying. She replied, smilingly, that it was wrong of him to make fun of her. "Oh, no! I am in earnest," he said, and put his left arm around her waist while they sauntered along. The air was soft, the stars were bright, and the huge load of hay oscillated in front of them, drawn by four horses whose ponderous hoofs raised clouds of dust. Without a word from their driver they turned to the right. He kissed her again and again, and then she went home. The following week, Théodore obtained meetings.

They met in yards, behind walls or under isolated trees. She was not ignorant, as girls of well-to-do families are—for the animals had instructed her—but her reason and her instinct of honor kept her from falling. Her resistance exasperated Théodore's love, and so in order to satisfy it (or perchance ingenuously), he offered to marry her. She would not believe him at first, so he made solemn promises. But in a short time he mentioned a difficulty: the previous year, his parents had purchased a substitute for

---

5. *theft of thirty sous*, an insignificant sum, the sou being worth a fraction of a cent.

him[6]; but any day he might be drafted, and the prospect of serving in the army alarmed him greatly. To Félicité his cowardice appeared a proof of his love for her, and her devotion to him grew stronger. When she met him, he would torture her with his fears and his entreaties. At last, he announced that he was going to the prefect himself for information, and would let her know everything on the following Sunday, between eleven o'clock and midnight.

When the time drew near, she ran to meet her lover.

But instead of Théodore, one of his friends was at the meeting place.

He informed her that she would never see her sweetheart again; for, in order to escape the conscription, he had married a rich old woman, Madame Lehoussais, of Toucques.

The poor girl's sorrow was frightful. She threw herself on the ground; she cried and called on the Lord, and wandered around desolately until sunrise. Then she went back to the farm, declared her intention of leaving, and at the end of the month, after she had received her wages, she packed all her belongings in a handkerchief and started for Pont-l'Évêque.

In front of the inn, she met a woman wearing widow's weeds, and upon questioning her, learned that she was looking for a cook. The girl did not know very much, but appeared so willing and so modest in her requirements, that Madame Aubain finally said: "Very well, I will give you a trial." And half an hour later Félicité was installed in her house.

At first she lived in a constant anxiety that was caused by "the style of the household" and the memory of "Monsieur," that hovered over everything. Paul and Virginia, the one aged seven, and the other barely four, seemed made of some precious material; she carried them pig-a-back, and was greatly mortified when Madame Aubain forbade her to kiss them every other minute.

But in spite of all this, she w
The comfort of her new surroun
obliterated her sadness.

Every Thursday, friends of ...dame Aubain dropped in for a game of cards, and it was Félicité's duty to prepare the table and heat the foot-warmers. They arrived at exactly eight o'clock and departed before eleven.

Every Monday morning, the dealer in secondhand goods, who lived under the alley-way, spread out his wares on the sidewalk. Then the city would be filled with a buzzing of voices in which the neighing of horses, the bleating of lambs, the grunting of pigs, could be distinguished, mingled with the sharp sound of wheels on the cobblestones. About twelve o'clock, when the market was in full swing, there appeared at the front door a tall, middle-aged peasant, with a hooked nose and a cap on the back of his head; it was Robelin, the farmer of Geffosses. Shortly afterwards came Liébard, the farmer of Toucques, short, rotund, and ruddy, wearing a gray jacket and spurred boots.

Both men brought their landlady either chickens or cheese. Félicité would inevitably thwart their ruses, and they held her in great respect.

At various times, Madame Aubain received a visit from the Marquis de Grémanville, one of her uncles, who was ruined and lived at Falaise on the remainder of his estates. He always came at dinner-time and brought an ugly poodle with him, whose paws soiled the furniture. In spite of his efforts to appear a man of breeding (he even went so far as to raise his hat every time he said "My deceased father"), his habits got the better of him, and he would fill his glass a little too often and relate broad stories. Félicité would show him out very politely and say: "You have had enough for this time,

---

6. *substitute for him.* This refers to the accepted nineteenth-century practice of paying a substitute to take one's place in order to be excused from military service.

Monsieur de Grémanville! Hoping to see you again!" and would close the door.

She opened it gladly for Monsieur Bourais, a retired lawyer. His bald head and white cravat, the ruffling of his shirt, his flowing brown coat, the manner in which he took snuff, his whole person, in fact, produced in her the kind of awe which we feel when we see extraordinary persons. As he managed Madame's estates, he spent hours with her in Monsieur's study; he was in constant fear of being compromised, had a great regard for the magistracy and some pretensions to learning.

In order to facilitate the children's studies, he presented them with an engraved geography which represented various scenes of the world: cannibals with feather head-dresses, a gorilla kidnapping a young girl, Arabs in the desert, a whale being harpooned, etc.

Paul explained the pictures to Félicité. And, in fact, this was her only literary education.

The children's studies were under the direction of a poor devil employed at the town-hall, who sharpened his pocket-knife on his boots and was famous for his penmanship.

When the weather was fine, they went to Geffosses. The house was built in the center of the sloping yard; and the sea looked like a gray spot in the distance. Félicité would take slices of cold meat from the lunch basket and they would sit down and eat in a room next to the dairy. The room was all that remained of a cottage that had been torn down. The dilapidated wall-paper trembled in the drafts. Madame Aubain, overwhelmed by recollections, would hang her head, while the children were afraid to open their mouths. Then, "Why don't you go and play?" their mother would say; and they would scamper off.

Paul would go to the old barn, catch birds, throw stones into the pond, or pound the trunks of trees with a stick till they resounded like drums. Virginia would feed the rabbits and run to pick the wild flowers in the fields, and her flying legs would disclose her little embroidered pantalettes. One autumn evening, they struck out for home through the meadows. The new moon illumined part of the sky, and a mist hovered like a veil over the sinuosities of the river. Oxen, lying in the pastures, gazed mildly at the passing persons. In the third field, however, several of them got up and surrounded them. "Don't be afraid," cried Félicité; and murmuring a sort of lament she passed her hand over the back of the nearest ox; he turned away and the others followed. But when they came to the next pasture, they heard frightful bellowing.

It was a bull which was hidden from them by the fog. He advanced towards the two women, and Madame Aubain prepared to flee for her life. "No, no! not so fast," warned Félicité. Still they hurried on for they could hear the noisy breathing of the bull close behind them. His hoofs pounded the grass like hammers, and presently he began to gallop! Félicité turned around and threw patches of grass in his eyes. He hung his head, shook his horns, and bellowed with fury. Madame Aubain and the children, huddled at the end of the field, were trying to jump over the ditch. Félicité continued to back before the bull, blinding him with dirt, while she shouted to them to make haste.

Madame Aubain finally slid into the ditch, after shoving first Virginia and then Paul into it, and though she stumbled several times, she managed, by dint of courage, to climb the other side of it.

The bull had driven Félicité up against a fence; the foam from his muzzle flew in her face, and in another minute he would have disembowelled her. She had just time to slip between two bars, and the huge animal, thwarted, paused.

For years, this occurrence was a topic of conversation in Pont-l'Évêque. But Félicité took no credit to herself, and probably never knew that she had been heroic.

Virginia occupied her thoughts solely, for the shock she had sustained gave her a nervous affliction, and the physician, M. Poupart, prescribed the salt-water bathing at Trouville. In those days, Trouville was not greatly patronized. Madame Aubain gathered information, consulted Bourais, and made preparations as if they were going on an extended trip.

The baggage was sent the day before on Liébard's cart. On the following morning, he brought around two horses, one of which had a woman's saddle with a velveteen back to it, while on the crupper of the other was a rolled shawl that was to be used for a seat. Madame Aubain mounted the second horse, behind Liébard. Félicité took charge of the little girl, and Paul rode M. Lechaptois's donkey, which had been lent for the occasion on the condition that they should be careful of it.

The road was so bad that it took two hours to cover the eight miles. The two horses sank knee-deep into the mud and stumbled into ditches; sometimes they had to jump over them. In certain places, Liébard's mare stopped abruptly. He waited patiently till she started again, and talked of the people whose estates bordered the road, adding his own moral reflections to the outline of their histories. Thus, when they were passing through Toucques, and came to some windows draped with nasturtiums, he shrugged his shoulders and said: "There's a woman, Madame Lehoussais, who, instead of taking a young man—" Félicité could not catch what followed; the horses began to trot, the donkey to gallop, and they turned into a lane; then a gate swung open, two farm-hands appeared, and they all dismounted at the very threshold of the farmhouse.

Mother Liébard, when she caught sight of her mistress, was lavish with joyful demonstrations. She got up a lunch which comprised a leg of mutton, tripe, sausages, a chicken fricassée, sweet cider, a fruit tart, and some preserved prunes; then to all this the good woman added polite remarks about Madame, who appeared to be in better health; Mademoiselle, who had grown to be "superb"; and Paul, who had become singularly sturdy; she spoke also of their deceased grandparents, whom the Liébards had known, for they had been in the service of the family for several generations.

Like its owners, the farm had an ancient appearance. The beams of the ceiling were mouldy, the walls black with smoke, and the windows gray with dust. The oak sideboard was filled with all sorts of utensils—plates, pitchers, tin bowls, wolf-traps. The children laughed when they saw a huge syringe. There was not a tree in the yard that did not have mushrooms growing around its foot, or a bunch of mistletoe hanging in its branches. Several of the trees had been blown down, but they had started to grow in the middle and all were laden with quantities of apples. The thatched roofs, which were of unequal thickness, looked like brown velvet and could resist the fiercest gales. But the wagon-shed was fast crumbling to ruins. Madame Aubain said that she would attend to it, and then gave orders to have the horses saddled.

It took another thirty minutes to reach Trouville. The little caravan dismounted in order to pass Les Ecores, a cliff that overhangs the bay, and a few minutes later, at the end of the dock, they entered the yard of the Golden Lamb, an inn kept by Mother David.

During the first few days, Virginia felt stronger, owing to the change of air and the action of the sea-baths. She took them in her little chemise, as she had no bathing suit, and afterwards her nurse dressed her in the cabin of a customs officer, which was used for that purpose by other bathers.

In the afternoon, they would take the donkey and go to the Roches-Noires near Hennequeville. The path led at first through undulating grounds, and thence to a plateau, where pastures and tilled fields alternated. At the edge of the road, mingled with the brambles, grew holly bushes, and here and there stood large dead trees whose branches traced zigzags upon the blue sky.

Ordinarily, they rested in a field facing the ocean, with Deauville on their left, and Havre on their right. The sea glittered brightly in the sun and was as smooth as a mirror, and so calm that they could scarcely distinguish its murmur; sparrows chirped joyfully, and the immense canopy of heaven spread over it all. Madame Aubain brought out her sewing, and Virginia amused herself by braiding reeds; Félicité wove lavender blossoms, while Paul was bored and wished to go home.

Sometimes they crossed the Toucques in a boat, and started to hunt for sea-shells. The outgoing tide exposed star-fish and sea-urchins, and the children tried to catch the flakes of foam which the wind blew away. The sleepy waves lapping the sand unfurled themselves along the shore, that extended as far as the eye could see; but where land began, it was limited by the downs which separated it from the "Swamp," a large meadow shaped like a hippodrome. When they went home that way, Trouville, on the slope of a hill below, grew larger and larger as they advanced, and, with all its houses of unequal height, seemed to spread out before them in a sort of giddy confusion.

When the heat was too oppressive, they remained in their rooms. The dazzling sunlight cast bars of light between the shutters. Not a sound in the village, not a soul on the sidewalk. This silence intensified the tranquility of everything. In the distance, the hammers of some caulkers pounded the hull of a ship, and the sultry breeze brought them an odor of tar.

The principal diversion consisted in watching the return of the fishing-smacks. As soon as they passed the beacons, they began to ply to windward. The sails were lowered to one-third of the masts, and with their fore-sails swelled up like balloons they glided over the waves and anchored in the middle of the harbor. Then they crept up alongside of the dock, and the sailors threw the quivering fish over the side of the boat; a line of carts was waiting for them, and women with white caps sprang forward to receive the baskets and embrace their men-folk.

One day, one of them spoke to Félicité, who, after a little while, returned to the house gleefully. She had found one of her sisters, and presently Nastasie Barette, wife of Léroux, made her appearance, holding an infant in her arms, another child by the hand, while on her left was a little cabin-boy, with his hands in his pockets and his cap on his ear.

At the end of fifteen minutes, Madame Aubain bade her go.

They always hung around the kitchen, or approached Félicité when she and the children were out walking. The husband, however, did not show himself.

Félicité developed a great fondness for them; she bought them a stove, some shirts and a blanket; it was evident that they exploited her. Her foolishness annoyed Madame Aubain, who, moreover, did not like the nephew's familiarity, for he called her son "thou"[7];—and, as Virginia began to cough and the season was over, she decided to return to Pont-l'Évêque.

Monsieur Bourais assisted her in the choice of a college. The one at Caen was considered the best. So Paul was sent away and bravely said good-bye to them all, for he was glad to go to live in a house where he would have boy companions.

Madame Aubain resigned herself to the separation from her son because it was unavoidable. Virginia brooded less and less over it. Félicité regretted the noise he made, but soon a new occupation diverted

7. *called her son "thou."* This is an indication of extreme familiarity. The French have two words for the singular *you,* one of which ("tu," *thou*) is used only with family and intimate friends.

her mind; beginning from Christmas, she accompanied the little girl to her catechism lesson every day.

After she had made a curtsey at the threshold, she would walk up the aisle between the double lines of chairs, open Madame Aubain's pew, sit down, and look around.

Girls and boys, the former on the right, the latter on the left-hand side of the church, filled the stalls of the choir; the priest stood beside the reading-desk; on one stained window of the side-aisle the Holy Ghost hovered over the Virgin; on another one, Mary knelt before the Child Jesus, and behind the altar, a wooden group represented Saint Michael felling the dragon.

The priest first read a condensed lesson of sacred history. Félicité evoked Paradise, the Flood, the Tower of Babel, the blazing cities, the dying nations, the shattered idols; and out of this she developed a great respect for the Almighty and a great fear of His wrath. Then, when she listened to the Passion, she wept. Why had they crucified Him who loved little children, nourished the people, made the blind see, and who, out of humility, had wished to be born among the poor, in a stable? The sowings, the harvests, the wine-presses, all those familiar things which the Scriptures mention, formed a part of her life; the word of God sanctified them; and she loved the lambs with increased tenderness for the sake of the Lamb, and the doves because of the Holy Ghost.

She found it hard, however, to think of the latter as a person, for was it not a bird, a flame, and sometimes only a breath?[8] Perhaps it is its light that at night hovers over swamps, its breath that propels the clouds, its voice that renders church-bells harmonious. And Félicité worshipped devoutly, while enjoying the coolness and the stillness of the church.

As for the dogma, she could not understand it and did not even try. The priest discoursed, the children recited, and she went to sleep, only to awaken with a start when they were leaving the church and their wooden shoes clattered on the stone pavement.

In this way, she learned her catechism, her religious education having been neglected in her youth; and thenceforth she imitated all Virginia's religious practices, fasted when she did, and went to confession with her. At the Corpus Christi Day[9] they both decorated an altar.

She worried in advance over Virginia's first communion. She fussed about the shoes, the rosary, the book and the gloves. With what nervousness she helped the mother dress the child!

During the entire ceremony, she felt anguished. Monsieur Bourais hid part of the choir from view, but directly in front of her, the flock of maidens, wearing white wreaths over their lowered veils, formed a snow-white field, and she recognized her darling by the slenderness of her neck and her devout attitude. The bell tinkled. All the heads bent, and there was a silence. Then, at the peals of the organ the singers and the worshippers struck up the Agnus Dei; the boys' procession began; behind them came the girls. With clasped hands, they advanced step by step to the lighted altar, knelt at the first step, received one by one the Host, and returned to their seats in the same order. When Virginia's turn came, Félicité leaned forward to watch her, and through that imagination which springs from true affection, she at once became the child, whose face and dress became hers, whose heart beat in her bosom, and when Virginia opened her

---

8. *a bird, a flame, and sometimes only a breath.* Félicité is confused by the church's use of different religious symbols to represent the Holy Ghost.
9. *Corpus Christi Day.* This festival in honor of the Eucharist is a very important holiday in Europe. It occurs in late spring and is observed with elaborate processions through the streets.

mouth and closed her lids, she did like-wise and came very near fainting.

The following day, she presented her-self early at the church so as to receive communion from the curé. She took it with the proper feeling, but did not ex-perience the same delight as on the previous day.

Madame Aubain wished to make an accomplished girl of her daughter; and as Guyot could not teach English nor music, she decided to send her to the Ursulines[10] at Honfleur.

The child made no objection, but Félicité sighed and thought Madame was heartless. Then she thought that perhaps her mistress was right, as these things were beyond her sphere. Finally, one day, an old *fiacre*[11] stopped in front of the door, and a nun stepped out. Félicité put Virginia's luggage on top of the carriage, gave the coachman some instructions, and smuggled six jars of jam, a dozen pears and a bunch of violets under the seat.

At the last minute Virginia had a fit of sobbing; she embraced her mother again and again, while the latter kissed her on her forehead, and said: "Now, be brave, be brave!" The step was pulled up, and the *fiacre* rumbled off.

Then Madame Aubain had a fainting spell, and that evening all her friends, including the two Lormeaus, Madame Lechaptois, the ladies Rochefeuille, Messieurs de Houppeville and Bourais, called on her and tendered their sym-pathy.

At first the separation proved very painful to her. But her daughter wrote her three times a week and the other days she, herself, wrote to Virginia. Then she walked in the garden, read a little, and in this way managed to fill out the empti-ness of the hours.

Each morning, out of habit, Félicité entered Virginia's room and gazed at the walls. She missed combing her hair, lacing her shoes, tucking her in her bed, and the bright face and little hand when they used to go out for a walk. In order to occupy herself she tried to make lace. But her clumsy fingers broke the threads; she had no heart for anything, lost her sleep, and "wasted away," as she put it.

In order to have some distraction, she asked leave to receive the visits of her nephew Victor.

He would come on Sunday, after church, with ruddy cheeks and bared chest, bringing with him the scent of the country. She would set the table and they would sit down opposite each other, and eat their dinner; she ate as little as possible, herself, to avoid any extra ex-pense, but would stuff him so with food that he would finally go to sleep. At the first stroke of vespers, she would wake him up, brush his trousers, tie his cravat and walk to church with him, leaning on his arm with maternal pride.

His parents always told him to get something out of her, either a package of brown sugar, or soap, or brandy, and sometimes even money. He brought her his clothes to mend, and she accepted the task gladly, because it meant another visit from him.

In August, his father took him on a coasting-vessel.

It was vacation time, and the arrival of the children consoled Félicité. But Paul was capricious, and Virginia was growing too old to be thee-and-thou'd, a fact which seemed to produce a sort of embarrass-ment in their relations.

Victor went successively to Morlaix, to Dunkirk, and to Brighton; whenever he returned from a trip, he would bring her a present. The first time it was a box of shells; the second, a coffee-cup; the third, a big doll of gingerbread. He was growing handsome, had a good figure, a tiny mous-tache, kind eyes, and a little leather cap that sat jauntily on the back of his head. He amused his aunt by telling her stories mingled with nautical expressions.

---

10. *Ursulines*, a religious order devoted to teach-ing. 11. *fiacre* (fē ä′ krə), a small hackney coach.

One Monday, the 14th of July, 1819 (she never forgot the date), Victor announced that he had been engaged to a merchant-vessel and that in two days he would take the steamer at Honfleur and join his sailer, which was going to start from Havre very soon. Perhaps he might be away two years.

The prospects of his departure filled Félicité with despair, and in order to bid him farewell, on Wednesday night, after Madame's dinner, she put on her pattens and trudged the four miles that separated Pont-l'Évêque from Honfleur.

When she reached the Calvary,[12] instead of turning to the right, she turned to the left and lost herself in the coalyards; she had to retrace her steps; some people she spoke to advised her to hasten. She walked helplessly around the harbor filled with vessels, and knocked against hawsers. Presently the ground sloped abruptly, lights flitted to and fro, and she thought all at once that she had gone mad when she saw horses in the sky.

Others, on the edge of the dock, neighed at the sight of the ocean. A derrick pulled them up in the air and dumped them into a boat, where passengers were bustling about among barrels of cider, baskets of cheese and bags of meal; chickens cackled, the captain swore, and a cabin-boy rested on the railing, apparently indifferent to his surroundings. Félicité, who did not recognize him, kept shouting: "Victor!" He suddenly raised his eyes, but while she was preparing to rush up to him, they withdrew the gangplank.

The packet, towed by singing women, glided out of the harbor. Her hull squeaked, and the heavy waves beat up against her sides. The sail had turned, and nobody was visible:—and on the ocean, silvered by the light of the moon, the vessel formed a black spot that grew dimmer and dimmer, and finally disappeared.

When Félicité passed the Calvary again, she felt as if she must entrust that which was dearest to her to the Lord; and for a long while she prayed, with uplifted eyes and a face wet with tears. The city was sleeping; some customs officials were taking the air; and the water kept pouring through the holes of the dam with a deafening roar. The town clock struck two.

The parlor of the convent would not open until morning, and surely a delay would annoy Madame; so, in spite of her desire to see the other child, she went home. The maids of the inn were just arising when she reached Pont-l'Évêque.

So the poor boy would be on the ocean for months! His previous trips had not alarmed her. One can come back from England and Brittany; but America, the colonies, the islands, were all lost in an uncertain region at the very end of the world.

From that time on, Félicité thought solely of her nephew. On warm days she feared he would suffer from thirst, and when it stormed, she was afraid he would be struck by lightning. When she hearkened to the wind that rattled in the chimney and dislodged the tiles on the roof, she imagined that he was being buffeted by the same storm, perched on top of a shattered mast, with his whole body bent backward and covered with sea-foam; or, —these were recollections of the engraved geography—he was being devoured by savages, or captured in a forest by apes, or dying on some lonely coast. She never mentioned her anxieties, however.

Madame Aubain worried about her daughter.

The sisters thought that Virginia was affectionate but delicate. The slightest emotion enervated her. She had to give up her piano lessons. Her mother insisted upon regular letters from the convent. One morning, when the postman failed to come, she grew impatient and began to pace to and fro, from her chair to the window. It was really extraordinary! No news since four days!

---

12. *Calvary,* a sculpture representing the Crucifixion, particularly common in northern France.

In order to console her mistress by her own example, Félicité said:

"Why, Madame, I haven't had any news since six months!"—

"From whom?"—

The servant replied gently:

"Why—from my nephew."

"Oh, yes, your nephew!" And shrugging her shoulders, Madame Aubain continued to pace the floor as if to say: "I did not think of it. Besides, I do not care, a cabin-boy, a pauper!—but my daughter—what a difference! just think of it!—"

Félicité, although she had been reared roughly, was very indignant. Then she forgot about it.

It appeared quite natural to her that one should lose one's head about Virginia.

The two children were of equal importance; they were united in her heart, and their fate was to be the same.

The chemist informed her that Victor's vessel had reached Havana. He had read the information in a newspaper.

Félicité imagined that Havana was a place where people did nothing but smoke, and that Victor walked around among Negroes in a cloud of tobacco. Could a person, in case of need, return by land? How far was it from Pont-l'Évêque? In order to learn these things, she questioned Monsieur Bourais. He reached for his map and began some explanations concerning longitudes, and smiled with superiority at Félicité's bewilderment. At last, he took his pencil and pointed out an oval blotch, adding: "There it is." She bent over the map; the maze of colored lines hurt her eyes without enlightening her; and when Bourais asked her what puzzled her, she requested him to show her the house Victor lived in. Bourais threw up his hands, sneezed, and then laughed uproariously; such ignorance delighted his soul; but Félicité failed to understand the cause of his mirth, she whose intelligence was so limited that she perhaps expected to see even the picture of her nephew!

It was two weeks later that Liébard came into the kitchen at market-time, and handed her a letter from her brother-in-law. As neither of them could read, she called upon her mistress.

Madame Aubain, who was counting the stitches of her knitting, laid her work down beside her, opened the letter, started, and in a low tone and with a searching look said: "They tell you of a—misfortune. Your nephew—"

He had died. The letter told nothing more.

Félicité dropped on a chair, leaned her head against the back and closed her lids; presently they grew pink. Then, with drooping head, inert hands and staring eyes, she repeated at intervals:

"Poor little chap! poor little chap!"

Liébard watched her and sighed. Madame Aubain was trembling.

She proposed to the girl to go to see her sister in Trouville.

With a single motion, Félicité replied that it was not necessary.

There was a silence. Old Liébard thought it about time for him to take leave.

Then Félicité said:

"They have no sympathy, they do not care!"

Her head fell forward again, and from time to time, mechanically, she toyed with the long knitting-needles on the work-table.

Some women passed through the yard with a basket of wet clothes.

When she saw them through the window, she suddenly remembered her own wash; as she had soaked it the day before, she must go and rinse it now. So she arose and left the room.

Her tub and her board were on the bank of the Toucques. She threw a heap of clothes on the ground, rolled up her sleeves, and grasped her bat; and her loud pounding could be heard in the neighboring gardens. The meadows were empty, the breeze wrinkled the stream, at the bottom of which were long grasses that looked like the hair of corpses floating in the water. She restrained her sorrow and was very brave until night; but, when she had gone to her own room, she gave way to it, burying her face in the pillow and pressing her two fists against her temples.

A long while afterward, she learned through Victor's captain the circumstances which surrounded his death. At the hospital they had bled him too much, treating him for yellow fever. Four doctors held him at one time. He died almost instantly, and the chief surgeon had said: "Here goes another one!"

His parents had always treated him barbarously; she preferred not to see them again, and they made no advances, either from forgetfulness or out of innate hardness.

Virginia was growing weaker.

A cough, continual fever, oppressive breathing, and spots on her cheeks indicated some serious trouble. Monsieur Poupart had advised a sojourn in Provence.[13] Madame Aubain decided that they would go, and she would have had her daughter come home at once, had it not been for the climate of Pont-l'Évêque.

She made an arrangement with a livery-stable man who drove her over to the convent every Tuesday. In the garden there was a terrace, from which the view extends to the Seine. Virginia walked in it, leaning on her mother's arm and treading the dead vine-leaves. Sometimes the sun, shining through the clouds, made her blink her lids, when she gazed at the sails in the distance, and let her eyes roam over the horizon from the chateau of Tankerville to the lighthouses of Havre. Then they rested in the arbor. Her mother had bought a little cask of fine Malaga wine, and Virginia, laughing at the idea of becoming intoxicated, would drink a few drops of it, but never more.

Her strength returned. Autumn passed. Félicité began to reassure Madame Aubain. But, one evening, when she returned home after an errand, she met M. Poupart's coach in front of the door; M. Poupart himself was standing in the vestibule, and Madame Aubain was tying the strings of her bonnet. "Give me my foot-warmer, my purse and my gloves; and be quick about it," she said.

Virginia had congestion of the lungs; perhaps it was desperate.

"Not yet," said the physician, and both got into the carriage, while the snow fell in thick flakes. It was almost night and very cold.

Félicité rushed to the church to light a candle. Then she ran after the coach, which she overtook after an hour's chase, sprang up behind, and held on to the straps. But suddenly a thought crossed her mind: "The yard has been left open; supposing the burglars got in!" And down she jumped.

The next morning, at daybreak, she called at the doctor's. He had been home, but had left again. Then she waited at the inn, thinking that strangers might bring her a letter. At last, at daylight she took the diligence for Honfleur.

The convent was at the end of a steep and narrow street. When she arrived at about the middle of it, she heard strange noises, a funeral knell. "It must be for some one else," thought she; and she pulled the knocker violently.

After several minutes had elapsed, she heard footsteps; the door was half opened, and a nun appeared. The good sister, with an air of compunction, told her that "she had just passed away." And at the same time the tolling of Saint-Léonard's increased.

Félicité reached the second floor. Already at the threshold, she caught sight of Virginia lying on her back, with clasped hands, her mouth open and her head thrown back, beneath a black crucifix inclined toward her, and stiff curtains which were less white than her face. Madame Aubain lay at the foot of the couch, clasping it with her arms and uttering groans of agony. The Mother Superior was standing on the right side

13. *Provence* (prô väns'), a province in southern France noted for its hot sun.

of the bed. The three candles on the bureau made red blurs, and the windows were dimmed by the fog outside. The nuns carried Madame Aubain from the room.

For two nights, Félicité never left the corpse. She would repeat the same prayers, sprinkle holy water over the sheets, get up, come back to the bed, and contemplate the body. At the end of the first vigil, she noticed that the face had taken on a yellow tinge, the lips grew blue, the nose grew pinched, the eyes were sunken. She kissed them several times and would not have been greatly astonished had Virginia opened them; to souls like these the supernatural is always quite simple. She washed her, wrapped her in a shroud, put her into the casket, laid a wreath of flowers on her head, and arranged her curls. They were blond and of an extraordinary length for her age. Félicité cut off a big lock and put half of it into her bosom, resolving never to part with it.

The body was taken to Pont-l'Évêque, according to Madame Aubain's wishes; she followed the hearse in a closed carriage.

After the ceremony it took three quarters of an hour to reach the cemetery. Paul, sobbing, headed the procession; Monsieur Bourais followed, and then came the principal inhabitants of the town, the women covered with black capes, and Félicité. The memory of her nephew, and the thought that she had not been able to render him these honors, made her doubly unhappy, and she felt as if he were being buried with Virginia.

Madame Aubain's grief was uncontrollable. At first she rebelled against God, thinking that he was unjust to have taken away her child—she who had never done anything wrong, and whose conscience was so pure! But no! she ought to have taken her South. Other doctors would have saved her. She accused herself, prayed to be able to join her child, and cried in the midst of her dreams. Of the latter, one more especially haunted her.

Her husband, dressed like a sailor, had come back from a long voyage, and with tears in his eyes told her that he had received the order to take Virginia away. Then they both consulted about a hiding-place.

Once she came in from the garden, all upset. A moment before (and she showed the place), the father and daughter had appeared to her, one after the other; they did nothing but look at her.

During several months she remained inert in her room. Félicité scolded her gently; she must keep up for her son and also for the other one, for "her memory."

"Her memory!" replied Madame Aubain, as if she were just awakening, "Oh! yes, yes, you do not forget her!" This was an allusion to the cemetery where she had been expressly forbidden to go.

But Félicité went there every day. At four o'clock exactly, she would go through the town, climb the hill, open the gate, and arrive at Virginia's tomb. It was a small column of pink marble with a flat stone at its base, and it was surrounded by a little plot enclosed by chains. The flower-beds were bright with blossoms. Félicité watered their leaves, renewed the gravel, and knelt on the ground in order to till the earth properly. When Madame Aubain was able to visit the cemetery, she felt very much relieved and consoled.

Years passed, all alike and marked by no other events than the return of the great Church holidays: Easter, Assumption, All Saints' Day. Household happenings constituted the only data to which in later years they often referred. Thus, in 1825, workmen painted the vestibule; in 1827, a portion of the roof almost killed a man by falling into the yard. In the summer of 1828, it was Madame's turn to offer the hallowed bread; at that time, Bourais disappeared mysteriously; and the old acquaintances: Guyot, Liébard, Madame Lechaptois, Robelin, old Grémanville, paralyzed since a long time, passed away one by one. One night, the driver of the mail in Pont-l'Évêque announced the Revolution of July.[14] A few days afterward a new sub-prefect was nominated, the Baron de Larsonnière, ex-counsul in America, who, besides his wife, had his sister-in-law and her three grown daughters with him. They were often seen on their lawn, dressed in loose blouses, and they had a parrot and a Negro servant. Madame Aubain received a call, which she returned promptly. As soon as she caught sight of them, Félicité would run and notify her mistress. But only one thing was capable of arousing her: a letter from her son.

He could not follow any profession, as he was absorbed in drinking. His mother paid his debts, and he made fresh ones; and the sighs that she heaved while she knitted at the window reached the ears of Félicité, who was spinning in the kitchen.

They walked in the garden together, always speaking of Virginia, and asking each other if such and such a thing would have pleased her, and what she would probably have said on this or that occasion.

All her little belongings were put away in a closet of the room which held the two little beds. But Madame Aubain looked them over as little as possible. One summer day, however, she resigned herself to the task, and when she opened the closet, the moths flew out.

Virginia's frocks were hung under a shelf, where there were three dolls, some hoops, a doll-house, and a basin which she had used. Félicité and Madame Aubain also took out the skirts, the handkerchiefs, and the stockings and spread them on the beds, before putting them away again. The sun fell on the pitiful things, disclosing their spots and the creases formed by the motions of the body. The atmosphere was warm and blue, and a blackbird trilled in the garden; everything seemed to live in happiness. They found a little hat of soft brown plush, but it was entirely moth-eaten. Félicité asked for it. Their eyes met and

filled with tears; at last the mistress opened her arms, and the servant threw herself against her breast, and they hugged each other and gave vent to their grief in a kiss which equalized them for a moment.

It was the first time that this had ever happened, for Madame Aubain was not of an expansive nature. Félicité was as grateful for it as if it had been some favor, and thenceforth loved her with animal-like devotion and a religious veneration.

Her kindheartedness developed. When she heard the drums of a marching regiment passing through the street, she would stand in the doorway with a jug of cider and give the soldiers a drink. She nursed cholera victims. She protected Polish refugees,[15] and one of them even declared that he wished to marry her. But they quarrelled, for one morning when she returned from the Angelus, she found him in the kitchen coolly eating a dish which he had prepared for himself during her absence.

After the Polish refugees came Colmiche, an old man who was credited with having committed frightful misdeeds in '93.[16] He lived near the river in the ruins of a pig-sty. The urchins peeped at him through the cracks in the walls and threw stones that fell on his miserable bed, where he lay gasping with catarrh, with long hair, inflamed eyelids, and a tumor as big as his head on one arm.

She got him some linen, tried to clean his hovel, and dreamed of installing him in the bake-house without his being in Madame's way. When the cancer broke, she dressed it every day; sometimes she brought him some cake and placed him in

---

14. *Revolution in July.* This refers to the 1830 revolution in France which ousted Charles X and put Louis Philippe in his place. 15. *cholera . . . refugees.* Asiatic cholera was rampant in France in 1832. The Polish refugees indicated were those fleeing the wrath of Czar Nicholas I, who suppressed with great severity the Polish revolt of 1832. 16. *frightful misdeeds in '93,* the Reign of Terror during the French Revolution.

the sun on a bundle of hay; and the poor old creature, trembling and drooling, would thank her in his broken voice, and put out his hands whenever she left him. Finally he died, and she had a mass said for the repose of his soul.

That day a great joy came to her: at dinner time, Madame de Larsonnière's servant called with the parrot, the cage, and the perch and chain and lock. A note from the baroness told Madame Aubain that, as her husband had been promoted to a prefecture, they were leaving that night, and she begged her to accept the bird as a remembrance and a token of her esteem.

Since a long time the parrot had been on Félicité's mind, because he came from America, which reminded her of Victor, and she had approached the Negro on the subject.

Once even, she had said:

"How glad Madame would be to have him!"

The man had repeated this remark to his mistress, who, not being able to keep the bird, took this means of getting rid of it.

He was called Loulou. His body was green, his head blue, the tips of his wings were pink, and his breast was golden.

But he had the tiresome tricks of biting his perch, pulling his feathers out, scattering refuse, and spilling the water of his bath. Madame Aubain grew tired of him and gave him to Félicité for good.

She undertook his education, and soon he was able to repeat: "Pretty boy! Your servant, sir! I salute you, Marie!" His perch was placed near the door, and several persons were astonished that he did not answer to the name of "Jacquot," for every parrot is called Jacquot. They called him a goose and a log, and these taunts were like so many dagger thrusts to Félicité. Strange stubbornness of the bird, which would not talk when people watched him!

Nevertheless, he sought society; for on Sunday, when the ladies Rochefeuille, Monsieur de Houppeville, and the new habitués, Onfroy, the chemist, Monsieur Varin, and Captain Mathieu, dropped in for their game of cards, he struck the window-panes with his wings, and made such a racket that it was impossible to talk.

Bourais's face must have appeared very funny to Loulou. As soon as he saw him, he would begin to roar. His voice re-echoed in the yard, and the neighbors would come to the windows and begin to laugh, too; and in order that the parrot might not see him, Monsieur Bourais edged along the wall, pushed his hat over his eyes to hide his profile, and entered by the garden door, and the looks he gave the bird lacked affection. Loulou, having thrust his head into the butcher-boy's basket, received a slap, and from that time he always tried to nip his enemy. Fabu threatened to wring his neck, although he was not cruelly inclined, notwithstanding his big whiskers and tattooings. On the contrary, he rather liked the bird, and, out of deviltry, tried to teach him oaths. Félicité, whom his manner alarmed, put Loulou in the kitchen, took off his chain, and let him walk all over the house.

When he went downstairs, he rested his beak on the steps, lifted his right foot and then his left one; but his mistress feared that such feats would give him vertigo. He became ill and was unable to eat. There was a small growth under his tongue like those chickens are sometimes afflicted with. Félicité pulled it off with her nails and cured him. One day, Paul was imprudent enough to blow the smoke of his cigar in his face; another time, Madame Lormeau was teasing him with the tip of her umbrella, and he swallowed the tip. Finally he got lost.

She had put him on the grass to cool him and went away only for a second; when she returned, she found no parrot! She hunted among the bushes, on the bank of the river, and on the roofs, without paying any attention to Madame Aubain, who screamed at her: "Take care! you must be insane!" Then she searched every garden in Pont-l'Évêque and stopped the passers-by to inquire of them: "Haven't you perhaps seen my parrot?" To those who had never seen the parrot, she described him minutely. Suddenly she thought she saw something green fluttering behind the mills at the foot of the hill. But when she got to the top of the hill she could not see it. A hod-carrier told her that he had just seen the bird in Saint-Melaine, in Mother Simon's store. She rushed to the place. The people did not know what she was talking about. At last she came home, exhausted, with her slippers worn to shreds, and despair in her heart. She sat down on the bench near Madame and was telling of her search when presently a light weight dropped on her shoulder— Loulou! What the deuce had he been doing? Perhaps he had just taken a little walk around the town!

She did not easily forget her scare; in fact, she never got over it. In consequence of a cold, she caught a sore throat; and some time afterward she had an earache. Three years later she was stone deaf, and spoke in a very loud voice even in church. Although her sins might have been proclaimed throughout the diocese without any shame to herself, or ill effects to the community, the curé thought it advisable to receive her confession in the vestry-room.

Imaginary buzzings also added to her bewilderment. Her mistress often said to her: "My goodness, how stupid you are!" and she would answer: "Yes, Madame," and look for something.

The narrow circle of her ideas grew more restricted than it already was; the bellowing of the oxen, the chime of the bells no longer reached her intelligence. All things moved silently, like ghosts. Only one noise penetrated her ears: the parrot's voice.

As if to divert her mind, he reproduced for her the tick-tack of the spit in the kitchen, the shrill cry of the fish-vendors, the saw of the carpenter who had a shop opposite, and when the door-bell rang, he would imitate Madame Aubain: "Félicité! go to the front door."

They held conversations together, Loulou repeating the three phrases of his repertory over and over, Félicité replying by words that had no greater meaning, but in which she poured out her feelings. In her isolation, the parrot was almost a son, a lover. He climbed upon her fingers, pecked at her lips, clung to her shawl, and when she rocked her head to and fro like a nurse, the big wings of her cap and the wings of the bird flapped in unison. When clouds gathered on the horizon and the thunder rumbled, Loulou would scream, perhaps because he remembered the storms in his native forests. The dripping of the rain would excite him to frenzy; he flapped around, struck the ceiling with his wings, upset everything, and would finally fly into the garden to play. Then he would come back into the room, light on one of the andirons, and hop around in order to get dry.

One morning during the terrible winter of 1837, when she had put him in front of the fireplace on account of the cold, she found him dead in his cage, hanging on to the wire bars with his head down. He had probably died of congestion. But she believed that he had been poisoned, and although she had no proof whatever, her suspicion rested on Fabu.

She wept so sorely that her mistress said: "Why don't you have him stuffed?"

She asked the advice of the chemist, who had always been kind to the bird.

He wrote to Havre for her. A certain man named Fellacher consented to do the work. But, as the diligence driver often lost parcels entrusted to him, Félicité resolved to take her pet to Honfleur herself.

Leafless apple trees lined the edges of the road. The ditches were covered with ice. The dogs on the neighboring farms barked; and Félicité, with her hands beneath her cape, her little black sabots and her basket, trotted along nimbly in the middle of the sidewalk. She crossed the forest, passed by the Haut-Chêne, and reached Saint-Gatien.

Behind her, in a cloud of dust and impelled by the steep incline, a mail-coach drawn by galloping horses advanced like a whirlwind. When he saw a woman in the middle of the road, who did not get out of the way, the driver stood up in his seat and shouted to her, and so did the postilion, while the four horses, which he could not hold back, accelerated their pace; the two leaders were almost upon her; with a jerk of the reins he threw them to one side, but, furious at the incident, he lifted his big whip and lashed her from her head to her feet with such violence that she fell to the ground unconscious.

Her first thought, when she recovered her senses, was to open the basket. Loulou was unharmed. She felt a sting on her right cheek; when she took her hand away, it was red, for the blood was flowing.

She sat down on a pile of stones, and sopped her cheek with her handkerchief; then she ate a crust of bread she had put in her basket, and consoled herself by looking at the bird.

Arriving at the top of Ecquemanville, she saw the lights of Honfleur shining in the distance like so many stars; farther on, the ocean spread out in a confused mass. Then a weakness came over her; the misery of her childhood, the disappointment of her first love, the departure of her nephew, the death of Virginia; all these things came back to her at once, and, rising like a swelling tide in her throat, almost choked her.

Then she wished to speak to the captain of the vessel, and without stating what she was sending, she gave him some instructions.

Fellacher kept the parrot a long time.

He always promised that it would be ready for the following week; after six months he announced the shipment of a case, and that was the end of it. Really, it seemed as if Loulou would never come back to his home. "They have stolen him," thought Félicité.

Finally he arrived, sitting bolt upright on a branch which could be screwed into a mahogany pedestal, with his foot in the air, his head on one side, and in his beak a nut which the naturalist, from love of the sumptuous, had gilded. She put him in her room.

This place, to which only a chosen few were admitted, looked like a chapel and a second-hand shop, so filled was it with devotional and heterogeneous things. The door could not be opened easily on account of the presence of a large wardrobe. Opposite the window that looked out into the garden, a bull's-eye opened on the yard; a table was placed by the cot and held a wash-basin, two combs, and a piece of blue soap in a broken saucer. On the walls were rosaries, medals, a number of Holy Virgins, and a holy-water basin made out of a cocoanut; on the bureau, which was covered with a napkin like an altar, stood the box of shells that Victor had given her; also a watering-can and a balloon, writing-books, the engraved geography and a pair of shoes; on the nail which held the mirror hung Virginia's little plush hat! Félicité carried this sort of respect so far that she even kept one of Monsieur's old coats. All the things which Madame Aubain discarded, Félicité begged for her own room. Thus, she had artificial flowers on the edge of the bureau, and the picture of the Comte d'Artois[17] in the recess of the window. By means of a board, Loulou was set on a portion of the chimney which advanced into the room. Every morning when she awoke, she saw him in the dim light of dawn and

17. *Comte d'Artois* (kōn′ där twä′), the former title of King Charles X of France. The picture implies that Madame Aubain was a royalist at heart.

recalled bygone days and the smallest details of insignificant actions, without any sense of bitterness or grief.

As she was unable to communicate with people, she lived in a sort of somnambulistic torpor. The processions of Corpus Christi Day seemed to wake her up. She visited the neighbors to beg for candlesticks and mats so as to adorn the temporary altars in the street.

In church, she always gazed at the Holy Ghost, and noticed that there was something about it that resembled a parrot. The likeness appeared even more striking on a colored picture by Espinai,[18] representing the baptism of our Saviour. With his scarlet wings and emerald body, it was really the image of Loulou. Having bought the picture, she hung it near the one of the Comte d'Artois so that she could take them in at one glance.

They associated in her mind, the parrot becoming sanctified through the neighborhood of the Holy Ghost, and the latter becoming more lifelike in her eyes and more comprehensible. In all probability the Father had never chosen as messenger a dove, as the latter has no voice, but rather one of Loulou's ancestors. And Félicité said her prayers in front of the colored picture, though from time to time she turned slightly toward the bird.

She desired very much to enter in the ranks of the "Daughters of the Virgin." But Madame Aubain dissuaded her from it.

A most important event occurred: Paul's marriage.

After being first a notary's clerk, then in business, then in the customs, and a tax collector, and having even applied for a position in the administration of woods and forests, he had at last, when he was thirty-six years old, by a divine inspiration, found his vocation: registrature! and he displayed such a high ability that an inspector had offered him his daughter and his influence.

Paul, who had become quite settled, brought his bride to visit his mother.

But she looked down upon the customs of Pont-l'Évêque, put on airs, and hurt Félicité's feelings. Madame Aubain felt relieved when she left.

The following week they learned of Monsieur Bourais's death in an inn. There were rumors of suicide, which were confirmed; doubts arose concerning his integrity. Madame Aubain looked over her accounts and soon discovered his numerous embezzlements; sales of wood which had been concealed from her, false receipts, noted. Furthermore, he had an illegitimate child, and entertained a friendship for "a person in Dozulé."

These base actions affected her very much. In March, 1853, she developed a pain in her chest; her tongue looked as if it were coated with smoke, and the leeches they applied did not relieve her oppression; and on the ninth evening she died, being just seventy-two years old.

People thought that she was younger, because her hair, which she wore in bands framing her pale face, was brown. Few friends regretted her loss, for her manner had been so haughty that she did not attract them. Félicité mourned for her as servants seldom mourn for their masters. The fact that Madame should die before herself perplexed her mind and seemed contrary to the order of things, and absolutely monstrous and inadmissible. Ten days later (the time to journey from Besançon),[19] the heirs arrived. Her daughter-in-law ransacked the drawers, kept some of the furniture, and sold the rest; then they went back to their own home.

Madame's armchair, foot-warmer, worktable, the eight chairs, everything was gone! The places occupied by the pictures formed yellow squares on the walls. They had taken the two little beds, and the

---

18. *Espinai* (es pin ĭ′), a Spanish painter who specialized in holy pictures (d. 1783). 19. *Besançon* (bə zän sōn′), a town of central France in the province of Burgundy, about thirty miles west of the Swiss border.

wardrobe had been emptied of Virginia's belongings! Félicité went upstairs, over-come with grief.

The following day a sign was posted on the door; the chemist screamed in her ear that the house was for sale.

For a moment she tottered, and had to sit down.

What hurt her most was to give up her room,—so nice for poor Loulou! She looked at him in despair and implored the Holy Ghost, and it was this way that she contracted the idolatrous habit of saying her prayers kneeling in front of the bird. Sometimes the sun fell through the window on his glass eye, and lighted a great spark in it, which sent Félicité into ecstasy.

Her mistress had left her an income of three hundred and eighty francs. The garden supplied her with vegetables. As for clothes, she had enough to last her till the end of her days, and she econo-mized on the light by going to bed at dusk.

She rarely went out, in order to avoid passing in front of the second-hand dealer's shop where there was some of the old furniture. Since her fainting spell, she dragged her leg, and as her strength was failing rapidly, old Mother Simon, who had lost her money in the grocery business, came every morning to chop the wood and pump the water.

Her eyesight grew dim. She did not open the shutters after that. Many years passed. But the house did not sell or rent. Fearing that she would be put out, Félicité did not ask for repairs. The lathes of the roof were rotting away, and during one whole winter her bolster was wet. After Easter she spit blood.

Then Mother Simon went for a doctor. Félicité wished to know what her com-plaint was. But, being too deaf to hear, she caught only one word: "Pneumonia." She was familiar with it and gently an-swered: "Ah! like Madame," thinking it quite natural that she should follow her mistress.

The time for the altars in the street drew near.

The first one was always erected at the foot of the hill, the second in front of the post-office, and the third in the middle of the street. This position occasioned some rivalry among the women, and they finally decided upon Madame Aubain's yard.

Félicité's fever grew worse. She was sorry that she could not do anything for the altar. If she could, at least, have con-tributed something toward it! Then she thought of the parrot. Her neighbors ob-jected that it would not be proper. But the curé gave his consent, and she was so grateful for it that she begged him to ac-cept after her death her only treasure, Loulou. From Tuesday until Saturday, the day before the event, she coughed more frequently. In the evening her face was contracted, her lips stuck to her gums, and she began to vomit; and on the following day, she felt so low that she called for a priest.

Three neighbors surrounded her when the dominie administered the Extreme Unction. Afterwards she said that she wished to speak to Fabu.

He arrived in his Sunday clothes, very ill at ease among the funereal surround-ings.

"Forgive me," she said, making an effort to extend her arm, "I believed it was you who killed him!"

What did such accusations mean? Suspect a man like him of murder! And Fabu became excited and was about to make trouble.

"Don't you see she is not in her right mind?"

From time to time Félicité spoke to shadows. The women left her, and Mother Simon sat down to breakfast.

A little later, she took Loulou and hold-ing him up to Félicité:

"Say good-bye to him now!" she com-manded.

Although he was not a corpse, he was eaten up by worms; one of his wings was broken, and the wadding was coming out of his body. But Félicité was blind now, and she took him and laid him against her cheek. Then Mother Simon removed him in order to set him on the altar.

The grass exhaled an odor of summer; flies buzzed in the air; the sun shone on the river and warmed the slate roof. Old Mother Simon had returned to Félicité and was peacefully falling asleep.

The ringing of bells woke her; the people were coming out of church. Félicité's delirium subsided. By thinking of the procession, she was able to see it as if she had taken part in it. All the schoolchildren, the singers, and the firemen walked on the sidewalks, while in the middle of the street came first the custodian of the church with his halberd, then the beadle with a large cross, the teacher in charge of the boys and a sister escorting the little girls; three of the smallest ones, with curly heads, threw rose leaves into the air; the deacon with outstretched arms conducted the music; and two incense-bearers turned with each step they took toward the Holy Sacrament, which was carried by M. le Curé, attired in his handsome chasuble and walking under a canopy of red velvet supported by four men. A crowd of people followed, jammed between the walls of the houses hung with white sheets; at last the procession arrived at the foot of the hill.

A cold sweat broke out on Félicité's forehead. Mother Simon wiped it away with a cloth, saying inwardly that some day she would have to go through the same thing herself.

The murmur of the crowd grew louder, was very distinct for a moment, and then died away. A volley of musketry shook the window-panes. It was the postilions saluting the Sacrament. Félicité rolled her eyes and said as loudly as she could: "Is he all right?" meaning the parrot.

Her death agony began. A rattle that grew more and more rapid shook her body. Froth appeared at the corners of her mouth, and her whole frame trembled. In a little while could be heard the music of the bass horns, the clear voices of the children, and the men's deeper notes. At intervals all was still, and their shoes sounded like a herd of cattle passing over the grass.

The clergy appeared in the yard. Mother Simon climbed on a chair to reach the bull's-eye, and in this manner could see the altar. It was covered with a lace cloth and draped with green wreaths. In the middle stood a little frame containing relics; at the corners were two little orange-trees, and all along the edge were silver candlesticks, porcelain vases containing sunflowers, lilies, peonies, and tufts of hydrangeas. This mound of bright colors descended diagonally from the first floor to the carpet that covered the sidewalk. Rare objects arrested one's eye. A golden sugar-bowl was crowned with violets, earrings set with Alençon stones were displayed on green moss, and two Chinese screens with their bright landscapes were near by. Loulou, hidden beneath roses, showed nothing but his blue head, which looked like a piece of lapis-lazuli.

The singers, the canopy-bearers, and the children lined up against the sides of the yard. Slowly the priest ascended the steps and placed his shining sun on the lace cloth. Everybody knelt. There was deep silence; and the censers, slipping on their chains, were swung high in the air. A blue vapor rose in Félicité's room. She opened her nostrils and inhaled it with a mystic sensuousness; then she closed her lids. Her lips smiled. The beats of her heart grew fainter and fainter, and vaguer, like a fountain giving out, like an echo dying away;—and when she exhaled her last breath, she thought she saw in the half-opened heavens a gigantic parrot[20] hovering about her head.

THE END

20. *in the half-opened heavens a gigantic parrot . . . :* Félicité's vision suggests some of the religious paintings depicting Christ's baptism.

Development

INTERPRETATION

1. Both the French word *simple* in the original title of Flaubert's short story ("Un Coeur Simple") and the English cognate can be used in three distinct connotative senses—one unfavorable (simple Simon), one neutral (simple solution), and one favorable (simple faith)—to suggest foolishness, directness, and innocence, respectively. Because Flaubert was intensely concerned with language, we can assume that he felt this wide range of meaning to be truer to his character than a more specific and limited word would be. Point out some of Félicité's divergent traits of character, and try to formulate a definition of *simple* as it applies to her.

2. Though Flaubert's style is usually labeled objective, some critics point out a romantic element in his writing. One aspect of romanticism is a sympathy for the poor. Considering Félicité's lowly social position, would it be fair to see Flaubert in the role of a champion of the lower classes? Why or why not?

TECHNIQUE

1. Flaubert's care in selecting details should alert us that every detail is very important. Reread the introduction to "A Simple Heart" carefully (page 61, column 1, paragraph 1 to page 62, column 1, paragraph 3), noting the kinds of information we are given about Félicité, about Madame Aubain, and about the setting. *(a)* Summarize your impression of Madame Aubain, explaining what the furnishings of the Aubain household reveal about her financial status, tastes, and general interests. *(b)* Summarize your impression of Félicité and discuss how her activities reveal her nature and how the reader's attitude toward her is affected by the setting in which she performs these activities.

2. *(a)* List the objects of Félicité's devotion in the order in which they occur in her life, and explain the way in which these attachments become increasingly less normal. *(b)* How is her sorrow over the broken engagement (her first attachment) finally relieved? Discuss how her reaction to the loss experienced in the other instances is a parallel to the broken engagement. *(c)* Considering your answers to *(a)* and *(b)*, show how Flaubert has made Félicité's adoration of the parrot seem believable, if not inevitable.

3. As mentioned previously, Flaubert is often thought of as an objective writer; however, as one of his critics has pointed out, "every literary work of any power . . . is in fact an elaborate system of controls over the reader's involvement and detachment along *various* lines of interest." *(a)* Point out some of the devices which comprise Flaubert's "system of controls" in "A Simple Heart." *(b)* If it is true that Flaubert directs his reader's sympathies, how does he avoid *appearing* to do so?

4. In Félicité's deathbed vision, she equates Loulou the parrot with the Holy Ghost. *(a)* What have been Félicité's previous feelings about the Holy Ghost? *(b)* What has been established about her intellect and attitude toward religion that makes this final vision believable?

EXTENSIONS

1. The care and expense which many people lavish on their pets is often criticized as frivolous and wasteful. What insights might Flaubert's story provide on this topic?

The Woman Scorned

MEDEA / EURIPIDES / GREECE

HEDDA GABLER / HENRIK IBSEN / NORWAY

Medea[1]

EURIPIDES[2] / Greece

(485 B.C.? — 441 B.C.)

freely adapted from the Greek by Robinson Jeffers

CHARACTERS

THE NURSE

THE TUTOR

THE CHILDREN

FIRST WOMAN OF CORINTH

SECOND WOMAN OF CORINTH

THIRD WOMAN OF CORINTH

MEDEA

CREON

JASON

AEGEUS

JASON'S SLAVE

ATTENDANTS TO MEDEA

SOLDIERS

The entire action of the play occurs before Medea's house in Corinth.

1. *Medea* (Mi dē′ ə) **2.** *Euripides* (yẻr ip′ i dēz)

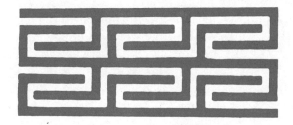

Act One

(The NURSE *comes from the door Left toward the front of the stage.)*
NURSE. I wish the long ship Argo had never passed that perilous channel between the Symplegades,
I wish the pines that made her mast and her oars still waved in the wind on Mount Pelion, and the gray fishhawk
Still nested in them, the great adventurers had never voyaged
Into the Asian sunrise to the shores of morning for the Golden Fleece,
 For then my mistress Medea
5 Would never have seen Jason, nor loved and saved him, nor cut herself off from home to come with him
Into this country of the smiling chattering Greeks and the roofs of Corinth[3]: over which I see evil
Hang like a cloud. For she is not meek but fierce, and the daughter of a king.
 Yet at first all went well.
The folk of Corinth were kind to her, they were proud of her beauty, and Jason loved her. Happy is the house
Where the man and the woman love and are faithful. Now all is changed; all is black hatred. For Jason has turned from her; he calls the old bond a barbarian mating, not a Greek marriage; he has cast her off
10 And wedded the yellow-haired child of Creon, the ruler here. He wants worldly advantage, fine friends,
And a high place in Corinth. For these he is willing to cast Medea like a harlot, and betray the children
That she has borne him. He is not wise, I think
 But Medea

---

3. *I wish . . . the roofs of Corinth.* Jason met Medea while seeking the legendary Golden Fleece, which had been shorn from a magical ram. The noblest heroes of Greece (the Argonauts) accompanied him on the ship Argo to Colchis, a barbarian country on the Black Sea. On the way they faced many dangers, among them the Clashing Rocks, or Symplegades, which roll continuously against one another and threaten to crush whatever comes between them. When "the great adventurers" finally arrived at Colchis, King Aetes, Medea's father and keeper of the Fleece, set Jason an impossible series of tasks as the price of winning the legendary treasure. Hera and Aphrodite sent down Cupid to inflame Medea with love for Jason. As a result, she used her magic to gain him the Fleece and then fled with him to Corinth.

Lies in the house, broken with pain and rage; she will neither eat nor drink,
   except her own tears,
She turns her face toward the earth, remembering her father's house and her
   native land, which she abandoned
15 For the love of this man: who now despises her.
And if I try to speak comfort to her she only stares at me, great eyes like stones.
   She is like a stone on the shore
Or a wave of the sea, and I think she hates
Even her children.
She is learning what it is to be a foreigner, cast out, alone and despised.
20 She will never learn to be humble, she will never learn to drink insult
Like harmless water. O I'm in terror of her: whether she'll thread a knife
   through her own heart,
Or whether she'll hunt the bridegroom and his new bride, or what more
   dreadful evil stalks in the forest
Of her dark mind. I know that Jason would have been wiser to tempt a lioness,
   or naked-handed
Steal the whelps of a tiger.
   (From up Right she sees MEDEA'S BOYS *coming with their* TUTOR, ELDER BOY
   first with seashell, YOUNGER BOY *on* TUTOR'S *back.)*
                         Here come the happy children. Little they know
25 Of their mother's grief.
   (During this speech TUTOR *lets* BOY *off his back.* BOYS *go up and sit up Right
   corner of house.* TUTOR *crosses down Center to Left of* NURSE.*)*
   TUTOR.   Old servant of my lady, why do you stand out here,
   keeping watch in solitude
With those grim eyes? Is it some trouble of your own that you are lamenting?
   I should think Medea
Would need your care.
   NURSE. It is all one to Medea, whether I am there or here. Yes, it is mine,
My trouble. My lady's grief is my grief. And it has hurt me
30 So that I had to come out and speak it to the earth and sky.
   TUTOR. Is she still in that deep despair?
   NURSE.   You are lucky,
Old watchdog of Jason's boys. I envy you,
You do not see her. This evil is not declining, it is just at dawn. I dread the
   lion-eyed
Glare of its noon.
   TUTOR.   Is she so wrought? Yet neither you nor Medea
Knows the latest and worst.
   NURSE *(rises from rock).* What? What?
   TUTOR *(crosses to Center).*   I shouldn't have spoken.
   NURSE.   Tell me the
   truth, old man. You and I are two slaves, we can trust each other,
35 We can keep secrets.
   TUTOR.   I heard them saying—when we walked beside the holy
   fountain Peirene,[4]
Where the old men sit in the sun on the stone benches—they were saying that

---

4. *Peirene* (pī rēn′).

Creon, the lord of this land,
Intends to drive out Medea and the children with her, these innocent boys,
    out of this house
And out of Corinth, and they must wander through the wild world
Homeless and helpless.
    NURSE.   I don't believe it. Ah, no! Jason may hate the mother,
    but he would hardly
40 Let his sons be cast out.
    TUTOR.   Well—he has made a new alliance.
He is not a friend of this house.
    NURSE *(she crosses below* TUTOR *to Left)*. If this were true!—
    MEDEA *(within house. She is Asiatic and laments loudly)*. Death.
    NURSE. Listen! I hear her voice.
    MEDEA *(within)*. Death. Death is my wish. For myself, my enemies, my
    children. Destruction.
45   NURSE. Take the children away, keep them away from her.
Take them to the other door. Quickly.
    (During "Deaths" YOUNGER BOY *rises from rock.* TUTOR *crosses, picks him*
    up and exits Left, followed by ELDER BOY. *They go out, toward rear door of*
    the house. THE NURSE *looks after them, wringing her hands.)*
    MEDEA. That's the word. Grind, crush, burn. Destruction. Ai— Ai—
    NURSE *(wringing her hands)*.   This is my terror:
To hear her always harking back to the children, like a fierce hound at fault.
    O unhappy one,
They're not to blame.
    (Sits step Right of pillar down Left.)
    MEDEA *(within)*. If any god hears me: let me die. Ah, rotten, rotten, rotten:
    death is the only
50 Water to wash this dirt.
    *(*FIRST *and* SECOND WOMAN *are coming in up Right, but the* NURSE *does not*
    yet notice them. She is intent on MEDEA'S *cries and her own thoughts.)*
    NURSE.   Oh, it's a bad thing
To be born of high race, and brought up wilful and powerful in a great house,
    unruled.
And ruling many: for then if misfortune comes it is unendurable, it drives you
    mad. I say that poor people
Are happier: the little commoners and humble people, the poor in spirit: they
    can lie low
Under the wind and live:
    (Enter THIRD WOMAN; *joins* FIRST *and* SECOND *up Right Center.)*
                while the tall oaks and cloud-raking mountain pines
    go mad in the storm,
55 Writhe, groan and crash.
    MEDEA. Ai!
    NURSE. This is the wild and terrible justice of God: it brings on great persons
The great disasters.
    MEDEA. Ai!!!
    NURSE *(becomes aware of the* WOMEN *who have come in, and is startled from*
    her reverie. FIRST WOMAN *crosses down Center)*. What do you want?
    FIRST WOMAN. I hear her crying again: it is dreadful.

SECOND WOMAN (*crosses down to Right of* FIRST WOMAN). Her lamentation.
60 She is beautiful and deep in grief: we couldn't help coming.
THIRD WOMAN (*crosses down to Right of* SECOND WOMAN). We are friends of
this house and its trouble hurts us.
NURSE. You are right, friends; it is not a home. It is broken.
A house of grief and of weeping.
MEDEA (*within*).   Hear me, God, let me die. What I need: all
dead, all dead, all dead
(THIRD WOMAN *crosses down Right of rock.*)
Under the great cold stones. For a year and a thousand years and another
thousand: cold as the stones, cold,
65 But noble again, proud, straight and silent, crimson-cloaked
In the blood of our wounds.
(FIRST WOMAN *crosses to third step, Center.*)
FIRST WOMAN.   O shining sky, divine earth,
Harken not to the song that this woman sings.
It is not her mind's music; her mind is not here.
She does not know what she prays for.
70 Pain and wrath are the singers.
SECOND WOMAN (*crosses to second step, facing door*). Unhappy one,
Never pray for death, never pray for death,
He is here all too soon.
He strikes from the clear sky like a hawk,
He hides behind green leaves, or he waits
75 Around the corner of the wall.
O never pray for death, never pray for death—
Because that prayer will be answered.
MEDEA (*the rise and fall of her voice indicates that she is prowling back and
forth beyond the main doorway, like a caged animal*). I know poisons. I
know the bright teeth of steel. I know fire. But I will not be mocked by my
enemies,
(THIRD WOMAN *crosses up Right of rock to Right Center.*)
And I will not endure pity. Pity and contempt are sister and brother, twin-born.
I will not die tamely.
80 I will not allow blubber-eyed pity, nor contempt either, to snivel over the stones
of my tomb.
I am not a Greek woman.
THIRD WOMAN (*crosses to step Center*). No, a barbarian woman from savage
Colchis, at the bitter end
Of the Black Sea. Does she boast of that?
SECOND WOMAN.   She doesn't know what she is saying.
MEDEA (*within*). Poisons. Death-magic. The sharp sword. The hemp rope.
Death-magic.
Death—
SECOND WOMAN (*crosses down Right of rock.* THIRD WOMAN *joins her*). I hate
Jason, who made this sorrow.
85 FIRST WOMAN (*crosses to* NURSE *in front of doors*). Old and honored servant
of a great house, do you think it is wise
To leave your lady alone in there, except perhaps a few slaves, building that
terrible acropolis

Of deadly thoughts? We Greeks believe that solitude is very dangerous, great
    passions grow into monsters
In the dark of the mind; but if you share them with loving friends they remain
    human, they can be endured.
    MEDEA *(within)*. Ai!

90   FIRST WOMAN. I think you ought to persuade Medea to come from the dark
    dwelling, and speak with us, before her heart breaks,
Or she does harm to herself. She has lived among us, we've learned to love her,
    we'd gladly tell her so.
It might comfort her spirit.
    NURSE.   Do you think so? She wouldn't listen.
    (Door bolt is heard. NURSE *rises.* FIRST WOMAN *crosses down Right, joining
    other two* WOMEN, *and sits on rock.)*
                                           —Oh, oh, she
    is coming!
Speak carefully to her: make your words a soft music.
    *(*MEDEA *comes through the doorway, propping herself against one of the
    pillars, and stands staring.)*
    NURSE. Oh, my dear, my poor child.
    *(*NURSE *sits.)*

95   SECOND WOMAN *(whispering)*. They say she is dangerous. Look at her eyes.
    FIRST WOMAN. She is a witch, but not evil. She can make old men young
    again: she did it for Jason's father.
    THIRD WOMAN. All the people of her country are witches. They know about
    drugs and magic. They are savages, but they have a wild wisdom.
    SECOND WOMAN. Poor soul, it hasn't helped this one much.
    MEDEA *(she does not see the gaping and whispering* WOMEN*)*. I will look at
    the light of the sun, this last time. I wish from that blue sky the white wolf
    of lightning

100 Would leap, and burst my skull and my brain, and like a burning babe cling
    to these breasts— Ai!—Ai!
    (She checks and looks fiercely at the WOMEN *below.)*
Someone is here?
    (Her hostile eyes range back and forth; she sees the WOMEN *clearly now,
    and assumes full self-control. Her voice is cautious and insincere.)*
                      I did not know I had visitors.—Women of Corinth:
If anything has been spoken too loudly here, consider
That I believed I was alone; and I have some provocation. You've come—let
    me suppose
With love and sympathy—to peer at my sorrow. I understand well enough

105 That nothing is ever private in a Greek city; whoever withholds anything
Is thought sullen or proud—
    (With irony.)
                           undemocratic
I think you call it. This is not always just, but we know that justice, at least on
    earth,
Is a name, not a fact; and as for me, I wish to avoid any appearance
Of being—proud. Of what? Of affliction? I will show you my naked heart.
    (The THREE WOMEN *rise; cross to Center.)*
                       You know that my lord Jason

110 Has left me and made a second marriage, with the bright-haired child
   Of wealth and power. I too was a child of power, but not in this country; and
      I spent my power
   For love of Jason. I poured it out before him like water, I made him drink it like
      wine. I gave him
   Success and fame; I saved him his precious life; not once, many times. You
      may have heard what I did for him:
   I betrayed my father for him, I killed my brother to save him; I made my own
      . land to hate me forever;
115 And I fled west with Jason in the Greek ship, under the thunder of the sail,
      weeping and laughing,
   That huge journey through the Black Sea and the Bosporus, where the rocks
      clang together, through the Sea of Marmora,
   And through Hellespont,
                           watched by the spearmen of wealthy Troy, and home
      to Greek water[5]: his home, my exile,
   My endless exile.
      (Crosses to pillar Left of house.)
                           And here I have loved him and borne him sons; and this—
      man—
   Has left me and taken Creon's daughter, to enjoy her fortune, and put aside her
      soft yellow hair
120 And kiss her young mouth.
      (MEDEA *stands rigid, struggling for self-control.)*
   FIRST WOMAN. She is terrible. Stone with stone eyes.
   SECOND WOMAN. Look: the foam-flake on her lip, that flickers with her
      breathing.
   THIRD WOMAN. She is pitiable: she is under great injuries.
   MEDEA *(low-voiced).* I do not know what other women—I do not know how
      much a Greek woman
125 Will endure. The people of my race are somewhat rash and intemperate. As
      for me, I want simply to die.
      (She sits at pillar Left.)
   But Jason is not to smile at his bride over my grave, nor that great man Creon
   Hang wreaths and make a feast-day in Corinth. Or let the wreaths be bright
      blinding fire, and the songs a high wailing,
   And the wine, blood.
      FIRST WOMAN *(crosses to Center).* Daughter of sorrow, beware.
   It is dangerous to dream of wine; it is worse
130 To speak of wailing or blood:
   For the images that the mind makes
   Find a way out, they work into life.
      MEDEA.   Let them work into life!

---

5. *I betrayed my father . . . to Greek water.* When King Aetes sent his son with an army in pursuit
of Medea and Jason, Medea tricked her brother into a lone meeting so that Jason could slay him.
Their journey to Corinth took them southwest from the Black Sea to the Aegean by way of the
Sea of Marmora. Bosporus and Hellespont (now the Dardanelles) are straits connecting Marmora
with the Black Sea and with the Aegean, respectively. Troy is called "wealthy" because the Argonauts' voyage took place a generation before the Trojan War.

FIRST WOMAN. There are evils that cannot be cured by evil.
Patience remains, and the gods watch all.

135 MEDEA *(dully, without hope)*. Let them watch my enemies go down in blood.
(First trumpet off up Right is heard. The THREE WOMEN *cross up Right.)*
SECOND WOMAN   Medea, beware!
Some great person is coming.—
(Second trumpet is heard.)
It is Creon himself.
(Third trumpet.)
THIRD WOMAN. Creon is coming.
(The THREE WOMEN *cross down stage of rock Right.)*
NURSE.   He is dark with anger. O my lady—my child
—bend in this wind,
And not be broken!
*(*MEDEA *rises.* CREON *comes in up Right with* MEN *attending him. The*
WOMEN *move to one side. He speaks to* MEDEA, *with an angry gesture toward*
WOMEN.)*
140 CREON *(at Center)*. You have admirers, I see. Abate your pride: these people
will not be with you where you are going.
(A pause. MEDEA *does not answer.* CREON *brings his wrath under control*
and crosses up to second step to Right of MEDEA.)*
Medea, woman of the stone forehead and hate-filled eyes: I have made my
decision. I have decided
That you must leave this land at once and go into banishment
THREE WOMEN. Oohh!
145 CREON.   with your children.
THREE WOMEN. Oohh.
CREON. I intend to remove
A root of disturbance out of the soil of Corinth. I am here to see to it. I will not
return home
Until it is done.
(The THREE WOMEN *sit.)*
MEDEA.   You mean—banishment?
CREON.   Exile: banishment: go where you may,
Medea, but here
You abide no more.
MEDEA.   —I with my children?
CREON.   I will not take them away from you.
MEDEA.   The children, my lord—
(Her lips move angrily, but the voice is not heard.)
CREON.   What are you muttering?
MEDEA. Nothing—I am praying to my gods for wisdom,
150 And you for mercy. My sons are still very young, tender and helpless. You
know, my lord,
What exile means—to wander with fear and famine for guide and driver,
through all the wild winter storms
And the rage of the sun; and beg a bread-crust and be derided; pelted with
stones in the villages,
Held a little lower than the scavenger dogs, kicked, scorned and slaved—the
children, my lord,

Are Jason's children. Your chosen friend, I believe, and now
155 Even closer bound. And as for me, your servant, O master of Corinth, what
    have I done? Why
Must I be cast?
    CREON.   I will tell you frankly: because you nourish rancorous ill will
    toward persons
Whom I intend to protect: I send you out before you've time to do harm here.
    And you are notorious
For occult knowledge: sorcery, poisons, magic. Men say you can even sing
    down the moon from heaven,
And make the holy stars to falter and run backward, against the purpose
160 And current of nature. Ha? As to that I know not: I know you are dangerous.
    You threaten my daughter: you have to go.
    MEDEA. But I wish her well, my lord! I wish her all happiness. I hope that
    Jason may be as kind to her
As—to me.
    CREON.   That is your wish?
    MEDEA.   I misspoke, I thought of old days—
    (She seems to weep.)
    CREON.   I acknowledge, Medea,
That you have some cause for grief. I all the more must guard against your dark
    wisdom and bitter heart.
    MEDEA. You misjudge me cruelly. It is true that I have some knowledge of
    drugs and medicines: I can sometimes cure sickness.
165 Is that a crime? These dark rumors, my lord,
Are only the noise of popular gratitude.
    (Crosses down to one step above him.)
You must have observed it often: if any person
Knows a little more than the common man, the people suspect him. If he brings
    a new talent,
How promptly the hateful whispers begin. But you are not a common man,
    lord of Corinth; you
170 Will not fear knowledge.
    CREON.   No. Nor change my decision. I am here to see you
    leave this house and the city:
And not much time. Move quickly, gather your things and go. I pity you,
    Medea,
But you must go.
    (He crosses off steps, with back to her down Right Center.)
    MEDEA.   You pity me? You—pity me?
    (She comes close to him, wild with rage.)
I will endure a dog's pity or a wart-grown toad's. May God who hears me—
    We shall see in the end
Who's to be pitied.
    (NURSE rises, crosses in to steps. MEDEA crosses down Left, then up Right
    between pillar and edge of house, then back to NURSE in her arms.)
    CREON.   Yes, and I'll keep her safe of your female hatred: therefore
    I send you
175 Out of this land.
    (NURSE resumes her sitting position down Left.)

MEDEA.   It is not true, I am not jealous. I never hated her.
Jealous for the sake of Jason? I am far past wanting Jason, my lord. You took
    him and gave him to her.
And I will say you did well, perhaps wisely. Your daughter is loved by all: she
    is beautiful: if I were near her
I would soon love her.
    CREON.   You can speak sweetly enough, you can make honey
        in your mouth like a brown bee
When it serves your turn.
    MEDEA.   Not honey: the truth.
    CREON.   Trust you or not, you are going
        out of this country, Medea.
180 What I decide is fixed;
        (MEDEA *crosses away from him to Center.*)
                    it is like the firm rocks of Acrocorinth,[6] which neither
        earthquake can move
Nor a flood of tears melt. Make ready quickly: I have a guest in my house. I
    should return to him.
    NURSE (*comes to Left of* MEDEA *and speaks to her*). What guest? O my lady,
        ask him
Who is the guest? If powerful and friendly
He might be a refuge for us—
185   MEDEA (*pays no attention to her. Crosses; kneels; to* CREON). I know that your
        will is granite. But even on the harsh face of a granite mountain some
        flowers of mercy
May grow in season. Have mercy on my little sons, Creon,
Though there is none for me.
        (*She reaches to embrace his knees. He steps backward from her.*)
    CREON.   How long, woman? This is decided; done;
        finished.
        (NURSE *crosses back Left and sits down.*)
    MEDEA (*rising from her knees, turns half away from him*). I am not a beggar.
I will not trouble you. I shall not live long.
        (*Crosses two steps to Left; turns to him again.*)
Sire: grant me a few hours yet, one day to prepare in, one little day
190 Before I go out of Corinth forever.
    CREON.   What? No! I told you. The day is today,
        Medea, this day.
And the hour is now.
    MEDEA.   There are no flowers on this mountain: not one violet,
        not one anemone.
Your face, my lord, is like flint. If I could find the right words, if some god
    would lend me a touch of eloquence,
I'd show you my heart.
        (*Crosses to* CREON.)
                    I'd lift it out of my breast and turn it over in my hands;
        You'd see how pure it is
Of any harm or malice toward you or your household.

---

6. *Acrocorinth* (from the Greek *akros*, meaning top or peak + *Corinth*), a high rock on which was
built a citadel and a temple of Aphrodite.

(She holds out her hands to him.)
195 Look at it: not a speck: look, my lord. They call mercy
The jewel of kings. I am praying
To you as to one of the gods: destroy us not utterly. To go out with no refuge,
    nothing prepared,
Is plain death: I would rather kill myself quickly and here. If I had time but to
    ask the slaves
And strolling beggars where to go, how to live: and I must gather some means:
    one or two jewels
200 And small gold things I have,
    (Crosses away from CREON *to Left.)*
                         to trade them for bread and goat's milk.
    (Crosses up steps to Center of doorway.)
Wretched, wretched, wretched I am,
I and my boys. *(She kneels again.)*
            I beseech you, Creon,
By the soft yellow hair and cool smooth forehead and the white knees
Of that young girl who is now Jason's bride: lend me this inch of time: one day
    —half a day.
For this one is now half gone—and I will go my sad course and vanish in the
    morning quietly as dew
205 That drops on the stones at dawn and is dry at sunrise. You will never again be
    troubled by any word
Or act of mine. And this I pray you for your dear child's sake. Oh Creon, what
    is half a day
In all the rich years of Corinth?
    CREON.   I will think of it. I am no tyrant.
I have been merciful to my own hurt, many times. Even to myself I seem to be
    foolish
If I grant you this thing— No, Medea,
210 I will not grant it.
    *(*THREE WOMEN *rise, cross down Right of* CREON, *imploringly.)*
              Well— We shall watch you: as a hawk does a viper. What
    harm could she do
In the tail of one day? A ruler ought to be ruthless; but I am not. I am a fool
In my own eyes, whatever the world may think. I can be gruff with warriors;
    a woman weeping
    *(*MEDEA *weeps.)*
Floods me off course. Take it, then. Make your preparations.
But if tomorrow's sun shines on you here—Medea, you die—
    *(*MEDEA *and* WOMEN *make a gesture of thanks.)*
                                  Enough words.
    Thank me not. I want my hands
215 Washed of this business.
    (He departs quickly up Right, followed by his MEN. MEDEA *rises from her
    knees.)*
    MEDEA.   I will thank you.
And the whole world will hear of it.
    *(*MEDEA *crosses around to Right of house on top step; makes a violent
    gesture after him, then sits at pillar Right.)*

FIRST WOMAN (*crosses up Center watching him out then turns to other* WOMEN). I have seen this man's arrogance, I watched and heard him.
I am of Corinth, and I say that Corinth
Is not well ruled.

220   SECOND WOMAN (*Crosses up Center.* THREE WOMEN *join hands at Center on end of this speech*). The city where even a woman, even a foreigner,
Suffers unjustly the rods of power
Is not well ruled.
    (THREE WOMEN *take a step to* MEDEA.)
    FIRST WOMAN. Unhappy Medea, what haven, what sanctuary, where will you wander?
Which of the gods, Medea,
225 Drives you through waves of woe, the mooring broken, the hawsers and the anchor-head,
Hopeless from harbor?
    MEDEA.   —This man—this barking dog—this gulled fool—
    (MEDEA *rises.*)

                                      gods of my father's country,
You saw me low on my knees before the great dog of Corinth; humble, holding my heart in my hands
For a dog to bite—break this dog's teeth!
    (WOMEN *cross down stage of rock Right.*)
                           Women: it is a bitter thing to be a woman.
A woman is weak for warfare, she must use cunning. Men boast their battles: I tell you this, and we know it:
(Starts down steps Center.)
230 It is easier to stand in battle three times, in the front line, in the stabbing fury, than to bear one child.
And a woman, they say, can do no good but in childbirth. It may be so. She can do evil;
    (WOMEN *make pleading gesture to her.*)
           she can do evil.
    (She snarls at them and they turn away.)
I wept before that tall dog, I wept my tears before him, I degraded my knees to him, I gulled and flattered him.
O triple fool, he has given me
    (She crosses up Right Center. FIRST WOMAN *sits on rock Right.)*
                     all that I needed: a little time, a space of time.
    (Crosses back to Left Center.)
                               Death is dearer to me
Than what I am now; and if today by sunset the world has not turned, and turned sharp too—let your dog Creon
235 Send two or three slaves to kill me and a cord to strangle me: I will stretch out
My throat to it. But I have a bitter hope, women. I begin to see light
Through the dark wood, between the monstrous trunks of the trees, at the end
   .   of the tangled forest an eyehole,
A pin-point of light:
                      I shall not die perhaps
As a pigeon dies. Nor like an innocent lamb, that feels a hand on its head and

looks up from the knife

240 To the man's face and dies. No, like some yellow-eyed beast that has killed its
hunters let me lie down

On the hounds' bodies and the broken spears. Then how to strike them? What
means to use? There are so many

Doors through which painful death may glide in and catch— Which one,
which one?

(She stands meditating down Left. The NURSE *comes from behind her and
speaks to the* FIRST WOMAN.)

NURSE.   Tell me: do you know what guest

Is in Creon's house?

FIRST WOMAN.   What? Oh. An Athenian ship came from the north last
night: it is Aegeus.[7]

The lord of Athens.

NURSE.   Aegeus! My lady knows him: I believe he will help us.
Some god has brought him here,

245 Some savior god.

FIRST WOMAN. He is leaving, I think, today.

NURSE *(hobbling back toward* MEDEA).   My lady!
Lord Aegeus

Is here in Corinth, Creon's guest. Aegeus of Athens.

*(*MEDEA *looks at her silently, without attention.)*

If you will see him and speak him fairly,

We have a refuge.

MEDEA.   I have things in my hand to do. Be quiet.

NURSE.   Oh, listen to me!

You are driven out of Corinth; you must find shelter. Aegeus of Athens is here.

*(*MEDEA *turns from her. The* NURSE *catches at her clothing, servile but eager,
slave and mother at the same time.)*

250 MEDEA *(angrily turning on her).* What's that to me?

NURSE *(kneels at her feet).* I lifted you in my arms when you were—this long.
I gave you milk from these breasts, that are now dead leaves.

I saw the little beautiful body straighten and grow tall: Oh—child—almost my
child—how can I

Not try to save you? Life is better than death—

MEDEA.   Not now.

NURSE. Time's running out!

MEDEA.   I have time. Oh, I have time.

It would be good to stand here a thousand years and think of nothing

255 But the deaths of three persons.

NURSE.   Ai! There's no hope then.

Ai, child, if you could do this red thing you dream of, all Corinth

Would pour against you.

MEDEA.   After my enemies are punished and I have heard the
last broken moan—Corinth?

What's that? I'll sleep. I'll sleep well. I am alone against all: and so weary

That it is pitiful.

---

7. *Aegeus* (ē′ jus), a legendary Athenian king, the father of Theseus.

(MEDEA *sits.* NURSE *rises, wringing her hands. On trumpet call the* THREE WOMEN *cross up Right.*)

FIRST WOMAN. Look: who is coming? I see the sunlight glitter on lanceheads.

260 SECOND WOMAN. Oh, it is Jason!

THIRD WOMAN. Jason's Medea's worst enemy, who should have been
Her dearest protector.

(MEDEA *leans wearily against one of the pillars of the doorway, her back to the stage, unconscious of what they are saying.* JASON *enters in haste up Right, followed by armed* ATTENDANTS, *and speaks angrily.*)

JASON (*crossing to Center on second step*). What business have you here, you women
Clustered like buzzing bees at the hive-door?
Where is Medea?

(*They do not answer for a moment, but look involuntarily toward* MEDEA, *and* JASON *sees her. She jerks and stiffens at the sound of his voice, but does not turn.*)

FIRST WOMAN (*pointing*). There: mourning for what you have done.

(NURSE *takes a step above* MEDEA, *disclosing her to* JASON.)

JASON. Ha? What she has done.
265 Not I. Not by my will are she and my sons exiled.

MEDEA (*slowly turns and faces him, her head high, rigid with inner violence.*)
Is there another dog here?

(THREE WOMEN *sit on steps up Right Center.*)

JASON. So, Medea,
You have once more affronted and insulted the head of Corinth. This is not the first time
I've seen what a fool anger is. You might have lived here happily, secure and honored—I hoped you would—
By being just a little decently respectful toward those in power. Instead you had to go mad with anger
270 And talk yourself into exile. To me it matters little what you say about me, but rulers are sensitive.
Time and again I've smoothed down Creon's indignation, then you like a mad-woman, like a possessed imbecile,
Wag your head and let the words flow again; you never cease
From speaking evil against him and his family. So now— Call yourself lucky, Medea,
Not to get worse than exile.

(*Crosses a few steps to* MEDEA *on second step.*)
In spite of all this, I have your interest at heart and am here to help you.
275 Exile's a bitter business. I want to make some provision for you. I wish you no harm,
Although you hate me.

(*He waits for her to speak, but she is silent. He continues.*)
And in particular the children, my sons; our sons.
You might have been decent enough
To have thought of our sons.

MEDEA (*slowly*). Did you consider them
When you betrayed this house?

JASON.   Certainly I considered them. It was my hope
  that they would grow up here,
And I, having married power, could protect and favor them. And if perhaps,
  after many years, I become
280 Dynast of Corinth—for that is Creon's desire, to make me his heir—our sons
Would have been a king's sons— I hope to help them wherever they go: but
  now of course must look forward
To younger children.
    (Steps down off steps and turns from her.)
  MEDEA *(trembling).* Ah—it's enough. Something might happen. It is—likely
    that—something might happen
To the bride and the marriage.
  JASON.   I'll guard against it. But evidently Creon is right
    to be rid of you.
    *(He crosses as if to go off Right. She stops him when he is up Right Center.
    He gives helmet to SLAVE; crosses down Right.)*
  MEDEA *(rises and crosses to Center).* Have you finished now? I thought I
    would let you speak on and spread out your shamelessness
285 Before these women the way a Tyrian trader[8] unrolls his rare fabrics: "Do you
    like it ladies?"
                              It is the
Dog's daughter's husband. It is a brave person: it has finally got up its courage
  —with a guard of spears—
To come and look me in the face.
    *(JASON turns away from her. MEDEA makes gestures as if to take him in her
    arms, then stops.)*
                              O Jason: how have you pulled me down
To this hell of vile thoughts? I did not use to talk like a common woman. I
  loved you once:
And I am ashamed of it:
    (JASON sits on rock Right. She crosses two steps Left.)
                              but there are some things
290 That ought to be remembered by you and me. That blue day when we drove
    through the Hellespont
Into Greek sea, and the great-shouldered heroes were singing at the oars, and
    those birds flying
Through the blown foam: that day was too fine I suppose
For Creon's daughter's man to remember
    (JASON rises as if to leave.)
                              —but you might remember
Whether I cheated my father for you and tamed the fire-breathing
295 Brazen-hoofed bulls; and whether I saved your life in the field of the teeth;
    and you might remember
Whether I poisoned the great serpent and got you the Golden Fleece; and fled
    with you, and killed my brother
When he pursued us, making myself abominable
In my own home: and then in yours I got your enemy Pelias hacked to death

---

8. *Tyrian trader.* The people of Tyre in Phoenicia were the greatest merchants of the ancient
world.

By his own daughters' hands⁹—whatever these fine Corinthian friends of
        yours
₃₀₀ May say against my rapid and tricky wisdom: you it has served,
You it has served well:
        (JASON starts to speak.)
                                here are five times, if I counted right—and all's not
        counted—
That your adventure would have been dusty death
If I'd not saved you—but now you think that your adventures are over; you are
        safe and high placed in Corinth,
And will need me no more.
                                It is a bit of a dog, isn't it, women? It is well
        qualified
₃₀₅ To sleep with the dog's daughter.
        (JASON makes a gesture of wrath.)
                                But for me, Jason, me driven by the hairy
        snouts from the quadruped marriage-bed,
What refuge does your prudent kindness advise? Shall I fly home to Colchis—
To put my neck in the coil of a knotted rope, for the crimes
I served you with? Or shall I go and kneel to the daughter of Pelias? They
        would indeed be happy
To lay their hands on my head: holding the very knives and the cleavers
₃₁₀ That carved their sire. The world is a little closed to me, eh?
By the things I have done for you.
        (Crosses away from him to down Center.)
        NURSE.   I'll go to the palace
And seek Aegeus. There is no other hope.
        (She hurries out door Left.)
        JASON *(slowly crossing to Center to Right of* MEDEA*)*. I see, Medea,
You have been a very careful merchant of benefits. You forget none, you keep
        a strict reckoning. But—
Some little things that I on my side have done for you
₃₁₅ Ought to be in the books too: as, for example, that I carried you
Out of the dirt and superstition of Asiatic Colchis into the rational
Sunlight of Greece, and the marble music of the Greek temples: is that no
        benefit? And I have brought you
To meet the first minds of our time, and to speak as an equal with the great
        heroes and the rulers of cities:
Is that no benefit? And now—this grievous thing that you hate me for:

---

9. *Whether I cheated . . . his own daughters' hands.* Medea recalls the magic she worked to help
Jason win and keep the Fleece. Jason was called upon to yoke two young bulls, whose feet were
bronze and whose breath was fire. With the bulls he was to sow dragons' teeth in the ground from
which would spring a crop of armed men. These he was to fight and conquer. Medea provided
him with an ointment that gave him strength and prevented any injury to him during the feat.
The great serpent was the guardian of the Fleece. Medea sang a magical song to lull it to sleep
so that Jason could steal the Fleece. By securing the Fleece, Jason sought to dethrone the Grecian
king Pelias, who had usurped the throne of Jason's father. On his return, Jason found that Pelias
had killed his father and caused his mother's death through grief. Medea avenged the crime for
Jason by persuading Pelias' daughters that they could rejuvenate their father if they would dis-
member his body while he slept. They did as she told them; but she vanished, leaving them horrified at their deed.

320 That I have married Creon's young daughter, little Creusa:
    (MEDEA sits on second step.)

                                              do you think I did
it like a boy or a woman,
Out of blind passion? I did it to achieve power here; and I'd have used that power to protect
You and our sons, but your jealous madness has muddled everything. And finally:
    (NURSE appears behind house and exits up Right. JASON crosses above MEDEA to top step.)
As to those acts of service you so loudly boast—whom do I thank for them? I thank divine Venus, the goddess
Who makes girls fall in love. You did them because you had to do them; Venus compelled you; I
325 Enjoyed her favor.
    (Crosses down two steps to her Left.)
                           A man dares things, you know; he makes his adventure
In the cold eye of death; and if the gods care for him
They appoint an instrument to save him; if not, he dies. You were that instrument.
    MEDEA. Here it is: the lowest.
The obscene dregs; the slime and the loathing; the muddy bottom of a mouthed cup: when a scoundrel begins
To invoke the gods.
330   JASON. Ha!
    MEDEA. You had better go, Jason. Vulgarity
Is a contagious disease; and in a moment what could I do but spit at you like a peasant, or curse you
Like a drunken slave? You had better take yourself back to
"Little Creusa."
    JASON.   I came to help you and save you if possible.
    (Reaches down and touches her arm.)
    MEDEA.
                                      Your help
335 Is not wanted. Go. Go.
    JASON *(crosses below her to Right Center, then stops).* If I could see my boys—
    MEDEA.   Go quickly.
    JASON.   Yours the regret then.
    (Exits up Right. Watching him go, MEDEA strokes her wrist and hand to the tips of the spread fingers, as if she were scraping off slime.)
    MEDEA. This is it. I did not surely know it: loathing is all. This flesh
He has touched and fouled. These hands that wrought for him, these knees
That ran his errands. This body that took his—what they call love, and made children of it. If I could peel off
The flesh, the children, the memory—
    (Again she scarifies one hand with the other. She looks at her hand.)
                          Poor misused hand; poor defiled arm; your bones
340 Are not unshapely. If I could tear off the flesh and be bones; naked bones;
Salt-scoured bones on the shore
At home in Colchis.

FIRST WOMAN (*rises and crosses down Right*). God keep me from fire and
 the hunger of the sword,
Save me from the hateful sea and the jagged lightning,
345 And the violence of love.
 SECOND WOMAN (*joins* FIRST WOMAN). A little love is a joy in the house,
A little fire is a jewel against frost and darkness.
 (*During these two speeches* THIRD WOMAN *goes up Right Center, then
 returns to* WOMEN *down Right.*)
 FIRST WOMAN. A great love is a fire
That burns the beams of the roof.
350 The doorposts are flaming and the house falls.
 (THIRD WOMAN *kneels.*)
A great love is a lion in the cattle-pen,
The herd goes mad, the heifers run bawling
And the claws are in their flanks.
Too much love is an armed robber in the treasury.
355 He has killed the guards and he walks in blood.
 SECOND WOMAN. And now I see the black end,
The end of great love, and God save me from it:
The unburied horror, the unbridled hatred,
The vultures tearing a corpse!
360 God keep me clean of those evil beaks.
 THIRD WOMAN. What is she doing, that woman,
Staring like stone, staring?
 (MEDEA *looks up.*)
Oh, she has moved now.
 MEDEA. Annihilation. The word is pure music: annihilation. To annihilate
 the past—
365 Is not possible: but its fruit in the present—
Can be nipped off. Am I to look in my sons' eyes
And see Jason's forever? How could I endure the endless defilement, those lives
That mix Jason and me? Better to be clean
Bones on the shore. Bones have no eyes at all, how could they weep? White
 bones
370 On the Black Sea shore—
        Oh, but that's far. Not yet. Corinth must howl first.
 FIRST WOMAN. The holy fountains flow up from the earth,
The smoke of sacrifice flows up from the earth,
The eagle and the wild swan fly up from the earth,
Righteousness also
375 Has flown up from the earth to the feet of God.
It is not here, but up there; peace and pity are departed;
Hatred is here; hatred is heavy, it clings to the earth.
Love blows away, hatred remains.
 SECOND WOMAN. Women hate war, but men will wage it again.
380 Women may hate their husbands, and sons their fathers,
But women will never hate their own children.
 FIRST WOMAN. But as for me, I will do good to my husband,
I will love my sons and daughters, and adore the gods.
 MEDEA. If I should go into the house with a sharp knife

385 To the man and his bride—
　　　(MEDEA *rises.* THIRD WOMAN *rises.)*
Or if I could fire the room they sleep in, and hear them
Wake in the white of the fire, and cry to each other, and howl like dogs.
　　　THREE WOMEN. Oh!!!
　　　(Cringe together.)
　　　MEDEA. And howl and die—
390 But I might fail; I might be cut down first;
The knife might turn in my hand, or the fire not burn, and my enemies could
　　　laugh at me.
No: I have subtler means, and more deadly cruel; I have my dark art
That fools call witchcraft. Not for nothing I have worshipped the wild gray
　　　goddess that walks in the dark, the wise one,
The terrible one, the sweet huntress, flower of night, Hecate,[10]
395 In my house at my hearth.
　　　(She crosses up to pillar Right and sits.)
　　　NURSE *(hurries in toward* MEDEA, *to her Right).* My lady: he was leaving
　　　Creon's door: he is coming.
　　　(MEDEA pays no attention.)
　　　　　　　　　　　　Aegeus is coming.
The power of Athens.
　　　MEDEA *(prays).* Ancient goddess to whom I and my people
Make the sacrifice of black lambs and black female hounds,
Holy one, haunter of crossroads, queen of night, Hecate,
400 Help me now: to remember in my mind the use of the venomous fire, the magic
　　　song
And the sharp gems.
　　　(She sits in deep thought. AEGEUS *comes in up Right.)*
　　　NURSE. He is here, my lady,
Athens is here.
　　　(MEDEA pays no attention. THREE WOMEN *curtsy, then resume their original
　　　positions at rock.* FIRST WOMAN *sits.)*
　　　AEGEUS *(crosses down Left and up steps to top step, Left of* MEDEA). Medea,
　　　rejoice! There is no fairer greeting from friend to friend.
　　　(She ignores him. He speaks more loudly.)
Hail and rejoice! Medea.
　　　MEDEA *(lifts her head and stares at him).* "Rejoice?" It may be so. It may be
　　　I shall—rejoice
405 Before the sun sets.
　　　AEGEUS.　　　　　What has happened to you?
　　　　　　　　　　　　　　　　Your eyes are cavernous!
And your mouth twitches.
　　　MEDEA.　　　　　　　Nothing: I am quite well: fools trouble me. Where
　　　are you travelling from,
Aegeus?
　　　AEGEUS. From Delphi,[11] where I went to consult
The ancient oracle of Apollo.
　　　MEDEA *(abstractedly).*　　Oh— Delphi— Did you get a good answer?

---

10. *Hecate* (hek′ ə tē), the goddess of the underworld. 11. *Delphi,* the location of the temple of
the god of truth, Apollo. Delphi was the source of the most famous and trustworthy prophecies.

AEGEUS. An obscure one.

410 Some god or other has made me unable to beget a child: that is my sorrow: but the oracle
Never gives plain responses.
   (Crosses two steps nearer her.)
                              I tell you these things because you are skilled in
   mysteries, and you might help me
To the god's meaning.
   MEDEA *(wearily).*   You want a child? What did Apollo
Say to you?
   AEGEUS. That I must not unloose the hanging foot of the wine-skin until I
   return
To the hearth of my fathers.
   MEDEA *(without interest, but understanding the anatomical reference).*
                     You have never had a child?
AEGEUS.   No.

415 And it is bitterness.
   (Turns away from her and takes one step down.)
   MEDEA.   But when misfortune comes it is bitter to have children,
   and watch their starlike
Faces grow dim to endure it.
   AEGEUS.   When death comes, Medea,
It is, for a childless man, utter despair, darkness, extinction. One's children
Are the life after death.
   MEDEA *(excited).*   Do you feel it so? Do you feel it so?
Then—if you had a dog-eyed enemy and needed absolute vengeance—you'd kill
420 The man's children first. Unchild him, ha?
And then unlife him.
   AEGEUS.   I do not care to think of such horrors.
I have no enemy.
   *(MEDEA rises, making violent movement; sits again. He stares, and slightly
   recoils from her. Crosses back up to her.)*
                    What is it? What is the matter, Medea? You are trembling;
   wild fever
Flames in your eyes.
   MEDEA.   I am well enough— Fools trouble me, and dogs; but not
   that— Oh—
   AEGEUS.   What has happened to you?
   NURSE *(crouches by her, trying to comfort her).* My dear—my love—
   MEDEA *(pushes her gently aside; looks up at AEGEUS).*   I would
   not hurt my children. Their father hurts them.
425 AEGEUS. What do you mean—Jason? What has Jason done?
   MEDEA.   He has betrayed
   and denied
Both me and them.
   AEGEUS.   Jason has done that? Why? Why?
   MEDEA. He has cast me off and married Creon's young daughter.
And Creon, this very day, is driving us
Into black exile.

AEGEUS.   Jason consents to that?

MEDEA.   He is glad of it.

AEGEUS *(crossing down steps to* WOMEN *down Right)*. Why—it's atrocious, it's past belief.

NURSE *(says in* MEDEA's *ear)*. Ask him for refuge! Ask him to receive you in Athens!

430 MEDEA *(straight and rigid)*.   Do you not think such men ought to be punished, Aegeus?

AEGEUS.   I think it is villainous.

They told me nothing of this—

MEDEA.   Do you not think such men ought to be punished, Aegeus?

(Crossing down steps to second step Center.)

AEGEUS. Where will you go?

MEDEA *(solemnly)*.   If there is any rightness on earth or in heaven, they will be punished.

AEGEUS.   Where

Will you go to, Medea?

MEDEA *(crossing Left, still on second step)*. What? To death, of course.

NURSE *(crosses to* AEGEUS*)*. Oh— She is all bewildered, sir,

In the deep storm and ocean of grief, or she would ask of you

435 Refuge in Athens.

MEDEA *(in bitter mockery, seeing* AEGEUS *hesitate)*. Ah? So I should. That startled the man. Aegeus:

Will *you* shelter me in *Athens?*

AEGEUS.   Why—yes. Yes—I will not take you now from Corinth; it would not be right.

I want no quarrel with Creon, I am his guest here.

(Crossing below NURSE *to Center.)*

         If you by your own means come to Athens

I will take care of you.

*(*THE NURSE *sits on first step to Right of* AEGEUS*.)*

MEDEA.   I would repay you for it. I know the remedies—that would make a dry stick flame into fire and fruit.

AEGEUS *(eagerly)*.   You'd cure my sterility?

MEDEA. I could do so.

AEGEUS.   You are famous for profound knowledge

Of drugs and charms.

(Eagerly.) You'll come to Athens?

MEDEA.   If I choose. If the gods decide it so. But, Aegeus,

440 Would you protect me if I came? I have certain enemies. If powerful enemies came, baying for my blood,

Would you protect me?

AEGEUS.   Why—yes. What enemies? Yes.

Athens protects.

MEDEA. I should need peace and a free mind

While I prepared the medicines to make you well.

AEGEUS. You'll have them, you'll have them, Medea. You've seen the huge stones

In the old sacred war-belt of Athens. Come the four ends of the world, they will
   not break in: you're safe there:
445 I am your pledge.
   (Extends arm, which she later takes.)
   MEDEA.   Will you swear it, Aegeus?
   AEGEUS.   Ah? Why? I promised.
   MEDEA *(she takes his arm)*.   I trust you:
   the oath is formal: your cure
Depends on it.
   *(She crosses below him to down Right and then turns to him, raising her
   hand.)*
              You swear by the fruitful earth and high shining heaven that
   you will protect me in Athens
Against all men. Swear it.
   AEGEUS *(raises his hand)*. I swear by the fruitful earth and high shining
   heaven to protect you in Athens
Against all men. *(*BOTH *lower their arms.)*
   MEDEA.   And if you should break this oath?
   AEGEUS.   I will not break it.
   MEDEA. If you should break it, the earth
Will give you no bread but death, and the sky no light
450 But darkness.
   AEGEUS *(visibly perturbed)*. I will not break it.
   MEDEA.   You must repeat the words,
   Aegeus.
   AEGEUS. If I break it, the earth
Will give me no bread but death, and the sky no light
But darkness.
   MEDEA.   You have sworn: the gods have heard you.
   (Crosses below AEGEUS *to Center. Pause.)*
   AEGEUS *(uneasily)*. When will you come to Athens?
   (Turning to her.)
   MEDEA.   To Athens? Oh,
To Athens. Why—if I come, if I live—it will be soon. The yoke's
455 On the necks of the horses.
   (Crosses up to top step at door of house.)
                         I have some things to do
That men will talk of afterwards with hushed voices: while I and my children
Safe in Athens laugh. Is that it? Farewell, Aegeus.
   *(She turns abruptly from him; goes slowly, deep in thought, into the house.
   The doors close.)*
   AEGEUS *(staring after her)*. May the gods comfort you, Medea—to you also
   farewell,
Women of Corinth.
   *(*THREE WOMEN *rise.)*
   FIRST WOMAN.   Fair be the gale behind you, sir, and the way ahead.
   (Exit AEGEUS *up Right. She turns to* NURSE.*)*
What is she plotting in her deep mind?
460 She is juggling with death and life, as a juggler
With a black ball and a white ball.

(NURSE *slowly goes up to second step, looking at door of house.*)

SECOND WOMAN (*crosses to Left of the* FIRST WOMAN). No: she is like some distracted city

Sharpening its weapons. Embassies visit her:

The heads of state come to her door:

465 She receives them darkly.

NURSE.   I beseech you, women,

Not to speak words against my lady whom I love. You know that wicked injustice she has to suffer.

(She prays.)

O God, protector of exiles, lord of the holy sky, lead us

To the high rock that Athens loves, and the olive

Garland of Athens.

(The NURSE *crosses down Left and sits on steps.)*

FIRST WOMAN.   Athens is beautiful

470 As a lamp on a rock.

The temples are marble-shafted; light shines and lingers there.

Honey-color among the carved stones

And silver-color on the leaves of the olives.

The maidens are crowned with violets: Athens and Corinth

475 Are the two crowns of time.

SECOND WOMAN (*crosses to* FIRST WOMAN *and they join hands*). Mycenae for spears and armor; Sparta

For the stern men and the tall blonde women; and Thebes I remember,

Old Thebes and the seven gates in the gray walls—

But rather I praise Athena, the ivory, the golden,

480 The gray-eyed Virgin, her city.

And also I praise Corinth of the beautiful fountains,

On the fair plain between the two gulfs.

FIRST WOMAN. God-favored cities of the Greek world.

Fortunate those that dwell in them, happy that behold them.

485 SECOND WOMAN. How can one wish to die? How can that woman

Be drowned in sorrow and bewildered with hatred?

(The bolt on door is heard opening. MEDEA *enters and stands in doorway.)*

For only to be alive and to see the light

Is beautiful. Only to see the light;

To see a blade of young grass,

490 Or the gray face of a stone.

FIRST WOMAN (*pointing toward* MEDEA). Hush.

MEDEA (*proudly and falsely*).   As you say. What a marvelous privilege it is

Merely to be alive. And how foolish it would be

To spend the one day of life that remains to me—at least in Corinth—this tag end of one day

On tears and hatred! Rather I should rejoice, and sing, and offer gifts; and as to my enemies—

495 I will be reconciled with them.

FIRST WOMAN (*amazed*).   Reconciled with them!

(THREE WOMEN *cross a few steps to* MEDEA.)

MEDEA.   As you say. Reconciled.

Why should they hate me?
Surely I can appease those people.
They say that gold will buy anything; even friendship, even love: at least in Greece,
Among you civilized people, you reasonable and civilized Hellenes. In fact,
We've seen it happen. They bought Jason; Jason's love. Well—
500 I shall buy theirs.
I still have two or three of the treasures that I brought from home, things of pure precious gold, which a god
Gave to the kings of my ancestors.
(The light darkens, a cloud passing over the sun. Harp effect offstage. The THREE WOMEN *huddle together.)*
                                        Is it late? It seems to me
That the light darkens.
        (To the NURSE.*)*
                ·   Is it evening?
NURSE *(trembling).*   No— No— A cloud.
MEDEA. I hope for thunder: let the sky rage: my gifts
        (Enter TWO SLAVES *from door with gift. Kneel on top step.)*
Will shine the brighter. Listen, old woman! I want you
        (The NURSE *rises.)*
505 To go to Jason and tell him—tell him— Tell him that I am sick of hating and weary of evil!
I wish for peace.
        *(*MEDEA *crosses and stands between* TWO SLAVES.*)*
I wish to send precious gifts to that pale girl with the yellow hair
Whom he has married: tell him to come and take them—and to kiss his boys
Before we go into exile. Tell him to come speedily. Now run, run, find him.
        *(*MEDEA *turns her head away.)*
510 NURSE *(crossing to* WOMEN *stage Center).* Oh, I'll go. I'll run.
        (Tremulously, to WOMEN.*)*
                                        Let me pass,
        please.
        *(*WOMEN *make way for the* NURSE. MEDEA *stands looking after her. The* NURSE *turns back at the limit of the scene, Right, and says, wringing her hands.)*
But I am terrified. I do not know— I am terrified.
        Pray to the gods, women, to keep
Evil birds from our hearts!
        (She hurries away up Right.)
514 MEDEA *(crossing down two steps).* Run! Run! Find him!!!!
        *(*MEDEA *goes into the house.)*

CURTAIN

Act Two

MEDEA *is sitting on the upper doorstep. A cloak of woven gold lies across her knee and down the stone steps. Beside her are two open cases of dark leather. From one she takes a coronet of gold vine leaves, looks at it and replaces it.*

TWO SERVING WOMEN *stand in the doorway behind her. On the Right, at some distance, the* THREE WOMEN *are huddled, like sheep in a storm.*

The scene is darker than it was, and the gold cloth shines.

MEDEA. These are the gifts I am sending to the young bride; this golden wreath

And this woven-gold veil. They are not without value; there is nothing like them in the whole world, or at least

The Western world; the God of the Sun[1] gave them to my father's father, and I have kept them

In the deep chest for some high occasion; which has now come.

5 I have great joy in giving these jewels to Creon's daughter, for the glory of life consists of being generous

To one's friends, and—merciless to one's enemies—you know what a friend she has been to me. All Corinth knows.

The slaves talk of it. The old stones in the walls

Have watched and laughed.

(MEDEA *looks at the gold cloth, and strokes it cautiously with her hand. It seems to scorch her fingers.* THIRD WOMAN *has come nearer to look; now starts backward.)*

MEDEA. See, it is almost alive. Gold is a living thing: such pure gold.

(NURSE *enters from up Right; crosses to foot of steps.)*

10 But when her body has warmed it, how it will shine!

(*To the* NURSE.)

Why doesn't he come? What keeps him?

NURSE (*evidently terrified*).   Oh, my lady: presently.

---

1. *God of the Sun,* Helios (hē′ lē os), grandfather of Medea.

I have but now returned from him. He was beyond the gate, watching the
   races—where a monstrous thing
Had happened: a young mare broke from the chariot
And tore with her teeth a stallion.
   MEDEA *(stands up, shakes out the golden cloak, which again smoulders. She
   folds it cautiously, lays it in the leather case. The light has darkened again.
   She looks anxiously at the clouded sun)*. He takes his time, eh? It is
   intolerable
15 To sit and wait.
   (To the SERVING WOMEN.*)*
                    Take these into the house. Keep them at hand
For when I call.
   (They take them in. MEDEA *moves restlessly, under extreme nervous tension;
   speaks to the* NURSE. NURSE *crosses below steps to stage Left, then up two
   steps.)*
                 You say that a mare attacked a stallion?
   NURSE.   She tore him cruelly.
I saw him being led away: a black racer: his blood ran down
From the throat to the fetlocks.
   MEDEA.   You're sure he's coming. You're sure?
   NURSE.   He said he would.
   MEDEA.   Let him make haste, then!
   SECOND WOMAN *(she crosses to Left below* NURSE*)*. Frightening irrational
      things
20 Have happened lately; the face of nature is flawed with omens.
   FIRST WOMAN *(crosses to Left, joining* SECOND WOMAN*)*.   Yesterday
      evening a slave
Came up to the harbor-gate, carrying a basket
Of new-caught fish: one of the fish took fire
And burned in the wet basket with a high flame: the thing was witnessed
By many persons.
   THIRD WOMAN *(crosses Left of other* TWO WOMEN, *joining them)*. And a black
      leopard was seen
25 Gliding through the marketplace—
   MEDEA *(abruptly, approaching the* WOMEN*)*. You haven't told me yet: do you
      not think that Creon's daughter
Will be glad of those gifts?
   FIRST WOMAN.   O Medea, too much wealth
Is sometimes dreadful.
   MEDEA.   She'll be glad, however. She'll take them and put them
      on, she'll wear them, she'll strut in them,
She'll peacock in them. I see him coming now—the
   *(*THREE WOMEN *retire to up Left corner.* NURSE *sits below Left pillar.)*
                                        whole palace will admire
   her. Stand away from me, women,
While I make my sick peace.
   *(*MEDEA *crosses way down Right as* JASON *enters up Right to stage Center.*
   NURSE *points at* MEDEA, *who goes across the scene to meet* JASON, *but more
   and more slowly, and stops. Her attitude indicates her aversion.)*
   JASON.   Well, I have come. I tell you plainly,

30 Not for your sake: the children's. Your woman says that you have your wits
        again, and are willing
To look beyond your own woes.
        (MEDEA *is silent.* JASON *observes her and says*)
                                It appears doubtful.
        (She turns from him.)
—Where are the children? I have made inquiry: I can find fosterage for them
In Epidarurus; or any other of several cities
That are Creon's friends. I'll visit them from time to time, and watch
35 That they're well kept.
        MEDEA *(with suppressed violence).* You mean—take them from me!
Be careful, Jason, I am not patient yet.
        (More quietly.)
                                I am the one who labored in pain to
        bear them, I cannot
Smile while I lose them. But I am learning: I am learning—
        No, Jason: I will not give up my little ones
To the cold care of strangers.
        Hard faces, harsh hands. It will be far better for them to share
My wandering ocean of beggary and bleak exile:
40 I love them, Jason. Only if you would keep them and care for them here in
        Corinth,
I might consent.
        JASON.   Gladly—but they are exiled.
        MEDEA.   —In your own house.
        JASON.   Gladly I'd do it—but you understand
They are exiled, as you are. I asked Creon and he refused it.
        MEDEA. You asked Creon to take my children from me?
        (She reaches her hands toward him.)
Forgive me, Jason,
As I do you.
        (Crosses up steps to his Right.)
                We have had too much wrath, and our acts
45 Are closing on us. On me, I mean. Retribution is from the gods, and it breaks
        our hearts: but you
Feel no guilt, you fear nothing, nothing can touch you. It is wonderful to stand
        serene above fate
While earthlings wince. If it lasts. It does not always last.
—Do you love the children, Jason?
        JASON.   Ha? Certainly. The children? Certainly!
I am their father.
        MEDEA. Oh, but that's not enough. If I am to give them up to you—be patient
        with me,
I must question you first. And very deeply; to the quick. If anything happens
        to them,
50 Would you be grieved?
        JASON.   Nothing will happen to them, Medea, if in my care.
        Rest your mind on it.
        MEDEA *(she crosses up to top step in back of* JASON*).* You must pardon me:
        it is not possible to be certain of that.

If they were—killed and their blood
Ran on the floor of the house or down the deep earth—
Would you be grieved?
    JASON.   You have a sick mind. What a weak thing a woman is,
    always dreaming of evil.
    MEDEA. Answer me!
    JASON.   Yes, after I'd cut their killer into red collops—I'd grieve.
    MEDEA.   That is true: vengeance
55 Makes grief bearable. But—Creon's daughter, your wife—no doubt will breed
Many other boys. But, if something should happen to—Creon's daughter—
    JASON.   Enough, Medea. Too much. Be silent!
    MEDEA. I am to conclude that you love—Creon's daughter—
More than your sons. They'll have to take the sad journey with me.
    (To the NURSE.*)*
Tell the boys to come out
60 And bid their father farewell.
    (The NURSE *goes into the house.)*
    JASON *(coming to her and taking her arm).* I could take them from you
By force, Medea.
    MEDEA *(violently).* Try it, you!
    (Controlling herself.)
                       No, Creon decided otherwise; he said
    *(*JASON *crosses down Right as if to go.)*
    they will share my exile. Come, Jason,
Let's be friends at last!
    (The BOYS *come out with their* TUTOR, *followed by the* NURSE. JASON *makes
    to clasp her arm. She pulls away to Center.)*
I am quite patient now; I have learned. Come, boys: come,
    *(*BOYS *run straight to* MEDEA.*)*
Speak to your father.
    *(*NURSE *and* TUTOR *remain on top step at either side of door. They shrink
    back.)*
                     No, no, we're friends again. We're not angry any more.
    JASON *(has gone eagerly to meet them on the steps. He drops to one knee to
    be more nearly level with them, but they are shy and reluctant).* Big boys.
    Tall fellows, ha?
65 You've grown up since I saw you.
    MEDEA.   Smile for him, children.
Give him
    (She turns, and stands rigidly turned away, her face sharp with pain.)
    your hands.
    NURSE *(to* JASON*).* I think he's afraid of you, sir.
    JASON *(to the* YOUNGER BOY*).*   What? What? You'll learn,
    my man,
    (During this speech ELDER BOY *crosses to him. He picks him up.)*
Not to fear me. You'll make your enemies run away from you
When you grow up.
    (To the ELDER BOY.*)* And you, Captain,
How would you like a horn-tipped bow to hunt rabbits with?
    Wolves, I mean.

(Takes ELDER BOY *by the hand and crosses with him to rock Right. He sits* YOUNGER BOY *on his lap.* ELDER BOY *sits on floor. He plays with the* BOYS. *They are less shy of him now.)*

FIRST WOMAN *(coming close to* MEDEA*)*. Don't give them to him,
70 Medea. If you do it will ache forever.

  SECOND WOMAN.   You have refuge; take them there.
Athens is beautiful—

  MEDEA *(fiercely)*. Be silent!
Look at him: he loves them—ah? Therefore his dear children
Are not going to that city but a darker city, where no games are played, no
  music is heard. Do you think
I am a cow lowing after the calf? Or a bitch with pups, licking
75 The hand that struck her? Watch and see. Watch this man, women: he is going
  to weep. I think
He is going to weep blood, and quite soon, and much more
Than I have wept. Watch and keep silence.

  (She goes toward the GROUP *on the steps.)*
               Jason,
Are the boys dear to you? I think I am satisfied that you love them,
These two young heroes.

  *(*JASON *stands up and turns to her, one of the* BOYS *clinging to each of his hands. He has made friends with them.)*
80 MEDEA *(she weeps)*. Oh—Oh—Oh!

  JASON. God's hand, Medea, what is it?
What is the matter?

  MEDEA *(makes with both hands a gesture of pushing down something, flings her head back proudly)*. Nothing. It is hard to let them go.
—This I have thought of:
You shall take them to—Creon's daughter, your wife—and make them kneel to
  her, and ask her
85 To ask her father to let them stay here in Corinth. He'll grant it, he is growing
  old, he denies her nothing.
Even that hard king loves his only child.
What she asks is done. You will go with the boys, Jason, and speak for them,
  —they are not skillful yet
In supplication—and I'll send gifts. I'll put gifts in their hands. People say
  that gifts
Will persuade even the gods. Is it well thought of?
90 Will she listen to us?

  JASON.   Why, if I ask it! She'd hardly refuse me anything. And I
  believe that you're right,
She can rule Creon.

  MEDEA *(to the* TUTOR*)*. Bring me those gold things.
  *(*TUTOR *exits main door.)*
  (She extends hands to BOYS. *Sits on step. They cross to her.)*
Dear ones, brave little falcons—little pawns of my agony—
Go, ask that proud breastless girl of her bitter charity
Whether she will let you nest here until your wings fledge, while far your
  mother
Flies the dark storm— *(She weeps again.)*

JASON.　　　　　　　　I'm sorry for you. Parting is hard.
　(He crosses down Right off steps.)
　MEDEA.　　　　　　　　　　　　　　I can bear it.
95 And worse too.
　(The TUTOR *and* SERVING WOMEN *bring the gifts.)*
　　　　　　　Oh, here: here are the things: take them, darlings,
Into your little hands.
　(Giving them to the BOYS. *Crown goes to* YOUNGER BOY. *Cloak to* ELDER BOY.
　Each show them to TUTOR *and* NURSE, *then sit on the third step.* SERVING
　WOMEN *exit as soon as gifts are taken from them.)*
　　　　　　　Hold carefully by the cases: don't touch the gold,
Or it might—tarnish.
　JASON.　　　　　　　Why! These are king's treasures. You shouldn't, Medea:
　it's too much. Creon's house
Has gold enough of its own.
　MEDEA.　　　　　　　Oh—if she'll wear them. What should I want with
　woven gold vanities. Black is my wear. The woman ought to be very happy
　(Throws wedding ring in box with cloak.)
With such jewels—and such a husband—ah? Her sun is rising,
　*(*MEDEA *crosses Left.)*
　mine going down—I hope
100 To a red sunset. The little gold wreath is pretty, isn't it?
　*(*YOUNGER BOY *holds it up to* JASON.*)*
　JASON *(doubtfully).* It looks like fire—
　MEDEA.　　　　　　　　　　Vine leaves: the flashing
Arrow-sharp leaves. They have weight, though.
　*(*BOYS *put down boxes.)*
　　　　　　　Gold is too heavy a burden for little hands. Carry
　them, you,
Until you come to the palace.
　*(*NURSE *takes gold wreath; exits up Right, followed by* TUTOR *with cloak.*
　JASON *follows with* BOYS *by the hand.)*
　　　　　　　Farewell, sweet boys: brave little trudging
　pilgrims from the black wave
To the white desert: take the stuff in, be sure you lay it in her own hands.
Come back and tell me what happens.
　*(Crosses up to front of pillar Right and waves goodbye to them as they
　leave. She turns abruptly away from them.)*
　　　　　　　Tell me what happens.
　(The BOYS *go out reluctantly,* JASON *holding their hands.)*
　　　　　　　　　　　　　　Rejoice, women,
　The gifts are given; the bait is laid.
105 The gods roll their great eyes over Creon's house and quietly smile:
That robe of bright-flowing gold, that bride-veil, that fish-net
To catch a young slender salmon—not mute, she'll sing: her delicate body
　writhes in the meshes,
The golden wreath binds her bright head with light: she'll dance, she'll sing
　loudly:
Would I were there to hear it, that proud one howling.
　(She crosses to Center between pillars.)

Look, the sun's out again, the clouds are gone,
110 All's gay and clear. Ai! I wish the deep earth would open and swallow us—
Before I do what comes next.
I wish all life would perish,
(Crosses down to third step and sits.)
       and the holy gods in high heaven die, before my
 little ones
Come home to my hands.
  FIRST WOMAN *(going to* MEDEA*)*. It would be better for you, Medea, if the earth
115 Opened her jaws and took you down into darkness.
But one thing you will not do, for you cannot,
You will not hurt your own children, though wrath like plague-boils
Aches, your mind in a fire-haze
Bites the purple apples of pain—no blood-lapping
120 Beast of the field, she-bear nor lioness,
Nor the lean wolf-bitch,
Hurts her own tender whelps, nor the yellow-eyed,
Scythe-beaked and storm-shouldered
Eagle that tears the lambs has ever made prey
125 Of the fruit of her own tree—
  MEDEA.   How could that girl's death slake me?
  THIRD WOMAN *(coming forward from the* OTHERS*)*. I am sick with terror.
I'll run to the palace, I'll warn them.
  MEDEA.   Will you? Go. Go if you will.
God and my vengeful goddess are doing these things: you cannot prevent them,
  but you could easily fall
In the same fire.
  THIRD WOMAN *(retreating)*. I am afraid to go.
  MEDEA.   You are wise. Anyone
130 Running between me and my justice will reap
What no man wants.
  FIRST WOMAN.   Not justice; vengeance.
You have suffered evil, you wish to inflict evil.
  MEDEA. I do according to nature what I have to do.
  FIRST WOMAN. I have heard evil
135 Answering evil as thunder answers the lightning.
A great waste voice in the hollow sky,
And all that they say is death. I have heard vengeance
Like an echo under a hill answering vengeance.
Great hollow voices: all that they say is death.
  SECOND WOMAN.   The sword speaks
140 And the spear answers: the city is desolate.
The nations remember old wrongs and destroy each other.
And no man binds up their wounds.
  FIRST WOMAN.   But justice
Builds a firm house.
  MEDEA.   The doors of her house are vengeance.
  SECOND WOMAN.   I dreamed that someone
Gave good for evil, and the world was amazed.
145 MEDEA *(rises. Crosses up between pillar and column Right)*. Only a coward

or a madman gives good for evil. Did you hear a thin music
Like a girl screaming? Or did I perhaps imagine it? Hark, it is music.

THIRD WOMAN *(crossing towards Center below steps)*. Let me go, Medea!
I'll be mute, I'll speak to no one. I cannot bear—
Let me go to my house!

MEDEA.   You will stay here,
150 And watch the end.
(The WOMEN *are beginning to mill like scared cattle, huddled and circular.)*
                    You will be quiet, you women. You came to see
How the barbarian woman endures betrayal: watch and you'll know.

SECOND WOMAN *(kneels)*. My heart is a shaken cup
Of terror: the thin black wine
Spills over all my flesh down to my feet.

155 FIRST WOMAN. She fled from her father's house in a storm of blood,
In a blood-storm she flew up from Thessaly,
Now here and dark over Corinth she widens
Wings to ride up the twisted whirlwind
And talons to hold with—
160 Let me flee this dark place and the pillared doorway.

SECOND WOMAN. I hear the man-wolf on the snow hill
Howl to the soaring moon—

THIRD WOMAN. The demon comes in through the locked door
And strangles the child—

165 SECOND WOMAN. Blood is the seed of blood, hundredfold the harvest,
The gleaners that follow it, their feet are crimson—

FIRST WOMAN. I see the whirlwind hanging from the black sky.
Like a twisted rope,
Like an erect serpent, its tail tears the earth,
170 It is braided of dust and lightning,
Who will fly in it? Let me hide myself
From these night-shoring pillars and the dark door.

MEDEA.   Have patience, women.
    Be quiet.
I am quite sure something has happened; presently someone
Will bring us news.

THIRD WOMAN.   Look! The children are coming.

175 SECOND WOMAN *(rises)*. They have bright things in their hands: their faces
    are clear and joyous; was all that fear
A dream, a dream?
*(MEDEA crosses to pillar Left. The TUTOR enters up Right with the BOYS.
The ELDER BOY carries a decorated bow and arrows; the YOUNGER BOY has
a doll, a brightly painted wooden warrior. MEDEA, gazing at the BOYS,
retreats slowly backward from them.)*

TUTOR *(crossing up to MEDEA on top step; BOYS stand behind him on second
    and third steps)*. Rejoice, Medea, I bring good news. The princess
    graciously
Received your presents and smiled: it is peace between you. She has welcomed
    the little boys, they are safe from exile.
They'll be kept here. Their father is joyful.

MEDEA *(coldly, her hands clenched in the effort of self control)*. Yes?

TUTOR. All Creon's house is well pleased. When we first went in
180 The serving-women came and fondled the children; it was rumored through
  all the household that you and Jason
Were at peace again: like word of a victory
Running through a wide city, when people gather in the streets to be glad
  together: and we brought the boys
Into the hall; we put those costly gifts in their hands; then Jason
Led them before the Princess. At first she looked angrily at them and turned
  away, but Jason said,
185 "Don't be angry at your friends. You ought to love
Those whom I love. Look what they've brought you, dear," and she looked
  and saw
In the dark boxes the brilliant gold: she smiled then,
And marveled at it. *(He turns to them and* YOUNGER BOY *crosses up to him.)*
       Afterwards she caressed the children; she even said that
  this little one's
Hair was like fine-spun gold. Then Jason gave them these toys and we came
  away.
  MEDEA. Yes. If this
190 Were all. If this were all, old man—
I'd have your bony loins beaten to a blood-froth
For the good news you bring.
  TUTOR.   My lady—
  MEDEA.   There's more, however
It will come soon.
  (The BOYS *shyly approach her and show their toys. She, with violent self-*
  constraint, looks at them; but folds her hands in her cloak, not to touch
  them.)
  ELDER BOY *(crosses to her. Drawing the little bow).* Look, Mother.
  MEDEA *(suddenly weeping).* Take them away from me!
195 I cannot bear. I cannot bear.
  TUTOR.   Children, come quickly.
  (He shepherds them up the steps, and disappears in the house.)
  FIRST WOMAN. If there is any mercy or forbearance in heaven
Let it reach down and touch the dark mind
To save it from what it dreams—
  SLAVE *(a young* SLAVE *dashes in up Right, panting and distraught. He has*
  run from CREON'S *house).* Where is Medea?
  *(*SLAVE *crosses to base of steps Right, throwing himself across them.)*
  SECOND WOMAN.   What has happened? What horror drives you?
Are spears hunting behind you?
  SLAVE *(he sees* MEDEA *on the steps).* Flee for your life, Medea! I am Jason's
  man, but you were good to me
200 While I was here in the house. Can you hear me? Escape, Medea!
  MEDEA.   I hear you.
Draw breath; say quietly
What you have seen. It must have been something notable, the way your eyes
Bulge in the whites.
  SLAVE.   If you have horses, Medea, drive! Or a boat on the shore,
Sail! *(Rises and crosses down stage Right.)*

MEDEA. But first you must tell me about the beautiful girl who was lately
married:

205   SLAVE. Ooh!

MEDEA.   Your great man's daughter:

SLAVE. Ooh!

MEDEA. Are they all quite well?

SLAVE.   My ears ring with the crying, my eyes are
scalded. She put on the gold garments—

Did you do it, Medea?

MEDEA.   I did it.

SLAVE. Ooooh!!!

210   MEDEA. Speak quietly.

SLAVE.   You are avenged.

You are horribly avenged. It is too much.

The gods will hate you.

    (Collapses on podium.)

MEDEA *(avid, but still sitting).* This is my care. Did anyone die with her?

SLAVE.   Creon!

THREE WOMEN. Oooh!!!!

MEDEA *(solemnly).* Where is pride now?

215 Tell me all that you saw. Speak slowly.

SLAVE.   He tried to save her—he died!

Corinth is masterless.

All's in amazed confusion, and some are looting, but they'll avenge him—

    (He hears someone coming behind him.)

                          I'm going on!

Someone is going to die.

    (He runs Left to the far side of the scene, and exits while MEDEA *speaks.*
    Meanwhile the light has been changing, and soon the sun will set.)

MEDEA.   Here comes a more stable witness.

    (The NURSE *enters from up Right.)*

                           Old friend:

Catch your breath; take your time. I want the whole tale, every gesture and cry.
I have labored for this.

NURSE. Death is turned loose! I've hobbled and run, and fallen—

    (Crosses to fourth step and sits.)

MEDEA.   Please,

Nurse: I am very happy: go slowly.

    *(*MEDEA *sits and puts her head in* NURSE's *lap.)*

220 Tell me these things in order from the beginning.

As when you used to dress me, when I was little, in my father's house: you
used to say

"One thing at a time; one thing and then the next."

    (The light has changed to a flare of sunset.)

    *(*THREE WOMEN *have assembled themselves after* NURSE's *entrance in*
    following fashion: FIRST *sitting first step Center,* SECOND *standing to her*
    Left, THIRD *standing to Left of* SECOND.)*

NURSE.   My eyes are blistered,

My throat's like a dry straw— There was a long mirror on the wall, and when
her eyes saw it—

After the children had gone with Jason—she put her hands in the case and took
    those gold things—and I
225 Watched, for I feared something might happen to her, but I never thought
  So horribly—she placed on her little head the bright golden wreath, she
    gathered the flowing gold robe
  Around her white shoulders,
  And slender flanks,
    (MEDEA *rises; crosses to below rock down Right.)*
  And gazed at the girl in the metal mirror, going back and forth
230 On tiptoe almost;
  But suddenly horror began. I— Oh, oh—
    MEDEA *(crosses up to Right of* NURSE, *shaking her by the shoulders).* You are
    not suffering.
  You saw it, you did not feel it. Speak plainly.
    NURSE.   Her face went white;
  She staggered a few steps, bending over, and fell
235 Into the great throne-chair; then a serving woman
  Began to call for water thinking she had fainted, but saw the foam
  Start on her lips, and the eyes rolling, and screamed instead. Then some of
    them
  Ran after Jason, others ran to fetch Creon: and that doomed girl
  Frightfully crying started up from the chair; she ran, she was like a torch, and
    the gold crown
    (MEDEA *races up to door of house writhing.)*
240 Like a comet streamed fire; she tore at it but it clung to her head; the golden
    cloak
  Was white-hot, flaying the flesh from the living bones: blood mixed with fire
    ran down, she fell, she burned
  On the floor, writhing. Then Creon came and flung himself on her, hoping to
    choke
  That rage of flame, but it ran through him, his own agony
  Made him forget his daughter's. The fire stuck to the flesh, it glued him to her;
    he tried to stand up,
245 He tore her body and his own. The burnt flesh broke
  In lumps from the bones.
    (She covers her eyes with her hands.)
    I have finished. They lie there.
  Eyeless, disfaced, untouchable; middens of smoking flesh—
    (Nearly a scream.)   No!
  I have no more.
    MEDEA *(crossing down to* NURSE; *takes her arms).* I want all.
  Had they died when you came away?
    NURSE.   I am not able—have mercy—No, the
    breath
250 Still whistled in the black mouths. No one could touch them.
                                         Jason stood in
    their smoke, and his hands tore
  His unhelmeted hair.
    MEDEA. You have told good news well: I'll reward you.
  As for those people, they will soon die. Their woes are over too soon.

(MEDEA crosses down, then paces up Right and back down Right; sees WOMEN at end of speech and crosses to them.)
Mine are not.
Jason's are not.
(She turns abruptly from them, toward the BOYS, who have been standing by the doorway, fascinated, not comprehending but watching.)
My little falcons! Listen to me! Laugh and be glad: we have accomplished it.
Our enemies were great and powerful, they were full of cold pride, they ruled
    all this country—they are down in the ashes.
(Sitting on steps with BOYS.)
255 Crying like dogs, cowering in the ashes, in their own ashes. They went down
    with the sun, and the sun will rise
And not see them again. He will think "Perhaps they are sleeping, they feasted
    late.
At noon they will walk in the garden." Oh, no, oh, no!
They will not walk in the garden. No one has ever injured me but suffered more
Than I had suffered.
(She turns from the BOYS.)
                Therefore this final sacrifice I intended glares in my eyes
260 Like a lion on a ridge.
(Turning back to the BOYS.)
              We still hate, you know; a person nearer than these, more vile, more contemptible,
Whom I—I cannot. If he were my own hands I would cut him off, or my eyes,
    I would gouge him out—
But not you: that was madness.
(She turns from them.)   So Jason will be able to say, "I have lost much,
But not all: I have children: My sons are well."
(She stands staring, agonized, one hand picking at the other.)
No! I want him crushed, boneless, crawling—
I have no choice.
(Resolutely, to the THREE WOMEN. She rises and crosses down Left to WOMEN.)
              You there! You thought me soft and submissive like a common woman—who takes a blow
265 And cries a little, and she wipes her face
And runs about the housework, loving her master? I am not such a woman.
   FIRST WOMAN. Awake, Medea!
Awake from the evil dream. Catch up your children and flee,
Farther than Athens, farther than Thrace or Spain, flee to the world's end.
270 Fire and death have done your bidding,
Are you not fed full with evil?
Is it not enough?
   MEDEA.   No, Loathing is endless.
Hate is a bottomless cup, I will pour and pour.
(She turns fiercely to the BOYS.)   Children—
(Suddenly melting.)   —O my
    little ones!
What was I dreaming? My babes, my own!
(She kneels to them, taking their hands.)

Never, never, never, never

275 Shall my own babes be hurt. Not if every war-hound and spear-slave in headless Corinth
Were on the track.

(Still kneeling; to WOMEN.*)*

Look, their sweet lips are trembling: look, women, the little mouths: I frightened them
With those wild words: they stood and faced me, they never flinched.
Look at their proud young eyes! My eaglets, my golden ones!

(She kisses them, then holds them off and gazes at them.)

O sweet small faces—like the pale wild-roses

280 That blossom where the cliff breaks toward the brilliant sea: the delicate form and color, the dear, dear fragrance
Of your sweet breath—

(She continues gazing at them; her face changes.)

NURSE *(sits up).*   My lady, make haste, haste!
Take them and flee. Flee away from here! Someone will come soon.

*(*MEDEA *still gazes at the* BOYS.*)*

Oh—listen to me.

Spears will come, death will come. All Corinth is in confusion and headless anarchy, unkinged and amazed
Around that horror you made: therefore they linger: yet in a moment

285 Its avengers come!

*(*MEDEA *looks up from staring at the* BOYS. *Her face has changed; the love has gone out of it. She speaks in a colorless, tired voice.)*

MEDEA. I have a sword in the house.
I can defend you.

(She stands up stiffly and takes the BOYS *by their shoulders; holds the* ELDER *in front of her, toward* WOMEN: *speaks with cold intensity.)*

Would you say that this child

Has Jason's eyes?

(The WOMEN *are silent, in terror gazing at her.)*

—They are his cubs. They have his blood.

As long as they live I shall be mixed with him.

(Crosses to pillar up Right. She looks down at the BOYS; *speaks tenderly but hopelessly.)*

Children:

It is evening. See, evening has come. Come, little ones.

290 Into the house.

*(*BOYS *cross to her; arms about her waist.)*

Evening brings all things home. It brings the bird to the bough and the lamb to the fold—
And the child to the mother.

(She pushes BOYS *gently into house.)*

We must not think too much: people go mad

If they think too much.

(In the doorway, behind BOYS, *she flings up her hands as if to tear her hair out by the roots; then quietly goes in. The great door closes; the iron noise of the bolt is driven home.)*

NURSE.   No!

(She rushes toward the door, helpless, her hand reaching up and beating feebly against the foot of the door.)

FIRST WOMAN. What is going to happen?

SECOND WOMAN. That crown of horrors—

(They speak like somnambulists, and stand frozen. There is a moment of silence.)

295 CHILD'S VOICE *(in the house, shrill, broken off)*. Mother! Ai—!

(The WOMEN press toward the door, crying more or less simultaneously.)

WOMEN. Medea, no!

Prevent her! Save them!

Open the door—

(They listen for an answer.)

THIRD WOMAN. A god is here, Medea, he calls to you, he forbids you—

(NURSE has risen, and beats feebly on the door, stooping and bent over. FIRST WOMAN stands beside her, very erect, with her back against the door, covering her ears with her hands. They are silent.)

ELDER BOY'S VOICE *(clear, but as if hypnotized)*. Mother— Mother—ai!

MEDEA. Aaahh!!!!

(Lamentation—keening—is heard in the house. It rises and falls, and continues to the end, but often nearly inaudible. It is now twilight.)

300 NURSE *(limps down the steps and says)*. There is no hope in heaven or earth.
It is done.
It was destined when she was born, now it is done.

(Wailing.)

Oh, oh, oh.

THIRD WOMAN *(with terror, looking into the shadows)*. Who is coming?
Someone is running at us!

FIRST WOMAN *(quietly)*. The accursed man.
Jason.

SECOND WOMAN. He has a sword.

FIRST WOMAN. I am more afraid of the clinging contagion of his misfortunes.

305 A man the gods are destroying.

JASON *(enters rapidly up Right, disheveled and shaking, a drawn sword in his hand. Crosses in to Right at foot of steps)*. Where is that murderess?
Here in the house?

Or has she fled? She'll have to hide in the heavy metal darkness and caves of the earth—and there
I'll crawl and find her.

(No answer. The THREE WOMEN draw away from him as he moves toward the door. He stops and turns on them, drawing his left hand across his face, as if his eyes were bewildered.)

JASON.　　　　　Are you struck dumb? Are you shielding her?
Where is Medea?

FIRST WOMAN. You caused these things. She was faithful to you and you broke faith.
Horror is here.

JASON.　　　Uncaused. There was no reason— Tell me at once—

310 Whether she took my boys with her? Creon's people would kill them for what she has done: I'd rather save them
Than punish her. Help me in this.

NURSE (*wailing, sinks to ground down Left*). Oh, oh, oh—

JASON (*looking sharply at* NURSE).   So she has killed herself.
Good. She never lacked courage— I'll take my sons away to the far end of the
   earth, and never
Speak of these things again.

NURSE (*wailing*).   Oh, oh, oh—
   (*Lamentation from the house answers.*)

JASON (*with a queer slyness, for he is trying to cheat himself out of believing
   what he dreads. He glances at the door, furtively, over his shoulder*). Is she
   lying in there?
Honorable at least in her death. I might have known it.
   (*They remain silent.*)

                                                   Well, answer!

FIRST WOMAN (*pointing toward* CREON'S *house*).   Death is
   there; death is here.
315 But you are both blind and deaf: how can I tell you?

JASON (*is silent, then says slowly*).   But—the—children are
   well?

FIRST WOMAN. I do not know
Whether Medea lives or is dead.

JASON (*flings down the sword and sets his shoulder against the door; pushes
   in vain*).   Open! Open! Open!
   (*Returns halfway down the steps, and says pitiably.*)

                                             Women, I am alone. Help
   me.
Help me to break the bolt.
                     Go and find help—
   (JASON *runs down Right as door opens. This stops him and he turns. It is
   now fairly dark; the interior of the house is lighted.* WOMEN *draw back in
   fear;* JASON *stands on the steps, bewildered.* MEDEA *comes into the doorway;
   her hand and clothing are blood-marked. The door closes.*)

MEDEA. What feeble night-bird overcome by misfortune beats at my door?
   (JASON *takes two steps up to her.*)
Can this be that great adventurer,
The famous lord of the seas and delight of women, the heir of rich Corinth—
   this crying drunkard
320 On the dark doorstep? Yet you've not had enough. You have come to drink the
   last bitter drops.
I'll pour them for you.
   (*She displays her hand which is covered with blood.*)

JASON. What's that stain on your hands?

MEDEA.   The wine I was pouring for you
   spilled on my hand—
Dear were the little grapes that were crushed to make it; dear were the
   vineyards.

JASON.   I came to kill you, Medea,
Like a caught beast, like a crawling viper. Give me my sons, that I may save
   them from Creon's men,
I'll go quietly away.

MEDEA.   Hush, they are sleeping. Perhaps I will let you look at them:

You cannot have them.

325 But the hour is late, you ought to go home to that highborn bride; the night has
fallen, surely she longs for you.

Surely her flesh is not crusted black, nor her forehead burned bald, nor her
mouth a horror.

(JASON *kneels on the steps, painfully groping for his sword.*)

She is very young. But surely she loves and desires you—
Surely she will be fruitful. Your sword you want?

There it is. Not that step, the next lower. No, the next higher.

JASON (*stands erect. Goes up two steps to her*). I'll kill you first and then find
my sons.

MEDEA.   You must be careful, Jason. Do you see the two fire-snakes

330 That guard this door?

(*Indicating the two snakes.*)

Here and here: one on each side: two serpents. Their
throats are swollen with poison,

Their eyes are burning coals and their tongues are fire. They are coiled ready
to strike: if you come near them,

They'll make you what Creon is. But stand there very quietly.
I'll let you
Look at your sons.

(MEDEA *crosses to pillar Left.*)

Open the doors that he may see them.

(*The doors open revealing the* TWO BOYS *soaked in blood.*)

JASON (*flinging his hands to his temples and crossing up to pillar Right*).
I knew it already.

I knew it before I saw it. No wild beast could have done it.

MEDEA.   I have done it:
because I loathed you more

335 Than I loved them.

JASON. Did you feel nothing, no pity, are you pure evil? I should have killed
you
The day I saw you.

MEDEA. I tore my own heart and laughed: I was tearing yours.

JASON. Will you laugh while I strangle you?

MEDEA. I would still laugh.

(JASON *lunges at her but is sent back by snakes.*)

——Beware my door holders, Jason! these eager
serpents.——I'd still be joyful

To know that every bone of your life is broken: you are left helpless, friendless,
mateless, childless,

Avoided by gods and men, unclean with awful excess of grief—childless.

JASON. It is no matter now

340 Who lives, or who dies.

(*As next speech is said* JASON *starts slowly down steps to Right.*)

MEDEA. You had love and betrayed it: now of all men
You are utterly the most miserable. As I of women. But I, as woman, despised,
a foreigner, alone
Against *you* and the might of Corinth,
Have met you, throat for throat, evil for evil, vengeance for vengeance.

JASON *(turning to her on bottom step)*. What does it matter now?
Only give me my boys: the little pitiful violated bodies: that I may bury them
345 In some kind place.
    MEDEA. To you? You would betray even the little bodies: coin them for
      silver.
Sell them for power. No!
    JASON *(crawling up two more steps at her feet)*. Let me touch their dear flesh,
      let me touch their hair!
    MEDEA. No. They are mine.
    (Harp effect off Right.)
They are going with me: the chariot is at the gate.
    (During this speech JASON *rises and goes slowly down Right.)*
    Go down to your ship Argo and weep beside it, that rotting hulk on the
    harbor-beach
Drawn dry astrand, never to be launched again—even the weeds and barnacles
    on the warped keel
350 Are dead and stink—that's your last companion—
Ana only hope: for some time one of the rotting timbers
Will fall on your head and kill you—meanwhile sit there and mourn,
    remembering the infinite evil, and the good
That you made evil.
                  Now I go forth
Under the cold eyes of heaven—those weakness-despising stars: not me they
    scorn.
    MEDEA *goes into the house—*JASON *starts after her but the door is bolted*
    in his face. He collapses to the ground in front of the doors. MEDEA *is seen*
    coming out Left door bearing the TWO BOYS. *Then, as final fanfare of music*
    comes, slow

CURTAIN

Development

INTERPRETATION

1. Medea is a good example of a character who is "larger than life." We accept her gigantic emotions and extravagant deeds because she seems to represent a superhuman force. Characterize this force, and cite incidents and lines to support your interpretation.

2. *(a)* Reread the passage in which the three women of Corinth comment on the lamentations of Medea (page 88, lines 66—83). Describe the conflict ex-

pressed in these lines. *(b)* In what other ways does this same conflict appear in the play?

3. *(a)* Medea tells the women, "I understand well enough/ That nothing is ever private in a Greek city" (page 89, lines 104—105). What does she mean? *(b)* Discuss the opposing views of life that the two societies (Corinth and Colchis) represent in the play.

4. *(a)* In the first meeting between

Jason and Medea, Jason calmly answers Medea's charges of ingratitude with three different arguments (page 99, line 312 to page 100, line 327). What are they and what is their tone? (b) What insights do they provide into the personality of Jason? (c) Is Jason or Medea the more sympathetic character in this scene? Discuss.

5. In Medea, as in most Greek plays, there are numerous suggestions that fate rules the actions of the characters. For example, Medea says, "I do according to nature what I have to do" (page 114, line 133). (a) Are statements like this indications that Medea's actions are inevitable and beyond her control, or are they rationalizations? Discuss. (b) Do Medea's actions seem any more or less fated when she kills her children than when she kills Creon and Creusa?

6. The sun is a commonly used symbol for the light of reason. Thus, Jason speaks of the "rational/ Sunlight of Greece" (page 99, lines 316—317). Other references to sunlight in the play, however, suggest a very different meaning: the gold cloth which kills Creusa was a gift to Medea from Helios, her grandfather and God of the Sun; and the murder itself is reported in the "flare of sunset." (a) Describe the conflict implied by such references to the sun. (b) Relate this symbol, with its contradictory meanings, to an important theme in the play.

TECHNIQUE

1. (a) Point out instances of foreshadowing in the dialogue between the tutor and the nurse which opens the play. (b) Characterize the mood of this scene, citing lines to support your case.

2. There are three "appeals" generally used in argumentation: to the logic of the case, to the emotional elements in the situation, and to the moral integrity of the arguer himself. (a) Which of these appeals does Medea depend on most in her argument to Creon? (b) What does her way of arguing reveal about her knowledge of Creon's personality? (c) What does the argument reveal about Medea herself?

3. (a) How does the meeting with Aegeus serve to focus Medea's plans for vengeance, and thus to advance the plot (page 102, line 404 to page 105, line 457)? (b) What is ironic in the thought which Aegeus' grief at being childless excites in Medea?

4. An important distinction exists between tragedy and pathos. In the pathetic there is little or no emphasis on the struggle, for the pathetic figure struggles so ineffectually that the audience reaction to him is one of pity. In the tragic, however, there is a great deal of emphasis on the struggle. The tragic figure fights back, and he fights so well that the audience is awed by him. (a) Is the death of Medea's children tragic or pathetic? Explain. (b) What emotions are evoked by Medea's exit carrying the bodies of the children? (c) Is the tragic tone of the play flawed or enforced by the presence of the bodies? Discuss.

EXTENSIONS

1. The women of Corinth accuse Medea of wanting "not justice; vengeance." (a) Do you agree? (b) What is the distinction between the two?

2. (a) What is there in Medea which forces our admiration? (b) Would you admire her more, or less, had she spared her children? (c) Discuss the difficulties involved in presenting a "good" character who inspires as much respect and awe as a powerful villain like Medea.

Hedda Gabler

HENRIK IBSEN / Norway
(1828 – 1906)

translated from the Norwegian by William Archer

CHARACTERS

GEORGE TESMAN
HEDDA TESMAN, *his wife*
MISS JULIANA TESMAN, *his aunt*
MRS. ELVSTED
JUDGE BRACK
EILERT LOVBORG
BERTA, *servant at the Tesmans'*

The scene of the action is Tesman's villa, in the west end of Christiania.

Act One

SCENE: *A spacious, handsome, and tastefully furnished drawing room, decorated in dark colors. In the back, a wide doorway with curtains drawn back, leading into a smaller room decorated in the same style as the drawing room. In the right-hand wall of the front room, a folding door leading out to the hall. In the opposite wall, on the Left, a glass door, also with curtains drawn back. Through the panes can be seen part of a veranda outside, and trees covered with autumn foliage. An oval table, with a cover on it, and surrounded by chairs, stands well forward. In front, by the wall on the Right, a wide stove of dark porcelain, a high-backed armchair, a cushioned footrest, and two footstools. A settee, with a small round table in front of it, fills the upper right-hand corner. In front, on the Left, a little way from the wall, a sofa. Farther back than the glass door, a piano. On either side of the doorway at the back a whatnot with terra-cotta and majolica ornaments.[1] Against the back wall of the inner room a sofa, with a table, and one or two chairs. Over the sofa hangs the portrait of a handsome elderly man in a general's uniform. Over the table a hanging lamp, with an opal glass shade. A number of bouquets are arranged about the drawing room, in vases and glasses.*

Hedda Gabler by Henrik Ibsen, translated by Archer from AN APPROACH TO LITERATURE, Fourth Edition. Copyright © 1964 by Meredith Publishing Company.
1. *terra-cotta and majolica* (mə jolʹ ə kə) *ornaments,* ornaments made of glazed earthenware.

Others lie upon the tables. The floors in both rooms are covered with thick carpets. Morning light. The sun shines in through the glass door.

MISS JULIANA TESMAN, *with her bonnet on and carrying a parasol, comes in from the hall, followed by* BERTA, *who carries a bouquet wrapped in paper.* MISS TESMAN *is a comely and pleasant looking lady of about sixty-five. She is nicely but simply dressed in a gray walking costume.* BERTA *is a middle-aged woman of plain and rather countrified appearance.*

MISS TESMAN (*stops close to the door, listens, and says softly*). Upon my word, I don't believe they are stirring yet!

BERTA (*also softly*). I told you so, Miss. Remember how late the steamboat got in last night. And then, when they got home! Good Lord, what a lot the young mistress had to unpack before she could get to bed.

MISS TESMAN. Well, well—let them have their sleep out. But let us see that they get a good breath of the fresh morning air when they do appear. (*She goes to the glass door and throws it open.*)

BERTA (*beside the table, at a loss what to do with the bouquet in her hand*). I declare there isn't a bit of room left. I think I'll put it down here, Miss. (*She places it on the piano.*)

MISS TESMAN. So you've got a new mistress now, my dear Berta. Heaven knows it was a wrench to me to part with you.

BERTA (*on the point of weeping*). And do you think it wasn't hard for me too, Miss? After all the blessed years I've been with you and Miss Rina.

MISS TESMAN. We must make the best of it, Berta. There was nothing else to be done. George can't do without you, you see—he absolutely can't. He has had you to look after him ever since he was a little boy.

BERTA. Ah, but, Miss Julia, I can't help thinking of Miss Rina lying helpless at home there, poor thing. And with

only that new girl, too! She'll never learn to take proper care of an invalid.

MISS TESMAN. Oh, I shall manage to train her. And of course, you know, I shall take most of it upon myself. You needn't be uneasy about my poor sister, my dear Berta.

BERTA. Well, but there's another thing, Miss. I'm so mortally afraid I shan't be able to suit the young mistress.

MISS TESMAN. Oh, well—just at first there may be one or two things——

BERTA. Most like she'll be terrible grand in her ways.

MISS TESMAN. Well, you can't wonder at that—General Gabler's daughter! Think of the sort of life she was accustomed to in her father's time. Don't you remember how we used to see her riding down the road along with the General? In that long black habit—and with feathers in her hat?

BERTA. Yes, indeed—I remember well enough! But good Lord, I should never have dreamt in those days that she and Master George would make a match of it.

MISS TESMAN. Nor I. But, by-the-bye, Berta—while I think of it: in future you mustn't say Master George. You must say Dr. Tesman.

BERTA. Yes, the young mistress spoke of that too—last night—the moment they set foot in the house. Is it true, then, Miss?

MISS TESMAN. Yes, indeed it is. Only think, Berta—some foreign university has made him a doctor—while he has been abroad, you understand. I hadn't heard a word about it, until he told me himself upon the pier.

BERTA. Well, well, he's clever enough for anything, he is. But I didn't think he'd have gone in for doctoring people too.

MISS TESMAN. No, no, it's not that sort of doctor he is. (*Nods significantly.*) But let me tell you, we may have to call him something grander before long.

BERTA. You don't say so! What can that be, Miss?

MISS TESMAN *(smiling)*. Wouldn't you like to know! *(With emotion.)* Ah, dear, dear—if my poor brother could only look up from his grave now, and see what his little boy has grown into! *(Looks around.)* But bless me, Berta—why have you done this? Taken the chintz covers off all the furniture?

BERTA. The mistress told me to. She can't abide covers on the chairs, she says.

MISS TESMAN. Are they going to make this their everyday sitting room then?

BERTA. Yes, that's what I understood —from the mistress. Master George— the doctor—he said nothing.

(GEORGE TESMAN comes from the Right into the inner room, humming to himself, and carrying an unstrapped empty portmanteau. He is a middle-sized, young-looking man of thirty-three, rather stout, with a round, open, cheerful face, fair hair and beard. He wears spectacles, and is somewhat carelessly dressed in comfortable indoor clothes.)

MISS TESMAN. Good morning, good morning, George.

TESMAN *(in the doorway between the rooms)*. Aunt Julia! Dear Aunt Julia! *(Goes up to her and shakes hands warmly.)* Come all this way so early! Eh?

MISS TESMAN. Why of course I had to come and see how you were getting on.

TESMAN. In spite of your having had no proper night's rest?

MISS TESMAN. Oh, that makes no difference to me.

TESMAN. Well, I suppose you got home all right from the pier? Eh?

MISS TESMAN. Yes, quite safely, thank goodness. Judge Brack was good enough to see me right to my door.

TESMAN. We were so sorry we couldn't give you a seat in the carriage. But you saw the pile of boxes Hedda had to bring with her.

MISS TESMAN. Yes, she had certainly plenty of boxes.

BERTA *(to TESMAN)*. Shall I go in and see if there's anything I can do for the mistress?

TESMAN. No, thank you, Berta, you needn't. She said she would ring if she wanted anything.

BERTA *(going toward the Right)*. Very well.

TESMAN. But look here, take this portmanteau with you.

BERTA *(taking it)*. I'll put it in the attic. *(She goes out by the hall door.)*

TESMAN. Fancy, Auntie, I had the whole of that portmanteau chock full of copies of documents. You wouldn't believe how much I have picked up from all the archives I have been examining, curious old details that no one has had any idea of——

MISS TESMAN. Yes, you don't seem to have wasted your time on your wedding trip, George.

TESMAN. No, that I haven't. But do take off your bonnet, Auntie. Look here! Let me untie the strings—eh?

MISS TESMAN *(while he does so)*. Well, well—this is just as if you were still at home with us.

TESMAN *(with the bonnet in his hand, looks at it from all sides)*. Why, what a gorgeous bonnet you've been investing in!

MISS TESMAN. I bought it on Hedda's account.

TESMAN. On Hedda's account? Eh?

MISS TESMAN. Yes, so that Hedda needn't be ashamed of me if we happened to go out together.

TESMAN *(patting her cheeks)*. You always think of everything, Aunt Julia. *(Lays the bonnet on a chair beside the table.)* And now, look here—suppose we sit comfortably on the sofa and have a little chat, till Hedda comes.

(They seat themselves. She places her parasol in the corner of the sofa.)

MISS TESMAN *(takes both his hands and looks at him)*. What a delight it is to have you again, as large as life, before my very eyes, George! My George, my poor brother's own boy!

TESMAN. And it's a delight for me, too, to see you again, Aunt Julia! You, who have been father and mother in one to me.

MISS TESMAN. Oh, yes, I know you will always keep a place in your heart for your old aunts.

TESMAN. And what about Aunt Rina? No improvement—eh?

MISS TESMAN. Oh, no, we can scarcely look for any improvement in her case, poor thing. There she lies, helpless, as she has lain for all these years. But heaven grant I may not lose her yet awhile! For if I did, I don't know what I should make of my life, George, especially now that I haven't you to look after any more.

TESMAN (patting her back). There, there, there——

MISS TESMAN (suddenly changing her tone). And to think that here you are a married man, George! And that you should be the one to carry off Hedda Gabler—the beautiful Hedda Gabler. Only think of it—she, that was so beset with admirers!

TESMAN (hums a little and smiles complacently). Yes, I fancy I have several good friends about town who would like to stand in my shoes—eh?

MISS TESMAN. And then this fine long wedding tour you have had! More than five, nearly six months——

TESMAN. Well, for me it has been a sort of tour of research as well. I have had to do so much grubbing among old records—and to read no end of books too, Auntie.

MISS TESMAN. Oh, yes, I suppose so. (More confidentially, and lowering her voice a little.) But listen now, George—have you nothing—nothing special to tell me?

TESMAN. As to our journey?

MISS TESMAN. Yes.

TESMAN. No, I don't know of anything except what I have told you in my letters. I had a doctor's degree conferred on me—but that I told you yesterday.

MISS TESMAN. Yes, yes, you did. But what I mean is—haven't you any—any—expectations——?

TESMAN. Expectations?

MISS TESMAN. Why, you know, George —I'm your old auntie!

TESMAN. Why, of course I have expectations.

MISS TESMAN. Ah!

TESMAN. I have every expectation of being a professor one of these days.

MISS TESMAN. Oh, yes, a professor——

TESMAN. Indeed, I may say I am certain of it. But my dear Auntie, you know all about that already!

MISS TESMAN (laughing to herself). Yes, of course I do. You are quite right there. (Changing the subject.) But we were talking about your journey. It must have cost a great deal of money, George?

TESMAN. Well, you see, my handsome traveling scholarship went a good way.

MISS TESMAN. But I can't understand how you can have made it go far enough for two.

TESMAN. No, that's not so easy to understand—eh?

MISS TESMAN. And especially traveling with a lady—they tell me that makes it ever so much more expensive.

TESMAN. Yes, of course it makes it a little more expensive. But Hedda had to have this trip, Auntie! She really had to. Nothing else would have done.

MISS TESMAN. No, no, I suppose not. A wedding tour seems to be quite indispensable nowadays. But tell me now —have you gone thoroughly over the house yet?

TESMAN. Yes, you may be sure I have. I have been afoot ever since daylight.

MISS TESMAN. And what do you think of it all?

TESMAN. I'm delighted! Quite delighted! Only I can't think what we are to do with the two empty rooms between this inner parlor and Hedda's bedroom.

MISS TESMAN (laughing). Oh, my dear George, I dare say you may find some use for them—in the course of time.

TESMAN. Why of course you are quite right, Aunt Julia! You mean as my library increases—eh?

MISS TESMAN. Yes, quite so, my dear boy. It was your library I was thinking of.

TESMAN. I am specially pleased on Hedda's account. Often and often, before we were engaged, she said that she would never care to live anywhere but in Secretary Falk's villa.

MISS TESMAN. Yes, it was lucky that this very house should come into the market, just after you had started.

TESMAN. Yes, Aunt Julia, the luck was on our side, wasn't it—eh?

MISS TESMAN. But the expense, my dear George! You will find it very expensive, all this.

TESMAN (looks at her, a little cast down). Yes, I suppose I shall, Aunt!

MISS TESMAN. Oh, frightfully!

TESMAN. How much do you think? In round numbers? Eh?

MISS TESMAN. Oh, I can't even guess until all the accounts come in.

TESMAN. Well, fortunately, Judge Brack has secured the most favorable terms for me, so he said in a letter to Hedda.

MISS TESMAN. Yes, don't be uneasy, my dear boy. Besides, I have given security for the furniture and all the carpets.

TESMAN. Security? You? My dear Aunt Julia, what sort of security could you give?

MISS TESMAN. I have given a mortgage on our annuity.

TESMAN (jumps up). What! On your and Aunt Rina's annuity!

MISS TESMAN. Yes, I knew of no other plan, you see.

TESMAN (placing himself before her). Have you gone out of your senses, Auntie! Your annuity—it's all that you and Aunt Rina have to live upon.

MISS TESMAN. Well, well, don't get so excited about it. It's only a matter of form you know—Judge Brack assured me of that. It was he that was kind enough to arrange the whole affair for me. A mere matter of form, he said.

TESMAN. Yes, that may be all very well. But nevertheless——

MISS TESMAN. You will have your own salary to depend upon now. And, good heavens, even if we did have to pay up a little! To eke things out a bit at the start! Why, it would be nothing but a pleasure to us.

TESMAN. Oh, Auntie, will you never be tired of making sacrifices for me!

MISS TESMAN (rises and lays her hands on his shoulders). Have I had any other happiness in this world except to smooth your way for you, my dear boy? You, who have had neither father nor mother to depend on. And now we have reached the goal, George! Things have looked black enough for us, sometimes; but, thank heaven, now you have nothing to fear.

TESMAN. Yes, it is really marvelous how everything has turned out for the best.

MISS TESMAN. And the people who opposed you—who wanted to bar the way for you—now you have them at your feet. They have fallen, George. Your most dangerous rival—his fall was the worst. And now he has to lie on the bed he has made for himself, poor misguided creature.

TESMAN. Have you heard anything of Eilert? Since I went away, I mean.

MISS TESMAN. Only that he is said to have published a new book.

TESMAN. What! Eilert Lovborg! Recently—eh?

MISS TESMAN. Yes, so they say. Heaven knows whether it can be worth anything! Ah, when your new book appears—that will be another story, George! What is it to be about?

TESMAN. It will deal with the domestic industries of Brabant[2] during the Middle Ages.

---

2. *Brabant,* during the Middle Ages, a duchy in the southern Low Countries, now a province in Belgium.

MISS TESMAN. Fancy, to be able to write on such a subject as that!

TESMAN. However, it may be some time before the book is ready. I have all these collections to arrange first, you see.

MISS TESMAN. Yes, collecting and arranging—no one can beat you at that. There you are my poor brother's own son.

TESMAN. I am looking forward eagerly to setting to work at it; especially now that I have my own delightful home to work in.

MISS TESMAN. And, most of all, now that you have got the wife of your heart, my dear George.

TESMAN (embracing her). Oh, yes, yes, Aunt Julia. Hedda—she is the best part of all! (Looks toward the doorway.) I believe I hear her coming—eh?

(HEDDA enters from the Left through the inner room. She is a woman of twenty-nine. Her face and figure show refinement and distinction. Her complexion is pale and opaque. Her steel gray eyes express a cold, unruffled repose. Her hair is of an agreeable medium brown, but not particularly abundant. She is dressed in a tasteful, somewhat loose-fitting morning gown.)

MISS TESMAN (going to meet HEDDA). Good morning, my dear Hedda! Good morning, and a hearty welcome.

HEDDA (holds out her hand). Good morning, dear Miss Tesman! So early a call! That is kind of you.

MISS TESMAN (with some embarrassment). Well, has the bride slept well in her new home?

HEDDA. Oh yes, thanks. Passably.

TESMAN (laughing). Passably! Come, that's good, Hedda! You were sleeping like a stone when I got up.

HEDDA. Fortunately. Of course one has always to accustom one's self to new surroundings, Miss Tesman, little by little. (Looking toward the Left.) Oh, there the servant has gone and opened the veranda door, and let in a whole flood of sunshine.

MISS TESMAN (going toward the door). Well, then, we will shut it.

HEDDA. No, no, not that! Tesman, please draw the curtains. That will give a softer light.

TESMAN (at the door). All right, all right. There now, Hedda, now you have both shade and fresh air.

HEDDA. Yes, fresh air we certainly must have, with all these stacks of flowers. But, won't you sit down, Miss Tesman?

MISS TESMAN. No, thank you. Now that I have seen that everything is all right here—thank heaven—I must be getting home again. My sister is lying longing for me, poor thing.

TESMAN. Give her my very best love, Auntie; and say I shall look in and see her later in the day.

MISS TESMAN. Yes, yes, I'll be sure to tell her. But by-the-bye, George, (Feeling in her dress pocket.) I have almost forgotten, I have something for you here.

TESMAN. What is it, Auntie? Eh?

MISS TESMAN (produces a flat parcel wrapped in newspaper and hands it to him). Look here, my dear boy.

TESMAN (opening the parcel). Well, I declare! Have you really saved them for me, Aunt Julia! Hedda! Isn't this touching—eh?

HEDDA (beside the whatnot on the right). Well, what is it?

TESMAN. My old morning shoes! My slippers.

HEDDA. Indeed. I remember you often spoke of them while we were abroad.

TESMAN. Yes, I missed them terribly. (Goes up to her.) Now you shall see them, Hedda!

HEDDA (going toward the stove). Thanks, I really don't care about it.

TESMAN (following her). Only think —ill as she was, Aunt Rina embroidered these for me. Oh you can't think how many associations cling to them.

HEDDA (at the table). Scarcely for me.

MISS TESMAN. Of course not for Hedda, George.

TESMAN. Well, but now she belongs to the family, I thought——

HEDDA (interrupting). We shall never get on with this servant, Tesman.

MISS TESMAN. Not get on with Berta?

TESMAN. Why, dear, what puts that in your head? Eh?

HEDDA (pointing). Look there! She has left her old bonnet lying about on a chair.

TESMAN (in consternation, drops the slippers on the floor). Why, Hedda——

HEDDA. Just fancy, if any one should come in and see it!

TESMAN. But Hedda, that's Aunt Julia's bonnet.

HEDDA. Is it!

MISS TESMAN (taking up the bonnet). Yes, indeed it's mine. And, what's more, it's not old, Madame Hedda.

HEDDA. I really did not look closely at it, Miss Tesman.

MISS TESMAN (tying on the bonnet). Let me tell you it's the first time I have worn it—the very first time.

TESMAN. And a very nice bonnet it is too—quite a beauty!

MISS TESMAN. Oh, it's no such great thing, George. (Looks around her.) My parasol? Ah, here. (Takes it.) For this is mine too, (Mutters.) not Berta's.

TESMAN. A new bonnet and a new parasol! Only think, Hedda!

HEDDA. Very handsome indeed.

TESMAN. Yes, isn't it? But Auntie, take a good look at Hedda before you go! See how handsome she is!

MISS TESMAN. Oh, my dear boy, there's nothing new in that. Hedda was always lovely. (She nods and goes toward the Right.)

TESMAN (following). Yes, but have you noticed what splendid condition she is in? How she has filled out on the journey?

HEDDA (crossing the room). Oh, do be quiet!

MISS TESMAN (who has stopped and turned). Filled out?

TESMAN. Of course you don't notice it so much now that she has that dress on. But I, who can see——

HEDDA (at the glass door, impatiently). Oh, you can't see anything.

TESMAN. It must be the mountain air in the Tyrol[3]——

HEDDA (curtly, interrupting). I am exactly as I was when I started.

TESMAN. So you insist; but I'm quite certain you are not. Don't you agree with me, Auntie?

MISS TESMAN (who has been gazing at her with folded hands). Hedda is lovely—lovely—lovely. (Goes up to her, takes her head between both hands, draws it downward, and kisses her hair.) God bless and preserve Hedda Tesman, for George's sake.

HEDDA (gently freeing herself). Oh! Let me go.

MISS TESMAN (in quiet emotion). I shall not let a day pass without coming to see you.

TESMAN. No you won't, will you, Auntie? Eh?

MISS TESMAN. Good-bye—good-bye!

(She goes out by the hall door. TESMAN accompanies her. The door remains half open. TESMAN can be heard repeating his message to Aunt Rina and his thanks for the slippers.

In the meantime, HEDDA walks about the room raising her arms and clenching her hands as if in desperation. Then she flings back the curtains from the glass door, and stands there looking out.

Presently TESMAN returns and closes the door behind him.)

TESMAN (picks up the slippers from the floor). What are you looking at, Hedda?

HEDDA (once more calm and mistress of herself). I am only looking at the leaves. They are so yellow, so withered.

TESMAN (wraps up the slippers and lays them on the table). Well you see, we are well into September now.

HEDDA (again restless). Yes, to think of it! Already in—in September.

---

3. Tyrol (tə rōl′), a mountainous region in western Austria noted for its scenic beauty.

TESMAN. Don't you think Aunt Julia's manner was strange, dear? Almost solemn? Can you imagine what was the matter with her? Eh?

HEDDA. I scarcely know her, you see. Is she often like that?

TESMAN. No, not as she was today.

HEDDA (leaving the glass door). Do you think she was annoyed about the bonnet?

TESMAN. Oh, scarcely at all. Perhaps a little, just at the moment . . .

HEDDA. But what an idea, to pitch her bonnet about in the drawing room! No one does that sort of thing.

TESMAN. Well you may be sure Aunt Julia won't do it again.

HEDDA. In any case, I shall manage to make my peace with her.

TESMAN. Yes, my dear, good Hedda, if you only would.

HEDDA. When you call this afternoon, you might invite her to spend the evening here.

TESMAN. Yes, that I will. And there's one thing more you can do that would delight her heart.

HEDDA. What is it?

TESMAN. If you could only prevail on yourself to say *du*[4] to her. For my sake, Hedda? Eh?

HEDDA. No, no, Tesman, you really mustn't ask that of me. I have told you so already. I shall try to call her "Aunt"; and you must be satisfied with that.

TESMAN. Well, well. Only I think now that you belong to the family, you——

HEDDA. H'm, I can't in the least see why —— (She goes up toward the middle doorway.)

TESMAN (after a pause). Is there anything the matter with you, Hedda? Eh?

HEDDA. I'm only looking at my old piano. It doesn't go at all well with all the other things.

TESMAN. The first time I draw my salary, we'll see about exchanging it.

HEDDA. No, no—no exchanging. I don't want to part with it. Suppose we put it there in the inner room, and then get another here in its place. When it's convenient, I mean.

TESMAN (a little taken aback). Yes—of course we could do that.

HEDDA (takes up the bouquet from the piano). These flowers were not here last night when we arrived.

TESMAN. Aunt Julia must have brought them for you.

HEDDA (examining the bouquet). A visiting card. (Takes it out and reads.) "Shall return later in the day." Can you guess whose card it is?

TESMAN. No. Whose? Eh?

HEDDA. The name is "Mrs. Elvsted."

TESMAN. Is it really? Sheriff Elvsted's wife? Miss Rysing that was.

HEDDA. Exactly. The girl with the irritating hair, that she was always showing off. An old flame of yours, I've been told.

TESMAN (laughing). Oh, that didn't last long; and it was before I knew you, Hedda. But fancy her being in town!

HEDDA. It's odd that she should call upon us. I have scarcely seen her since we left school.

TESMAN. I haven't seen her either for—heaven knows how long. I wonder how she can endure to live in such an out-of-the-way hole, eh?

HEDDA (after a moment's thought says suddenly). Tell me, Tesman—isn't it somewhere near there that he—that—Eilert Lovborg is living?

TESMAN. Yes, he is somewhere in that part of the country.

(BERTA enters by the hall door.)

BERTA. That lady, ma'am, that brought some flowers a little while ago, is here again. (Pointing.) The flowers you have in your hand, ma'am.

HEDDA. Ah, is she? Well, please show her in.

(BERTA opens the door for MRS. ELVSTED, and goes out herself. MRS. ELVSTED is a woman of fragile figure,

---

4. *du*, the familiar form of *you* in Norwegian. It is customarily used only with family and intimate friends. *De* is the formal expression for *you*.

with pretty, soft features. Her eyes are light blue, large, round, and somewhat prominent, with a startled, inquiring expression. Her hair is remarkably light, almost flaxen, and unusually abundant and wavy. She is a couple of years younger than HEDDA. *She wears a dark visiting dress, tasteful, but not quite in the latest fashion.)*

HEDDA *(receives her warmly).* How do you do, my dear Mrs. Elvsted? It's delightful to see you again.

MRS. ELVSTED *(nervously, struggling for self-control).* Yes, it's a very long time since we met.

TESMAN *(gives her his hand).* And we too—eh?

HEDDA. Thanks for your lovely flowers——

MRS. ELVSTED. Oh, not at all. I would have come straight here yesterday afternoon; but I heard that you were away——

TESMAN. Have you just come to town? Eh?

MRS. ELVSTED. I arrived yesterday, about midday. Oh, I was quite in despair when I heard that you were not at home.

HEDDA. In despair? How so?

TESMAN. Why, my dear Mrs. Rysing —I mean Mrs. Elvsted——

HEDDA. I hope that you were not in any trouble?

MRS. ELVSTED. Yes, I am. And I don't know another living creature here that I can turn to.

HEDDA *(laying the bouquet on the table).* Come, let us sit here on the sofa——

MRS. ELVSTED. Oh, I am too restless to sit down.

HEDDA. Oh no, you're not. Come here. *(She draws* MRS. ELVSTED *down upon the sofa and sits at her side.)*

TESMAN. Well? What is it, Mrs. Elvsted?

HEDDA. Has anything special happened to you at home?

MRS. ELVSTED. Yes and no. Oh, I am so anxious you should not misunderstand me——

HEDDA. Then your best plan is to tell us the whole story, Mrs. Elvsted.

TESMAN. I suppose that's what you have come for—eh?

MRS. ELVSTED. Yes, yes—of course it is. Well then, I must tell you, if you don't already know, that Eilert Lovborg is in town, too.

HEDDA. Lovborg!

TESMAN. What! Has Eilert Lovborg come back? Fancy that, Hedda!

HEDDA. Well, well—I hear it.

MRS. ELVSTED. He has been here a week already. Just fancy, a whole week! In this terrible town, alone! With so many temptations on all sides.

HEDDA. But my dear Mrs. Elvsted, how does he concern you so much?

MRS. ELVSTED *(looks at her with a startled air, and says rapidly).* He was the children's tutor.

HEDDA. Your children's?

MRS. ELVSTED. My husband's. I have none.

HEDDA. Your stepchildren's, then?

MRS. ELVSTED. Yes.

TESMAN *(somewhat hesitatingly).* Then was he—I don't know how to express it —was he—regular enough in his habits to be fit for the post? Eh?

MRS. ELVSTED. For the last two years his conduct has been irreproachable.

TESMAN. Has it indeed? Fancy that, Hedda!

HEDDA. I hear it.

MRS. ELVSTED. Perfectly irreproachable. I assure you! In every respect. But all the same, now that I know he is here, in this great town and with a large sum of money in his hands, I can't help being in mortal fear for him.

TESMAN. Why did he not remain where he was? With you and your husband? Eh?

MRS. ELVSTED. After his book was published he was too restless and unsettled to remain with us.

TESMAN. Yes, by-the-bye, Aunt Julia told me he had published a new book.

MRS. ELVSTED. Yes, a big book, dealing with the march of civilization—in broad outline, as it were. It came out about a fortnight ago. And since it has sold so well, and been so much read and made such a sensation——

TESMAN. Has it indeed? It must be something he has had lying by since his better days.

MRS. ELVSTED. Long ago, you mean?

TESMAN. Yes.

MRS. ELVSTED. No, he has written it all since he has been with us—within the last year.

TESMAN. Isn't that good news, Hedda? Think of that.

MRS. ELVSTED. Ah, yes, if only it would last!

HEDDA. Have you seen him here in town?

MRS. ELVSTED. No, not yet. I have had the greatest difficulty in finding out his address. But this morning I discovered it at last.

HEDDA (looks searchingly at her). Do you know, it seems to me a little odd of your husband—h'm——

MRS. ELVSTED (starting nervously). Of my husband. What?

HEDDA. That he should send you to town on such an errand—that he does not come himself and look after his friend.

MRS. ELVSTED. Oh no, no, my husband has no time. And besides, I—I had some shopping to do.

HEDDA (with a slight smile). Ah, that is a different matter.

MRS. ELVSTED (rising quickly and uneasily). And now I beg and implore you, Mr. Tesman, receive Eilert Lovborg kindly if he comes to you! And that he is sure to do. You see you were such great friends in the old days. And then you are interested in the same studies—the same branch of science—so far as I can understand.

TESMAN. We used to be, at any rate.

MRS. ELVSTED. That is why I beg so earnestly that you—you too—will keep a sharp eye upon him. Oh, you will promise me that, Mr. Tesman—won't you?

TESMAN. With the greatest of pleasure, Mrs. Rysing.

HEDDA. Elvsted.

TESMAN. I assure you I shall do all I possibly can for Eilert. You may rely upon me.

MRS. ELVSTED. Oh, how very, very kind of you! (Presses his hands.) Thanks, thanks, thanks! (Frightened.) You see, my husband is very fond of him!

HEDDA (rising). You ought to write to him, Tesman. Perhaps he may not care to come to you of his own accord.

TESMAN. Well, perhaps it would be the right thing to do, Hedda? Eh?

HEDDA. And the sooner the better. Why not at once?

MRS. ELVSTED (imploringly). Oh, if you only would!

TESMAN. I'll write this moment. Have you his address, Mrs.—Mrs. Elvsted?

MRS. ELVSTED. Yes. (Takes a slip of paper from her pocket, and hands it to him.) Here it is.

TESMAN. Good, good. Then I'll go in—— (Looks about him.) By-the-bye, my slippers? Oh, here. (Takes the packet, and is about to go.)

HEDDA. Be sure you write him a cordial, friendly letter. And a good long one too.

TESMAN. Yes, I will.

MRS. ELVSTED. But please, please don't say a word to show that I have suggested it.

TESMAN. No, how could you think I would? Eh? (He goes out to the Right, through the inner room.)

HEDDA (goes up to MRS. ELVSTED, smiles, and says in a low voice). There. We have killed two birds with one stone.

MRS. ELVSTED. What do you mean?

HEDDA. Could you not see that I wanted him to go?

MRS. ELVSTED. Yes, to write the letter——

HEDDA. And that I might speak to you alone.

MRS. ELVSTED (confused). About the same thing?

HEDDA. Precisely.

MRS. ELVSTED (apprehensively). But there is nothing more, Mrs. Tesman! Absolutely nothing!

HEDDA. Oh, yes, but there is. There is a great deal more, I can see that. Sit here and we'll have a cozy, confidential chat. (She forces MRS. ELVSTED to sit in the easy chair beside the stove, and seats herself on one of the footstools.)

MRS. ELVSTED (anxiously, looking at her watch). But, my dear Mrs. Tesman, I was really on the point of going.

HEDDA. Oh, you can't be in such a hurry. Well? Now tell me something about your life at home.

MRS. ELVSTED. Oh, that is just what I care least to speak about.

HEDDA. But to me, dear? Why, weren't we schoolfellows?

MRS. ELVSTED. Yes, but you were in the class above me. Oh, how dreadfully afraid of you I was then!

HEDDA. Afraid of me?

MRS. ELVSTED. Yes, dreadfully. For when we met on the stairs you used always to pull my hair.

HEDDA. Did I, really?

MRS. ELVSTED. Yes, and once you said you would burn it off my head.

HEDDA. Oh, that was all nonsense, of course.

MRS. ELVSTED. Yes, but I was so silly in those days. And since then, too—we have drifted so far—far apart from each other. Our circles have been so entirely different.

HEDDA. Well then, we must try to drift together again. Now listen! At school we said du to each other; and we called each other by our Christian names——

MRS. ELVSTED. No, I am sure you must be mistaken.

HEDDA. No, not at all! I can remember quite distinctly. So now we are going to renew our old friendship. (Draws the footstool closer to MRS. ELVSTED.) There now! (Kisses her cheek.) You must say du to me and call me Hedda.

MRS. ELVSTED (presses and pats her hands). Oh, how good and kind you are! I am not used to such kindness.

HEDDA. There, there, there! And I shall say du to you, as in the old days, and call you my dear Thora.

MRS. ELVSTED. My name is Thea.

HEDDA. Why, of course! I meant Thea. (Looks at her compassionately.) So you are not accustomed to goodness and kindness, Thea? Not in your own home?

MRS. ELVSTED. Oh, if I only had a home! But I haven't any; I have never had a home.

HEDDA (looks at her for a moment). I almost suspected as much.

MRS. ELVSTED (gazing helplessly before her). Yes—yes—yes.

HEDDA. I don't quite remember—was it not as housekeeper that you first went to Mr. Elvsted's?

MRS. ELVSTED. I really went as governess. But his wife—his late wife—was an invalid, and rarely left her room. So I had to look after the housekeeping as well.

HEDDA. And then—at last—you became mistress of the house.

MRS. ELVSTED (sadly). Yes, I did.

HEDDA. Let me see—about how long ago was that?

MRS. ELVSTED. My marriage?

HEDDA. Yes.

MRS. ELVSTED. Five years ago.

HEDDA. To be sure; it must be that.

MRS. ELVSTED. Oh, those five years! Or at all events the last two or three of them! Oh, if you[5] could only imagine——

HEDDA (giving her a little slap on the hand). De? Fie, Thea!

MRS. ELVSTED. Yes, yes, I will try. Well if you could only imagine and understand——

HEDDA (lightly). Eilert Lovborg has been in your neighborhood about three years, hasn't he?

MRS. ELVSTED (looks at her doubtfully). Eilert Lovborg? Yes—he has.

---

5. Oh, if you. Mrs. Elvsted uses the formal word for you and thus Hedda rebukes her in the next line.

HEDDA. Had you known him before, in town here?

MRS. ELVSTED. Scarcely at all. I mean —I knew him by name of course.

HEDDA. But you saw a good deal of him in the country?

MRS. ELVSTED. Yes, he came to us every day. You see, he gave the children lessons; for in the long run I couldn't manage it all myself.

HEDDA. No, that's clear. And your husband? I suppose he is often away from home?

MRS. ELVSTED. Yes. Being sheriff, you know, he has to travel about a good deal in his district.

HEDDA (leaning against the arm of the chair). Thea—my poor, sweet Thea —now you must tell me everything— exactly as it stands.

MRS. ELVSTED. Well, then, you must question me.

HEDDA. What sort of a man is your husband, Thea? I mean—you know— in everyday life. Is he kind to you?

MRS. ELVSTED (evasively). I am sure he means well in everything.

HEDDA. I should think he must be altogether too old for you. There is at least twenty years' difference between you, is there not?

MRS. ELVSTED (irritably). Yes, that is true, too. Everything about him is repellent to me! We have not a thought in common. We have no single point of sympathy—he and I.

HEDDA. But is he not fond of you all the same? In his own way?

MRS. ELVSTED. Oh, I really don't know. I think he regards me simply as a useful property. And then it doesn't cost much to keep me. I am not expensive.

HEDDA. That is stupid of you.

MRS. ELVSTED (shakes her head). It cannot be otherwise—not with him. I don't think he really cares for any one but himself—and perhaps a little for the children.

HEDDA. And for Eilert Lovborg, Thea.

MRS. ELVSTED (looking at her). For Eilert Lovborg? What puts that into your head?

HEDDA. Well, my dear—I should say, when he sends you after him all the way to town—— (Smiling almost imperceptibly.) And besides, you said so yourself, to Tesman.

MRS. ELVSTED (with a little nervous twitch). Did I? Yes, I suppose I did. (Vehemently, but not loudly.) No—I may just as well make a clean breast of it at once! For it must all come out in any case.

HEDDA. Why, my dear Thea?

MRS. ELVSTED. Well, to make a long story short, my husband did not know that I was coming.

HEDDA. What! Your husband didn't know it!

MRS. ELVSTED. No, of course not. For that matter, he was away from home himself—he was traveling. Oh, I could bear it no longer, Hedda! I couldn't indeed—so utterly alone as I should have been in the future.

HEDDA. Well? And then?

MRS. ELVSTED. So I put together some of my things—what I needed most—as quietly as possible. And then I left the house.

HEDDA. Without a word?

MRS. ELVSTED. Yes—and took the train straight to town.

HEDDA. Why, my dear, good Thea— to think of you daring to do it!

MRS. ELVSTED (rises and moves about the room). What else could I possibly do?

HEDDA. But what do you think your husband will say when you go home again?

MRS. ELVSTED (at the table, looks at her). Back to him?

HEDDA. Of course.

MRS. ELVSTED. I shall never go back to him again.

HEDDA (rising and going towards her). Then you have left your home—for good and all?

MRS. ELVSTED. Yes. There was nothing else to be done.

HEDDA. But then—to take flight so openly.

MRS. ELVSTED. Oh, it's impossible to keep things of that sort secret.

HEDDA. But what do you think people will say of you, Thea?

MRS. ELVSTED. They may say what they like for aught *I* care. *(Seats herself wearily and sadly on the sofa.)* I have done nothing but what I had to do.

HEDDA *(after a short silence).* And what are your plans now? What do you think of doing?

MRS. ELVSTED. I don't know yet. I only know this, that I must live here, where Eilert Lovborg is, if I am to live at all.

HEDDA *(takes a chair from the table, seats herself beside her, and strokes her hands).* My dear Thea—how did this— this friendship—between you and Eilert Lovborg come about?

MRS. ELVSTED. Oh, it grew up gradually. I gained a sort of influence over him.

HEDDA. Indeed?

MRS. ELVSTED. He gave up his old habits. Not because I asked him to, for I never dared do that. But of course he saw how repulsive they were to me; and so he dropped them.

HEDDA *(concealing an involuntary smile of scorn).* Then you have reclaimed him, as the saying goes, my little Thea.

MRS. ELVSTED. So he says himself, at any rate. And he, on his side, has made a real human being of me—taught me to think, and to understand so many things.

HEDDA. Did he give you lessons too, then?

MRS. ELVSTED. No, not exactly lessons. But he talked to me—talked about such an infinity of things. And then came the lovely, happy time when I began to share in his work—when he allowed me to help him!

HEDDA. Oh, he did, did he?

MRS. ELVSTED. Yes! He never wrote anything without my assistance.

HEDDA. You were two good comrades, in fact?

MRS. ELVSTED *(eagerly).* Comrades! Yes, fancy, Hedda, that is the very word he used! Oh, I ought to feel perfectly happy; and yet I cannot; for I don't know how long it will last.

HEDDA. Are you no surer of him than that?

MRS. ELVSTED *(gloomily).* A woman's shadow stands between Eilert Lovborg and me.

HEDDA *(looks at her anxiously).* Who can that be?

MRS. ELVSTED. I don't know. Someone he knew in his—in his past. Someone he has never been able wholly to forget.

HEDDA. What has he told you—about this?

MRS. ELVSTED. He has only once— quite vaguely—alluded to it.

HEDDA. Well! And what did he say?

MRS. ELVSTED. He said that when they parted, she threatened to shoot him with a pistol.

HEDDA *(with cold composure).* Oh, nonsense! No one does that sort of thing here.

MRS. ELVSTED. No. And that is why I think it must have been that red-haired singing woman whom he once——

HEDDA. Yes, very likely.

MRS. ELVSTED. For I remember they used to say of her that she carried loaded firearms.

HEDDA. Oh—then of course it must have been she.

MRS. ELVSTED *(wringing her hands).* And now just fancy, Hedda—I hear this singing woman—that she is in town again! Oh, I don't know what to do——

HEDDA *(glancing towards the inner room).* Hush! Here comes Tesman. *(Rises and whispers.)* Thea—all this must remain between you and me.

MRS. ELVSTED *(springing up).* Oh, yes, yes! for heaven's sake!

(GEORGE TESMAN, with a letter in his hand, comes from the Right through the inner room.)

TESMAN. There now—the epistle is finished.

HEDDA. That's right. And now Mrs. Elvsted is just going. Wait a moment—I'll go with you to the garden gate.

TESMAN. Do you think Berta could post the letter, Hedda dear?

HEDDA (takes it). I will tell her to.

(BERTA enters from the hall.)

BERTA. Judge Brack wishes to know if Mrs. Tesman will receive him.

HEDDA. Yes, ask Judge Brack to come in. And look here—put this letter in the post.

BERTA (taking the letter). Yes, ma'am. (She opens the door for JUDGE BRACK and goes out herself. BRACK is a man of forty-five; thick-set, but well-built and elastic in his movements. His face is roundish with an aristocratic profile. His hair is short, still almost black, and carefully dressed. His eyes are lively and sparkling, his eyebrows thick. His moustaches are also thick, with short-cut ends. He wears a well-cut walking suit, a little too youthful for his age. He uses an eyeglass, which he now and then lets drop.)

BRACK (with his hat in his hand, bowing). May one venture to call so early in the day?

HEDDA. Of course one may.

TESMAN (presses his hand). You are welcome at any time. (Introducing him.) Judge Brack, Miss Rysing.

HEDDA. Oh!

BRACK (bowing). Ah, delighted.

HEDDA (looks at him and laughs). It's nice to have a look at you by daylight, Judge!

BRACK. Do you find me altered?

HEDDA. A little younger, I think.

BRACK. Thank you so much.

TESMAN. But what do you think of Hedda—eh? Doesn't she look flourishing? She has actually——

HEDDA. Oh, do leave me alone. You haven't thanked Judge Brack for all the trouble he has taken——

BRACK. Oh, nonsense—it was a pleasure to me——

HEDDA. Yes, you are a friend indeed. But here stands Thea all impatience to be off—so au revoir Judge. I shall be back again presently.

(Mutual salutations. MRS. ELVSTED and HEDDA go out by the hall door.)

BRACK. Well, is your wife tolerably satisfied——

TESMAN. Yes, we can't thank you sufficiently. Of course she talks a little rearrangement here and there; and one or two things are still wanting. We shall have to buy some additional trifles.

BRACK. Indeed!

TESMAN. But we won't trouble you about these things. Hedda says she herself will look after what is wanting. Shan't we sit down? Eh?

BRACK. Thanks, for a moment. (Seats himself beside the table.) There is something I wanted to speak to you about, my dear Tesman.

TESMAN. Indeed? Ah, I understand! (Seating himself.) I suppose it's the serious part of the frolic that is coming now. Eh?

BRACK. Oh, the money question is not so very pressing; though, for that matter, I wish we had gone a little more economically to work.

TESMAN. But that would never have done, you know! Think of Hedda, my dear fellow! You, who know her so well. I couldn't possibly ask her to put up with a shabby style of living!

BRACK. No, no, that is just the difficulty.

TESMAN. And then, fortunately, it can't be long before I receive my appointment.

BRACK. Well, you see, such things are often apt to hang fire for a time.

TESMAN. Have you heard anything definite? Eh?

BRACK. Nothing exactly definite—— (Interrupting himself.) But, by-the-bye—I have one piece of news for you.

TESMAN. Well?

BRACK. Your old friend, Eilert Lovborg, has returned to town.

TESMAN. I know that already.

BRACK. Indeed! How did you learn it?

TESMAN. From that lady who went out with Hedda.

BRACK. Really? What was her name? I didn't quite catch it.

TESMAN. Mrs. Elvsted.

BRACK. Aha, Sheriff Elvsted's wife? Of course, he has been living up in their regions.

TESMAN. And fancy, I'm delighted to hear that he is quite a reformed character!

BRACK. So they say.

TESMAN. And then he has published a new book—eh?

BRACK. Yes, indeed he has.

TESMAN. And I hear it has made some sensation!

BRACK. Quite an unusual sensation.

TESMAN. Fancy, isn't that good news! A man of such extraordinary talents—— I felt so grieved to think that he had gone irretrievably to ruin.

BRACK. That was what everybody thought.

TESMAN. But I cannot imagine what he will take to now! How in the world will he be able to make his living? Eh?

(During the last words, HEDDA *has entered by the hall door.)*

HEDDA *(to* BRACK, *laughing with a touch of scorn).* Tesman is forever worrying about how people are to make their living.

TESMAN. Well, you see, dear, we were talking about poor Eilert Lovborg.

HEDDA *(glancing at him rapidly).* Oh, indeed? *(Seats herself in the arm chair beside the stove and asks indifferently.)* What is the matter with him?

TESMAN. Well, no doubt he has run through all his property long ago; and he can scarcely write a new book every year —eh? So I really can't see what is to become of him.

BRACK. Perhaps I can give you some information on that point.

TESMAN. Indeed!

BRACK. You must remember that his relations have a good deal of influence.

TESMAN. Oh, his relations, unfortunately, have entirely washed their hands of him.

BRACK. At one time they called him the hope of the family.

TESMAN. At one time, yes! But he has put an end to all that.

HEDDA. Who knows? *(With a slight smile.)* I hear they have reclaimed him up at Sheriff Elvsted's.

BRACK. And then this book that he has published——

TESMAN. Well, well, I hope to goodness they may find something for him to do. I have just written to him. I asked him to come and see us this evening, Hedda dear.

BRACK. But, my dear fellow, you are booked for my bachelors' party this evening. You promised on the pier last night.

HEDDA. Have you forgotten, Tesman?

TESMAN. Yes, I had utterly forgotten.

BRACK. But it doesn't matter, for you may be sure he won't come.

TESMAN. What makes you think that, eh?

BRACK *(with a little hesitation, rising and resting his hands on the back of his chair).* My dear Tesman—and you too, Mrs. Tesman—I think I ought not to keep you in the dark about something that— that——

TESMAN. That concerns Eilert?

BRACK. Both you and him.

TESMAN. Well, my dear Judge, out with it.

BRACK. You must be prepared to find your appointment deferred longer than you desired or expected.

TESMAN *(jumping up uneasily).* Is there some hitch about it? Eh?

BRACK. The nomination may perhaps be made conditional on the result of a competition——

TESMAN. Competition! Think of that, Hedda!

HEDDA *(leans farther back in the chair).* Aha—aha!

TESMAN. But who can my competitor be? Surely not——

BRACK. Yes, precisely—Eilert Lovborg.

TESMAN (*clasping his hands*). No, no—it's quite inconceivable! Quite impossible!

BRACK. H'm—that is what it may come to, all the same.

TESMAN. Well but, Judge Brack—it would show the most incredible lack of consideration for me. (*Gesticulates with his arms.*) For—just think—I'm a married man. We have been married on the strength of these prospects, Hedda and I; and run deep into debt; and borrowed money from Aunt Julia too. Good heavens, they had as good as promised me the appointment. Eh?

BRACK. Well, well, well—no doubt you will get it in the end; only after a contest.

HEDDA (*immovable in her arm chair*). Fancy, Tesman, there will be a sort of sporting interest in that.

TESMAN. Why, my dearest Hedda, how can you be so indifferent about it.

HEDDA (*as before*). I am not at all indifferent. I am most eager to see who wins.

BRACK. In any case, Mrs. Tesman, it is best that you should know how matters stand. I mean—before you set about the little purchases I hear you are threatening.

HEDDA. This can make no difference.

BRACK. Indeed! Then I have no more to say. Good-bye! (*To* TESMAN.) I shall look in on my way back from my afternoon walk, and take you home with me.

TESMAN. Oh, yes, yes—your news has quite upset me.

HEDDA (*reclining, holds out her hand*). Good-bye, Judge; and be sure you call in the afternoon.

BRACK. Many thanks. Good-bye, good-bye!

TESMAN (*accompanying him to the door*). Good-bye, my dear Judge! You must really excuse me—— (JUDGE BRACK *goes out by the hall door.*)

TESMAN (*crosses the room*). Oh, Hedda—one should never rush into adventures. Eh?

HEDDA (*looks at him, smiling*). Do you do that?

TESMAN. Yes, dear—there is no denying—it was adventurous to go and marry and set up house upon mere expectations.

HEDDA. Perhaps you are right there.

TESMAN. Well, at all events, we have our delightful home, Hedda! Fancy, the home we both dreamed of—the home we were in love with, I may almost say. Eh?

HEDDA (*rising slowly and wearily*). It was part of our compact that we were to go into society—to keep open house.

TESMAN. Yes, if you only knew how I had been looking forward to it! Fancy, to see you as hostess in a select circle. Eh? Well, well, well, for the present we shall have to get on without society, Hedda, only to invite Aunt Julia now and then. Oh, I intended you to lead such an utterly different life, dear!

HEDDA. Of course I cannot have my man in livery just yet.

TESMAN. Oh no, unfortunately. It would be out of the question for us to keep a footman, you know.

HEDDA. And the saddle horse I was to have had——

TESMAN (*aghast*). The saddle horse!

HEDDA. I suppose I must not think of that now.

TESMAN. Good heavens, no! That's as clear as daylight.

HEDDA (*goes up the room*). Well, I shall have one thing at least to kill time with in the meanwhile.

TESMAN (*beaming*). Oh, thank heaven for that! What is it, Hedda? Eh?

HEDDA (*in the middle doorway, looks at him with covert scorn*). My pistols, George.

TESMAN (*in alarm*). Your pistols!

HEDDA (*with cold eyes*). General Gabler's pistols. (*She goes out through the inner room, to the Left.*)

TESMAN (*rushes up to the middle doorway and calls after her*). No, for heaven's sake, Hedda darling—don't touch those dangerous things! For my sake, Hedda! Eh?

CURTAIN

Act Two

SCENE: *The room at the* TESMANS' *as in the first act, except that the piano has been removed, and an elegant little writing table with bookshelves put in its place. A smaller table stands near the sofa at the Left. Most of the bouquets have been taken away.* MRS. ELVSTED's *bouquet is upon the large table in front. It is afternoon.*

HEDDA, *dressed to receive callers is alone in the room. She stands by the open glass door, loading a revolver. The fellow to it lies in an open pistol case on the writing table.*

HEDDA *(looks down the garden, and calls).* So you are here again, Judge!

BRACK *(is heard calling from a distance).* As you see, Mrs. Tesman!

HEDDA *(raises the pistol and points).* Now I'll shoot you, Judge Brack!

BRACK *(calling unseen).* No, no, no! Don't stand aiming at me!

HEDDA. This is what comes of sneaking in the back way. *(She fires.)*

BRACK *(nearer).* Are you out of your senses!

HEDDA. Dear me—did I happen to hit you?

BRACK *(still outside).* I wish you would let these pranks alone!

HEDDA. Come in then, Judge.

(JUDGE BRACK, dressed as though for a men's party, enters by the glass door. He carries a light overcoat over his arm.)

BRACK. What the deuce—haven't you tired of that sport, yet? What are you shooting at?

HEDDA. Oh, I am only firing in the air.

BRACK *(gently takes the pistol out of her hand).* Allow me, madam! *(Looks at it.)* Ah—I know this pistol well! *(Looks around.)* Where is the case? Ah, here it is. *(Lays the pistol in it, and shuts it.)* Now we won't play at that game any more today.

HEDDA. Then what in heaven's name would you have me do with myself?

BRACK. Have you had no visitors?

HEDDA (*closing the glass door*). Not one. I suppose all our set are still out of town.

BRACK. And is Tesman not at home either?

HEDDA (*at the writing table, putting the pistol case in a drawer which she shuts*). No. He rushed off to his aunt's directly after lunch; he didn't expect you so early.

BRACK. H'm—how stupid of me not to have thought of that!

HEDDA (*turning her head to look at him*). Why stupid?

BRACK. Because if I had thought of it I should have come a little—earlier.

HEDDA (*crossing the room*). Then you would have found no one to receive you; for I have been in my room changing my dress ever since lunch.

BRACK. And is there no sort of little chink that we could hold a parley through?

HEDDA. You have forgotten to arrange one.

BRACK. That was another piece of stupidity.

HEDDA. Well, we must just settle down here and wait. Tesman is not likely to be back for some time yet.

BRACK. Never mind; I shall not be impatient.

(HEDDA *seats herself in the corner of the sofa.* BRACK *lays his overcoat over the back of the nearest chair, and sits down, but keeps his hat in his hand. A short silence. They look at each other.*)

HEDDA. Well?

BRACK (*in the same tone*). Well?

HEDDA. I spoke first.

BRACK (*bending a little forward*). Come, let us have a cozy little chat, Mrs. Hedda.

HEDDA (*leaning farther back in the sofa*). Does it not seem like a whole eternity since our last talk? Of course I don't count those few words yesterday evening and this morning.

BRACK. You mean since our last confidential talk? Our last tête-à-tête?

HEDDA. Well, yes—since you put it so.

BRACK. Not a day has passed but I have wished that you were home again.

HEDDA. And I have done nothing but wish the same thing.

BRACK. You? Really, Mrs. Hedda? And I thought you had been enjoying your tour so much!

HEDDA. Oh, yes, you may be sure of that!

BRACK. But Tesman's letters spoke of nothing but happiness.

HEDDA. Oh, Tesman! You see, he thinks nothing so delightful as grubbing in libraries and making copies of old parchments, or whatever you call them.

BRACK (*with a spice of malice*). Well, that is his vocation in life—or part of it at any rate.

HEDDA. Yes, of course; and no doubt when it's your vocation—— But *I!* Oh, my dear Mr. Brack, how mortally bored I have been.

BRACK (*sympathetically*). Do you really say so? In downright earnest?

HEDDA. Yes, you can surely understand it! To go for six whole months without meeting a soul that knew anything of our circle, or could talk about the things we are interested in.

BRACK. Yes, yes, I too should feel that a deprivation.

HEDDA. And then, what I found most intolerable of all——

BRACK. Well?

HEDDA.—— was being everlastingly in the company of one and the same person.

BRACK (*with a nod of assent*). Morning, noon, and night, yes—at all possible times and seasons.

HEDDA. I said "everlastingly."

BRACK. Just so. But I should have thought, with our excellent Tesman, one could——

HEDDA. Tesman is—a specialist, my dear Judge.

BRACK. Undeniably.

HEDDA. And specialists are not at all

amusing to travel with. Not in the long run at any rate.

BRACK. Not even—the specialist one happens to love?

HEDDA. Faugh—don't use that sickening word!

BRACK *(taken aback)*. What do you say, Mrs. Hedda?

HEDDA *(half laughing, half irritated)*. You should just try it! To hear nothing but the history of civilization, morning, noon, and night——

BRACK. Everlastingly.

HEDDA. Yes, yes, yes! And then all this about the domestic industry of the Middle Ages! That's the most disgusting part of it!

BRACK *(looks searchingly at her)*. But tell me in that case how am I to understand your——

HEDDA. My accepting George Tesman, you mean?

BRACK. Well, let us put it so.

HEDDA. Good heavens, do you see anything so wonderful in that?

BRACK. Yes and no—Mrs. Hedda.

HEDDA. I had positively danced myself tired, my dear Judge. My day was done. *(With a slight shudder.)* Oh no—I won't say that; nor think it either!

BRACK. You have assuredly no reason to.

HEDDA. Oh, reasons—— *(Watching him closely.)* And George Tesman—after all, you must admit that he is correctness itself.

BRACK. His correctness and respectability are beyond all question.

HEDDA. And I don't see anything absolutely ridiculous about him. Do you?

BRACK. Ridiculous? No—I shouldn't exactly say so——

HEDDA. Well—and his powers of research, at all events, are untiring. I see no reason why he should not one day come to the front, after all.

BRACK *(looks at her hesitatingly)*. I thought that you, like every one else, expected him to attain the highest distinction.

HEDDA *(with an expression of fatigue)*. Yes, so I did. And then, since he was bent, at all hazards, on being allowed to provide for me—I really don't know why I should not have accepted his offer.

BRACK. No, if you look at it in that light——

HEDDA. It was more than my other adorers were prepared to do for me, my dear Judge.

BRACK *(laughing)*. Well, I can't answer for all the rest; but as for myself, you know quite well that I have always entertained a—a certain respect for the marriage tie—for marriage as an institution, Mrs. Hedda.

HEDDA *(jestingly)*. Oh, I assure you I have never cherished any hopes with respect to you.

BRACK. All I require is a pleasant and intimate interior, where I can make myself useful in every way, and am free to come and go as—as a trusted friend——

HEDDA. Of the master of the house, do you mean?

BRACK *(bowing)*. Frankly, of the mistress first of all; but of course of the master, too, in the second place. Such a triangular friendship—if I may call it so—is really a great convenience for all parties, let me tell you.

HEDDA. Yes, I have many a time longed for some one to make a third on our travels. Oh, those railway carriage tête-à-têtes!

BRACK. Fortunately your wedding journey is over now.

HEDDA *(shaking her head)*. Not by a long, long way. I have only arrived at a station on the line.

BRACK. Well, then the passengers jump out and move about a little, Mrs. Hedda.

HEDDA. I never jump out.

BRACK. Really?

HEDDA. No—because there is always some one standing by to——

BRACK *(laughing)*. To look at your ankles, do you mean?

HEDDA. Precisely.

BRACK. Well but, dear me——

HEDDA (with a gesture of repulsion). I won't have it. I would rather keep my seat where I happen to be—and continue the tête-à-tête.

BRACK. But suppose a third person were to jump in and join the couple.

HEDDA. Ah, that is quite another matter!

BRACK. A trusted friend——

HEDDA. ——with a fund of conversation on all sorts of lively topics——

BRACK. ——and not the least bit of a specialist!

HEDDA (with an audible sigh). Yes, that would be a relief indeed.

BRACK (hears the front door open, and glances in that direction). The triangle is completed.

HEDDA (half aloud). And on goes the train.

(GEORGE TESMAN, in a gray walking suit, with a soft felt hat, enters from the hall. He has a number of unbound books under his arm and in his pockets.)

TESMAN (goes up to the table beside the corner settee). Ouf—what a load for a warm day—all these books. (Lays them on the table.) I'm positively perspiring, Hedda. Hallo—are you there already, my dear Judge? Eh? Berta didn't tell me.

BRACK (rising). I came in through the garden.

HEDDA. What books have you got there?

TESMAN (stands looking them through). Some new books on my special subjects—quite indispensable to me.

HEDDA. Your special subjects?

BRACK. Yes, books on his special subjects, Mrs. Tesman. (BRACK and HEDDA exchange a confidential smile.)

HEDDA. Do you need still more books on your special subjects?

TESMAN. Yes, my dear Hedda, one can never have too many of them. Of course one must keep up with all that is written and published.

HEDDA. Yes, I suppose one must.

TESMAN (searching among his books). And look here—I have got hold of Eilert Lovborg's new book too. (Offering it to her.) Perhaps you would like to glance through it, Hedda? Eh?

HEDDA. No, thank you. Or rather—afterwards perhaps.

TESMAN. I looked into it a little on the way home.

BRACK. Well, what do you think of it—as a specialist?

TESMAN. I think it shows quite remarkable soundness of judgment. He never wrote like that before. (Putting the books together.) Now I shall take all these into my study. I'm longing to cut the leaves! And then I must change my clothes. (To BRACK.) I suppose we needn't start just yet? Eh?

BRACK. Oh, dear no—there is not the slightest hurry.

TESMAN. Well then, I will take my time. (Is going with his books, but stops in the doorway and turns.) By-the-bye, Hedda, Aunt Julia is not coming this evening.

HEDDA. Not coming? Is it that affair of the bonnet that keeps her away?

TESMAN. Oh, not at all. How could you think such a thing of Aunt Julia? Just fancy! The fact is, Aunt Rina is very ill.

HEDDA. She always is.

TESMAN. Yes, but today she is much worse than usual, poor dear.

HEDDA. Oh, then it's only natural that her sister should remain with her. I must bear my disappointment.

TESMAN. And you can't imagine, dear, how delighted Aunt Julia seemed to be—because you had come home looking so flourishing!

HEDDA (half aloud, rising). Oh, those everlasting aunts!

TESMAN. What?

HEDDA (going to the glass door). Nothing.

TESMAN. Oh, all right. (He goes through the inner room, out to the Right.)

BRACK. What bonnet were you talking about?

HEDDA. Oh, it was a little episode with Miss Tesman this morning. She had laid down her bonnet on the chair there

(*Looks at him and smiles.*) and I pretended to think it was the servant's.

BRACK (*shaking his head*). Now my dear Mrs. Hedda, how could you do such a thing? To that excellent old lady, too!

HEDDA (*nervously crossing the room*). Well, you see, these impulses come over me all of a sudden; and I cannot resist them. (*Throws herself down in the easy chair by the stove.*) Oh, I don't know how to explain it.

BRACK (*behind the easy chair*). You are not really happy—that is at the bottom of it.

HEDDA (*looking straight before her*). I know of no reason why I should be—happy. Perhaps you can give me one?

BRACK. Well, amongst other things, because you have got exactly the home you had set your heart on.

HEDDA (*looks up at him and laughs*). Do you too believe in that legend?

BRACK. Is there nothing in it, then?

HEDDA. Oh, yes, there is something in it.

BRACK. Well?

HEDDA. There is this in it, that I made use of Tesman to see me home from evening parties last summer——

BRACK. I, unfortunately, had to go quite a different way.

HEDDA. That's true. I know you were going a different way last summer.

BRACK (*laughing*). Oh fie, Mrs. Hedda! Well, then—you and Tesman?

HEDDA. Well, we happened to pass here one evening; Tesman, poor fellow, was writhing in the agony of having to find conversation; so I took pity on the learned man——

BRACK (*smiles doubtfully*). You took pity? H'm——

HEDDA. Yes, I really did. And so—to help him out of his torment—I happened to say, in pure thoughtlessness, that I should like to live in this villa.

BRACK. No more than that?

HEDDA. Not that evening.

BRACK. But afterwards?

HEDDA. Yes, my thoughtlessness had consequences, my dear Judge.

BRACK. Unfortunately that too often happens, Mrs. Hedda.

HEDDA. Thanks! So you see it was this enthusiasm for Secretary Falk's villa that first constituted a bond of sympathy between George Tesman and me. From that came our engagement and our marriage, and our wedding journey, and all the rest of it. Well, well, my dear Judge—as you make your bed so you must lie, I could almost say.

BRACK. This is exquisite! And you really cared not a rap about it all the time.

HEDDA. No, heaven knows I didn't.

BRACK. But now? Now that we have made it so homelike for you?

HEDDA. Ugh—the rooms all seem to smell of lavender and dried love-leaves. But perhaps it's Aunt Julia that has brought that scent with her.

BRACK (*laughing*). No, I think it must be a legacy from the late Mrs. Secretary Falk.

HEDDA. Yes, there is an odor of mortality about it. It reminds me of a bouquet—the day after the ball. (*Clasps her hands behind her head, leans back in her chair and looks at him.*) Oh, my dear Judge—you cannot imagine how horribly I shall bore myself here.

BRACK. Why should not you, too, find some sort of vocation in life, Mrs. Hedda?

HEDDA. A vocation—that should attract me?

BRACK. If possible, of course.

HEDDA. Heaven knows what sort of a vocation that could be. I often wonder whether—— (*Breaking off.*) But that would never do either.

BRACK. Who can tell? Let me hear what it is.

HEDDA. Whether I might not get Tesman to go into politics, I mean.

BRACK (*laughing*). Tesman? No, really now, political life is not the thing for him—not at all in his line.

HEDDA. No, I daresay not. But if I could get him into it all the same?

BRACK. Why—what satisfaction could

you find in that? If he is not fitted for that sort of thing, why should you want to drive him into it?

HEDDA. Because I am bored, I tell you! *(After a pause.)* So you think it quite out of the question that Tesman should ever get into the ministry?

BRACK. H'm—you see, my dear Mrs. Hedda—to get into the ministry, he would have to be a tolerably rich man.

HEDDA *(rising impatiently).* Yes, there we have it! It is this genteel poverty I have managed to drop into! *(Crosses the room.)* That is what makes life so pitiable! So utterly ludicrous! For that's what it is.

BRACK. Now *I* should say the fault lay elsewhere.

HEDDA. Where, then?

BRACK. You have never gone through any really stimulating experience.

HEDDA. Anything serious, you mean?

BRACK. Yes, you may call it so. But now you may perhaps have one in store.

HEDDA *(tossing her head).* Oh, you're thinking of the annoyances about this wretched professorship! But that must be Tesman's own affair. I assure you I shall not waste a thought upon it.

BRACK. No, no, I daresay not. But suppose now that what people call—in elegant language—a solemn responsibility were to come upon you? *(Smiling.)* A new responsibility, Mrs. Hedda.

HEDDA *(angrily).* Be quiet! Nothing of that sort will ever happen!

BRACK *(warily).* We will speak of this again a year hence—at the very outside.

HEDDA *(curtly).* I have no turn for anything of the sort, Judge Brack. No responsibilities for me!

BRACK. Are you so unlike the generality of women as to have no turn for duties which——

HEDDA *(beside the glass door).* Oh, be quiet, I tell you! I often think there is only one thing in the world I have any turn for.

BRACK *(drawing near to her).* And what is that, if I may ask?

HEDDA *(stands looking out).* Boring myself to death. Now you know it. *(Turns,* looks towards the inner room, and laughs.) Yes, as I thought! Here comes the Professor.

BRACK *(softly, in a tone of warning).* Come, come, come, Mrs. Hedda!

(GEORGE TESMAN, *dressed for the party, with his gloves and hat in his hand, enters from the Right through the inner room.)*

TESMAN. Hedda, has no message come from Eilert Lovborg? Eh?

HEDDA. No.

TESMAN. Then you'll see he'll be here presently.

BRACK. Do you really think he will come?

TESMAN. Yes, I am almost sure of it. For what you were telling us this morning must have been a mere floating rumor.

BRACK. You think so?

TESMAN. At any rate, Aunt Julia said she did not believe for a moment that he would ever stand in my way again. Fancy that!

BRACK. Well then, that's all right.

TESMAN *(placing his hat and gloves on a chair on the Right).* Yes, but you must really let me wait for him as long as possible.

BRACK. We have plenty of time yet. None of my guests will arrive before seven or half-past.

TESMAN. Then meanwhile we can keep Hedda company, and see what happens. Eh?

HEDDA *(placing BRACK's hat and overcoat upon the corner settee).* And at the worst Mr. Lovborg can remain here with me.

BRACK *(offering to take his things).* Oh, allow me, Mrs. Tesman! What do you mean by "At the worst"?

HEDDA. If he won't go with you and Tesman.

TESMAN *(looks dubiously at her).* But, Hedda dear—do you think it would quite do for him to remain with you? Eh? Remember, Aunt Julia can't come.

HEDDA. No, but Mrs. Elvsted is coming. We three can have a cup of tea together.

TESMAN. Oh, yes, that will be all right.

BRACK (*smiling*). And that would perhaps be the safest plan for him.

HEDDA. Why so?

BRACK. Well, you know, Mrs. Tesman, how you used to gird at my little bachelor parties. You declared they were adapted only for men of the strictest principles.

HEDDA. But no doubt Mr. Lovborg's principles are strict enough now. A converted sinner—— (BERTA *appears at the hall door.*)

BERTA. There's a gentleman asking if you are at home, ma'am——

HEDDA. Well, show him in.

TESMAN (*softly*). I'm sure it is he! Fancy that!

(EILERT LOVBORG *enters from the hall. He is slim and lean; of the same age as* TESMAN, *but looks older and somewhat worn-out. His hair and beard are of a blackish brown, his face long and pale, but with patches of color on the cheekbones. He is dressed in a well-cut black visiting suit, quite new. He has dark gloves and a silk hat. He stops near the door, and makes a rapid bow, seeming somewhat embarrassed.*)

TESMAN (*goes up to him and shakes him warmly by the hand*). Well, my dear Eilert—so at last we meet again!

LOVBORG (*speaks in a subdued voice*). Thanks for your letter, Tesman. (*Approaching* HEDDA.) Will you too shake hands with me, Mrs. Tesman?

HEDDA (*taking his hand*). I am glad to see you, Mr. Lovborg. (*With a motion of her hand.*) I don't know whether you two gentlemen——

LOVBORG (*bowing slightly*). Judge Brack, I think.

BRACK (*doing likewise*). Oh, yes, in the old days——

TESMAN (*to* LOVBORG, *with his hands on his shoulders*). And now you must make yourself entirely at home, Eilert! Mustn't he, Hedda? For I hear you are going to settle in town again? Eh?

LOVBORG. Yes, I am.

TESMAN. Quite right, quite right. Let me tell you, I have got hold of your new book; but I haven't had time to read it yet.

LOVBORG. You may spare yourself the trouble.

TESMAN. Why so?

LOVBORG. Because there is very little in it.

TESMAN. Just fancy, how can you say so?

BRACK. But it has been much praised, I hear.

LOVBORG. That was what I wanted; so I put nothing into the book but what everyone would agree with.

BRACK. Very wise of you.

TESMAN. Well but, my dear Eilert!

LOVBORG. For now I mean to win myself a position again—to make a fresh start.

TESMAN (*a little embarrassed*). Ah, that is what you wish to do? Eh?

LOVBORG (*smiling, lays down his hat, and draws a packet, wrapped in paper, from his coat pocket*). But when this one appears, George Tesman, you will have to read it. For this is the real book—the book I have put my true self into.

TESMAN. Indeed? And what is it?

LOVBORG. It is the continuation.

TESMAN. The continuation? Of what?

LOVBORG. Of the book.

TESMAN. Of the new book?

LOVBORG. Of course.

TESMAN. Why, my dear Eilert—does it not come down to our own days?

LOVBORG. Yes, it does; and this one deals with the future.

TESMAN. With the future! But, good heavens, we know nothing of the future!

LOVBORG. No; but there is a thing or two to be said about it all the same. (*Opens the packet.*) Look here——

TESMAN. Why, that's not your handwriting.

LOVBORG. I dictated it. (*Turning over the pages.*) It falls into two sections. The first deals with the civilizing forces of the future. And here is the second—(*Running* *through the pages towards the end.)—*forecasting the probable line of development.

TESMAN. How odd now! I should never have thought of writing anything of that sort.

HEDDA *(at the glass door, drumming on the pane).* H'm—I daresay not.

LOVBORG *(replacing the manuscript in its paper and laying the packet on the table).* I brought it, thinking I might read you a little of it this evening.

TESMAN. That was very good of you, Eilert. But this evening—— *(Looking at* BRACK.) I don't quite see how we can manage it——

LOVBORG. Well then, some other time. There is no hurry.

BRACK. I must tell you, Mr. Lovborg—there is a little gathering at my house this evening—mainly in honor of Tesman, you know——

LOVBORG *(looking for his hat).* Oh—then I won't detain you——

BRACK. No, but listen—will you not do me the favor of joining us?

LOVBORG *(curtly and decidedly).* No, I can't, thank you very much.

BRACK. Oh, nonsense—do! We shall be quite a select little circle. And I assure you we shall have a "lively time" as Mrs. Hed—as Mrs. Tesman says.

LOVBORG. I have no doubt of it. But nevertheless——

BRACK. And then you might bring your manuscript with you, and read it to Tesman at my house. I could give you a room to yourselves.

TESMAN. Yes, think of that, Eilert, why shouldn't you? Eh?

HEDDA *(interposing).* But, Tesman, if Mr. Lovborg would really rather not! I am sure Mr. Lovborg is much more inclined to remain here and have supper with me.

LOVBORG *(looking at her).* With you, Mrs. Tesman?

HEDDA. And with Mrs. Elvsted.

LOVBORG. Ah—— *(Lightly.)* I saw her for a moment this morning.

HEDDA. Did you? Well, she is coming this evening. So you see you are almost bound to remain, Mr. Lovborg, or she will have no one to see her home.

LOVBORG. That's true. Many thanks, Mrs. Tesman—in that case I will remain.

HEDDA. Then I have one or two orders to give the servant——

(She goes to the hall door and rings. BERTA *enters.* HEDDA *talks to her in a whisper, and points towards the inner room.* BERTA *nods and goes out again.)*

TESMAN *(at the same time, to* LOVBORG). Tell me, Eilert—is it this new subject—the future—that you are going to lecture about?

LOVBORG. Yes.

TESMAN. They told me at the bookseller's that you are going to deliver a course of lectures this autumn.

LOVBORG. That is my intention. I hope you won't take it ill, Tesman.

TESMAN. Oh no, not in the least! But——

LOVBORG. I can quite understand that it must be disagreeable to you.

TESMAN *(cast down).* Oh, I can't expect you, out of consideration for me, to——

LOVBORG. But I shall wait till you have received your appointment.

TESMAN. Will you wait? Yes, but—yes, but—are you not going to compete with me? Eh?

LOVBORG. No; it is only the moral victory I care for.

TESMAN. Why, bless me—then Aunt Julia was right after all! Oh yes—I knew it! Hedda! Just fancy—Eilert Lovborg is not going to stand in our way!

HEDDA *(curtly).* Our way? Pray leave me out of the question.

(She goes up towards the inner room, where BERTA *is placing a tray with decanters and glasses on the table.* HEDDA *nods approval, and comes forward again.* BERTA *goes out.)*

TESMAN *(at the same time).* And you, Judge Brack—what do you say to this? Eh?

BRACK. Well, I say that a moral victory —h'm—may be all very fine——

TESMAN. Yes, certainly. But all the same——

HEDDA (*looking at* TESMAN *with a cold smile*). You stand there looking as if you were thunderstruck——

TESMAN. Yes, so I am, I almost think——

BRACK. Don't you see, Mrs. Tesman, a thunderstorm has just passed over?

HEDDA (*pointing toward the inner room*). Will you not take a glass of cold punch, gentlemen?

BRACK (*looking at his watch*). A stirrup cup?[1] Yes, it wouldn't come amiss.

TESMAN. A capital idea, Hedda! Just the thing! Now that the weight has been taken off my mind——

HEDDA. Will you not join them, Mr. Lovborg?

LOVBORG (*with a gesture of refusal*). No, thank you. Nothing for me.

BRACK. Why, bless me—cold punch is surely not poison.

LOVBORG. Perhaps not for everyone.

HEDDA. I will keep Mr. Lovborg company in the meantime.

TESMAN. Yes, yes, Hedda dear, do.

(*He and* BRACK *go into the inner room, seat themselves, drink punch, smoke cigarettes, and carry on a lively conversation during what follows.* LOVBORG *remains beside the stove.* HEDDA *goes to the writing table.*)

HEDDA (*raising her voice a little*). Do you care to look at some photographs, Mr. Lovborg? You know Tesman and I made a tour in the Tyrol on our way home?

(*She takes up an album, and places it on the table beside the sofa, in the farther corner of which she seats herself.* LOVBORG *approaches, stops, and looks at her. Then he takes a chair and seats himself at her Left, with his back toward the inner room.*)

HEDDA (*opening the album*). Do you see this range of mountains, Mr. Lovborg? It's the Ortler group. Tesman has written the name underneath. Here it is: "The Ortler group near Meran."

LOVBORG (*who has never taken his eyes off her, says softly and slowly*). Hedda —Gabler!

HEDDA (*glancing hastily at him*). Ah, hush!

LOVBORG (*repeats softly*). Hedda Gabler!

HEDDA (*looking at the album*). That was my name in the old days—when we two knew each other.

LOVBORG. And I must teach myself never to say Hedda Gabler again—never, as long as I live.

HEDDA (*still turning over the pages*). Yes, you must. And I think you ought to practice in time. The sooner the better, I should say.

LOVBORG (*in a tone of indignation*). Hedda Gabler married? And married to —George Tesman!

HEDDA. Yes—so the world goes.

LOVBORG. Oh, Hedda, Hedda—how could you[2] throw yourself away!

HEDDA (*looks sharply at him*). What? I can't allow this!

LOVBORG. What do you mean? (TESMAN *comes into the room and goes toward the sofa.*)

HEDDA (*hears him coming and says in an indifferent tone*). And this is a view from the Val d'Ampezzo, Mr. Lovborg. Just look at these peaks! (*Looks affectionately up at* TESMAN.) What's the name of these curious peaks, dear?

TESMAN. Let me see? Oh, those are the Dolomites.

HEDDA. Yes, that's it! Those are the Dolomites, Mr. Lovborg.

TESMAN. Hedda dear, I only wanted to ask whether I shouldn't bring you a little punch after all? For yourself at any rate —eh?

HEDDA. Yes, do, please; and perhaps a few biscuits.

TESMAN. No cigarettes?

HEDDA. No.

TESMAN. Very well.

(*He goes into the inner room and out to the Right.* BRACK *sits in the inner room, and keeps an eye from time to time on* HEDDA *and* LOVBORG.)

1. *stirrup cup,* a farewell drink, usually one offered to a mounted rider. 2. *how could you.* Lovborg uses the familiar form *du.*

LOVBORG (softly, as before). Answer me, Hedda—how could you go and do this?

HEDDA (apparently absorbed in the album). If you continue to say du to me I won't talk to you.

LOVBORG. May I not say du when we are alone?

HEDDA. No. You may think it; but you mustn't say it.

LOVBORG. Ah, I understand. It is an offense against George Tesman, whom you[3]—love.

HEDDA (glances at him and smiles). Love? What an idea!

LOVBORG. You don't love him then!

HEDDA. But I won't hear of any sort of unfaithfulness! Remember that.

LOVBORG. Hedda, answer me one thing.

HEDDA. Hush!

(TESMAN enters with a small tray from the inner room.)

TESMAN. Here you are! Isn't this tempting? (He puts the tray on the table.)

HEDDA. Why do you bring it yourself?

TESMAN (filling the glasses). Because I think it's such fun to wait upon you, Hedda.

HEDDA. But you have poured out two glasses. Mr. Lovborg said he wouldn't have any——

TESMAN. No, but Mrs. Elvsted will soon be here, won't she?

HEDDA. Yes, by-the-bye, Mrs. Elvsted——

TESMAN. Had you forgotten her? Eh?

HEDDA. We were so absorbed in these photographs. (Shows him a picture.) Do you remember this little village?

TESMAN. Oh, it's that one just below the Brenner Pass. It was there we passed the night——

HEDDA. ——and met that lively party of tourists.

TESMAN. Yes, that was the place. Fancy, if we could only have had you with us, Eilert! Eh? (He returns to the inner room and sits beside BRACK.)

LOVBORG. Answer me this one thing, Hedda——

HEDDA. Well?

LOVBORG. Was there no love in your friendship for me either? Not a spark—not a tinge of love in it?

HEDDA. I wonder if there was? To me it seems as though we were two good comrades—two thoroughly intimate friends. (Smilingly.) You especially were frankness itself.

LOVBORG. It was you that made me so.

HEDDA. As I look back upon it all, I think there was really something beautiful, something fascinating—something daring—in—in that secret intimacy—that comradeship which no living creature so much as dreamed of.

LOVBORG. Yes, yes, Hedda! Was there not? When I used to come to your father's in the afternoon, and the General sat over at the window reading his papers, with his back towards us——

HEDDA. And we two on the corner sofa——

LOVBORG. Always with the same illustrated paper before us ——

HEDDA. For want of an album, yes.

LOVBORG. Yes, Hedda, and when I made my confessions to you—told you about myself, things that at that time no one else knew! There I would sit and tell you of my escapades—my days and nights of devilment. Oh, Hedda—what was the power in you that forced me to confess these things?

HEDDA. Do you think it was any power in me?

LOVBORG. How else can I explain it? And all those—those roundabout questions you used to put to me——

HEDDA. Which you understood so particularly well——

LOVBORG. How could you sit and question me like that? Question me quite frankly——

HEDDA. In roundabout terms, please observe.

LOVBORG. Yes, but frankly nevertheless. Cross-question me about all that sort of thing?

---

3. whom you. From this point, Lovborg uses the formal De.

HEDDA. And how could you answer, Mr. Lovborg?

LOVBORG. Yes, that is just what I can't understand—in looking back upon it. But tell me now, Hedda, was there not love at the bottom of our friendship? On your side, did you not feel as though you might purge my stains away if I made you my confessor? Was it not so?

HEDDA. No, not quite.

LOVBORG. What was your motive, then?

HEDDA. Do you think it quite incomprehensible that a young girl—when it can be done—without any one knowing——

LOVBORG. Well?

HEDDA. ——should be glad to have a peep, now and then, into a world which——

LOVBORG. Which——

HEDDA. ——which she is forbidden to know anything about?

LOVBORG. So that was it?

HEDDA. Partly. Partly—I almost think.

LOVBORG. Comradeship in the thirst for life. But why should not that, at any rate, have continued?

HEDDA. The fault was yours.

LOVBORG. It was you that broke with me.

HEDDA. Yes, when our friendship threatened to develop into something more serious. Shame upon you, Eilert Lovborg! How could you think of wronging your—your frank comrade?

LOVBORG (clenching his hands). Oh, why did you not carry out your threat? Why did you not shoot me down?

HEDDA. Because I have such a dread of scandal.

LOVBORG. Yes, Hedda, you are a coward at heart.

HEDDA. A terrible coward. (Changing her tone.) But it was a lucky thing for you. And now you have found ample consolation at the Elvsteds'.

LOVBORG. I know what Thea has confided to you.

HEDDA. And perhaps you have confided to her something about us?

LOVBORG. Not a word. She is too stupid to understand anything of that sort.

HEDDA. Stupid?

LOVBORG. She is stupid about matters of that sort.

HEDDA. And I am cowardly. (Bends over toward him, without looking him in the face, and says more softly.) But now I will confide something to you.

LOVBORG (eagerly). Well?

HEDDA. The fact that I dared not shoot you down——

LOVBORG. Yes!

HEDDA. ——that was not my most arrant cowardice—that evening.

LOVBORG (looks at her a moment, understands, and whispers passionately). Oh, Hedda! Hedda Gabler! Now I begin to see a hidden reason beneath our comradeship! You[4] and I! After all, then, it was your craving for life——

HEDDA (softly, with a sharp glance). Take care! Believe nothing of the sort!

(Twilight has begun to fall. The hall door is opened from without by BERTA.)

HEDDA (closes the album with a bang and calls smilingly). Ah, at last! My darling Thea, come along!

(MRS. ELVSTED enters from the hall. She is in evening dress. The door is closed behind her.)

HEDDA (on the sofa, stretches out her arms towards her). My sweet Thea—you can't think how I have been longing for you!

(MRS. ELVSTED, in passing, exchanges slight salutations with the gentlemen in the inner room, then goes up to the table and gives HEDDA her hands. LOVBORG has risen. He and MRS. ELVSTED greet each other with a silent nod.)

MRS. ELVSTED. Ought I to go in and talk to your husband for a moment?

HEDDA. Oh, not at all. Leave those two alone. They will soon be going.

MRS. ELVSTED. Are they going out?

4. *You.* Lovborg once again addresses Hedda as *du.*

HEDDA. Yes, to a supper party.

MRS. ELVSTED (*quickly, to* LOVBORG). Not you?

LOVBORG. No.

HEDDA. Mr. Lovborg remains with us.

MRS. ELVSTED (*takes a chair and is about to seat herself at his side*). Oh, how nice it is here!

HEDDA. No, thank you, my little Thea! Not there! You'll be good enough to come over here to me. I will sit between you.

MRS. ELVSTED. Yes, just as you please. (*She goes around the table and seats herself on the sofa on* HEDDA'*s right.* LOVBORG *reseats himself on his chair.*)

LOVBORG (*after a short pause, to* HEDDA). Is not she lovely to look at?

HEDDA (*lightly stroking her hair*). Only to look at?

LOVBORG. Yes. For we two—she and I—we are two real comrades. We have absolute faith in each other; so we can sit and talk with perfect frankness——

HEDDA. Not roundabout, Mr. Lovborg?

LOVBORG. Well——

MRS. ELVSTED (*softly clinging close to* HEDDA). Oh, how happy I am, Hedda; for, only think, he says I have inspired him too.

HEDDA (*looks at her with a smile*). Ah! Does he say that, dear?

LOVBORG. And then she is so brave, Mrs. Tesman!

MRS. ELVSTED. Good heavens—am I brave?

LOVBORG. Exceedingly — where your comrade is concerned.

HEDDA. Ah, yes—courage! If one only had that!

LOVBORG. What then? What do you mean?

HEDDA. Then life would perhaps be livable, after all. (*With a sudden change of tone.*) But now, my dearest Thea, you really must have a glass of cold punch.

MRS. ELVSTED. No, thanks, I never take anything of that kind.

HEDDA. Well then, you, Mr. Lovborg.

LOVBORG. Nor I, thank you.

MRS. ELVSTED. No, he doesn't either.

HEDDA (*looks fixedly at him*). But if I say you shall?

LOVBORG. It would be no use.

HEDDA (*laughing*). Then I, poor creature, have no sort of power over you?

LOVBORG. Not in that respect.

HEDDA. But seriously, I think you ought to—for your own sake.

MRS. ELVSTED. Why, Hedda!

LOVBORG. How so?

HEDDA. Or rather on account of other people.

LOVBORG. Indeed?

HEDDA. Otherwise people might be apt to suspect that—in your heart of hearts—you did not feel quite secure—quite confident of yourself.

MRS. ELVSTED (*softly*). Oh please, Hedda——

LOVBORG. People may suspect what they like for the present.

MRS. ELVSTED (*joyfully*). Yes, let them!

HEDDA. I saw it plainly in Judge Brack's face a moment ago.

LOVBORG. What did you see?

HEDDA. His contemptuous smile, when you dared not go with them into the inner room.

LOVBORG. Dared not? Of course I preferred to stop here and talk to you.

MRS. ELVSTED. What could be more natural, Hedda?

HEDDA. But the Judge could not guess that. And I saw, too, the way he smiled and glanced at Tesman when you dared not accept his invitation to this wretched little supper party of his.

LOVBORG. Dared not! Do you say I dared not?

HEDDA. *I* don't say so. But that was how Judge Brack understood it.

LOVBORG. Well, let him.

HEDDA. Then you are not going with them?

LOVBORG. I will stay here with you and Thea.

MRS. ELVSTED. Yes, Hedda—how can you doubt that?

HEDDA (*smiles and nods approvingly to* LOVBORG). Firm as a rock! Faithful to your principles, now and forever! Ah, that is how a man should be! *(Turns to* MRS. ELVSTED *and caresses her.)* Well now, what did I tell you, when you came to us this morning in such a state of distraction——

LOVBORG *(surprised).* Distraction!

MRS. ELVSTED *(terrified).* Hedda, oh Hedda!

HEDDA. You can see for yourself; you haven't the slightest reason to be in such mortal terror—— *(Interrupting herself.)* There! Now we can all three enjoy ourselves!

LOVBORG *(who has given a start).* Ah—what is all this, Mrs. Tesman?

MRS. ELVSTED. Oh my God, Hedda! What are you saying? What are you doing?

HEDDA. Don't get excited! That horrid Judge Brack is sitting watching you.

LOVBORG. So she was in mortal terror! On my account!

MRS. ELVSTED *(softly and piteously).* Oh, Hedda—now you have ruined everything!

LOVBORG *(looks fixedly at her for a moment. His face is distorted).* So that was my comrade's frank confidence in me?

MRS. ELVSTED *(imploringly).* Oh, my dearest friend, only let me tell you——

LOVBORG *(takes one of the glasses of punch, raises it to his lips, and says in a low, husky voice).* Your health, Thea!
(He empties the glass, puts it down, and takes the second.)

MRS. ELVSTED *(softly).* Oh, Hedda, Hedda—how could you do this?

HEDDA. *I* do it? *I*? Are you crazy?

LOVBORG. Here's to your health too, Mrs. Tesman. Thanks for the truth. Hurrah for the truth!
(He empties the glass and is about to refill it.)

HEDDA *(lays her hand on his arm).* Come, come—no more for the present. Remember you are going out to supper.

MRS. ELVSTED. No, no, no!

HEDDA. Hush! They are sitting watching you.

LOVBORG *(putting down the glass).* Now, Thea, tell me the truth.

MRS. ELVSTED. Yes.

LOVBORG. Did your husband know that you had come after me?

MRS. ELVSTED *(wringing her hands).* Oh, Hedda—do you hear what he is asking?

LOVBORG. Was it arranged between you and him that you were to come to town and look after me? Perhaps it was the Sheriff himself that urged you to come? Aha, my dear—no doubt he wanted my help in his office! Or was it at the card table that he missed me?

MRS. ELVSTED *(softly, in agony).* Oh, Lovborg, Lovborg!

LOVBORG *(seizes a glass and is on the point of filling it).* Here's a glass for the old Sheriff too!

HEDDA *(preventing him).* No more just now. Remember you have to read your manuscript to Tesman.

LOVBORG *(calmly, putting down the glass).* It was stupid of me—all this, Thea—to take it in this way, I mean. Don't be angry with me, my dear, dear comrade. You shall see—both you and the others—that if I was fallen once—now I have risen again! Thanks to you, Thea.

MRS. ELVSTED *(radiant with joy).* Oh, heaven be praised!
(BRACK has in the meantime looked at his watch. He and TESMAN rise and come into the drawing room.)

BRACK *(takes his hat and overcoat).* Well, Mrs. Tesman, our time has come.

HEDDA. I suppose it has.

LOVBORG *(rising).* Mine too, Judge Brack.

MRS. ELVSTED *(softly and imploringly).* Oh, Lovborg, don't do it!

HEDDA *(pinching her arm).* They can hear you!

MRS. ELVSTED *(with a suppressed shriek).* Ow!

LOVBORG *(to* BRACK*).* You were good enough to invite me.

BRACK. Well, are you coming after all?

LOVBORG. Yes, many thanks.

BRACK. I'm delighted.

LOVBORG (to TESMAN, *putting the parcel of manuscript in his pocket*). I should like to show you one or two things before I send it to the printers.

TESMAN. Fancy—that will be delightful. But, Hedda dear, how is Mrs. Elvsted to get home? Eh?

HEDDA. Oh, that can be managed somehow.

LOVBORG (*looking toward the ladies*). Mrs. Elvsted? Of course, I'll come again and fetch her. (*Approaching.*) At ten or thereabouts, Mrs. Tesman? Will that do?

HEDDA. Certainly. That will do capitally.

TESMAN. Well, then, that's all right. But you must not expect me so early, Hedda.

HEDDA. Oh, you may stop as long—as long as ever you please.

MRS. ELVSTED (*trying to conceal her anxiety*). Well then, Mr. Lovborg—I shall remain here until you come.

LOVBORG (*with his hat in his hand*). Pray do, Mrs. Elvsted.

BRACK. And now off goes the excursion train, gentlemen! I hope we shall have a lively time, as a certain lady puts it.

HEDDA. Ah, if only the fair lady could be present unseen!

BRACK. Why unseen?

HEDDA. In order to hear a little of your liveliness at first hand, Judge Brack.

BRACK (*laughing*). I should not advise the fair lady to try it.

TESMAN (*also laughing*). Come, you're a nice one Hedda! Fancy that!

BRACK. Well, good-bye, good-bye, ladies.

LOVBORG (*bowing*). About ten o'clock, then.

(BRACK, LOVBORG, *and* TESMAN *go out by the hall door. At the same time* BERTA *enters from the inner room with a lighted lamp, which she places on the dining-room table; she goes out by the way she came.*)

MRS. ELVSTED (*who has risen and is wandering restlessly about the room*). Hedda, Hedda, what will come of all this?

HEDDA. At ten o'clock he will be here. I can see him already—with vine leaves in his hair—flushed and fearless——

MRS. ELVSTED. Oh, I hope he may.

HEDDA. And then, you see, then he will have regained control over himself. Then he will be a free man for all his days.

MRS. ELVSTED. Oh God! If he would only come as you see him now!

HEDDA. He will come as I see him—so, and not otherwise! (*Rises and approaches* THEA.) You may doubt him as long as you please; I believe in him. And now we will try——

MRS. ELVSTED. You have some hidden motive in this, Hedda!

HEDDA. Yes, I have. I want for once in my life to have power to mold a human destiny.

MRS. ELVSTED. Have you not the power?

HEDDA. I have not—and have never had it.

MRS. ELVSTED. Not your husband's?

HEDDA. Do you think that is worth the trouble? Oh, if you could only understand how poor I am. And fate has made you so rich! (*Clasps her passionately in her arms.*) I think I must burn your hair off, after all.

MRS. ELVSTED. Let me go! Let me go! I am afraid of you, Hedda!

BERTA (*in the middle doorway*). Tea is laid in the dining room, ma'am.

HEDDA. Very well. We are coming.

MRS. ELVSTED. No, no, no! I would rather go home alone! At once!

HEDDA. Nonsense! First you shall have a cup of tea, you little stupid. And then—at ten o'clock—Eilert Lovborg will be here—with vine leaves in his hair.

(*She drags* MRS. ELVSTED *almost by force toward the middle doorway.*)

CURTAIN

Act Three

SCENE: *The room at the* TESMANS'. *The curtains are drawn over the middle doorway, and also over the glass door. The lamp, half turned down, and with a shade over it, is burning on the table. In the stove, the door of which stands open, there has been a fire, which is now nearly burnt out.*

MRS. ELVSTED, *wrapped in a large shawl, and with her feet upon a footrest, sits close to the stove, sunk back in the arm chair.* HEDDA, *fully dressed, lies sleeping upon the sofa, with a blanket over her.*

MRS. ELVSTED *(after a pause, suddenly sits up in her chair, and listens eagerly. Then she sinks back again wearily, moaning to herself).* Not yet! Oh God, oh God, not yet!

(BERTA *slips in by the hall door. She has a letter in her hand.)*

MRS. ELVSTED *(turns and whispers eagerly).* Well, has anyone come?

BERTA *(softly).* Yes, a girl has brought this letter.

MRS. ELVSTED *(quickly, holding out her hand).* A letter! Give it to me!

BERTA. No, it's for Dr. Tesman, ma'am.

MRS. ELVSTED. Oh, indeed.

BERTA. It was Miss Tesman's servant that brought it. I'll lay it here on the table.

MRS. ELVSTED. Yes, do.

BERTA *(laying down the letter).* I think I had better put out the lamp. It's smoking.

MRS. ELVSTED. Yes, put it out. It must soon be daylight now.

BERTA *(putting out the lamp).* It is daylight already, ma'am.

MRS. ELVSTED. Yes, broad day! And no one come back yet!

BERTA. Lord bless you, ma'am! I guessed how it would be.

MRS. ELVSTED. You guessed?

BERTA. Yes, when I saw that a certain person had come back to town—and that he went off with them. For we've heard enough about that gentleman before now.

MRS. ELVSTED. Don't speak so loud. You will waken Mrs. Tesman.

BERTA *(looks towards the sofa and sighs).* No, no, let her sleep, poor thing. Shan't I put some wood on the fire?

MRS. ELVSTED. Thanks, not for me.

BERTA. Oh, very well. *(She goes softly out by the hall door.)*

HEDDA *(is awakened by the shutting of the door, and looks up).* What's that?

MRS. ELVSTED. It was only the servant.

HEDDA *(looking about her).* Oh, we're here! Yes now I remember. *(Sits erect upon the sofa, stretches herself, and rubs her eyes.)* What o'clock is it, Thea?

MRS. ELVSTED *(looks at her watch).* It's past seven.

HEDDA. When did Tesman come home?

MRS. ELVSTED. He has not come.

HEDDA. Not come home yet?

MRS. ELVSTED *(rising).* No one has come.

HEDDA. Think of our watching and waiting here till four in the morning——

MRS. ELVSTED *(wringing her hands).* And how I watched and waited for him!

HEDDA *(yawns, and says with her hand before her mouth).* Well, well—we might have spared ourselves the trouble.

MRS. ELVSTED. Did you get a little sleep?

HEDDA. Oh yes; I believe I have slept pretty well. Have you not?

MRS. ELVSTED. Not for a moment. I couldn't, Hedda! Not to save my life.

HEDDA *(rises and goes towards her).*

There, there, there! There's nothing to be so alarmed about. I understand quite well what has happened.

MRS. ELVSTED. Well, what do you think? Won't you tell me?

HEDDA. Why, of course it has been a very late affair at Judge Brack's.

MRS. ELVSTED. Yes, yes, that is clear enough. But all the same——

HEDDA. And then, you see, Tesman hasn't cared to come home and ring us up in the middle of the night. *(Laughing.)* Perhaps he wasn't inclined to show himself either—immediately after a jollification.

MRS. ELVSTED. But in that case, where can he have gone?

HEDDA. Of course he has gone to his aunts' and slept there. They have his old room ready for him.

MRS. ELVSTED. No, he can't be with them; for a letter has just come for him from Miss Tesman. There it lies.

HEDDA. Indeed? *(Looks at the address.)* Why yes, it's addressed in Aunt Julia's own hand. Well then, he has remained at Judge Brack's. And as for Eilert Lovborg—he is sitting, with vine leaves in his hair, reading his manuscript.

MRS. ELVSTED. Oh Hedda, you are just saying things you don't believe a bit.

HEDDA. You really are a little blockhead, Thea.

MRS. ELVSTED. Oh yes, I suppose I am.

HEDDA. And how mortally tired you look.

MRS. ELVSTED. Yes, I am mortally tired.

HEDDA. Well then, you must do as I tell you. You must go into my room and lie down for a little while.

MRS. ELVSTED. Oh no, no. I shouldn't be able to sleep.

HEDDA. I am sure you would.

MRS. ELVSTED. Well, but your husband is certain to come soon now; and then I want to know at once.

HEDDA. I shall take care to let you know when he comes.

MRS. ELVSTED. Do you promise me, Hedda?

HEDDA. Yes, rely upon me. Just you go in and have a sleep in the meantime.

MRS. ELVSTED. Thanks; then I'll try to. *(She goes off through the inner room.)*

(HEDDA goes up to the glass door and draws back the curtains. The broad daylight streams into the room. Then she takes a little hand glass from the writing table, looks at herself in it, and arranges her hair. Next she goes to the hall door and presses the bell button. BERTA *presently appears at the hall door.)*

BERTA. Did you want anything, ma'am?

HEDDA. Yes; you must put some more wood in the stove. I am shivering.

BERTA. Bless me—I'll make up the fire at once. *(She rakes the embers together and lays a piece of wood upon them; then stops and listens.)* That was a ring at the front door, ma'am.

HEDDA. Then go to the door. I will look after the fire.

BERTA. It'll soon burn up. *(She goes out by the hall door.)*

(HEDDA kneels on the footrest and lays some more pieces of wood in the stove. After a short pause, GEORGE TESMAN *enters from the hall. He looks tired and rather serious. He steals on tiptoe towards the middle doorway and is about to slip through the curtains.)*

HEDDA *(at the stove, without looking up).* Good morning.

TESMAN *(turns).* Hedda! *(Approaching her.)* Good heavens—are you up so early?

HEDDA. Yes, I am up very early this morning.

TESMAN. And I never doubted you were still sound asleep! Fancy that, Hedda!

HEDDA. Don't speak so loud. Mrs. Elvsted is resting in my room.

TESMAN. Has Mrs. Elvsted been here all night?

HEDDA. Yes, since no one came to fetch her.

TESMAN. Ah, to be sure.

HEDDA *(closes the door of the stove and rises).* Well, did you enjoy yourself at Judge Brack's?

TESMAN. Have you been anxious about me? Eh?

HEDDA. No, I should never think of being anxious. But I asked if you had enjoyed yourself.

TESMAN. Oh yes, for once in a way. Especially the beginning of the evening; for then Eilert read me part of his book. We arrived more than an hour too early, fancy that! And Brack had all sorts of arrangements to make, so Eilert read to me.

HEDDA (seating herself by the table on the Right). Well? Tell me, then——

TESMAN (sitting on a footstool near the stove). Oh Hedda, you can't conceive what a book that is going to be! I believe it is one of the most remarkable things that have ever been written. Fancy that!

HEDDA. Yes, yes; I don't care about that——

TESMAN. I must make a confession to you, Hedda. When he had finished reading, a horrid feeling came over me.

HEDDA. A horrid feeling?

TESMAN. I felt jealous of Eilert for having had it in him to write such a book. Only think, Hedda!

HEDDA. Yes, yes, I am thinking!

TESMAN. And then how pitiful to think that he, with all his gifts, should be irreclaimable after all.

HEDDA. I suppose you mean that he has more courage than the rest?

TESMAN. No, not at all; I mean that he is incapable of taking his pleasures in moderation.

HEDDA. And what came of it all—in the end?

TESMAN. Well, to tell the truth, I think it might best be described as an orgy, Hedda.

HEDDA. Had he vine leaves in his hair?

TESMAN. Vine leaves? No, I saw nothing of the sort. But he made a long, rambling speech in honor of the woman who had inspired him in his work—that was the phrase he used.

HEDDA. Did he name her?

TESMAN. No, he didn't; but I can't help thinking he meant Mrs. Elvsted. You may be sure he did.

HEDDA. Well—where did you part from him?

TESMAN. On the way to town. We broke up—the last of us at any rate—all together; and Brack came with us to get a breath of fresh air. And then, you see, we agreed to take Eilert home; for he had had far more than was good for him.

HEDDA. I daresay.

TESMAN. But now comes the strange part of it, Hedda; or, I should rather say, the melancholy part of it. I declare I am almost ashamed—on Eilert's account—to tell you——

HEDDA. Oh, go on——

TESMAN. Well, as we were getting near town, you see, I happened to drop a little behind the others. Only for a minute or two, fancy that!

HEDDA. Yes, yes, yes, but?

TESMAN. And then, as I hurried after them, what do you think I found by the wayside? Eh?

HEDDA. Oh, how should I know!

TESMAN. You mustn't speak of it to a soul, Hedda! Do you hear! Promise me, for Eilert's sake. (Draws a parcel, wrapped in paper, from his coat pocket.) Fancy, dear, I found this.

HEDDA. Is not that the parcel he had with him yesterday?

TESMAN. Yes, it is the whole of his precious, irreplaceable manuscript! And he had gone and lost it, and knew nothing about it. Only fancy, Hedda! So deplorably——

HEDDA. But why did you not give him back the parcel at once?

TESMAN. I didn't dare to—in the state he was then in.

HEDDA. Did you not tell any of the others that you had found it?

TESMAN. Oh, far from it. You can surely understand that, for Eilert's sake, I wouldn't do that.

HEDDA. So no one knows that Eilert Lovborg's manuscript is in your possession?

TESMAN. No. And no one must know it.

HEDDA. Then what did you say to him afterwards?

TESMAN. I didn't talk to him again at all; for when we got in among the streets, he and two or three of the others gave us the slip and disappeared. Fancy that!

HEDDA. Indeed! They must have taken him home then.

TESMAN. Yes, so it would appear. And Brack, too, left us.

HEDDA. And what have you been doing with yourself since?

TESMAN. Well, I and some of the others went home with one of the party, a jolly fellow, and took our morning coffee with him; or perhaps I should rather call it our night coffee—eh? But now, when I have rested a little, and given Eilert, poor fellow, time to have his sleep out, I must take this back to him.

HEDDA (holds out her hand for the packet). No—don't give it to him! Not in such a hurry, I mean. Let me read it first.

TESMAN. No, my dearest Hedda, I mustn't, I really mustn't.

HEDDA. You must not?

TESMAN. No—for you can imagine what a state of despair he will be in when he awakens and misses the manuscript. He has no copy of it, you know! He told me so.

HEDDA (looking searchingly at him). Can such a thing not be reproduced? Written over again?

TESMAN. No, I don't think that would be possible. For the inspiration, you see——

HEDDA. Yes, yes—I suppose it depends on that. (Lightly.) But, by-the-bye—here is a letter for you.

TESMAN. Fancy!

HEDDA (handing it to him). It came early this morning.

TESMAN. It's from Aunt Julia! What can it be? (He lays the packet on the other footstool, opens the letter, runs his eye through it, and jumps up.) Oh, Hedda—she says that poor Aunt Rina is dying!

HEDDA. Well, we were prepared for that.

TESMAN. And that if I want to see her again, I must make haste. I'll run in to them at once.

HEDDA (suppressing a smile). Will you run?

TESMAN. Oh, dearest Hedda—if you could only make up your mind to come with me! Just think!

HEDDA (rises and says wearily, repelling the idea). No, no, don't ask me. I will not look upon sickness and death. I loathe all sorts of ugliness.

TESMAN. Well, well, then! (Bustling around.) My hat—My overcoat? Oh, in the hall—I do hope I mayn't come too late, Hedda! Eh?

HEDDA. Oh, if you run——

BERTA. Judge Brack is at the door, and wishes to know if he may come in.

TESMAN. At this time! No, I can't possibly see him.

HEDDA. But I can. (To BERTA.) Ask Judge Brack to come in. (BERTA goes out.)

HEDDA (quickly whispering). The parcel, Tesman! (She snatches it up from the stool.)

TESMAN. Yes, give it to me!

HEDDA. No, no, I will keep it till you come back.

(She goes to the writing table and places it in the bookcase. TESMAN stands in a flurry of haste, and cannot get his gloves on. JUDGE BRACK enters from the hall.)

HEDDA (nodding to him). You are an early bird, I must say.

BRACK. Yes, don't you think so? (To TESMAN.) Are you on the move, too?

TESMAN. Yes, I must rush off to my aunts'. Fancy, the invalid one is lying at death's door, poor creature.

BRACK. Dear me, is she indeed? Then on no account let me detain you. At such a critical moment——

TESMAN. Yes, I must really rush—Good-bye! Good-bye! (He hastens out by the hall door.)

HEDDA (approaching). You seem to

have made a particularly lively night of it at your rooms, Judge Brack.

BRACK. I assure you I have not had my clothes off, Mrs. Hedda.

HEDDA. Not you, either?

BRACK. No, as you may see. But what has Tesman been telling you of the night's adventures?

HEDDA. Oh, some tiresome story. Only that they went and had coffee somewhere or other.

BRACK. I have heard about that coffee party already. Eilert Lovborg was not with them, I fancy?

HEDDA. No, they had taken him home before that.

BRACK. Tesman, too?

HEDDA. No, but some of the others, he said.

BRACK (smiling). George Tesman is really an ingenuous creature, Mrs. Hedda.

HEDDA. Yes, heaven knows he is. Then is there something behind all this?

BRACK. Yes, perhaps there may be.

HEDDA. Well then, sit down, my dear Judge, and tell your story in comfort.

(She seats herself to the Left of the table. BRACK sits near her, at the long side of the table.)

HEDDA. Now then?

BRACK. I had special reasons for keeping track of my guests—or rather of some of my guests—last night.

HEDDA. Of Eilert Lovborg among the rest, perhaps?

BRACK. Frankly, yes.

HEDDA. Now you make me really curious——

BRACK. Do you know where he and one or two of the others finished the night, Mrs. Hedda?

HEDDA. If it is not quite unmentionable, tell me.

BRACK. Oh no, it's not at all unmentionable. Well, they put in an appearance at a particularly animated soirée.

HEDDA. Of the lively kind?

BRACK. Of the very liveliest——

HEDDA. Tell me more of this, Judge Brack.

BRACK. Lovborg, as well as the others, had been invited in advance. I knew all about it. But he had declined the invitation; for now, as you know, he has become a new man.

HEDDA. Up at the Elvsteds', yes. But he went after all, then?

BRACK. Well, you see, Mrs. Hedda—unhappily the spirit moved him at my rooms last evening——

HEDDA. Yes, I hear he found inspiration.

BRACK. Pretty violent inspiration. Well, I fancy that altered his purpose; for we men folk are unfortunately not always so firm in our principles as we ought to be.

HEDDA. Oh, I am sure you are an exception, Judge Brack. But as to Lovborg?

BRACK. To make a long story short—he landed at last in Mademoiselle Diana's rooms.

HEDDA. Mademoiselle Diana's?

BRACK. It was Mademoiselle Diana that was giving the soirée, to a select circle of her admirers and her lady friends.

HEDDA. Is she a red-haired woman?

BRACK. Precisely.

HEDDA. A sort of a—singer?

BRACK. Oh yes—in her leisure moments. And moreover a mighty huntress of men, Mrs. Hedda. You have no doubt heard of her. Eilert Lovborg was one of her most enthusiastic protectors—in the days of his glory.

HEDDA. And how did all this end?

BRACK. Far from amicably, it appears. After a most tender meeting, they seem to have come to blows——

HEDDA. Lovborg and she?

BRACK. Yes. He accused her or her friends of having robbed him. He declared that his pocketbook had disappeared—and other things as well. In short, he seems to have made a furious disturbance.

HEDDA. And what came of it all?

BRACK. It came to a general scrimmage, in which the ladies as well as the gentlemen took part. Fortunately the police at last appeared on the scene.

HEDDA. The police too?

BRACK. Yes. I fancy it will prove a costly frolic for Eilert Lovborg, crazy being that he is.

HEDDA. How so?

BRACK. He seems to have made a violent resistance—to have hit one of the constables on the head and torn the coat off his back. So they had to march him off to the police station with the rest.

HEDDA. How have you learnt all this?

BRACK. From the police themselves.

HEDDA (gazing straight before her). So that is what happened. Then he had no vine leaves in his hair.

BRACK. Vine leaves, Mrs. Hedda?

HEDDA (changing her tone). But tell me now, Judge—what is your real reason for tracking out Eilert Lovborg's movements so carefully?

BRACK. In the first place, it could not be entirely indifferent to me if it should appear in the police court that he came straight from my house.

HEDDA. Will the matter come into court, then?

BRACK. Of course. However, I should scarcely have troubled so much about that. But I thought that, as a friend of the family, it was my duty to supply you and Tesman with a full account of his nocturnal exploits.

HEDDA. Why so, Judge Brack?

BRACK. Why, because I have a shrewd suspicion that he intends to use you as a sort of blind.

HEDDA. Oh, how can you think such a thing!

BRACK. Good heavens, Mrs. Hedda—we have eyes in our head. Mark my words! This Mrs. Elvsted will be in no hurry to leave town again.

HEDDA. Well, even if there should be anything between them, I suppose there are plenty of other places where they could meet.

BRACK. Not a single home. Henceforth, as before, every respectable house will be closed against Eilert Lovborg.

HEDDA. And so ought mine to be, you mean?

BRACK. Yes. I confess it would be more than painful to me if this personage were to be made free of your house. How superfluous, how intrusive, he would be, if he were to force his way into——

HEDDA. ——into the triangle?

BRACK. Precisely. It would simply mean that I should find myself homeless.

HEDDA (looks at him with a smile). So you want to be the one cock in the basket—that is your aim.

BRACK (nods slowly and lowers his voice). Yes, that is my aim. And for that I will fight—with every weapon I can command.

HEDDA (her smile vanishing). I see you are a dangerous person—when it comes to the point.

BRACK. Do you think so?

HEDDA. I am beginning to think so. And I am exceedingly glad to think that you have no sort of hold over me.

BRACK (laughing equivocally). Well, well, Mrs. Hedda—perhaps you are right there. If I had, who knows what I might be capable of?

HEDDA. Come, come now, Judge Brack. That sounds almost like a threat.

BRACK (rising). Oh, not at all! The triangle, you know, ought, if possible, to be spontaneously constructed.

HEDDA. There I agree with you.

BRACK. Well, now I have said all I had to say; and I had better be getting back to town. Good-bye, Mrs. Hedda. (He goes towards the glass door.)

HEDDA (rising). Are you going through the garden?

BRACK. Yes, it's a short cut for me.

HEDDA. And then it is the back way, too.

BRACK. Quite so. I have no objection to back ways. They may be piquant enough at times.

HEDDA. When there is ball practice[1] going on, you mean?

---

1. *ball practice,* shooting.

BRACK (*in the doorway, laughing to her*). Oh, people don't shoot their tame poultry, I fancy.

HEDDA (*also laughing*). Oh no, when there is only one cock in the basket—— (*They exchange laughing nods of farewell. He goes. She closes the door behind him.* HEDDA, *who has become quite serious, stands for a moment looking out. Presently she goes and peeps through the curtain over the middle doorway. Then she goes to the writing table, takes* LOVBORG's *packet out of the bookcase, and is on the point of looking through its contents.* BERTA *is heard speaking loudly in the hall.* HEDDA *turns and listens. Then she hastily locks up the packet in the drawer, and lays the key on the inkstand.* EILERT LOVBORG, *with his greatcoat on and his hat in his hand, tears open the hall door. He looks somewhat confused and irritated.*)

LOVBORG (*looking towards the hall*). And I tell you I must and will come in! There!

(*He closes the door, turns and sees* HEDDA, *at once regains his self-control, and bows.*)

HEDDA (*at the writing table*). Well, Mr. Lovborg, this is rather a late hour to call for Thea.

LOVBORG. You mean rather an early hour to call on you. Pray pardon me.

HEDDA. How do you know that she is still here?

LOVBORG. They told me at her lodgings that she had been out all night.

HEDDA (*going to the oval table*). Did you notice anything about the people of the house when they said that?

LOVBORG (*looks inquiringly at her*). Notice anything about them?

HEDDA. I mean, did they seem to think it odd?

LOVBORG (*suddenly understanding*). Oh yes, of course! I am dragging her down with me! However, I didn't notice anything. I suppose Tesman is not up yet?

HEDDA. No—I think not——

LOVBORG. When did he come home?

HEDDA. Very late.

LOVBORG. Did he tell you anything?

HEDDA. Yes, I gathered that you had had an exceedingly jolly evening at Judge Brack's.

LOVBORG. Nothing more?

HEDDA. I don't think so. However, I was so dreadfully sleepy——

(MRS. ELVSTED *enters through the curtains of the middle doorway.*)

MRS. ELVSTED (*going towards him*). Ah, Lovborg! At last!

LOVBORG. Yes, at last. And too late!

MRS. ELVSTED (*looks anxiously at him*). What is too late?

LOVBORG. Everything is too late now. It is all over with me.

MRS. ELVSTED. Oh no, no—don't say that.

LOVBORG. You will say the same when you hear——

MRS. ELVSTED. I won't hear anything!

HEDDA. Perhaps you would prefer to talk to her alone! If so, I will leave you.

LOVBORG. No, stay—you too. I beg you to stay.

MRS. ELVSTED. Yes, but I won't hear anything, I tell you.

LOVBORG. It is not last night's adventures that I want to talk about.

MRS. ELVSTED. What is it then?

LOVBORG. I want to say that now our ways must part.

MRS. ELVSTED. Part!

HEDDA (*involuntarily*). I knew it!

LOVBORG. You can be of no more service to me, Thea.

MRS. ELVSTED. How can you stand there and say that! No more service to you! Am I not to help you now, as before? Are we not to go on working together?

LOVBORG. Henceforward I shall do no work.

MRS. ELVSTED (*despairingly*). Then what am I to do with my life?

LOVBORG. You must try to live your life as if you had never known me.

MRS. ELVSTED. But you know I cannot do that!

LOVBORG. Try if you cannot, Thea. You must go home again——

MRS. ELVSTED (*in vehement protest*). Never in this world! Where you are, there will I be also! I will not let myself be driven away like this! I will remain here! I will be with you when the book appears.

HEDDA (*half aloud, in suspense*). Ah yes—the book!

LOVBORG (*looks at her*). My book and Thea's for that is what it is.

MRS. ELVSTED. Yes, I feel that it is. And that is why I have a right to be with you when it appears! I will see with my own eyes how respect and honor pour in upon you afresh. And the happiness— the happiness—oh, I must share it with you!

LOVBORG. Thea—our book will never appear.

HEDDA. Ah!

MRS. ELVSTED. Never appear!

LOVBORG. Can never appear.

MRS. ELVSTED (*in agonized foreboding*). Lovborg—what have you done with the manuscript?

HEDDA (*looks anxiously at him*). Yes, the manuscript?

MRS. ELVSTED. Where is it?

LOVBORG. Oh Thea—don't ask me about it!

MRS. ELVSTED. Yes, yes, I will know. I demand to be told at once.

LOVBORG. The manuscript. Well then— I have torn the manuscript into a thousand pieces.

MRS. ELVSTED (*shrieks*). Oh no, no!

HEDDA (*involuntarily*). That's not——

LOVBORG (*looks at her*). Not true, you think?

HEDDA (*collecting herself*). Oh well, of course, since you say so. But it sounded so improbable——

LOVBORG. It is true, all the same.

MRS. ELVSTED (*wringing her hands*). Oh God, oh God, Hedda—torn his own work to pieces!

LOVBORG. I have torn my own life to pieces. So why should I not tear my life-work too?

MRS. ELVSTED. And you did this last night?

LOVBORG. Yes, I tell you! Tore it into a thousand pieces and scattered them on the fiord—far out. There there is cool sea water at any rate—let them drift upon it— drift with the current and the wind. And then presently they will sink—deeper and deeper—as I shall, Thea.

MRS. ELVSTED. Do you know, Lovborg, that what you have done with the book— I shall think of it to my dying day as though you had killed a little child.

LOVBORG. Yes, you are right. It is a sort of child murder.

MRS. ELVSTED. How could you, then! Did not the child belong to me too?

HEDDA (*almost inaudibly*). Ah, the child——

MRS. ELVSTED (*breathing heavily*). It is all over then. Well, well, now I will go, Hedda.

HEDDA. But you are not going away from town?

MRS. ELVSTED. Oh, I don't know what I shall do. I see nothing but darkness before me. (*She goes out by the hall door.*)

HEDDA (*stands waiting for a moment*). So you are not going to see her home, Mr. Lovborg?

LOVBORG. I? Through the streets? Would you have people see her walking with me?

HEDDA. Of course I don't know what else may have happened last night. But is it so utterly irretrievable?

LOVBORG. It will not end with last night—I know that perfectly well. And the thing is that now I have no taste for that sort of life either. I won't begin it anew. She has broken my courage and my power of braving life out.

HEDDA (*looking straight before her*). So that pretty little fool has had her fingers in a man's destiny. (*Looks at him.*) But all the same, how could you treat her so heartlessly?

LOVBORG. Oh, don't say that it was heartless!

HEDDA. To go and destroy what has

filled her whole soul for months and years! You do not call that heartless!

LOVBORG. To you I can tell the truth, Hedda.

HEDDA. The truth?

LOVBORG. First promise me—give me your word—that what I now confide to you Thea shall never know.

HEDDA. I give you my word.

LOVBORG. Good. Then let me tell you that what I said just now was untrue.

HEDDA. About the manuscript?

LOVBORG. Yes. I have not torn it to pieces—nor thrown it into the fiord.

HEDDA. No, n— But—where is it then?

LOVBORG. I have destroyed it none the less—utterly destroyed it, Hedda!

HEDDA. I don't understand.

LOVBORG. Thea said that what I had done seemed to her like a child murder.

HEDDA. Yes, so she said.

LOVBORG. But to kill his child—that is not the worst thing a father can do to it.

HEDDA. Not the worst?

LOVBORG. No. I wanted to spare Thea from hearing the worst.

HEDDA. Then what is the worst?

LOVBORG. Suppose now, Hedda, that a man—in the small hours of the morning—came home to his child's mother after a night of riot and debauchery, and said: "Listen—I have been here and there—in this place and in that. And I have taken our child with me—to this place and to that. And I have lost the child—utterly lost it. The devil knows into what hands it may have fallen—who may have had their clutches on it."

HEDDA. Well, but when all is said and done, you know, that was only a book——

LOVBORG. Thea's pure soul was in that book.

HEDDA. Yes, so I understand.

LOVBORG. And you can understand, too, that for her and me together no future is possible.

HEDDA. What path do you mean to take then?

LOVBORG. None. I will only try to make an end of it all—the sooner the better.

HEDDA *(a step nearer to him)*. Eilert Lovborg—listen to me. Will you not try to—to do it beautifully?

LOVBORG. Beautifully? *(Smiling.)* With vine leaves in my hair, as you used to dream in the old days?

HEDDA. No, no. I have lost my faith in the vine leaves. But beautifully, nevertheless! For once in a way! Good-bye! You must go now—and do not come here any more.

LOVBORG. Good-bye, Mrs. Tesman. And give George Tesman my love. *(He is on the point of going.)*

HEDDA. No, wait! I must give you a memento to take with you.

(She goes to the writing table and opens the drawer and the pistol case; then returns to LOVBORG *with one of the pistols.)*

LOVBORG *(looks at her)*. This? Is this the memento?

HEDDA *(nodding slowly)*. Do you recognize it? It was aimed at you once.

LOVBORG. You should have used it then.

HEDDA. Take it—and do you use it now.

LOVBORG *(puts the pistol in his breast pocket)*. Thanks!

HEDDA. And beautifully, Eilert Lovborg. Promise me that!

LOVBORG. Good-bye, Hedda Gabler. *(He goes out by the hall door.)*

*(*HEDDA *listens for a moment at the door. Then she goes up to the writing table, takes out the packet of manuscript, peeps under the cover, draws a few of the sheets half out, and looks at them. Next she goes over and seats herself in the armchair beside the stove, with the packet in her lap. Presently she opens the stove door, and then the packet.)*

HEDDA *(throws one of the quires into the fire and whispers to herself)*. Now I am burning your child, Thea! Burning it, curly-locks! *(Throwing one or two more quires into the stove.)* Your child and Eilert Lovborg's. *(Throws the rest in.)* I am burning—I am burning your child.

CURTAIN

Act Four

SCENE: *The same rooms at the* TESMANS'. *It is evening. The drawing room is in darkness. The back room is lighted by the hanging lamp over the table. The curtains over the glass door are drawn close.*

HEDDA, *dressed in black, walks to and fro in the dark room. Then she goes into the back room and disappears for a moment to the Left. She is heard to strike a few chords on the piano. Presently she comes in sight again, and returns to the drawing room.*

BERTA *enters from the Right, through the inner room, with a lighted lamp, which she places on the table in front of the corner settee in the drawing room. Her eyes are red with weeping, and she has black ribbons in her cap. She goes quietly and circumspectly out to the Right.*

HEDDA *goes up to the glass door, lifts the curtain a little aside, and looks out into the darkness.*

Shortly afterwards, MISS TESMAN, *in mourning, with a bonnet and veil on, comes in from the hall.* HEDDA *goes towards her and holds out her hand.*

MISS TESMAN. Yes, Hedda, here I am, in mourning and forlorn; for now my poor sister has at last found peace.

HEDDA. I have heard the news already, as you see. Tesman sent me a card.

MISS TESMAN. Yes, he promised me he would. But nevertheless I thought that to Hedda—here in the house of life—I ought myself to bring the tidings of death.

HEDDA. That was very kind of you.

MISS TESMAN. Ah, Rina ought not to have left us just now. This is not the time for Hedda's house to be a house of mourning.

HEDDA *(changing the subject).* She died quite peacefully, did she not, Miss Tesman?

MISS TESMAN. Oh, her end was so calm, so beautiful. And then she had the unspeakable happiness of seeing George once more—and bidding him good-bye. Has he come home yet?

HEDDA. No. He wrote that he might be detained. But won't you sit down?

MISS TESMAN. No thank you, my dear, dear Hedda. I should like to, but I have so much to do. I must prepare my dear one for her rest as well as I can. She shall go to her grave looking her best.

HEDDA. Can I not help you in any way?

MISS TESMAN. Oh, you must not think of it! Hedda Tesman must have no hand in such mournful work. Nor let her thoughts dwell on it either—not at this time.

HEDDA. One is not always mistress of one's thoughts——

MISS TESMAN *(continuing).* Ah yes, it is the way of the world. At home we shall be sewing a shroud; and here there will soon be sewing too, I suppose—but of another sort, thank God!

(GEORGE TESMAN *enters by the hall door.)*

HEDDA. Ah, you have come at last!

TESMAN. You here, Aunt Julia? With Hedda? Fancy that!

MISS TESMAN. I was just going, my dear boy. Well, have you done all you promised?

TESMAN. No; I'm really afraid I have forgotten half of it. I must come to you again tomorrow. Today my brain is all in a whirl. I can't keep my thoughts together.

MISS TESMAN. Why, my dear George, you mustn't take it in this way.

TESMAN. Mustn't? How do you mean?

MISS TESMAN. Even in your sorrow you must rejoice, as I do—rejoice that she is at rest.

TESMAN. Oh yes, yes—you are thinking of Aunt Rina.

HEDDA. You will feel lonely now, Miss Tesman.

MISS TESMAN. Just at first, yes. But that will not last very long, I hope. I daresay I shall soon find an occupant for poor Rina's little room.

TESMAN. Indeed? Who do you think will take it? Eh?

MISS TESMAN. Oh, there's always some poor invalid or other in want of nursing, unfortunately.

HEDDA. Would you really take such a burden upon you again?

MISS TESMAN. A burden! Heaven forgive you, child—it has been no burden to me.

HEDDA. But suppose you had a total stranger on your hands——

MISS TESMAN. Oh, one soon makes friends with sick folk; and it's such an absolute necessity for me to have some one to live for. Well, heaven be praised, there may soon be something in this house, too, to keep an old aunt busy.

HEDDA. Oh, don't trouble about anything here.

TESMAN. Yes, just fancy what a nice time we three might have together, if——

HEDDA. If?

TESMAN *(uneasily).* Oh, nothing. It will all come right. Let us hope so—eh?

MISS TESMAN. Well, well, I daresay you two want to talk to each other. *(Smiling.)* And perhaps Hedda may have something to tell you too, George. Good-bye! I must go home to Rina. *(Turning at the door.)* How strange it is to think that now Rina is with me and with my poor brother as well!

TESMAN. Yes, fancy that, Aunt Julia! Eh?

(MISS TESMAN *goes out by the hall door.)*

HEDDA *(follows* TESMAN *coldly and searchingly with her eyes).* I almost believe your Aunt Rina's death affects you more than it does your Aunt Julia.

TESMAN. Oh, it's not that alone. It's Eilert I am so terribly uneasy about.

HEDDA *(quickly).* Is there anything new about him?

TESMAN. I looked in at his rooms this afternoon, intending to tell him the manuscript was in safe keeping.

HEDDA. Well, did you not find him?

TESMAN. No. He wasn't at home. But afterwards I met Mrs. Elvsted, and she told me that he had been here early this morning.

HEDDA. Yes, directly after you had gone.

TESMAN. And he said that he had torn his manuscript to pieces—eh?

HEDDA. Yes, so he declared.

TESMAN. Why, good heavens, he must have been completely out of his mind! And I suppose you thought it best not to give it back to him, Hedda?

HEDDA. No, he did not get it.

TESMAN. But of course you told him that we had it?

HEDDA. No. *(Quickly.)* Did you tell Mrs. Elvsted?

TESMAN. No; I thought I had better not. But you ought to have told him. Fancy, if, in desperation, he should go and do himself some injury! Let me have the manuscript, Hedda! I will take it to him at once. Where is it?

HEDDA *(cold and immovable, leaning on the armchair).* I have not got it.

TESMAN. Have not got it? What in the world do you mean?

HEDDA. I have burnt it—every line of it.

TESMAN (with a violent movement of terror). Burnt! Burnt Eilert's manuscript!

HEDDA. Don't scream so. The servant might hear you.

TESMAN. Burnt! Why, good God! No, no, no! It's impossible!

HEDDA. It is so, nevertheless.

TESMAN. Do you know what you have done, Hedda? It's unlawful appropriation of lost property. Fancy that! Just ask Judge Brack, and he'll tell you what it is.

HEDDA. I advise you not to speak of it —either to Judge Brack, or to any one else.

TESMAN. But how could you do anything so unheard-of? What put it into your head? What possessed you? Answer me that—eh?

HEDDA (suppressing an almost imperceptible smile). I did it for your sake, George.

TESMAN. For my sake!

HEDDA. This morning, when you told me about what he had read to you——

TESMAN. Yes, yes—what then?

HEDDA. You acknowledged that you envied him his work.

TESMAN. Oh, of course I didn't mean that literally.

HEDDA. No matter—I could not bear the idea that any one should throw you into the shade.

TESMAN (in an outburst of mingled doubt and joy). Hedda! Oh, is this true? But—but—I never knew you to show your love like that before. Fancy that!

HEDDA. Well, I may as well tell you that —just at this time—— (Impatiently, breaking off.) No, no; you can ask Aunt Julia. She will tell you, fast enough.

TESMAN. Oh, I almost think I understand you, Hedda! (Clasps his hands together.) Great heavens! do you really mean it! Eh?

HEDDA. Don't shout so. The servant might hear.

TESMAN (laughing in irrepressible glee). The servant! Why, how absurd you are, Hedda. It's only my old Berta! Why, I'll tell Berta myself.

HEDDA (clenching her hands together in desperation). Oh, it is killing me, it is killing me, all this!

TESMAN. What is, Hedda? Eh?

HEDDA (coldly, controlling herself). All this—absurdity—George.

TESMAN. Absurdity! Do you see anything absurd in my being overjoyed at the news! But after all perhaps I had better not say anything to Berta.

HEDDA. Oh—why not that too?

TESMAN. No, no, not yet! But I must certainly tell Aunt Julia. And then that you have begun to call me George too! Fancy that! Oh, Aunt Julia will be so happy—so happy.

HEDDA. When she hears that I have burnt Eilert Lovborg's manuscript— for your sake?

TESMAN. No, by-the-bye—that affair of the manuscript—of course nobody must know about that. But that you love me so much, Hedda—Aunt Julia must really share my joy in that! I wonder, now, whether this sort of thing is usual in young wives? Eh?

HEDDA. I think you had better ask Aunt Julia that question too.

TESMAN. I will indeed, some time or other. (Looks uneasy and downcast again.) And yet the manuscript—the manuscript! Good God! it is terrible to think what will become of poor Eilert now.

(MRS. ELVSTED, dressed as in the first act, with hat and cloak, by the hall door.)

MRS. ELVSTED (greets them hurriedly, and says in evident agitation). Oh, dear Hedda, forgive my coming again.

HEDDA. What is the matter with you, Thea?

TESMAN. Something about Eilert Lovborg again—eh?

MRS. ELVSTED. Yes! I am dreadfully afraid some misfortune has happened to him.

HEDDA (*seizes her arm*). Ah, do you think so?

TESMAN. Why, good Lord—what makes you think that, Mrs. Elvsted?

MRS. ELVSTED. I heard them talking of him at my boarding house—just as I came in. Oh, the most incredible rumors are afloat about him today.

TESMAN. Yes, fancy, so I heard too! And I can bear witness that he went straight home to bed last night. Fancy that!

HEDDA. Well, what did they say at the boarding house?

MRS. ELVSTED. Oh, I couldn't make out anything clearly. Either they knew nothing definite, or else—— They stopped talking when they saw me; and I did not dare to ask.

TESMAN (*moving about uneasily*). We must hope—we must hope that you misunderstood them, Mrs. Elvsted.

MRS. ELVSTED. No, no; I am sure it was of him they were talking. And I heard something about the hospital or——

TESMAN. The hospital?

HEDDA. No—surely that cannot be!

MRS. ELVSTED. Oh, I was in such mortal terror! I went to his lodgings and asked for him there.

HEDDA. You could make up your mind to that, Thea!

MRS. ELVSTED. What else could I do? I really could bear the suspense no longer.

TESMAN. But you didn't find him either—eh?

MRS. ELVSTED. No. And the people knew nothing about him. He hadn't been home since yesterday afternoon, they said.

TESMAN. Yesterday! Fancy, how could they say that?

MRS. ELVSTED. Oh, I am sure something terrible must have happened to him.

TESMAN. Hedda dear—how would it be if I were to go and make inquiries?

HEDDA. No, no—don't you mix yourself up in this affair.

(JUDGE BRACK, *with his hat in his hand, enters by the hall door, which* BERTA *opens, and closes behind him. He looks grave and bows in silence.*)

TESMAN. Oh, is that you, my dear Judge? Eh?

BRACK. Yes. It was imperative I should see you this evening.

TESMAN. I can see you have heard the news about Aunt Rina.

BRACK. Yes, that among other things.

TESMAN. Isn't it sad—eh?

BRACK. Well, my dear Tesman, that depends on how you look at it.

TESMAN (*looks doubtfully at him*). Has anything else happened?

BRACK. Yes.

HEDDA (*in suspense*). Anything sad, Judge Brack?

BRACK. That, too, depends on how you look at it, Mrs. Tesman.

MRS. ELVSTED (*unable to restrain her anxiety*). Oh! it is something about Eilert Lovborg!

BRACK (*with a glance at her*). What makes you think that, Madam? Perhaps you have already heard something?

MRS. ELVSTED (*in confusion*). No, nothing at all, but——

TESMAN. Oh, for heaven's sake, tell us!

BRACK (*shrugging his shoulders*). Well, I regret to say Eilert Lovborg has been taken to the hospital. He is lying at the point of death.

MRS. ELVSTED (*shrieks*). Oh God! Oh God!

TESMAN. To the hospital! And at the point of death.

HEDDA (*involuntarily*). So soon then——

MRS. ELVSTED (*wailing*). And we parted in anger, Hedda!

HEDDA (*whispers*). Thea—Thea—be careful!

MRS. ELVSTED (*not heeding her*). I must go to him! I must see him alive!

BRACK. It is useless, Madam. No one will be admitted.

MRS. ELVSTED. Oh, at least tell me what has happened to him? What is it?

TESMAN. You don't mean to say that he has himself—— Eh?

HEDDA. Yes, I am sure he has.

TESMAN. Hedda, how can you——

BRACK (keeping his eyes fixedly upon her). Unfortunately you have guessed quite correctly, Mrs. Tesman.

MRS. ELVSTED. Oh, how horrible!

TESMAN. Himself, then! Fancy that!

HEDDA. Shot himself!

BRACK. Rightly guessed again, Mrs. Tesman.

MRS. ELVSTED (with an effort at self-control). When did it happen, Mr. Brack?

BRACK. This afternoon—between three and four.

TESMAN. But, good Lord, where did he do it? Eh?

BRACK (with some hesitation). Where? Well, I suppose at his lodgings.

MRS. ELVSTED. No, that cannot be; for I was there between six and seven.

BRACK. Well, then, somewhere else. I don't know exactly. I only know that he was found—— He had shot himself —in the breast.

MRS. ELVSTED. Oh, how terrible! That he should die like that!

HEDDA (to BRACK). Was it in the breast?

BRACK. Yes—as I told you.

HEDDA. Not in the temple?

BRACK. In the breast, Mrs. Tesman.

HEDDA. Well, well—the breast is a good place, too.

BRACK. How do you mean, Mrs. Tesman?

HEDDA (evasively). Oh, nothing—nothing.

TESMAN. And the wound is dangerous, you say—eh?

BRACK. Absolutely mortal. The end has probably come by this time.

MRS. ELVSTED. Yes, yes, I feel it. The end! The end! Oh, Hedda!

TESMAN. But tell me, how have you learnt all this?

BRACK (curtly). Through one of the police. A man I had some business with.

HEDDA (in a clear voice). At last a deed worth doing!

TESMAN (terrified). Good heavens, Hedda; what are you saying?

HEDDA. I say there is beauty in this.

BRACK. H'm, Mrs. Tesman——

TESMAN. Beauty! Fancy that!

MRS. ELVSTED. Oh, Hedda, how can you talk of beauty in such an act!

HEDDA. Eilert Lovborg has himself made up his account with life. He has had the courage to do—the one right thing.

MRS. ELVSTED. No, you must never think that was how it happened! It must have been in delirium that he did it.

TESMAN. In despair!

HEDDA. That he did not. I am certain of that.

MRS. ELVSTED. Yes, yes! In delirium! Just as he tore up our manuscript.

BRACK (starting). The manuscript? Has he torn that up?

MRS. ELVSTED. Yes, last night.

TESMAN (whispers softly). Oh, Hedda, we shall never get over this.

BRACK. H'm, very extraordinary.

TESMAN (moving about the room). To think of Eilert going out of the world in this way! And not leaving behind him the book that would have immortalized his name——

MRS. ELVSTED. Oh, if only it could be put together again!

TESMAN. Yes, if it only could! I don't know what I would not give——

MRS. ELVSTED. Perhaps it can, Mr. Tesman.

TESMAN. What do you mean?

MRS. ELVSTED (searches in the pocket of her dress). Look here. I have kept all the loose notes he used to dictate from.

HEDDA (a step forward). Ah!

TESMAN. You have kept them, Mrs. Elvsted! Eh?

MRS. ELVSTED. Yes, I have them here. I put them in my pocket when I left home. Here they still are——

TESMAN. Oh, do let me see them!

MRS. ELVSTED (hands him a bundle of papers). But they are in such disorder— all mixed up.

TESMAN. Fancy, if we could make

something out of them, after all! Perhaps if we two put our heads together——

MRS. ELVSTED. Oh, yes, at least let us try——

TESMAN. We will manage it! We must! I will dedicate my life to this task.

HEDDA. You, George! Your life?

TESMAN. Yes, or rather all the time I can spare. My own collections must wait in the meantime. Hedda—you understand, eh? I owe this to Eilert's memory.

HEDDA. Perhaps.

TESMAN. And so, my dear Mrs. Elvsted, we will give our whole minds to it. There is no use in brooding over what can't be undone—eh? We must try to control our grief as much as possible, and——

MRS. ELVSTED. Yes, yes, Mr. Tesman, I will do the best I can.

TESMAN. Well then, come here. I can't rest until we have looked through the notes. Where shall we sit? Here? No, in there, in the back room. Excuse me, my dear Judge. Come with me, Mrs. Elvsted.

MRS. ELVSTED. Oh, if only it were possible!

(TESMAN *and* MRS. ELVSTED *go into the back room. She takes off her hat and cloak. They both sit at the table under the hanging lamp, and are soon deep in an eager examination of the papers.* HEDDA *crosses to the stove and sits in the armchair. Presently* BRACK *goes up to her.*)

HEDDA (*in a low voice*). Oh, what a sense of freedom it gives one, this act of Eilert Lovborg's.

BRACK. Freedom, Mrs. Hedda? Well, of course, it is a release for him——

HEDDA. I mean for me. It gives me a sense of freedom to know that a deed of deliberate courage is still possible in this world, a deed of spontaneous beauty.

BRACK (*smiling*). H'm—my dear Mrs. Hedda——

HEDDA. Oh, I know what you are going to say. For you are a kind of a specialist too, like—you know!

BRACK (*looking hard at her*). Eilert Lovborg was more to you than perhaps you are willing to admit to yourself. Am I wrong?

HEDDA. I don't answer such questions. I only know Eilert Lovborg has had the courage to live his life after his own fashion. And then—the last great act, with its beauty! Ah! that he should have the will and the strength to turn away from the banquet of life—so early.

BRACK. I am sorry, Mrs. Hedda, but I fear I must dispel an amiable illusion.

HEDDA. Illusion?

BRACK. Which could not have lasted long in any case.

HEDDA. What do you mean?

BRACK. Eilert Lovborg did not shoot himself voluntarily.

HEDDA. Not voluntarily?

BRACK. No. The thing did not happen exactly as I told it.

HEDDA (*in suspense*). Have you concealed something? What is it?

BRACK. For poor Mrs. Elvsted's sake I idealized the facts a little.

HEDDA. What are the facts?

BRACK. First, that he is already dead.

HEDDA. At the hospital?

BRACK. Yes—without regaining consciousness.

HEDDA. What more have you concealed?

BRACK. This—the event did not happen at his lodgings.

HEDDA. Oh, that can make no difference.

BRACK. Perhaps it may. For I must tell you—Eilert Lovborg was found shot in—in Mademoiselle Diana's boudoir.

HEDDA (*makes a motion as if to rise, but sinks back again*). That is impossible, Judge Brack! He cannot have been there again today.

BRACK. He was there this afternoon. He went there, he said, to demand the return of something which they had taken from him. Talked wildly about a lost child——

HEDDA. Ah—so that was why——

BRACK. I thought probably he meant his manuscript; but now I hear he destroyed that himself. So I suppose it must have been his pocketbook.

HEDDA. Yes, no doubt. And there— there he was found?

BRACK. Yes, there. With a pistol in his breast-pocket, discharged. The ball had lodged in a vital part.

HEDDA. In the breast—yes.

BRACK. No—in the bowels.

HEDDA (looks up at him with an expression of loathing). That too! Oh, what curse is it that makes everything I touch turn ludicrous and mean?

BRACK. There is one point more, Mrs. Hedda—another disagreeable feature in the affair.

HEDDA. And what is that?

BRACK. The pistol he carried——

HEDDA (breathless). Well? What of it?

BRACK. He must have stolen it.

HEDDA (leaps up). Stolen it! That is not true! He did not steal it!

BRACK. No other explanation is possible. He must have stolen it. Hush!

(TESMAN and MRS. ELVSTED have risen from the table in the back room, and come into the drawing room.)

TESMAN (with the papers in both his hands). Hedda dear, it is almost impossible to see under that lamp. Think of that!

HEDDA. Yes, I am thinking.

TESMAN. Would you mind our sitting at your writing table—eh?

HEDDA. If you like. (Quickly.) No, wait! Let me clear it first!

TESMAN. Oh, you needn't trouble, Hedda. There's plenty of room.

HEDDA. No, no; let me clear it, I say! I will take these things in and put them on the piano. There!

(She has drawn out an object, covered with sheet music, from under the bookcase, places several other pieces of music upon it, and carries the whole into the inner room, to the Left. TESMAN lays the scraps of paper on the writing table, and moves the lamp there from the corner table. HEDDA returns.)

HEDDA (behind MRS. ELVSTED's chair, gently ruffling her hair). Well, my sweet Thea, how goes it with Eilert Lovborg's monument?

MRS. ELVSTED (looks dispiritedly up at her). Oh, it will be terribly hard to put in order.

TESMAN. We must manage it. I am determined. And arranging other people's papers is just the work for me.

(HEDDA goes over to the stove, and seats herself on one of the footstools. BRACK stands over her, leaning on the armchair.)

HEDDA (whispers). What did you say about the pistol?

BRACK (softly). That he must have stolen it.

HEDDA. Why stolen it?

BRACK. Because every other explanation ought to be impossible, Mrs. Hedda.

HEDDA. Indeed?

BRACK (glances at her). Of course Eilert Lovborg was here this morning. Was he not?

HEDDA. Yes.

BRACK. Were you alone with him?

HEDDA. Part of the time.

BRACK. Did you not leave the room whilst he was here?

HEDDA. No.

BRACK. Try to recollect. Were you not out of the room a moment?

HEDDA. Yes, perhaps just a moment— out in the hall.

BRACK. And where was your pistol case during this time?

HEDDA. I had it locked up in——

BRACK. Well, Mrs. Hedda?

HEDDA. The case stood there on the writing table.

BRACK. Have you looked since, to see whether both the pistols are there?

HEDDA. No.

BRACK. Well, you need not. I saw the pistol found in Lovborg's pocket, and I knew it at once as the one I had seen yesterday—and before, too.

HEDDA. Have you it with you?

BRACK. No; the police have it.

HEDDA. What will the police do with it?

BRACK. Search till they find the owner.

HEDDA. Do you think they will succeed?

BRACK (bends over her and whispers). No, Hedda Gabler—not so long as I say nothing.

HEDDA (looks frightened at him). And if you do not say nothing, what then?

BRACK (shrugs his shoulders). There is always the possibility that the pistol was stolen.

HEDDA (firmly). Death rather than that.

BRACK (smiling). People say such things—but they don't do them.

HEDDA (without replying). And supposing the pistol was stolen, and the owner is discovered? What then?

BRACK. Well, Hedda—then comes the scandal.

HEDDA. The scandal!

BRACK. Yes, the scandal—of which you are mortally afraid. You will, of course, be brought before the court—both you and Mademoiselle Diana. She will have to explain how the thing happened—whether it was an accidental shot or murder. Did the pistol go off as he was trying to take it out of his pocket, to threaten her with? Or did she tear the pistol out of his hand, shoot him, and push it back into his pocket? That would be quite like her; for she is an able-bodied young person, this same Mademoiselle Diana.

HEDDA. But *I* have nothing to do with all this repulsive business.

BRACK. No. But you will have to answer the question: Why did you give Eilert Lovborg the pistol? And what conclusions will people draw from the fact that you did give it to him?

HEDDA (lets her head sink). That is true. I did not think of that.

BRACK. Well, fortunately, there is no danger, so long as I say nothing.

HEDDA (looks up at him). So I am in your power, Judge Brack. You have me at your beck and call, from this time forward.

BRACK (whispers softly). Dearest Hedda —believe me—I shall not abuse my advantage.

HEDDA. I am in your power none the less. Subject to your will and your demands. A slave, a slave then! (Rises impetuously.) No, I cannot endure the thought of that! Never!

BRACK (looks half-mockingly at her). People generally get used to the inevitable.

HEDDA (returns his look). Yes, perhaps. (She crosses to the writing table. Suppressing an involuntary smile, she imitates TESMAN's intonations.) Well? Are you getting on, George? Eh?

TESMAN. Heaven knows, dear. In any case it will be the work of months.

HEDDA (as before). Fancy that! (Passes her hands softly through MRS. ELVSTED's hair.) Doesn't it seem strange to you, Thea? Here are you sitting with Tesman —just as you used to sit with Eilert Lovborg?

MRS. ELVSTED. Ah, if I could only inspire your husband in the same way.

HEDDA. Oh, that will come too—in time.

TESMAN. Yes, do you know, Hedda— I really think I begin to feel something of the sort. But won't you go and sit with Brack again?

HEDDA. Is there nothing I can do to help you two?

TESMAN. No, nothing in the world. (Turning his head.) I trust to you to keep Hedda company, my dear Brack.

BRACK (with a glance at HEDDA). With the greatest of pleasure.

HEDDA. Thanks. But I am tired this evening. I will go in and lie down a little on the sofa.

TESMAN. Yes, do dear—eh?

(HEDDA goes into the back room and draws the curtains. A short pause. Suddenly she is heard playing a wild dance on the piano.)

MRS. ELVSTED (starts from her chair). Oh—what is that?

TESMAN (runs to the doorway). Why, my

dearest Hedda—don't play dance music tonight! Just think of Aunt Rina! And of Eilert too!

HEDDA *(puts her head out between the curtains)*. And of Aunt Julia. And of all the rest of them. After this, I will be quiet. *(Closes the curtains again.)*

TESMAN *(at the writing table)*. It's not good for her to see us at this distressing work. I'll tell you what, Mrs. Elvsted, you shall take the empty room at Aunt Julia's, and then I will come over in the evenings, and we can sit and work there—eh?

HEDDA *(in the inner room)*. I hear what you are saying, Tesman. But how am *I* to get through the evenings out here?

TESMAN *(turning over the papers)*. Oh, I daresay Judge Brack will be so kind as to look in now and then, even though I am out.

BRACK *(in the armchair, calls out gaily)*. Every blessed evening, with all the pleasure in life, Mrs. Tesman! We shall get on capitally together, we two!

HEDDA *(speaking loud and clear)*. Yes, don't you flatter yourself we will, Judge Brack? Now that you are the one cock in the basket——

(A shot is heard within. TESMAN, MRS. ELVSTED, *and* BRACK *leap to their feet.)*

TESMAN. Oh, now she is playing with those pistols again.

(He throws back the curtains and runs in, followed by MRS. ELVSTED. HEDDA *lies stretched on the sofa, lifeless. Confusion and cries.* BERTA *enters in alarm from the Right.)*

TESMAN *(shrieks to* BRACK*)*. Shot herself! Shot herself in the temple! Fancy that!

BRACK *(half-fainting in the armchair)*. Good God! People don't do such things.

CURTAIN

Development

INTERPRETATION

1. In the course of the play we find that Hedda Gabler either has been or is now in conflict with each of the following characters: Lovborg, Thea, Tesman, Judge Brack. *(a)* Briefly explain the nature of each of these conflicts. *(b)* What aspects of Hedda's personality are revealed by these conflicts? *(c)* Do you find more to pity or to condemn in her personality? Discuss.

2. *(a)* Compare the Hedda-Lovborg relationship with the Thea-Lovborg relationship. Why does Thea succeed where Hedda seemed to fail? *(b)* What is symbolized by Thea's hair? by Hedda's burning the book Thea worked on with Lovborg? *(c)* Does Hedda wish she were more like Thea? Discuss.

3. *(a)* When did Hedda threaten to shoot Lovborg with a pistol, and why? *(b)* At what points in the play does she again take up the pistols? *(c)* What do the pistols symbolize about her attitude toward herself as a woman? *(d)* Relate the meaning of this symbol to her marriage to George Tesman and to her attitude toward having a child.

4. Considering the play as a whole,

what irony do you find in the fact that Hedda's main ambition in life is to control a man's destiny?

5. *(a)* When Hedda learns of Lovborg's death, she exclaims, "At last a deed worth doing!" (page 169, column 1, lines 47-48). What does she mean? *(b)* Why is Lovborg's suicide particularly important to her? *(c)* Explain the horror of her reaction when she learns the manner of his death. *(d)* Is her own suicide an act of courage or of cowardice? Discuss.

6. Discuss the merits and limitations of the following interpretation of Hedda's character:

> Hedda Gabler is a victim of a static, lifeless society. Born with beauty and intelligence, she finds these qualities wasted on a stupid husband and a shallow life of leisure. Only Lovborg could have provided her with an escape, but his sensual nature dooms their pure love, and forces her down the path of self-destruction. Hedda is truly a fallen angel.

7. Hedda, Thea, and Aunt Julia share a problem common to women of their day and social standing: the need to do something worthwhile with their lives. *(a)* How does each of them solve this problem or fail to solve it? *(b)* In drawing attention to this problem, what might Ibsen be saying about the world in which he lived?

TECHNIQUE

1. *(a)* We begin to know Hedda through the conversation between Miss Tesman and Berta which opens the play. What do the following lines, spoken by Berta, contribute to this knowledge?

(1) ". . . what a lot the young mistress had to unpack before she could get to bed" (page 127, column 1, lines 20-22).
(2) ". . . I should never have dreamt in those days that she and Master George would make a match of it" (page 127, column 2, lines 24-26).

(3) "She can't abide covers on the chairs, she says" (page 128, column 1, lines 9-11).

(b) What do the discussions about Miss Tesman's bonnet and about George Tesman's "expectations" reveal about the young husband's attitude toward his wife? *(c)* Summarize the impression you have received of the Tesman marriage by the time Hedda appears.

2. Explain what each of the following details contributes to the characterization of Tesman: *(a)* the incident in which he receives his old slippers; *(b)* his repeated use of the phrase, "Fancy that!" *(c)* his reaction to Hedda's announcement that she has burned Lovborg's book, "It's unlawful appropriation of lost property" (page 167, column 1, lines 13-14); *(d)* his comment on himself, ". . . arranging other people's papers is just the work for me" (page 171, column 2, lines 9-10).

3. At the conclusion of Act II, Hedda says excitedly that she expects to see Lovborg returning with vine leaves in his hair. *(a)* Describe the scene which opens Act III. *(b)* Describe the change in tone between the end of Act II and the beginning of Act III. *(c)* What other instance in the play involves the same type of abrupt change in tone?

4. Hedda has at least one key phrase for each of the men in her life: George is "a specialist"; Lovborg has "vine leaves in his hair"; Judge Brack prefers to come "sneaking in by the back way" and wants to be "the only cock in the basket." *(a)* Explain the appropriateness of these phrases to the men they describe. *(b)* Ibsen employs a similar device for Hedda by titling the play *Hedda Gabler,* not *Hedda Tesman.* What might have been his purpose?

EXTENSIONS

1. Matthew Arnold's *Culture and Anarchy* revolves, to a great extent, around

a quotation from the clergyman Bishop Wilson: "First, never go against the best light you have; secondly, take care that your light be not darkness." *(a)* Explain the meaning of this figurative statement, as you understand it. *(b)* Discuss Hedda's tragedy in the light of this quotation; does she follow her best light, and is this light darkness?

2. Hedda tries to explain her cruel treatment of Aunt Julia by saying, ". . . these impulses come over me all of a sudden; and I cannot resist them" (page 146, column 1, lines 7-9). Judge Brack replies, "You are not really happy— that is at the bottom of it" (page 146, column 1, lines 12-14). What do you think of this as a general explanation of why people do apparently motiveless cruel acts?

Comparison

1. Medea and Hedda Gabler both seek to control the destiny of the men they once loved. *(a)* Compare the reasons the two women have for wanting this control. *(b)* What basic personality differences are reflected in their respective motives, actions, and degrees of success? *(c)* Which woman's actions seem to you more defensible?

2. Both women are fiercely proud in a way that accounts for much of their strength. *(a)* Compare their backgrounds as a source of this pride. *(b)* Compare the extent of their strength. Which character seems more vulnerable? Discuss.

3. Comment on the following statement about the role of society in the two plays:

Hedda Gabler and *Medea* are both tragedies of women outside their natural element. Hedda was born to live among people of wealth and breeding, and Medea can exist only among the exotic wilds of her native Colchis. Medea is like an eagle in a canary cage, and Hedda, like a peacock in a chicken coop. Nature forces each to violence as the only means of escape.

4. Lovborg fails to live up to Hedda's expectations just as Jason fails to live up to Medea's. *(a)* Which man's failure is more shameful in your opinion? Why? *(b)* Which man's fate is more pathetic? Discuss.

5. In the *Medea* the women of Corinth act as a chorus to interpret the action of the play. *Hedda Gabler* does not include such a chorus, however. *(a)* To what extent do Aunt Julia and Judge Brack perform this choric function? *(b)* What are their limitations as a chorus? *(c)* Summarize the "interpretations" of Hedda's tragedy which these two characters might give if they were asked to do so directly.

6. Poets often speak of the destructive potential in love: for example, there is Oscar Wilde's famous line, "Yet each man kills the thing he loves." *(a)* Do you feel that Medea and Hedda continue to love the men they destroy? Explain. *(b)* In what way might these two plays help to explain the meaning of Wilde's line?

7. Comment on the following assessment of these two plays, pointing out both its merits and limitations: Medea destroys her lover because she is angry; Hedda Gabler destroys hers because she is bored.

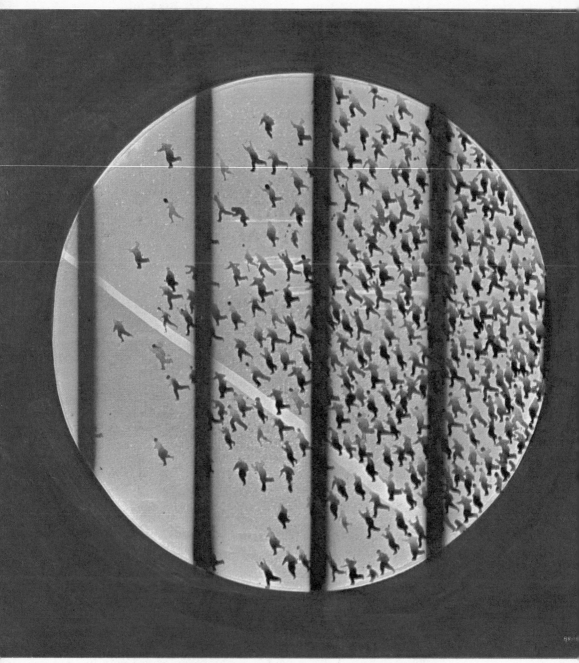

LA REJA by Juan Genovés. Courtesy of Mr. William Janss, Thousand Oaks, California.

The Prisoners

A PRISONER IN THE CAUCASUS / LEO TOLSTOY / RUSSIA

THE WALL / JEAN-PAUL SARTRE / FRANCE

THE TRIAL / JERZY ANDRZEJEWSKI / POLAND

A Prisoner in the Caucasus

LEO TOLSTOY[1] / Russia
(1828 – 1910)
translated from the Russian by Nathan Haskell Dole

A Russian gentleman was serving as an officer in the army of the Caucasus.[2] His name was Zhilin.[3]

One day a letter from his home came to him. His old mother wrote him:

I am now getting along in years, and I should like to see my beloved son before I die. Come and bid me farewell, lay me in the ground, and then with my blessing return again to your service. And I have been finding a bride for you, and she is intelligent and handsome and has property. If she pleases you, why then you can marry and settle down together.

Zhilin thought the matter over. "It is very true: the old lady has been growing feeble; maybe I shall not have a chance to see her again. I'll go, and if the girl is pretty—then I might marry."

He went to his colonel, got his leave of absence, bade his comrades farewell, gave the soldiers of his command nine gallons of vodka as a parting treat, and made his arrangements to leave.

There was war at that time in the Caucasus. The roads were not open for travel either by day or night. If any Russian rode or walked outside of the fortress, the Tartars[4] were likely either to kill him or carry him off to the mountains. And it was arranged that twice a week an escort of soldiers should go from fortress to fortress. In front and behind marched the soldiers, and the travelers rode in the middle.

It was now summertime. At sunrise the baggage train was made up behind the fortification; the guard of soldiery marched ahead, and the procession moved along the road.

Zhilin was on horseback, and his effects were on a cart which formed part of the train.

They had twenty-five versts[5] to travel. The train proceeded slowly; sometimes the soldiers halted; sometimes a wagon wheel came off, or a horse balked, and all had to stop and wait.

The sun was already past the zenith, but the train had only gone halfway. It was dusty and hot, the sun was fierce, and there was no shelter. A bald steppe; not a tree or a shrub along the road.

Zhilin rode on ahead, occasionally stopping and waiting till the train caught up with him. He would listen, and hear the signal on the horn to halt again. And Zhilin thought, "Had I now better go on alone without the soldiers? I have a good horse under me; if I fall in with the Tartars, I can escape. Or shall I wait?"

He kept stopping and pondering. And just then another officer, also on horseback, rode up to him; his name was Kostuilin,[6] and he had a musket. He said,

"A Prisoner in the Caucasus" from TOLSTOY'S TALES OF COURAGE AND CONFLICT, edited by Charles Neider. Copyright © 1958 by Charles Neider. Published by Doubleday & Company, Inc.
1. *Tolstoy* (tol/ stoi; Russ. tol stoi/). **2.** *Caucasus* (kô/kə səs), a mountain range in Caucasia, a region of southwest Russia between the Black and Caspian seas. **3.** *Zhilin* (zhiн/ lin). **4.** *Tartars* (tär/ tərs), various tribes in eastern Europe and western Asia, chiefly of Mongolian and Turkish origin. **5.** *versts*. A verst is a Russian measure of distance equal to .66 miles. **6.** *Kostuilin* (kôs/ tyüē lin).

"Zhilin, let us ride on ahead together. I am so hungry that I cannot stand it any longer, and the heat too—you could wring my shirt out!"

Kostuilin was a heavy, stout, ruddy man, and the sweat was dripping from him.

Zhilin reflected, and said, "And your musket is loaded?"

"It is."

"All right, let us go. Only one condition: not to separate."

And they started on up the road. They rode along the steppe, talking and looking on each side. There was a wide sweep of view in all directions. As soon as the steppe came to an end, the road went into a pass between two mountains.

And Zhilin said, "I must ride up on that mountain, and reconnoiter; otherwise you see they might come down from the mountain and surprise us."

But Kostuilin said, "What is there to reconnoiter? Let us go ahead."

Zhilin did not heed him.

"No," says he, "you wait for me here below. I'll just glance around."

And he spurred his horse up the mountain to the left.

The horse that Zhilin rode was a hunter; he had bought her out of a drove of colts, paying a hundred rubles for her, and he had himself trained her. She bore him up the steep slope as if on wings. He had hardly reached the summit when before him, on a place a little less than three acres, mounted Tartars were standing. There were thirty of them.

He saw them, and started to turn back, but the Tartars had caught sight of him; they set out in pursuit of him, unstrapping their weapons as they galloped. Zhilin dashed down the precipice with all the speed of his horse, and cried to Kostuilin, "Fire your gun!" and to his horse he said, though not aloud, "Little mother, carry me safely, don't stumble; if you trip up, I am lost. If we get back to the gun, we won't fall into their hands."

But Kostuilin, as soon as he saw the Tartars, instead of waiting for him, galloped on with all his might toward the fortress. With his whip he belabored his horse, first on one side, then on the other; all that could be seen through the dust was the horse switching her tail.

Zhilin saw that his case was desperate. The gun was gone; nothing was to be done with a saber alone. He turned his horse back toward the train; he thought he might escape that way.

But in front of him he saw that six were galloping down the slope. His horse was good, but theirs were better; and besides, they had got the start of him. He attempted to wheel about, and was going to dash ahead again, but his horse had got momentum, and could not be held back; he flew straight down toward them.

He saw a red-bearded Tartar approaching him on a gray horse. He was gaining on him; he was gnashing his teeth; he was getting his gun ready.

"Well," thought Zhilin, "I know you devils; if you should take me prisoner, you would put me into a hold, and flog me with a whip. I won't give myself up alive."

Now, Zhilin was not of great size, but he was a uhlan.[7] He drew his saber, spurred his horse straight at the red-bearded Tartar. He said to himself, "Either I will crush him with my horse, or I will hack him down with my saber."

Zhilin, however, did not reach the place on horseback; suddenly, from behind him, gunshots were fired at the horse. The horse fell headlong and pinned Zhilin's leg to the ground.

He tried to arise; but already two ill-smelling Tartars were sitting on him, and pinioning his hands behind his back.

He burst from them, knocking the Tartars over; but three others had leaped from their horses, and began to beat him on the head with their gun-stocks.

His sight failed him, and he staggered. The Tartars seized him, took from their

7. *uhlan* (yü′ län), one of a group of horse-mounted lancers, usually the leaders in a cavalry charge.

saddles extra saddle-girths, bent his arms behind his back, fastened them with a Tartar knot, and lifted him up.

They took his saber from him, pulled off his boots, made a thorough search of him, relieved him of his money and his watch, and tore his clothes in pieces.

Zhilin glanced at his horse. The poor beast lay as she had fallen, on her side, and was kicking, vainly trying to rise. In her head was a hole, and from the hole the black blood was pouring; the dust for an arshin[8] around was wet with it.

A Tartar went to the horse to remove the saddle. She was still kicking, so the man took out his dagger and cut her throat. The throat gave a whistling sound, a trembling ran over the body, and all was over.

The Tartars took off the saddle and the other trappings. The one with the red beard mounted his horse, and the others lifted Zhilin behind him; and, in order to keep him from falling, they fastened him with the reins to the Tartar's belt, and thus they carried him off to the mountains.

Zhilin sat behind, swaying, and bumping his face against the stinking Tartar's back.

All that he could see before him was the healthy Tartar back, and the sinewy neck, and a smooth-shaven nape, showing blue beneath the cap.

Zhilin's head ached; the blood trickled into his eyes. And it was impossible for him to get a more comfortable position on the horse, or wipe away the blood. His arms were so tightly bound that his collarbones ached.

They rode along from mountain to mountain; they forded a river; then they entered a highway, and rode along a valley.

Zhilin tried to follow the route that they took him; but his eyes were glued together with blood, and it was impossible for him to turn round.

It began to grow dark; they crossed still another river, and began to climb a rocky mountain. There was an odor of smoke. The barking of dogs was heard.

They had reached an *aul* (a Tartar village). The Tartars dismounted. The Tartar children came running up and surrounded Zhilin, whistling and exulting. Finally they began to hurl stones at him.

The Tartar drove away the children, lifted Zhilin from the horse, and called a menial.

A Nogayets,[9] with prominent cheekbones, came at the call. He wore only a shirt. The shirt was torn; his whole breast was bare. The Tartar gave him some order. The menial brought a foot-stock. It consisted of two oaken blocks provided with iron rings, and in one of the rings was a clamp with a lock. They unfastened Zhilin's arms, put on the clog, and took him to a shed, pushed him in, and shut the door.

Zhilin fell on the manure. As he lay there, he felt round in the darkness, and when he had found a place that was less foul, he stretched himself out.

2

Zhilin scarcely slept that night. The nights were short. He saw through a crack that it was growing light. Zhilin got up, widened the crack, and managed to look out.

Through the crack he could see a road leading down from the mountain; at the right, a Tartar hut with two trees near it. A black dog was lying on the road; a she-goat with her kids was walking by; they were shaking their tails.

He saw coming down the mountain a young Tartar girl in a variegated shirt, ungirdled, in pantalettes and boots; her head was covered with a kaftan,[10] and on it she bore a great tin water-jug.

She walked along, swaying and bending

---

8. *arshin* (är shĕn′), a Russian measure equaling twenty-eight inches. 9. *Nogayets* (nô′ gä yetz), a footman or general domestic servant. 10. *kaftan* (kaf′ tən), a long, flowing garment tied at the waist, in this instance rolled up and used as a cushion.

her back, and holding by the hand a little shaven-headed Tartar urchin, who wore a single shirt.

After the Tartar maiden had gone into the saklia[11] with her water-jug, the red-bearded Tartar of the evening before came out, wearing a silk beshmet,[12] a silver dagger in his belt, and *bashmaks,* or sandals, on his bare feet. On the back of his head was a high cap of sheepskin, dyed black. He came out, stretched himself, stroked his red beard. He paused, gave some order to the menial, and went off somewhere.

Then two children on horseback came along on their way to the watering-trough. The snouts of the horses were wet.

Other shaven-headed youngsters, with nothing but shirts on, and nothing on their legs, formed a little band, and came to the shed; they got a dry stick, and stuck it through the crack.

Zhilin growled "ukh" at them. The children began to squeal, and scatter in every direction as fast as their legs would carry them; only their bare knees glistened. But Zhilin began to be thirsty; his throat was parched. He said to himself, "I wonder if they won't come to look after me?"

While he was listening, the barn doors were thrown open. The red Tartar came in, and with him another, of slighter stature and of dark complexion. His eyes were bright and black, his cheeks ruddy, his little beard well trimmed, his face jolly and always enlivened with a grin.

The dark man's clothing was still richer —a beshmet of blue silk, embroidered with gold lace. In his belt, a great silver dagger; red morocco bashmaks, embroidered with silver, and over the fine bashmaks he wore a larger pair of stout ones. His cap was tall, of white lamb's-wool.

The red Tartar came in, muttered something, gave vent to some abusive language, and then stood leaning against the wall, fingering his dagger, and scowling under his brows at Zhilin, like a wolf.

But the dark Tartar, nervous and active, and always on the go, as if he were made of springs, came straight up to Zhilin, squatted down on his heels, showed his teeth, tapped him on the shoulder, began to gabble something in his own language, winked his eyes, and, clucking his tongue, kept saying, "A fine Russ, a fine Russ!"

Zhilin did not understand him, and said, "Drink; give me some water."

The dark one grinned, and all the time he kept babbling, "A fine Russ!"

Zhilin signified by his hands and lips that they should give him water.

The dark one understood, grinned, put his head out of the door, and cried, "Dina!"

A young girl came running in—a slender, lean creature of thirteen, with a face like the dark man's. Evidently she was his daughter. She also had black, luminous eyes, and she was very pretty.

She was dressed in a long, blue shirt, with wide sleeves and without a belt. On the bottom, on the breast, and on the cuffs it was relieved with red trimmings. She wore on her legs pantalettes and bashmaks, and over the bashmaks another pair with high heels. On her neck was a necklace wholly composed of Russian half-ruble pieces.[13] Her head was uncovered; she had her hair in a black braid, and on the braid was a ribbon, and to the ribbon were attached various ornaments and a silver ruble.

Her father gave her some command. She ran out, and quickly returned, bringing a little tin pitcher. After she had handed him the water, she also squatted on her heels in such a way that her knees were higher than her shoulders.

She sat that way, and opened her eyes, and stared at Zhilin while he was drinking, as if he were some wild beast.

Zhilin offered to return the pitcher to

11. *saklia* (säk/ lē yä), a hut. 12. *beshmet* (besh/ met), a garment worn under a tunic. 13. *half-ruble pieces,* silver coins worth one half of a ruble, the Russian standard monetary measure. The ruble equaled fifty-two cents in the mid-nineteenth century. The U.S. dollar at that time had a value five times as great as today.

her. She darted away like a wild goat. Even her father laughed. He sent her after something else. She took the pitcher, ran out, and brought back some unleavened bread on a small, round board, and again squatted down, and stared without taking her eyes from him.

The Tartars went out, and again bolted the door.

After a while the Nogayets also came to Zhilin, and said, *"Aï-da, khozyaïn. aï-da!"*[14]

But he did not know Russian either. Zhilin, however, perceived that he wished him to go somewhere. Zhilin hobbled out with his clog; it was impossible to walk, so he had to drag one leg. The Nogayets led the way for him.

He saw a Tartar village, a dozen houses, and the native mosque with its minaret. In front of one house stood three horses saddled. Lads held them by their bridles. From this house came the dark Tartar, and beckoned with his hand, signifying that Zhilin was to come to him. He grinned, and kept saying something in his own tongue, and went into the house.

Zhilin followed him.

The room was decent; the walls were smoothly plastered with clay. Against the front wall were placed feather-beds; on the sides hung costly rugs; on the rugs were guns, pistols, and sabers, all silver-mounted.

On one side a little oven was set in, on a level with the floor. The floor was of earth, clean as a threshing-floor, and the whole of the front part was covered with felt; rugs were distributed over the felt, and on the rugs were down pillows.

On the rugs were sitting some Tartars with bashmaks only on their feet—the dark Tartar, the red-bearded one, and three guests. Behind their backs, down cushions were placed; and before them on wooden plates were pancakes of millet flour, and melted butter in a cup, and the Tartar beer, called *buza,* in a pitcher. They ate with their fingers and all dipped into the butter.

The dark man leaped up, bade Zhilin sit on one side, not on a rug but on the bare floor; going back again to his rug, he served his guests with cakes and buza.

The menial showed Zhilin his place; he himself took off his outside bashmaks, placed them by the door in a row with the bashmaks of the other guests, and took his seat on the felt as near as possible to his masters; and while they ate he looked at them, and his mouth watered.

After the Tartars had finished eating the pancakes, a Tartar woman entered, dressed in the same sort of shirt as the girl wore, and in pantalettes; her head was covered with a handkerchief. She carried out the butter and the cakes, and brought a handsome finger bowl, and a pitcher with a narrow nose.

The Tartars proceeded to wash their hands, then they folded their arms, knelt down, and puffed on all sides, and said their prayers. Then they talked together in their own tongue.

Finally one of the guests, a Tartar, approached Zhilin, and began to speak to him in Russian.

"Kazi Muhamet made you prisoner," said he, pointing to the red-bearded Tartar, "and he has given you to Abdul Murat," indicating the dark one. "Abdul Murat is now your master."

Zhilin said nothing.

Abdul Murat began to talk, all the time pointing toward Zhilin, and grinned as he talked, *"Soldat Urus, korosho Urus."*[15]

The dragoman[16] went on to say, "He commands you to write a letter home, and have them send money to ransom you. As soon as money is sent, he will set you free."

Zhilin pondered a little, and then said, "Does he wish a large ransom?"

The Tartars took counsel together, and then the dragoman said, "Three thousand silver rubles."

---

14. *Aï-da, khozyaïn, aï-da!* Let's go Cossack, let's go! 15. *Soldat Urus, korosho Urus,* Russian soldier, good Russian. 16. *dragoman* (drag′ ə mən), a professional interpreter.

"No," replied Zhilin, "I can't pay that."

Abdul leaped up, began to gesticulate and talk to Zhilin; he seemed all the time to think that Zhilin understood him.

The dragoman translated his words.

"He means," says he, "how much will you give?"

Zhilin, after pondering a little, said, "Five hundred rubles."

Then the Tartars all began to talk at once. Abdul began to scream at the red-bearded Tartar. He grew so excited as he talked that the spittle flew from his mouth. But the red-bearded Tartar only frowned, and clucked with his tongue.

When all became silent again, the dragoman said, "Five hundred rubles is not enough to buy you of your master. He himself has paid two hundred for you. Kazi Muhamet was in debt to him. He took you for the debt. Three thousand rubles; it is no use to send less. But if you don't write, they will put you in a hole, and flog you with a whip."

"Ekh!" said Zhilin to himself, "the more cowardly one is, the worse it is for him."

He leaped to his feet, and said, "Now you tell him, dog that he is, that if he thinks he is going to frighten me, then I will not give him a single kopek[17] nor will I write. I am not afraid of you, and you will never make me afraid of you, you dog!" The dragoman interpreted this to them, and again they all began to talk at once.

They gabbled a long time, then the dark one got up and came to Zhilin.

"Urus," says he, "jigit, jigit[18] Urus!"

The word jigit in their language signifies a brave young man. And he grinned, said something to the dragoman, and the dragoman said, "Give a thousand rubles."

Zhilin would not give in: "I will not pay more than five hundred. But if you kill me, you will get nothing at all."

The Tartars consulted together, sent out the menial, and they themselves looked first at the door, then at Zhilin.

The menial returned, followed by a rather stout man in bare feet and almost stripped. His feet also were fastened to a clog.

Zhilin uttered an exclamation; he saw it was Kostuilin. So they had captured him too. They placed him next to his comrade; the two began to talk together, and the Tartars looked on and listened in silence.

Zhilin told how it had gone with him; Kostuilin told how his horse had stood stock-still, and his gun had misfired, and that this same Abdul had overtaken him and captured him.

Abdul sprang to his feet, pointed to Kostuilin, and made some remark. The dragoman translated his words to mean that they now both belonged to the same master, and that the one who paid the ransom first would be freed first.

"Now," said he to Zhilin, "you lose your temper so easily, but your comrade is calm; he has written a letter home; they will send five thousand silver rubles. And so he will be well fed, and he won't be hurt."

And Zhilin said, "Let my comrade do as he pleases. Maybe he is rich. But I am not rich; I will do as I have already told you. Kill me if you wish, but it would not do you any good, and I will not pay you more than five hundred rubles."

They were silent.

Suddenly Abdul leaped up, brought a little chest, took out a pen, a sheet of paper, and ink, and pushed them into Zhilin's hands, then tapped him on the shoulder and said by signs, "Write."

He had agreed to take the five hundred rubles.

"Wait a moment," said Zhilin to the dragoman. "Tell him that he must feed us well, clothe us, and give us good decent footwear, and let us stay together so that it may be pleasanter for us. And lastly, that he take off these clogs."

He looked at his Tartar master, and smiled. The master also smiled, and when he learned what was wanted, said, "I will

17. kopek (kō′ pek), a coin worth one hundredth of a ruble. 18. jigit (djē′ gēt).

give you the very best clothes; a cloak and boots, fit for a wedding. And I will feed you like princes. And if you want to live together, why, you can live in the shed. But it won't do to take away the clogs; you would run away. Only at night will I have them taken off." Then he jumped up and tapped him on the shoulder: "You good, me good."

Zhilin wrote his letter, but he put on it the wrong address so that it might never reach its destination. He said to himself, "I shall run away."

They took Zhilin and Kostuilin to the shed, strewed cornstalks, gave them water in a pitcher, and bread, two old cherkeski,[19] and some worn-out military boots. It was evident that they had been stolen from some dead soldier. When night came they took off their clogs, and locked them up in the shed.

3

Thus Zhilin and his comrade lived a whole month. Their master was always on the grin.

"You, Ivan, good—me, Abdul, good."

But he gave them wretched food—unleavened bread made of millet flour, cooked in the form of cakes, but often not heated through.

Kostuilin wrote home again, and was anxiously awaiting the arrival of the money, and lost his spirits. Whole days at a time he sat in the shed, and counted the days till his money should arrive, or else he slept.

But Zhilin knew that his letter would not reach its destination, and he did not write another.

"Where," he asked himself, "where would my mother get so much money for my ransom? And besides, she lived for the most part on what I used to send her. If she made out to raise five hundred rubles, she would be in want till the end of her days. If God wills it, I may escape."

And all the time he kept his eyes open, and made plans to elude his captors.

He walked about the aul; he amused himself by whistling; or else he sat down and fashioned things, either modeling dolls out of clay or plaiting baskets of osiers, for Zhilin was a master at all sorts of handiwork.

One time he made a doll with nose and hands and feet, and dressed in a Tartar shirt, and he set the doll on the roof. The Tartar women were going for water. Dina, the master's daughter, caught sight of the doll.

She called the Tartar women. They set down their jugs, and looked and laughed.

Zhilin took the doll, and offered it to them. They kept laughing, but did not dare to take it.

He left the doll, went to the barn, and watched what would take place.

Dina ran up to the doll, looked around, seized the doll, and fled.

The next morning at dawn he saw Dina come out on the doorstep with the doll. And she had already dressed it up in pieces of red cloth, and was rocking it like a little child, and singing a lullaby in her own language.

The old woman came out, gave her a scolding, snatched the doll away, broke it in pieces, and sent Dina off to work.

Zhilin made another doll, a still better one, and gave it to Dina.

One time Dina brought a little jug, put it down, took a seat, and looked at him. Then she laughed, and pointed to the jug.

"What is she so gay about?" wondered Zhilin.

---

19. *cherkeski* (cher′ kes kē), garments worn in a region of the Caucasus called Circassia.

He took the jug, and began to drink. He supposed that it was water, but it was milk.

He drank up the milk.

"Good," says he.

How delighted Dina was! "Good, Ivan, good!"

And she jumped up, clapped her hands, snatched the jug, and ran away. And from that time she began to bring him secretly fresh milk every day. Now, sometimes the Tartars would make cheesecakes out of goat's milk, and dry them on their roofs; so she used to carry some of these cakes secretly to him. And another time, when her father had killed a sheep, she brought him a piece of mutton in her sleeve. She threw it down, and ran away.

One time there was a heavy shower, and for a whole hour the rain poured as from buckets; and all the brooks grew roily. Wherever there had been a ford, the depth of the water increased to a fathom, and boulders were rolled along by it. Everywhere torrents were rushing, the mountains were full of the roaring.

Now, when the shower was over, streams were pouring all through the village. Zhilin asked his master for a knife, whittled out a cylinder and some paddles, and made a water-wheel, and fastened manikins at the two ends.

The little girls brought him some rags, and he dressed up the manikins, one like a man, the other like a woman. He fastened them on, and put the wheel in a brook. The wheel revolved, and the dolls danced.

The whole village collected; the little boys and the little girls, the women, and even the Tartars, came and clucked with their tongues, *"Aï, Urus! aï, Ivan!"*

Abdul had a Russian watch, which had been broken. He took it, and showed it to Zhilin, and clucked with his tongue. Zhilin said, "Let me have it, I will mend it."

He took it, opened the penknife, took it apart. Then he put it together again, and gave it back. The watch ran.

The Tartar was delighted, brought him his old beshmet, which was all in rags, and gave it to him. Nothing else was to be done — he took it, and used it as a covering at night.

From that time, Zhilin's fame went abroad, that he was a "master." Even from distant villages, they came to him. One brought him a gunlock or a pistol to repair, another a watch.

His master furnished him with tools—a pair of pincers and gimlets and a little file.

One time a Tartar fell ill; they came to Zhilin: "Come, cure him!"

Zhilin knew nothing of medicine. He went, looked at the sick man, said to himself, "Perhaps he will get well, anyway." He went into the shed, took water and sand, and shook them up together. He whispered a few words to the water in presence of the Tartars, and gave it to the sick man to drink.

Fortunately for him, the Tartar got well.

Zhilin had by this time learned something of their language. And some of the Tartars became accustomed to him; when they wanted him, they called him by name, "Ivan, Ivan"; but others always looked at him as if he was a wild beast.

The red-bearded Tartar did not like Zhilin; when he saw him, he scowled and turned away, or else insulted him.

There was another old man among them; he did not live in the aul, but came from down the mountain. Zhilin never saw him except when he came to the mosque to prayer. He was of small stature; on his cap he wore a white towel as an ornament. His beard and mustaches were trimmed; they were white as wool, and his face was wrinkled and brick-red. His nose was hooked like a hawk's, and his eyes were gray and cruel, and he had no teeth except two tusks.

He used to come in his turban, leaning on his staff, and glare like a wolf; whenever he saw Zhilin, he would snort, and turn his back.

One time Zhilin went down the mountain to see where the old man lived. He descended a narrow path, and saw a little stone-walled garden. On the other side of the wall were cherry trees, peach trees, and a little hut with a flat roof.

He went nearer; he saw beehives made of straw, and bees flying and humming around them. And the old man was on his knees busy doing something to one of the hives.

Zhilin raised himself up, so as to get a better view, and his clog made a noise.

The old man looked up—squealed; he whipped his pistol from his belt, and fired at Zhilin, who had barely time to hide behind the wall.

The old man came to make his complaint to Zhilin's master. Abdul called him in, grinned, and asked him, "Why did you go to the old man's?"

"I didn't do him any harm. I wanted to see how he lived."

Abdul explained it to the old man; but he was angry, hissed, mumbled something, showed his tusks, and threatened Zhilin with his hands.

Zhilin did not understand it all; but he made out that the old man wished Abdul to kill the two Russians, and not keep them in the aul.

The old man went off.

Zhilin began to ask his master, "Who is that old man?"

And the master replied, "He is a great man. He used to be our first jigit; he has killed many Russians. He used to be rich. He had three wives and eight sons. All lived in one village. The Russians came, destroyed his village, and killed seven of his sons. One son was left, and surrendered to the Russians. The old man went and gave himself up to the Russians also. He lived among them three months, found his son, killed him with his own hand, and escaped. Since that time he has stopped fighting. He went to Mecca to pray to God, and that's why he wears a turban. Whoever has been to Mecca is called a hadji,[20] and wears a chalma.[21] But he does not love you Russians. He has bade me kill you, but I don't intend to kill you. I have paid out money for you, and be-

sides, Ivan, I have come to like you. And so far from wishing to kill you, I would rather not let you go from me at all, if I had not given my word."

He laughed, and began to repeat in broken Russian, *"Tvoya Ivan, khorosh, moya, Abdul, khorosh*—Ivan, you good; Abdul, me good."

4

Thus Zhilin lived a month. In the daytime he walked about the aul or did some handiwork, but when night came, and it grew quiet in the aul, he burrowed in his shed. It was hard work digging because of the stones, and he sometimes had to use his file on them; and thus he dug a hole under the wall big enough to crawl through.

"Only," he thought, "I must know the region a little first, so as to escape in the right direction. And the Tartars wouldn't tell me anything."

He chose a time when his master was absent, then he went after dinner behind the aul to a mountain. His idea was to reconnoiter the country.

Now when Abdul went away he commanded his little son to follow Zhilin, and not take his eyes from him. The little fellow tagged after Zhilin, and kept crying, "Don't go there. Father won't allow it. I will call the men if you go!"

Zhilin began to reason with him.

"I am not going far," says he, "only to that hill; I want to find some herbs so as to cure your people. Come with me; I can't run away with this clog. If you will, I will make you a bow and arrows tomorrow."

He persuaded the lad, they went together. To look at, the mountain was not far, but it was hard work with the clog; he went a little distance at a time, pulling himself up by main strength.

Zhilin sat down on the summit, and began to survey the ground.

20. *hadji* (haj′ē). 21. *chalma* (chäl′mä), a turban.

To the south behind the shed lay a valley through which a herd was grazing, and another aul was in sight at the foot of it. Back of the village was another mountain still steeper, and back of that still another. Between the mountains lay a further stretch of forest, and then still other mountains rising ever higher and higher. And higher than all, stood snow-capped peaks white as sugar, and one snowy peak rose like a dome above them all.

To the east and west also were mountains. In every direction the smoke of auls was to be seen in the ravines.

"Well," he said to himself, "this is all their country."

He began to look in the direction of the Russian possessions. At his very feet was a little river, his aul surrounded by gardens. By the river some women, no larger in appearance than little dolls, were standing and washing. Behind the aul was a lower mountain, and beyond it two other mountains covered with forests. And between the two mountains a plain stretched far, far away in the blue distance; and on the plain lay what seemed like smoke.

Zhilin tried to remember in what direction, when he lived at home in the fortress, the sun used to rise, and where it set. He looked.

"Just about there," says he, "in that valley, our fortress ought to be. There, between those two mountains, I must make my escape."

The little sun began to slope toward the west. The snowy mountains changed from white to purple; the wooded mountains grew dark; a mist arose from the valley; and the valley itself, where the Russian fortress must be, glowed in the sunset as if it were on fire. Zhilin strained his gaze. Something seemed to hang waving in the air, like smoke arising from chimneys.

And so it seemed to him that it must be from the fortress itself—the Russian fortress.

It was already growing late. The voice of the mulla[22] calling to prayer was heard. The herds began to return; the kine were lowing. The little lad kept repeating, "Let us go!" but Zhilin could not tear himself away.

They returned home.

"Well," thinks Zhilin, "now I know the place; I must make my escape."

He proposed to make his escape that very night. The nights were dark; it was the wane of the moon.

Unfortunately the Tartars returned in the evening. Usually they came in driving the cattle with them, and came in hilarious. But this time they had no cattle; but they brought a Tartar, dead, on his saddle. It was the red-headed Tartar's brother who had been killed. They rode in solemnly, and all collected for the burial.

Zhilin also went out to look.

They did not put the dead body in a coffin, but wrapped it in linen, and placed it under a plane tree behind the village, where it lay on the sward.

The mulla came; the old men gathered together, their caps bound around with towels. They took off their shoes, and sat in rows on their heels before the dead.

In front was the mulla, behind him three old men in turbans, and behind them the rest of the Tartars. They sat there, with their heads bent low and kept silence. Long they kept silence. The mulla lifted his head and said, "Allah!" (That means God.) He said this one word, and again they hung their heads, and were silent a long time; they sat motionless.

Again the mulla lifted his head, saying, "Allah!" and all repeated it after him: "Allah!"

Then silence again.

The dead man lay on the sward; he was motionless, and they sat as if they were dead. Not one made a motion. The only sound was the rustling of the foliage of the plane tree, stirred by the breeze.

Then the mulla offered a prayer. All

22. *mulla* (mul′ ə), a title of respect for one who is learned in and teaches the sacred law.

got to their feet; they took the dead body in their arms, and carried it away. They brought it to a pit. The pit was not a mere hole, but was hollowed out under the earth like a cellar.

They took the body under the armpits and by the legs, doubled it up, and let it down gently, shoved it forcibly under the ground, and laid the arms along the belly. The Nogayets brought a green osier.[23] They laid it in the pit; then they quickly filled it up with earth, and over the dead man's head they placed a gravestone. They smoothed the earth over, and again sat around the grave in rows. There was a long silence.

"Allah! Allah! Allah!"

They sighed and got up.

The red-bearded Tartar gave money to the old men, then he got up, struck his forehead three times with a whip, and went home.

The next morning Zhilin saw the red-haired Tartar leading a mare through the village, and three Tartars following him. They went behind the village. Kazi Muhamet took off his beshmet, rolled up his sleeves—his hands were powerful—took out his dagger, and sharpened it on a whetstone. The Tartars held back the mare's head. Kazi Muhamet approached, and cut the throat; then, he turned the animal over, and began to flay it, pulling away the hide with his mighty fists.

The women and maidens came, and began to wash the intestines and the viscera. Then they cut up the mare, and carried the meat to the hut. And the whole village collected at the Kazi Muhamet's to celebrate the dead.

For three days they feasted on the mare and drank buza, and they celebrated the dead. All the Tartars were at home.

On the fourth day about noon, Zhilin saw that they were collecting for some expedition. Their horses were brought out. They put on their gear, and started off, ten men of them, under the command of the red-headed Tartar; only Abdul

stayed at home. There was a new moon, but the nights were still dark.

"Now," said Zhilin to himself, "we must escape today." And he told Kostuilin.

But Kostuilin was afraid. "How can we escape? We don't know the way."

"I know the way."

"But we should not get there during the night."

"Well, if we don't get there we will spend the night in the woods. I have some cakes. What are you going to do? It will be all right if they send you the money, but you see, your friends may not collect so much. And the Tartars are angry now because the Russians have killed one of their men. They say they are thinking of killing us."

Kostuilin thought and thought. "All right, let us go!"

5

Zhilin crept down into his hole, and widened it so that Kostuilin also could get through, and then they sat and waited till all should be quiet in the aul.

As soon as the people were quiet in the aul, Zhilin crept under the wall, and came out on the other side. He whispered to Kostuilin, "Crawl under."

Kostuilin also crept under, but in doing so he hit a stone with his leg, and it made a noise.

Now, the master had a brindled dog as a watch—a most ferocious animal;

---

23. *osier* (ō′ zhər), usually meaning any of various flexible willows, twigs, or branches. In this instance it probably means a mat made from the same.

they called him Ulyashin.[24] Zhilin had been in the habit of feeding him. Ulyashin heard the noise, and began to bark and jump about, and the other dogs joined in. Zhilin gave a little whistle, threw him a piece of cake. Ulyashin recognized him, began to wag his tail, and ceased barking. Abdul had heard the disturbance, and cried from within the saklia,—"Haït! haït![25] Ulyashin."

But Zhilin scratched the dog behind the ears. The dog made no more sound, rubbed against his legs, and wagged his tail.

They waited behind the corner.

All became silent again; the only sound was the bleating of a sheep in the fold, and far below them the water roaring over the boulders. It was dark, but the sky was studded with stars. Over the mountain the young moon hung red, with its horns turned upward.

In the valleys a mist was rising, white as milk. Zhilin started up, and said to his comrade. "Well, brother, *aï-da!*"

They set out again.

But as they got under way, they heard the call of the mulla on the minaret: *"Allah! Bis'm Allah! el Rakhman!"*[26]

"That means, the people will be going to the mosque."

Again they sat down and hid under the wall.

They sat there long, waiting until the people should pass. Again it grew still.

"Now God be with us!"

They crossed themselves, and started.

They went across the dvor,[27] and down the steep bank to the stream, crossed the stream, and proceeded along the valley. The mist was thick, and closed in all around them, but above their heads the stars could still be seen.

Zhilin used the stars to guide him which way to go. It was cool in the mist, it was easy walking, only their boots were troublesome—they were worn at the heels. Zhilin took his off, threw them away, and walked barefoot. He sprang from stone to stone, and kept glancing at the stars.

Kostuilin began to grow weary.

"Go slower," said he; "my boots chafe me, my whole foot is raw."

"Then take them off, it will be easier."

Kostuilin began to go barefoot, but that was still worse; he kept scraping his feet on the stones and having to stop.

Zhilin said to him, "You may cut your feet, but you will save your life; but if you are caught, they will kill you, which would be worse."

Kostuilin said nothing, but crept along, groaning. For a long time they went down the valley. Suddenly they heard dogs barking at the right. Zhilin halted, looked around, climbed up the bank, and felt about with his hands.

"Ekh!" said he, "we have made a mistake; we have gone too far to the right. Here is a strange aul. I could see it from the hill. We must go back to the left, up the mountain. There must be a forest there."

But Kostuilin objected: "Just wait a little while, let us get breath. My feet are all blood."

"Eh, brother! They will get well. You should walk more lightly. This way."

And Zhilin turned back toward the left, and uphill toward the forest.

Kostuilin kept halting and groaning. Zhilin tried to hush him up, and still hastened on.

They climbed the mountain. And there they found the forest. They entered it; their clothes were all torn to pieces on the thorns. They found a little path through the woods. They walked along it.

"Halt!"

There was the sound of hoofs on the path. They stopped to listen. It sounded like the tramping of a horse: then it also stopped. They set out once more; again

---

24. *Ulyashin* (ủl′ yä shin), a Tartar name meaning "Enforcer." 25. *Haït! haït!* (hä-yit), Calm down! quiet! 26. *Allah! Bis'm Allah! el Rakhman!*, a Moslem call to prayer. 27. *dvor* (dvôr), a yard or plaza.

the tramping hoofs. When they stopped, it stopped. Zhilin crept ahead, and investigated a light spot on the path.

Something was standing there. Whether it was a horse or not, on it there was something strange, not at all like a man.

It snorted—plainly!

"What a strange thing!"

Zhilin gave a slight whistle. There was a dash of feet from the path into the forest, a crackling in the underbrush, and something rushed along like a hurricane, with a crashing of dry boughs.

Kostuilin almost fell to the ground in fright. But Zhilin laughed, and said, "That was a stag. Do you hear how it crashes through the woods with its horns? We were afraid of him, and he is afraid of us."

They went on their way. Already the Great Bear was beginning to set; the dawn was not distant. And they were in doubt whether they should come out right or not. Zhilin was inclined to think that they were on the right track, and that it would be about ten versts farther before they reached the Russian fortress, but there was no certain guide; you could not tell in the night.

They came to a little clearing. Kostuilin sat down and said, "Do as you please, but I will not go any farther; my legs won't carry me."

Zhilin tried to persuade him.

"No," said he, "I won't go, I can't go."

Zhilin grew angry; he threatened him, he scolded him.

"Then I will go on without you. Good-by!"

Kostuilin jumped up and followed. They went four versts farther. The fog began to grow thicker in the forest. Nothing could be seen before them; the stars were barely visible.

Suddenly they heard the tramping of a horse just in front of them; they could hear his shoes striking on the stones.

Zhilin threw himself down on his belly, and tried to listen by laying his ear to the ground.

"Yes, it is—it is someone on horseback coming in our direction."

They slipped off to one side of the road, crouched down in the bushes, and waited. Zhilin crept close to the path, and looked.

He saw a mounted Tartar riding along, driving a cow, and muttering to himself. When the Tartar had ridden by, Zhilin returned to Kostuilin.

"Well, God has saved us. Up with you! Come along!"

Kostuilin tried to rise, and fell back.

"I can't; by God, I can't. My strength is all gone."

The man was staggered, and was bloated, and the sweat poured from him; and as they were caught in the forest in the midst of the cold fog, and his feet were torn, he lost all courage. Zhilin tried to lift him by main force. Then Kostuilin cried, "Ai! it hurts."

Zhilin was frightened to death.

"What are you screaming for? Don't you know that Tartar is near? He will hear you." But he said to himself, "Now, if he is really played out, what can I do with him? I can't abandon a comrade. Now," says he, "get up; climb on my back. I will carry you if you can't walk any longer." He took Kostuilin on his shoulders, holding him by the thighs, and went along the path with his burden. "Only," says he, "don't put your hands on my throat, for Christ's sake! Hold on by my shoulders."

It was hard for Zhilin. His feet were also bloody, and he was weary. He stopped, and made it a little easier for himself by setting Kostuilin down, and getting him higher up on his shoulders. Then he went on again.

Evidently the Tartar had heard Kostuilin scream. Zhilin caught the sound of some one following them, and shouting in his language. Zhilin hid among the bushes. The Tartar aimed his gun; he fired it off but missed, began to whine in his native tongue, and galloped up the path.

"Well," said Zhilin, "we are lost,

brother. The dog . . . he will be right back with a band of Tartars on our track. . . . If we don't succeed in putting three versts between us, we are lost." And he thinks to himself, "The devil take it, that I had to bring this clod along with me! Alone, I should have got there long ago."

Kostuilin said, "Go alone. Why should you be lost on my account?"

"No, I will not go; it would not do to abandon a comrade."

He lifted him again on his shoulders, and started on. Thus he made a verst. It was forest all the way, and no sign of outlet. But the fog was now beginning to lift, and seemed to be floating away in little clouds; not a star was any longer to be seen. Zhilin was tired out.

A little spring gushed out by the road; it was walled in with stones. There he stopped, and dropped Kostuilin.

"Let me rest a little," said he, "and get a drink. We will eat our cakes. It can't be very far now."

He had just stretched himself out to drink, when the sound of hoofs was heard behind them. Again they hid in the bushes at the right under the crest, and crouched down.

They heard Tartar voices. The Tartars stopped at the very spot where they had turned in from the road. After discussing awhile, they seemed to be setting dogs on the scent.

The refugees heard the sound of a crashing through the bushes; a strange dog came directly to them. He stopped and barked.

The Tartars followed on their track. They also were strangers. They seized them, bound them, lifted them on horses, and carried them off.

After they had ridden three versts, Abdul, their master, with two Tartars, met them. He said something to their new captors. They were transferred to Abdul's horses, and were brought back to the aul.

Abdul was no longer grinning, and he said not a word to them.

They reached the village at daybreak; the prisoners were left in the street. The children gathered around them, tormenting them with stones and whips, and howling.

The Tartars gathered around them in a circle, and the old man from the mountain was among them. They began to discuss. Zhilin made out that they were deciding on what should be done with them. Some said that they ought to be sent farther into the mountains, but the old man declared that they must be killed. Abdul argued against it.

"I have paid out money for them," said he. "I shall get a ransom for them."

But the old man said: "They won't pay anything; they will only be an injury to us. And it is a sin to feed Russians. Kill them, and that is the end of it."

They separated. Abdul came to Zhilin, and reported the decision.

"If," says he, "the ransom is not sent in two weeks, I will flog you. And if you try to run away again, I will kill you like a dog. Write your letter, and write it good!"

Paper was brought them; they wrote their letters. Clogs were put on their feet again; they were taken behind the mosque. There was a pit twelve feet deep, and they were thrust down into this pit.

6

Life was made utterly wretched for them. Their clogs were not taken off even at night, and they were not let out at all. Unbaked dough was thrown down to them as if they were dogs, and water was let down in a jug. In the pit it was damp and suffocating.

Kostuilin became ill, and swelled up, and had rheumatism all over his body, and he groaned or slept all the time. Even Zhilin lost his spirits; he saw that they were in desperate straits. And he did not know how to get out of it. He had begun to make an excavation, but there was nowhere to hide the earth; Abdul discovered it, and threatened to kill him.

He was squatting down one time in the pit, and thinking about liberty, and he grew sad.

Suddenly a cake fell directly into his lap, then another, and some cherries followed.

He looked up, and there was Dina. She peered down at him, laughed, and then ran away. And Zhilin began to conjecture, "Couldn't Dina help me?"

He cleared out a little place in the pit, picked up some clay, and made some dolls. He made men and women, horses and dogs; he said to himself, "When Dina comes, I will toss them up to her."

But Dina did not make her appearance on the next day. And Zhilin heard the trampling of horses' hoofs; men came riding up; the Tartars collected at the mosque, arguing, shouting, and talking about the Russians.

And he also heard the voice of the old man. Zhilin could not understand very well, but he gathered that the Russians were somewhere near, and the Tartars were afraid that they would attack the aul, and they did not know what to do with the prisoners. They talked awhile, and went away.

Suddenly Zhilin heard a rustling at the edge of the pit.

He saw Dina squatting on her heels, with her knees higher than her head; she leaned over, her necklace hung down, and swung over the pit. And her little eyes twinkled like stars. She took from her sleeve two cheese-cakes, and threw them down to him. Zhilin accepted them, and said, "Why did you stay away so long? I have been making you some dolls. Here they are."

He began to toss them up to her, one at a time.

But she shook her head, and would not look at them. "I can't take them," said she. She was silent for a while, but sat there; then she said, "Ivan, they want to kill you."

She made a significant motion across her throat.

"Who wants to kill me?"

"Father. The old men have ordered him to. But I am sorry for you."

And Zhilin said, "Well, then, if you are sorry for me, bring me a long pole."

She shook her head, meaning that it was impossible.

He clasped his hands in supplication to her. "Dina, please! Bring one to me, Dinushka!"

"I can't," said she. "They would see me; they are all at home."

And she ran away.

Afterward, Zhilin was sitting there in the evening, and wondering what was going to happen. He kept looking up. He could see the stars, but the moon had not yet risen. The mulla uttered his call, then all became silent.

Zhilin began already to doze, thinking to himself, "The little maid is afraid."

Suddenly a piece of clay fell on his head; he glanced up; a long pole was sliding over the edge of the pit; it slid out, began to descend toward him; it reached the bottom of the pit. Zhilin was delighted. He seized it, pulled it along—it was a strong pole. He had noticed it before on his master's roof.

He gazed up; the stars were shining high in the heavens, and Dina's eyes, at the edge of the pit, gleamed in the darkness like a cat's.

She craned her head over, and whispered, "Ivan, Ivan." And she waved her hands before her face, meaning, "Softly, please."

"What is it?" said Zhilin.

"All have gone, there are only two at home."

And Zhilin said, "Well, Kostuilin, let us go, let us make our last attempt. I will help you."

Kostuilin, however, would not hear of it.

"No," says he, "it is not meant for me to get away from here. How could I go when I haven't even strength to turn over?"

"All right, then. Good-by. Don't think me unkind."

He kissed Kostuilin.

He clasped the pole, told Dina to hold it firmly, and tried to climb up. Twice he fell back—his clog so impeded him. Kostuilin pushed him from below; he managed to get to the top; Dina pulled on the sleeves of his shirt with all her might, laughing heartily.

Zhilin pulled up the pole, and said, "Carry it back to its place, Dina, for if they found it they would flog you."

She dragged off the pole, and Zhilin began to go down the mountain. When he had reached the bottom of the cliff he took a sharp stone and tried to break the padlock of his clog. But the lock was strong; he could not strike it fairly.

He heard some one hurrying down the hill, with light, skipping steps. He said to himself, "That is probably Dina again."

Dina ran to him, took a stone, and said, "*Dai ya.* Let me try it."

She knelt down, and began to work with all her might. But her hands were as delicate as osiers. She had no strength. She threw down the stone, and burst into tears.

Zhilin again tried to break the lock, and Dina squatted by his side, and leaned against his shoulder. Zhilin glanced up, and saw at the left behind the mountain a red glow like a fire; it was the moon just rising.

"Well," he said to himself, "I must cross the valley and get into the woods before the moon rises." He stood up and threw away the stone. He would have to go as he was, even with the clog.

"Good-by," says he. "Dinushka, I shall always remember you."

Dina clung to him, searched with her hands for a place to stow away some cakes. He took the cakes.

"Thank you," said he; "you are a thoughtful darling. Who will make you dolls after I am gone?" and he stroked her hair.

Dina burst into tears, hid her face in her hands, and scrambled up the hillside like a kid. He could hear, in the darkness, the jingling of the coins on her braids.

Zhilin crossed himself, picked up the lock of his clog so that it might not make a noise, and started on his way, dragging his leg all the time, and keeping his eyes all the time on the glow where the moon was rising.

He knew the way. He had eight versts to go in a direct course, but he would have to strike into the forest before the moon became entirely visible. He crossed the stream, and now the light was increasing behind the mountain.

He proceeded down the valley; and as he walked along, he kept glancing around; still the moon was not visible. The glow was now changing to white light, and one side of the valley grew brighter and brighter. The shadow kept creeping nearer and nearer to the mountain, till it reached its very foot.

Zhilin still hurried along, all the time keeping in the shadow.

He hurried as fast as he could, but the moon rose still faster; and now, at the right, the mountain tops began to be illuminated.

He struck into the forest just as the moon rose above the mountains. It became as light and white as day. On the trees all the leaves were visible. It was warm and bright on the mountain side; everything seemed as if it were dead. The only sound was the roaring of a torrent far below. He walked along in the forest and met no one. Zhilin found a little spot in the forest where it was still darker, and sat down to rest.

While he rested he ate one of his cakes. He procured a stone and once more tried to break the padlock, but he only bruised his hands, and failed to break the lock.

He arose and went on his way. When he had gone a verst his strength gave out, his sore feet tortured him. He had to walk ten steps at a time and then stop.

"There's nothing to be done for it," says he to himself. "I will push on as long as my strength holds out; for if I sit down, then I shall not get up again. If I do not reach the fortress before it is daylight, then I will lie down in the woods and spend the day, and start on tomorrow night again."

He walked all night. Once he passed two Tartars on horseback, but he heard them at some distance, and hid behind a tree.

Already the moon was beginning to pale, the dew had fallen, it was near dawn, and Zhilin had not reached the end of the forest.

"Well," said he to himself, "I will go thirty steps farther, strike into the forest, and sit down."

He went thirty steps, and saw the end of the forest. He went to the edge; it was broad daylight. Before him, as on the palm of his hand, were the steppe and the fortress; and on the left, not far away on the mountain side, fires were burning, or dying out; the smoke rose, and men were moving around the watch-fires.

He looked, and saw the gleaming of firearms; Cossacks,[28] soldiers!

Zhilin was overjoyed.

He gathered his remaining strength, and walked down the mountain. And he said to himself, "God help me, if a mounted Tartar should get sight of me on this bare field! I should not escape him, even though I am so near."

Even while these thoughts were passing through his mind, he saw at the left, on a hillock not fourteen hundred feet away, three Tartars on the watch. They caught sight of him—bore down upon him. Then his heart failed within him. Waving his arms, he shouted at the top of his voice, "Brothers! help, brothers!"

Our men heard him—mounted Cossacks dashed out toward him. They spurred their horses so as to outstrip the Tartars.

The Cossacks were far off, the Tartars near. And now Zhilin collected his last remaining energies, seized his clog in his hand, ran toward the Cossacks, and, without any consciousness of feeling, crossed himself and cried, "Brothers, brothers, brothers!"

The Cossacks were fifteen in number.

The Tartars were dismayed. Before they reached him, they stopped short. And Zhilin was running toward the Cossacks.

The Cossacks surrounded him, and questioned him: "Who are you?" "What is your name?" "Where did you come from?"

But Zhilin was almost beside himself; he wept, and kept shouting, "Brothers, brothers!"

The soldiers hastened up, and gathered around him; one brought him bread, another kasha-gruel,[29] another vodka, another threw a cloak around him, still another broke off his clog.

The officers recognized him, they brought him into the fortress. The soldiers were delighted, his comrades pressed into Zhilin's room.

Zhilin told them what had happened to him, and he ended his tale with the words, "That's the way I went home and got married! No, I see such is not to be my fate."

And he remained in the service in the Caucasus.

At the end of a month Kostuilin was ransomed for five thousand rubles.

He was brought home scarcely alive.

THE END

---

28. *Cossacks* (kos′ aks), members of an elite corps of horsemen in Russia. 29. *kasha-gruel*, a cooked food prepared from crushed grain.

Development

INTERPRETATION

1. Zhilin is a familiar type of romantic hero, an adventurer who lives by his will and his wits. Determine for yourself what qualities distinguish this type of hero by answering the following questions for each of the six episodes in "A Prisoner in the Caucasus." *(a)* What different challenges does Zhilin meet in each episode? *(b)* With what particular virtue or ability does Zhilin respond to each challenge? *(c)* What are the factors in each episode which create a high level of reader interest or appeal?

2. *(a)* Why is dependence upon property alien to the spirit symbolized by Zhilin? *(b)* What is ironic about Zhilin's constant loyalty to Kostuilin? *(c)* In what ways does Kostuilin's presence emphasize Zhilin's heroic proportions?

3. Dina is essential to the mood and feeling of this story, although a nearly identical plot could have been constructed without her. *(a)* What are Dina's most appealing qualities? *(b)* What spirit might Dina be said to symbolize? *(c)* What are the reasons for the rapport between Zhilin and Dina? *(d)* How might Zhilin's adventure with Dina have influenced his decision that a wife, property, and a settled life were not for him?

4. One reader of this story said she "knew what would happen from the time Dina took the doll to the very end." *(a)* What expectations does this story inspire and satisfy which might give credence to this statement? *(b)* Is your enjoyment lessened by Tolstoy's use of a conventional hero? Why or why not?

TECHNIQUE

1. A good adventure story needs more than a wily hero to insure its success; our interest must flow willingly from one episode to the next. *(a)* What methods does Tolstoy use to heighten the tempo of his narration? *(b)* In what ways does the story benefit from its exotic setting?

2. Study the description of Abdul as an example of Tolstoy's narrative technique (page 181, column 1, paragraph 8). *(a)* Take the phrase "as if he were made of springs" as the principal descriptive image applied to Abdul and explain the way each action attributed to him involves or expands this image. *(b)* Read the description aloud to determine the way Tolstoy's syntax and rhythm contribute to the central image. *(c)* In what way does Tolstoy's choice of details in this description convey his attitude toward Abdul?

3. Writers often repeat gestures from scene to scene in order to recall a previous situation or emotion. *(a)* What happened to Zhilin's horse at the end of part 1 and to the Tartar horse after the burial in part 4? *(b)* With what gesture does Dina convey to Zhilin his fate in part 6? *(c)* Why is it dramatically appropriate that the gesture be repeated in part 6?

EXTENSIONS

1. Tolstoy once advised a young writer that "when you criticize your work, always put yourself in the position of the most limited reader, who is looking only for entertainment in a book." What do you think are the strengths or weaknesses of this philosophy?

2. Take the general plot of "A Prisoner in the Caucasus" and graft it onto a contemporary setting. Briefly discuss what you would make the main scenes of a new story, remembering that you are still trying to entertain your readers with a romantic adventure.

The Wall

JEAN-PAUL SARTRE[1] / France

(1905–1980)

translated from the French by Marie Jolas

They pushed us into a large white room and my eyes began to blink because the light hurt them. Then I saw a table and four fellows seated at the table, civilians, looking at some papers. The other prisoners were herded together at one end and we were obliged to cross the entire room to join them. There were several I knew, and others who must have been foreigners. The two in front of me were blond with round heads. They looked alike. I imagine they were French. The smaller one kept pulling at his trousers, out of nervousness.

This lasted about three hours. I was dog-tired and my head was empty. But the room was well-heated, which struck me as rather agreeable; we had not stopped shivering for twenty-four hours. The guards led the prisoners in one after the other in front of the table. Then the four fellows asked them their names and what they did. Most of the time that was all— or perhaps from time to time they would ask such questions as: "Did you help sabotage the munitions?" or, "Where were you on the morning of the ninth and what were you doing?" They didn't even listen to the replies, or at least they didn't seem to. They just remained silent for a moment and looked straight ahead, then they began to write. They asked Tom if it was true he had served in the International Brigade.[2] Tom couldn't say he hadn't because of the papers they had found in his jacket. They didn't ask Juan anything, but after he told them his name, they wrote for a long while.

"It's my brother José who's the anarchist," Juan said. "You know perfectly well he's not here now. I don't belong to

1. *Sartre* (sär′ trə, särt). 2. *International Brigade*, a group of volunteers from numerous countries who fought with the Spanish Republicans against the Fascists during the Spanish Civil War (1936-1939).

any party. I never did take part in politics."
They didn't answer.

Then Juan said, "I didn't do anything. And I'm not going to pay for what the others did."

His lips were trembling. A guard told him to stop talking and led him away. It was my turn.

"Your name is Pablo Ibbieta?"[3]

I said yes.

The fellow looked at his papers and said, "Where is Ramon Gris?"

"I don't know."

"You hid him in your house from the sixth to the nineteenth."

"I did not."

They continued to write for a moment and the guards led me away. In the hall, Tom and Juan were waiting between two guards. We started walking. Tom asked one of the guards, "What's the idea?" "How do you mean?" the guard said. "Was that just the preliminary questioning, or was that the trial?" "That was the trial," the guard said. "So now what? What are they going to do with us?" The guard answered drily, "The verdict will be told you in your cell."

In reality, our cell was one of the cellars of the hospital. It was terribly cold there because it was very drafty. We had been shivering all night long and it had hardly been any better during the day. I had spent the preceding five days in a cellar in the archbishop's palace, a sort of dungeon that must have dated back to the Middle Ages. There were lots of prisoners and not much room, so they housed them just anywhere. But I was not homesick for my dungeon. I hadn't been cold there, but I had been alone, and that gets to be irritating. In the cellar I had company. Juan didn't say a word; he was afraid, and besides, he was too young to have anything to say. But Tom was a good talker and knew Spanish well.

In the cellar there were a bench and four straw mattresses. When they led us back we sat down and waited in silence. After a while Tom said, "Our goose is cooked."

"I think so too," I said. "But I don't believe they'll do anything to the kid."

Tom said, "They haven't got anything on him. He's the brother of a fellow who's fighting, and that's all."

I looked at Juan. He didn't seem to have heard.

Tom continued, "You know what they do in Saragossa?[4] They lay the guys across the road and then they drive over them with trucks. It was a Moroccan deserter who told us that. They say it's just to save ammunition."

I said, "Well, it doesn't save gasoline."

I was irritated with Tom; he shouldn't have said that.

He went on, "There are officers walking up and down the roads with their hands in their pockets, smoking, and they see that it's done right. Do you think they'd put 'em out of their misery? Like hell they do. They just let 'em holler. Sometimes as long as an hour. The Moroccan said the first time he almost puked."

"I don't believe they do that here," I said, "unless they really are short of ammunition."

The daylight came in through four air vents and a round opening that had been cut in the ceiling, to the left, and which opened directly onto the sky. It was through this hole, which was ordinarily closed by means of a trapdoor, that they unloaded coal into the cellar. Directly under the hole, there was a big pile of coal dust; it had been intended for heating the hospital, but at the beginning of the war they had evacuated the patients and the coal had stayed there unused; it even got rained on from time to time, when they forgot to close the trapdoor.

Tom started to shiver. "God damn it," he said, "I'm shivering. There, it is starting again."

He rose and began to do gymnastic exercises. At each movement, his shirt opened and showed his white, hairy

3. *Ibbieta* (ē byā′ tä) 4. *Saragossa*, a city in northeastern Spain captured by the Fascists, who employed Moroccan mercenary soldiers in their army.

chest. He lay down on his back, lifted his legs in the air and began to do the scissors movement. I watched his big buttocks tremble. Tom was tough, but he had too much fat on him. I kept thinking that soon bullets and bayonet points would sink into that mass of tender flesh as though it were a pat of butter.

I wasn't exactly cold, but I couldn't feel my shoulders or my arms. From time to time, I had the impression that something was missing and I began to look around for my jacket. Then I would suddenly remember they hadn't given me a jacket. It was rather awkward. They had taken our clothes to give them to their own soldiers and had left us only our shirts and these cotton trousers the hospital patients wore in midsummer. After a moment, Tom got up and sat down beside me, breathless.

"Did you get warmed up?"

"Damn it, no. But I'm all out of breath."

Around eight o'clock in the evening, a Major came in with two Falangists.[5]

"What are the names of those three over there?" he asked the guard.

"Steinbock, Ibbieta and Mirbal," said the guard.

The Major put on his glasses and examined his list.

"Steinbock—Steinbock . . . Here it is. You are condemned to death. You'll be shot tomorrow morning."

He looked at his list again.

"The other two, also," he said.

"That's not possible," said Juan. "Not me."

The Major looked at him with surprise. "What's your name?"

"Juan Mirbal."

"Well, your name is here," said the Major, "and you're condemned to death."

"I didn't do anything," said Juan.

The Major shrugged his shoulders and turned toward Tom and me.

"You are both Basque?"[6]

"No, nobody's Basque."

He appeared exasperated.

"I was told there were three Basques. I'm not going to waste my time running after them. I suppose you don't want a priest?"

We didn't even answer.

Then he said, "A Belgian doctor will be around in a little while. He has permission to stay with you all night."

He gave a military salute and left.

"What did I tell you?" Tom said. "We're in for something swell."

"Yes," I said. "It's a damned shame for the kid."

I said that to be fair, but I really didn't like the kid. His face was too refined and it was disfigured by fear and suffering, which had twisted all his features. Three days ago, he was just a kid with a kind of affected manner some people like. But now he looked like an aging fairy, and I thought to myself he would never be young again, even if they let him go. It wouldn't have been a bad thing to show him a little pity, but pity makes me sick, and besides, I couldn't stand him. He hadn't said anything more, but he had turned gray. His face and hands were gray. He sat down again and stared, round-eyed, at the ground. Tom was good-hearted and tried to take him by the arm, but the kid drew himself away violently and made an ugly face. "Leave him alone," I said quietly. "Can't you see he's going to start to bawl?" Tom obeyed regretfully. He would have liked to console the kid; that would have kept him occupied and he wouldn't have been tempted to think about himself. But it got on my nerves. I had never thought about death, for the reason that the question had never come up. But now it had come up, and there was nothing else to do but think about it.

Tom started talking. "Say, did you ever bump anybody off?" he asked me. I didn't answer. He started to explain to me that he had bumped off six fellows since August. He hadn't yet realized what we were in

5. *Falangists* (fə lan′ jists), members of the Spanish Fascist party that won the Civil War. 6. *Basque* (bask), one of a people of unknown origin inhabiting the northern region of Spain.

for, and I saw clearly he didn't *want* to realize it. I myself hadn't quite taken it in. I wondered if it hurt very much. I thought about the bullets; I imagined their fiery hail going through my body. All that was beside the real question; but I was calm, we had all night in which to realize it. After a while Tom stopped talking and I looked at him out of the corner of my eye. I saw that he, too, had turned gray and that he looked pretty miserable. I said to myself, "It's starting." It was almost dark, a dull light filtered through the air vents across the coal pile and made a big spot under the sky. Through the hole in the ceiling I could already see a star. The night was going to be clear and cold.

The door opened and two guards entered. They were followed by a blond man in a tan uniform. He greeted us.

"I'm the doctor," he said. "I've been authorized to give you any assistance you may require in these painful circumstances."

He had an agreeable, cultivated voice.

I said to him, "What are you going to do here?"

"Whatever you want me to do. I shall do everything in my power to lighten these few hours."

"Why did you come to us? There are lots of others: the hospital's full of them."

"I was sent here," he answered vaguely. "You'd probably like to smoke, wouldn't you?" he added suddenly. "I've got some cigarettes and even some cigars."

He passed around some English cigarettes and some *puros*,[7] but we refused them. I looked him straight in the eye and he appeared uncomfortable.

"You didn't come here out of compassion," I said to him. "In fact, I know who you are. I saw you with some fascists in the barracks yard the day I was arrested."

I was about to continue, when all at once something happened to me which surprised me: the presence of this doctor had suddenly ceased to interest me. Usually, when I've got hold of a man I don't let go. But somehow the desire to speak had left me. I shrugged my shoulders and turned away. A little later, I looked up and saw he was watching me with an air of curiosity. The guards had sat down on one of the mattresses. Pedro, the tall thin one, was twiddling his thumbs, while the other one shook his head occasionally to keep from falling asleep.

"Do you want some light?" Pedro suddenly asked the doctor. The other fellow nodded, "Yes." I think he was not over-intelligent, but doubtless he was not malicious. As I looked at his big, cold, blue eyes, it seemed to me the worst thing about him was his lack of imagination. Pedro went out and came back with an oil lamp which he set on the corner of the bench. It gave a poor light, but it was better than nothing; the night before we had been left in the dark. For a long while I stared at the circle of light the lamp threw on the ceiling. I was fascinated. Then, suddenly, I came to, the light circle paled, and I felt as if I were being crushed under an enormous weight. It wasn't the thought of death, and it wasn't fear; it was something anonymous. My cheeks were burning hot and my head ached.

I roused myself and looked at my two companions. Tom had his head in his hands and only the fat, white nape of his neck was visible. Juan was by far the worst off; his mouth was wide open and his nostrils were trembling. The doctor came over to him and touched him on the shoulder, as though to comfort him; but his eyes remained cold. Then I saw the Belgian slide his hand furtively down Juan's arm to his wrist. Indifferent, Juan let himself be handled. Then, as though absent-mindedly, the Belgian laid three fingers over his wrist; at the same time, he drew away somewhat and managed to turn his back to me. But I leaned over backward and saw him take out his watch and look at it a moment before relinquishing the boy's wrist. After a moment, he let the in-

---

7. *puros*, cigars.

ert hand fall and went and leaned against the wall. Then, as if he had suddenly remembered something very important that had to be noted down immediately, he took a notebook from his pocket and wrote a few lines in it. "The son-of-a-bitch," I thought angrily. "He better not come and feel my pulse; I'll give him a punch in his dirty jaw."

He didn't come near me, but I felt he was looking at me. I raised my head and looked back at him. In an impersonal voice, he said, "Don't you think it's frightfully cold here?"

He looked purple with cold.

"I'm not cold," I answered him.

He kept looking at me with a hard expression. Suddenly I understood, and I lifted my hands to my face. I was covered with sweat. Here, in this cellar, in midwinter, right in a draft, I was sweating. I ran my fingers through my hair, which was stiff with sweat; at the same time, I realized my shirt was damp and sticking to my skin. I had been streaming with perspiration for an hour, at least, and had felt nothing. But this fact hadn't escaped that Belgian swine. He had seen the drops rolling down my face and had said to himself that it showed an almost pathological terror; and he himself had felt normal and proud of it because he was cold. I wanted to get up and go punch his face in, but I had hardly started to make a move before my shame and anger had disappeared. I dropped back onto the bench with indifference.

I was content to rub my neck with my handkerchief because now I felt the sweat dripping from my hair onto the nape of my neck and that was disagreeable. I soon gave up rubbing myself, however, for it didn't do any good; my handkerchief was already wringing wet and I was still sweating. My buttocks, too, were sweating, and my damp trousers stuck to the bench.

Suddenly, Juan said, "You're a doctor, aren't you?"

"Yes," said the Belgian.

"Do people suffer—very long?"

"Oh! When . . . ? No, no," said the Belgian, in a paternal voice, "it's quickly over."

His manner was as reassuring as if he had been answering a paying patient.

"But I . . . Somebody told me—they often have to fire two volleys."

"Sometimes," said the Belgian, raising his head, "it just happens that the first volley doesn't hit any of the vital organs."

"So they have to reload their guns and aim all over again?" Juan thought for a moment, then added hoarsely, "But that takes time!"

He was terribly afraid of suffering. He couldn't think about anything else, but that went with his age. As for me, I hardly thought about it any more and it certainly was not fear of suffering that made me perspire.

I rose and walked toward the pile of coal dust. Tom gave a start and looked at me with a look of hate. I irritated him because my shoes squeaked. I wondered if my face was as putty-colored as his. Then I noticed that he, too, was sweating. The sky was magnificient; no light at all came into our dark corner and I had only to lift my head to see the Big Bear. But it didn't look the way it had looked before. Two days ago, from my cell in the archbishop's palace, I could see a big patch of sky and each time of day brought back a different memory. In the morning, when the sky was a deep blue, and light, I thought of beaches along the Atlantic; at noon, I could see the sun, and I remembered a bar in Seville where I used to drink manzanilla and eat anchovies and olives; in the afternoon, I was in the shade, and I thought of the deep shadow which covers half of the arena while the other half gleams in the sunlight: it really gave me a pang to see the whole earth reflected in the sky like that. Now, however, no matter how much I looked up in the air, the sky no longer recalled anything. I liked it better that way. I came back and sat down next to Tom. There was a long silence.

Then Tom began to talk in a low voice. He had to keep talking, otherwise he lost his way in his own thoughts. I believe he was talking to me, but he didn't look at me. No doubt he was afraid to look at me, because I was gray and sweating. We were both alike and worse than mirrors for each other. He looked at the Belgian, the only one who was alive.

"Say, do you understand? I don't."

Then I, too, began to talk in a low voice. I was watching the Belgian.

"Understand what? What's the matter?"

"Something's going to happen to us that I don't understand."

There was a strange odor about Tom. It seemed to me that I was more sensitive to odors than ordinarily. With a sneer, I said, "You'll understand, later."

"That's not so sure," he said stubbornly. "I'm willing to be courageous, but at least I ought to know . . . Listen, they're going to take us out into the courtyard. All right. The fellows will be standing in line in front of us. How many of them will there be?"

"Oh, I don't know. Five, or eight. Not more."

"That's enough. Let's say there'll be eight of them. Somebody will shout 'Shoulder arms!' and I'll see all eight rifles aimed at me. I'm sure I'm going to feel like going through the wall. I'll push against the wall as hard as I can with my back, and the wall won't give in. The way it is in a nightmare . . . I can imagine all that. Ah, if you only knew how well I can imagine it!"

"Skip it!" I said. "I can imagine it too."

"It must hurt like the devil. You know they aim at your eyes and mouth so as to disfigure you," he added maliciously. "I can feel the wounds already. For the last hour I've been having pains in my head and neck. Not real pains—it's worse still. They're the pains I'll feel tomorrow morning. And after that, then what?"

I understood perfectly well what he meant, but I didn't want to seem to understand. As for the pains, I, too, felt them all through my body, like a lot of little gashes. I couldn't get used to them, but I was like him, I didn't think they were very important.

"After that," I said roughly, "you'll be eating daisies."

He started talking to himself, not taking his eyes off the Belgian, who didn't seem to be listening to him. I knew what he had come for, and that what we were thinking didn't interest him. He had come to look at our bodies, our bodies which were dying alive.

"It's like in a nightmare," said Tom. "You want to think of something, you keep having the impression you've got it, that you're going to understand, and then it slips away from you, it eludes you and it's gone again. I say to myself, afterward, there won't be anything. But I don't really understand what that means. There were moments when I almost do—and then it's gone again. I start to think of the pains, the bullets, the noise of the shooting. I am a materialist,[8] I swear it; and I'm not going crazy, either. But there's something wrong. I see my own corpse. That's not hard, but it's *I* who see it, with *my* eyes. I'll have to get to the point where I think—where I think I won't see anything more. I won't hear anything more, and the world will go on for the others. We're not made to think that way, Pablo. Believe me, I've already stayed awake all night waiting for something. But this is not the same thing. This will grab us from behind, Pablo, and we won't be ready for it."

"Shut up," I said. "Do you want me to call a father confessor?"

He didn't answer. I had already noticed that he had a tendency to prophesy and call me "Pablo" in a kind of pale voice. I didn't like that very much, but it seems all the Irish are like that. I had a vague impression that he smelled of urine. Actually, I didn't like Tom very much, and I didn't see why, just because we were

---

8. *a materialist,* one whose interests are mainly tangible and who denies any spiritual influences in human affairs.

going to die together, I should like him any better. There are certain fellows with whom it would be different—with Ramon Gris, for instance. But between Tom and Juan, I felt alone. In fact, I liked it better that way. With Ramon I might have grown soft. But I felt terribly hard at that moment, and I wanted to stay hard.

Tom kept on muttering, in a kind of absent-minded way. He was certainly talking to keep from thinking. Naturally, I agreed with him, and I could have said everything he was saying. It's not *natural* to die. And since I was going to die, nothing seemed natural any more: neither the coal pile, nor the bench, nor Pedro's dirty old face. Only it was disagreeable for me to think the same things Tom thought. And I knew perfectly well that all night long, within five minutes of each other, we would keep on thinking things at the same time, sweating or shivering at the same time. I looked at him sideways and, for the first time, he seemed strange to me. He had death written on his face. My pride was wounded. For twenty-four hours I had lived side by side with Tom, I had listened to him, I had talked to him, and I knew we had nothing in common. And now we were as alike as twin brothers, simply because we were going to die together. Tom took my hand without looking at me.

"Pablo, I wonder . . . I wonder if it's true that we just cease to exist."

I drew my hand away.

"Look between your feet, you dirty dog."

There was a puddle between his feet and water was dripping from his trousers.

"What's the matter?" he said, frightened.

"You're wetting your pants," I said to him.

"It's not true," he said furiously. "I can't be . . . I don't feel anything."

The Belgian had come closer to him. With an air of false concern, he asked, "Aren't you feeling well?"

Tom didn't answer. The Belgian looked at the puddle without comment. "I don't know what that is," Tom said savagely, "but I'm not afraid. I swear to you, I'm not afraid."

The Belgian made no answer. Tom rose and went to the corner. He came back, buttoning his fly, and sat down, without a word. The Belgian was taking notes.

We were watching the doctor. Juan was watching him too. All three of us were watching him because he was alive. He had the gestures of a living person, the interests of a living person; he was shivering in this cellar the way living people shiver; he had an obedient, well-fed body. We, on the other hand, didn't feel our bodies any more—not the same way, in any case. I felt like touching my trousers, but I didn't dare to. I looked at the Belgian, well-planted on his two legs, master of his muscles—and able to plan for tomorrow. We were like three shadows deprived of blood; we were watching him and sucking his life like vampires.

Finally he came over to Juan. Was he going to lay his hand on the nape of Juan's neck for some professional reason, or had he obeyed a charitable impulse? If he had acted out of charity, it was the one and only time during the whole night. He fondled Juan's head and the nape of his neck. The kid let him do it, without taking his eyes off him. Then, suddenly, he took hold of the doctor's hand and looked at it in a funny way. He held the Belgian's hand between his own two hands and there was nothing pleasing about them, those two gray paws squeezing that fat red hand. I sensed what was going to happen and Tom must have sensed it, too. But all the Belgian saw was emotion, and he smiled paternally. After a moment, the kid lifted the big red paw to his mouth and started to bite it. The Belgian drew back quickly and stumbled toward the wall. For a second, he looked at us with horror. He must have suddenly understood that we were not men like himself. I began to laugh, and one of the guards started up. The other had fallen asleep with his eyes wide open, showing only the whites.

I felt tired and over-excited at the same time. I didn't want to think any more about what was going to happen at dawn —about death. It didn't make sense, and I never got beyond just words, or emptiness. But whenever I tried to think about something else I saw the barrels of rifles aimed at me. I must have lived through my execution twenty times in succession; one time I thought it was the real thing; I must have dozed off for a moment. They were dragging me toward the wall and I was resisting; I was imploring their pardon. I woke with a start and looked at the Belgian. I was afraid I had cried out in my sleep. But he was smoothing his mustache; he hadn't noticed anything. If I had wanted to, I believe I could have slept for a while. I had been awake for the last forty-eight hours, and I was worn out. But I didn't want to lose two hours of life. They would have had to come and wake me at dawn. I would have followed them, drunk with sleep, and I would have gone off without so much as "Gosh!" I didn't want it that way, I didn't want to die like an animal. I wanted to understand. Besides, I was afraid of having nightmares. I got up and began to walk up and down and, so as to think about something else, I began to think about my past life. Memories crowded in on me, helter-skelter. Some were good and some were bad—at least that was how I had thought of them *before*. There were faces and happenings. I saw the face of a little *nivolero* who had gotten himself horned during the *Feria*,[9] in Valencia. I saw the face of one of my uncles, of Ramon Gris. I remembered all kinds of things that had happened: how I had been on strike for three months in 1926, and had almost died of hunger. I recalled a night I had spent on a bench in Granada; I hadn't eaten for three days. I was nearly wild, I didn't want to give up the sponge. I had to smile. With what eagerness I had run after happiness, and women, and liberty! And to what end? I

had wanted to liberate Spain, I admired Py Margall, I had belonged to the anarchist movement, I had spoken at public meetings. I took everything as seriously as if I had been immortal.

At that time I had the impression that I had my whole life before me, and I thought to myself, "It's all a god-damned lie." Now it wasn't worth anything because it was finished. I wondered how I had ever been able to go out and have a good time with girls. I wouldn't have lifted my little finger if I had ever imagined that I would die like this. I saw my life before me, finished, closed, like a bag, and yet what was inside was not finished. For a moment I tried to appraise it. I would have liked to say to myself, "It's been a good life." But it couldn't be appraised, it was only an outline. I had spent my time writing checks on eternity, and had understood nothing. Now, I didn't miss anything. There were a lot of things I might have missed: the taste of manzanilla, for instance, or the swims I used to take in summer in a little creek near Cadiz. But death had taken the charm out of everything.

Suddenly the Belgian had a wonderful idea.

"My friends," he said to us, "if you want me to—and providing the military authorities give their consent—I could undertake to deliver a word or some token from you to your loved ones . . ."

Tom growled, "I haven't got anybody."

I didn't answer. Tom waited for a moment, then he looked at me with curiosity. "Aren't you going to send any message to Concha?"

"No."

I hated that sort of sentimental conspiracy. Of course, it was my fault, since I had mentioned Concha the night before, and I should have kept my mouth shut. I had been with her for a year. Even as late as last night, I would have cut my arm

---

9. *nivolero . . . Feria.* Nivolero is probably a corruption of *novillero*, an aspiring but untrained bullfighter. A *Feria* is a fair or holiday festival.

off with a hatchet just to see her again for five minutes. That was why I had mentioned her. I couldn't help it. Now I didn't care any more about seeing her. I hadn't anything more to say to her. I didn't even want to hold her in my arms. I loathed my body because it had turned gray and was sweating—and I wasn't even sure that I didn't loathe hers too. Concha would cry when she heard about my death; for months she would have no more interest in life. But still it was I who was going to die. I thought of her beautiful, loving eyes. When she looked at me something went from her to me. But I thought to myself that it was all over; if she looked at me *now* her gaze would not leave her eyes, it would not reach out to me. I was alone.

Tom, too, was alone, but not the same way. He was seated astride his chair and had begun to look at the bench with a sort of smile, with surprise, even. He reached out his hand and touched the wood cautiously, as though he were afraid of breaking something, then he drew his hand back hurriedly, and shivered. I wouldn't have amused myself touching that bench, if I had been Tom, that was just some more Irish play-acting. But somehow it seemed to me too that the different objects had something funny about them. They seemed to have grown paler, less massive than before. I had only to look at the bench, the lamp or the pile of coal dust to feel I was going to die. Naturally, I couldn't think clearly about my death, but I saw it everywhere, even on the different objects, the way they had withdrawn and kept their distance, tactfully, like people talking at the bedside of a dying person. It was *his own death* Tom had just touched on the bench.

In the state I was in, if they had come and told me I could go home quietly, that my life would be saved, it would have left me cold. A few hours, or a few years of waiting are all the same, when you've lost the illusion of being eternal. Nothing mattered to me any more. In a way, I was calm. But it was a horrible kind of calm—because of my body. My body—I saw with its eyes and I heard with its ears, but it was no longer I. It sweat and trembled independently, and I didn't recognize it any longer. I was obliged to touch it and look at it to know what was happening to it, just as if it had been someone else's body. At times I still felt it, I felt a slipping, a sort of headlong plunging, as in a falling airplane, or else I heard my heart beating. But this didn't give me confidence. In fact, everything that came from my body had something damned dubious about it. Most of the time it was silent, it stayed put and I didn't feel anything other than a sort of heaviness, a loathsome presence against me. I had the impression of being bound to an enormous vermin.

The Belgian took out his watch and looked at it.

"It's half-past three," he said.

The son-of-a-bitch! He must have done it on purpose. Tom jumped up. We hadn't yet realized the time was passing. The night surrounded us like a formless, dark mass; I didn't even remember it had started.

Juan started to shout. Wringing his hands, he implored, "I don't want to die! I don't want to die!"

He ran the whole length of the cellar with his arms in the air, then he dropped down onto one of the mattresses, sobbing. Tom looked at him with dismal eyes and didn't even try to console him any more. The fact was, it was no use; the kid made more noise than we did, but he was less affected, really. He was like a sick person who defends himself against his malady with a high fever. When there's not even any fever left, it's much more serious.

He was crying. I could tell he felt sorry for himself; he was thinking about death. For one second, one single second, I too felt like crying, crying out of pity for myself. But just the contrary happened. I took one look at the kid, saw his thin, sobbing shoulders, and I felt I was inhuman. I couldn't feel pity either for these others or for myself. I said to myself, "I want to die decently."

Tom had gotten up and was standing just under the round opening looking out for the first signs of daylight. I was determined, I wanted to die decently, and I only thought about that. But underneath, ever since the doctor had told us the time, I felt time slipping, flowing by, one drop at a time.

It was still dark when I heard Tom's voice.

"Do you hear them?"

"Yes."

People were walking in the courtyard.

"What the hell are they doing? After all, they can't shoot in the dark."

After a moment, we didn't hear anything more. I said to Tom, "There's the daylight."

Pedro got up yawning, and came and blew out the lamp. He turned to the man beside him. "It's hellish cold."

The cellar had grown gray. We could hear shots at a distance.

"It's about to start," I said to Tom. "That must be in the back courtyard."

Tom asked the doctor to give him a cigarette. I didn't want any; I didn't want either cigarettes or alcohol. From that moment on, the shooting didn't stop.

"Can you take it in?" Tom said.

He started to add something, then he stopped and began to watch the door. The door opened and a lieutenant came in with four soldiers. Tom dropped his cigarette.

"Steinbock?"

Tom didn't answer. Pedro pointed him out.

"Juan Mirbal?"

"He's the one on the mattress."

"Stand up," said the Lieutenant.

Juan didn't move. Two soldiers took hold of him by the armpits and stood him up on his feet. But as soon as they let go of him he fell down.

The soldiers hesitated a moment.

"He's not the first one to get sick," said the Lieutenant. "You'll have to carry him, the two of you. We'll arrange things when we get there." He turned to Tom. "All right, come along."

Tom left between two soldiers. Two other soldiers followed, carrying the kid by his arms and legs. He was not unconscious; his eyes were wide open and tears were rolling down his cheeks. When I started to go out, the Lieutenant stopped me.

"Are you Ibbieta?"

"Yes."

"You wait here. They'll come and get you later on."

They left. The Belgian and the two jailers left too, and I was alone. I didn't understand what had happened to me, but I would have liked it better if they had ended it all right away. I heard the volleys at almost regular intervals; at each one, I shuddered. I felt like howling and tearing my hair. But instead, I gritted my teeth and pushed my hands deep into my pockets, because I wanted to stay decent.

An hour later, they came to fetch me and took me up to the first floor in a little room which smelt of cigar smoke and was so hot it seemed to me suffocating. Here there were two officers sitting in comfortable chairs, smoking, with papers spread out on their knees.

"Your name is Ibbieta?"

"Yes."

"Where is Ramon Gris?"

"I don't know."

The man who questioned me was small and stocky. He had hard eyes behind his glasses.

"Come nearer," he said to me.

I went nearer. He rose and took me by the arms, looking at me in a way calculated to make me go through the floor. At the same time he pinched my arms with all his might. He didn't mean to hurt me; it was quite a game; he wanted to dominate me. He also seemed to think it was necessary to blow his fetid breath right into my face. We stood like that for a moment, only I felt more like laughing than anything else. It takes a lot more than that to intimidate a man who's about to die: it didn't work. He pushed me away violently and sat down again.

"It's your life or his," he said. "You'll be allowed to go free if you tell us where he is."

After all, these two bedizened fellows with their riding crops and boots were just men who were going to die one day. A little later than I, perhaps, but not a great deal. And there they were, looking for names among their papers, running after other men in order to put them in prison or do away with them entirely. They had their opinions on the future of Spain and on other subjects. Their petty activities seemed to me to be offensive and ludicrous. I could no longer put myself in their place. I had the impression they were crazy.

The little fat fellow kept looking at me, tapping his boots with his riding crop. All his gestures were calculated to make him appear like a spirited, ferocious animal.

"Well? Do you understand?"

"I don't know where Gris is," I said. "I thought he was in Madrid."

The other officer lifted his pale hand indolently. This indolence was also calculated. I saw through all their little tricks, and I was dumbfounded that men should still exist who took pleasure in that kind of thing.

"You have fifteen minutes to think it over," he said slowly. "Take him to the linen-room, and bring him back here in fifteen minutes. If he continues to refuse, he'll be executed at once."

They knew what they were doing. I had spent the night waiting. After that, they had made me wait another hour in the cellar, while they shot Tom and Juan, and now they locked me in the linen-room. They must have arranged the whole thing the night before. They figured that sooner or later people's nerves wear out and they hoped to get me that way.

They made a big mistake. In the linen-room I sat down on a ladder because I felt very weak, and I began to think things over. Not their proposition, however. Naturally I knew where Gris was. He was hiding in his cousins' house, about two miles outside of the city. I knew, too, that I would not reveal his hiding place, unless they tortured me (but they didn't seem to be considering that). All that was definitely settled and didn't interest me in the least. Only I would have liked to understand the reasons for my own conduct. I would rather die than betray Gris. Why? I no longer liked Ramon Gris. My friendship for him had died shortly before dawn along with my love for Concha, along with my own desire to live. Of course I still admired him—he was hard. But it was not for that reason that I was willing to die in his place; his life was no more valuable than mine. No life was of any value. A man was going to be stood up against a wall and fired at till he dropped dead. It didn't make any difference whether it was I or Gris or somebody else. I knew perfectly well he was more useful to the Spanish cause than I was, but I didn't give a God damn about Spain or anarchy, either; nothing had any importance now. And yet, there I was. I could save my skin by betraying Gris and I refused to do it. It seemed more ludicrous to me than anything else; it was stubbornness.

I thought to myself, "Am I hard-headed!" And I was seized with a strange sort of cheerfulness.

They came to fetch me and took me back to the two officers. A rat darted out under our feet and that amused me. I turned to one of the Falangists and said to him, "Did you see that rat?"

He made no reply. He was gloomy, and took himself very seriously. As for me, I felt like laughing, but I restrained myself because I was afraid that if I started, I wouldn't be able to stop. The Falangist wore mustaches. I kept after him, "You ought to cut off those mustaches, you fool."

I was amused by the fact that he let

hair grow all over his face while he was still alive. He gave me a kind of half-hearted kick, and I shut up.

"Well," said the fat officer, "have you thought things over?"

I looked at them with curiosity, like insects of a very rare species.

"I know where he is," I said. "He's hiding in the cemetery. Either in one of the vaults, or in the gravediggers' shack."

I said that just to make fools of them. I wanted to see them get up and fasten their belts and bustle about giving orders.

They jumped to their feet.

"Fine. Moles, go ask Lieutenant Lopez for fifteen men. And as for you," the little fat fellow said to me, "if you've told the truth, I don't go back on my word. But you'll pay for this, if you're pulling our leg."

They left noisily and I waited in peace, still guarded by the Falangists. From time to time I smiled at the thought of the face they were going to make. I felt dull and malicious. I could see them lifting up the grave stones, or opening the doors of the vaults one by one. I saw the whole situation as though I were another person: the prisoner determined to play the hero, the solemn Falangists with their mustaches and the men in uniform running around among the graves. It was irresistibly funny.

After half an hour, the little fat fellow came back alone. I thought he had come to give the order to execute me. The others must have stayed in the cemetery.

The officer looked at me. He didn't look at all foolish.

"Take him out in the big courtyard with the others," he said. "When military operations are over, a regular tribunal will decide his case."

I thought I must have misunderstood.

"So they're not—they're not going to shoot me?" I asked.

"Not now, in any case. Afterward, that doesn't concern me."

I still didn't understand.

"But why?" I said to him.

He shrugged his shoulders without replying, and the soldiers led me away. In the big courtyard there was a hundred or so prisoners, women, children and a few old men. I started to walk around the grass plot in the middle. I felt absolutely idiotic. At noon we were fed in the dining hall. Two or three fellows spoke to me. I must have known them, but I didn't answer. I didn't even know where I was.

Toward evening, about ten new prisoners were pushed into the courtyard. I recognized Garcia, the baker.

He said to me, "Lucky dog! I didn't expect to find you alive."

"They condemned me to death," I said, "and then they changed their minds. I don't know why."

"I was arrested at two o'clock," Garcia said.

"What for?"

Garcia took no part in politics.

"I don't know," he said. "They arrest everybody who doesn't think the way they do."

He lowered his voice.

"They got Gris."

I began to tremble.

"When?"

"This morning. He acted like a damned fool. He left his cousins' house Tuesday because of a disagreement. There were any number of fellows who would have hidden him, but he didn't want to be indebted to anybody any more. He said, 'I would have hidden at Ibbieta's, but since they've got him, I'll go hide in the cemetery.'"

"In the cemetery?"

"Yes. It was the god-damnedest thing. Naturally they passed by there this morning; that had to happen. They found him in the gravediggers' shack. They opened fire at him and they finished him off."

"In the cemetery!"

Everything went around in circles, and when I came to I was sitting on the ground. I laughed so hard the tears came to my eyes.

THE END

Development

INTERPRETATION

1. Above all else, Pablo Ibbieta fears being drawn into a "sentimental conspiracy" and dying "like an animal." (a) Define what you think Pablo means by each of these expressions. (b) What forces at work in the story might trap him in either of these postures? (c) What attitudes does Pablo adopt toward his fellow prisoners and captors to protect himself from entrapment?

2. (a) What does Pablo feel motivates Tom's restlessness? (b) Though Tom calls himself a *materialist*, Pablo offers to call a "father confessor" for him after Tom tells of seeing his own corpse. What inconsistency in Tom's philosophy does this underline? (c) Why, after this incident, is Pablo so intent upon degrading Tom?

3. Pablo says that the worst thing about the Belgian doctor was his "lack of imagination" and that he "felt normal and was proud of it." (a) Why shouldn't the Belgian doctor be proud to feel normal? (b) What does Pablo gain by his vivid imagination?

4. When Tom anticipates the experience of pressing his back against the wall, he likens it to "the way it is in a nightmare." (a) What fear is embodied in the image of the wall which makes it as universal as the nightmare? (b) Why is an understanding of the limits of existence essential for understanding its value?

5. With two hours left before dawn, Pablo thinks of his body and most of his past life as being "dubious." (a) If the value of experience is doubtful because life doesn't last forever, why is Pablo so concerned about the way he faces death? (b) Why does it matter whether he betrays Ramon Gris or not?

(c) Why is Pablo so elated by his decision to be "hard-headed"? (d) In what way could the wall now be considered a support, rather than a barrier, to Pablo's freedom?

6. If you were to make a film of the short story "The Wall," the quality of Pablo's final laugh would be all-important. (a) What instructions would you give the actor playing Pablo to suggest the emotional quality you wanted in his laugh? (b) How would you defend your interpretation with reference to the story?

TECHNIQUE

1. Many of Sartre's fictional characters, once they realize that man is vulnerable, are overcome with a loathing for the physical facts of existence. Through what images and references does Pablo convey this emotion?

2. Contemporary world literature has spawned a group of unconventional fictional characters who have been called anti-heroes. By what methods does Sartre undermine traditional heroic attitudes and expectations in "The Wall"?

EXTENSIONS

1. Pablo says of Juan that he was "too young to have anything to say." (a) What do you think he means? (b) Do you agree or disagree with Pablo's statement? Why? (c) Defend or criticize the following interpretation: Juan lives for the possibilities of his future. Anticipation of losing these possibilities leaves him speechless. Only those men who have tasted the fullness of experience can come to terms with their lives and resolve themselves for death.

The Trial

JERZY ANDRZEJEWSKI[1] / Poland
(1909–   )
translated from the Polish by Adam Gillon and Ludwik Krzyzanowski

It happened during the first days of October 1939.[2]

The forest ranger of Rudawica[3] gave the same replies to all of the questions. The arms found by the Germans near his house were left the day before by the Polish soldiers from the division routed in the vicinity of Zamosc.[4] Accustomed to many years of solitary life he was caught too suddenly by the whole thing to invent a plausible lie on the spur of the moment. He confessed truthfully: he himself had buried all the rifles, the revolvers and the box of ammunition—without anyone's help. That is precisely what the Germans from the panzer unit[5] refused to believe.

They had two officers, both under thirty. They were sitting at the table without having removed their raincoats and steel helmets. Their battle attire alone gave the impression that the hastily called court-martial would end immediately. Peter was standing on the opposite side of the table between two hefty soldiers. Kaczynski,[6] the shopkeeper from Rudawica, pale and frightened, served as interpreter with his poor German.

The elder of the two officers, a lieutenant, conducted the interrogation. His tanned sportsman's face, of harsh regular features, expressed coldness and contempt. The other officer, with light blond hair and the appearance of a Prussian

1. *Andrzejewski* (än′ dje yev′ skē). 2. *October 1939*, the month Poland surrendered to the German invasion. 3. *Rudawica* (rü′ dä vē tsä), the region around the city of Ruda in southern Poland. 4. *Zamosc* (zä′ môshch), a city in eastern Poland near the German frontier. 5. *panzer unit*, an armored division of the German army. 6. *Kaczynski* (kä chin′ skē).

Junker,[7] was leaning his head back against the wall, indifferently looking out the window. The small windowpanes revealed a checkered landscape; the brown mud of the yard, a wooden fence, a rusty patch of the sky cut across by the crane of the well, two blackish apple trees, and beyond them a pine forest steeped in the misty blue of an October afternoon.

Peter saw nothing of this. From the beginning of the hearing he gazed stubbornly at the floor. In the place where he was standing there were traces of the mud brought in by the retreating Polish soldiers the night before. The dried clods had partly sunk into the rough boards of the floor.

There were five of them. They were all thin, dirty and unshaven; their faces were dark with fatigue, their boots torn, their coats bespattered with mud and soaked through. They stayed briefly. They fell upon the remnants of brown bread and old lard ravenously like men who had not eaten for many days. This was all the food Peter had. During the month of September the poor household of the forest ranger was completely cleaned out by crowds of fleeing civilians.

That night resembled the present night. From afar through the stillness of the forest came the hollow rumble of artillery. It was the surrounded division of General Kleeberg, the last of the routed and defeated Polish army, making its last stand. The Germans had not yet reached the Rudawica forests. Although the soldiers could hardly stand on their feet, they did not want to spend the night at the ranger's house. Their weariness and fear of being taken prisoner heightened their anxiety. Every now and then one of them would jump up and come to the window or look out into the yard, listening for the rumble of tanks from the nearby highway. They were gone before it grew dark. Actually not one of them thought of returning home. They intended to retreat further south to the Carpathians[8] in order to get to the Hungarian border across the German

positions. But they had no more strength to carry the arms that they had salvaged. Each retaining two revolvers, they left the rifles and the box of ammunition in the hall. Peter asked what he was to do, and they advised him to bury the things. They were hoping to return here shortly. Peter agreed.

Night fell when he started digging. He selected what seemed to him the best place, at the back of the yard by the fence behind the well. He brought out an old chest from the attic, lined it with hay and carefully placed the arms inside. He worked in complete darkness, by the dim light of a lantern covered by an old rag. The digging was hard. The clayey ground was heavy from the recent rains. Besides, the chest was quite tall so that he had to dig a hole of at least three feet deep. This took several hours. When he awoke at dawn the German panzer units were rumbling along the highway. He got up and throwing the sheepskin on his shirt went into the yard to check whether he had evenly and thoroughly covered up the hole. It seemed to him that this was so and this reassured him. But despite his fatigue he did not go back to sleep. He spent the whole morning loafing around the house. The enemy tanks rumbled on ceaselessly from the forest. The air shook with the roar of cars and motorcycles. A chilling dread came from that unseen might which like a flood of iron and steel seemed to trample the earth and life with immensity. The day was as the one before—wet and rainy. At times there rose gusts of a keen autumn wind.

At noon Charles Walitzki[9] came from Rudawica. He wanted to warn Peter of the Germans' arrival. He also brought a quarter loaf of bread, a few eggs and a piece of butter. Peter took him to the yard

---

7. *Prussian Junker,* a member of the aristocracy of Prussia, a German state traditionally devoted to militarism. **8.** *Carpathians* (kär pā′ thē əns), a mountain range in central Europe running from northern Czechoslovakia to central Rumania. **9.** *Walitzki* (vä litz′ kē).

and showed him the spot where he had dug the hole. He wanted someone else, besides himself, to know about the hidden arms. Charles stayed only a short while. He was in a hurry to get back home, not wishing to alarm his mother by prolonged absence. The Germans' arrival had frightened her. Thus, Peter was left alone once more. He waited. Only in the late afternoon a number of storm troopers rode up to the ranger's house on their motorcycles. From their vehement shouts and menacing faces Peter guessed that they were asking about arms and Polish soldiers. He denied everything. He was not worried about his security.

Meantime, the soldiers with drawn revolvers scattered around the house and began to search in every corner. Some of them came up to the barn. Others looked in the yard. Peter saw through the window how one of them—a young, tall fellow—evidently bored with inactivity, wandered to the back of the yard. However, even when the man stopped exactly on the spot in which the chest was buried he felt no anxiety. Suddenly the soldier stopped and began to tap the earth gingerly with his heel. "Heinrich!" he shouted without turning. Another soldier came running to him. Soon there were several of them.

From that moment on—he was not aware how long it could have taken—Peter fell into a state of numbness. While he appeared calm on the surface, inwardly he reacted as though he were dreaming a dream that could not be interrupted. He penetrated into a deep darkness that was drawing him into its bottomless void, like a dark mirror reflecting the motion of tormenting shadows.

At a certain moment the lieutenant asked Kaczynski the same question for the second time. The unfamiliar, sharp and raucous sounds intensified Peter's sensation of being in a dream. But he did not dare to lift his eyes. He feared to find hostile judges in the officers sitting behind the table, to find the well-known shopkeeper in Kaczynski, and his own house in the darkness of his room. Meanwhile, it became more and more difficult for Kaczynski to control his trembling. He stood with a lowered head, a fat and stocky man, constantly rubbing his sweaty hands that had turned red from cold. Only when the lieutenant repeated his last question again did he stop rubbing his hands. A minute later he bent down sideways to Peter and stammered to him rapidly.

Peter understood nothing. Yet he did not raise his head. A cold paralyzed his feet and hands. He felt an emptiness in his chest. "Now I shall wake!" he thought. He was jolted by the fear that this would have to happen immediately so that he might bury the arms that the soldiers had piled under the wall in the hall.

Suddenly he heard the muffled whisper of Kaczynski, "Mr. Ranger!"

The shopkeeper was standing so close that Peter's lowered eyes saw his shoes. They were old, clumsy and mud-bespattered gaiters. A soiled lace from his drawers stuck out from under the trousers, equally torn and muddy. Looking at the formless shoes, Peter asked, dreaming it was his own voice:

"What's the matter?"

Kaczynski swallowed, moving his neck.

"He says he's asking you for the last time."

"The last time?" Peter repeated.

"He wants to know who helped you."

A more severe cold swept over Peter. He gritted his teeth to stop his shaking.

"No one helped me," he said at last, surprised at the clarity and the loudness of his own voice. "No one was here."

The silence which fell after his words seemed to him very long. At length Kaczynski began his stammering translation. Peter listened carefully to those awkward and hesitant sounds. When they ceased he heard the quiet voice of the lieutenant. And suddenly a violent blow to his jaw from below threw his head backward. Before he could understand what happened, he received a second, even stronger blow in his face. He reeled, dazed by pain. Trying to keep his balance he instinctively grasped the chair standing beside the table. It fell. Then, losing the only point of support, he collapsed heavily against the wall. The blows rained on him but he did not defend himself. He did not even try to shield his face with his arm. He thought, however, that what he was experiencing could not be a dream. But the pain obliterated this thought, and it hardly reached his consciousness. Everything in him turned to torture. Even his voice froze in his throat, as if he had lost it. And this seemed the most terrible thing. It was only when he was kicked in his abdomen that an inarticulate howl broke out from behind his clenched teeth. He coiled up. Then a soldier who towered over him, caught him by his arms like a manikin and propping him up against the wall began to kick him in the groin repeatedly at close range. Peter howled. Suddenly he choked and grew still. He was seized with convulsions.

"Halt!" the lieutenant nodded calmly.

When the soldier stepped back, Peter sank to the floor. Pressed into a corner of the room, his knees drawn up under his bowed head, he vomited on himself. At a certain moment he felt that he was being lifted from the floor and sat on a stool. Then they threw some cold water in his face. He came to somewhat. The pain still lingered in him, but in comparison with what it had been a minute ago, it seemed almost a relief. It was quiet in the room. A fly was buzzing on the window pane. The Junker looking out the window was whistling through his teeth. The tanks were rattling on the highway. More closely, a motorcycle was growling.

The hunched Peter, holding his belly with both hands, almost stopped breathing, fearing to unleash the pain again with a careless motion. Suddenly he felt a warm moisture on his face. When he raised his hand mechanically, he felt that his fingers were sticky with thick blood. It

was flowing from his nose, and further below he touched his cut lips and bruised gums. He straightened his body. At first he saw everything through a ruddy, flowing mist. "My forehead must be injured," he thought indifferently. He wiped his eyes with his palm. Now he could see a little better.

Grey dusk began to fall on the room. The silhouettes of the two officers were outlined very clearly against the window and the forest, whose greyish-blue image appeared to reach the very house. Their immobility and their eyes turned to Peter from under the steel helmets, but, passing him by indifferently as though he were an object without importance, made them look like two stone statues. Slightly closer, he noticed Kaczynski, his grey, rough-hewn face and eyes under reddened lids, almost unseeing from fright. Behind him he felt the presence of the soldiers. Instinctively he cringed.

Suddenly the officers exchanged a few brief words. Although he did not want to do it, he looked at them. The pain froze in him at once. He only felt an icy cold within his head. He could neither move nor cry out. He no longer belonged to himself. And feeling more dead than alive for a moment, he now fell into the horror of the last conscious second, its almost inhuman loneliness, that penetrated beyond death, into silence and darkness. No sooner had he shaken himself out of this dread, than he understood that he was lost and there was no escape for him. Then suddenly a thought broke through the frozen tension of terror, the thought that were he to find the hand of a friendly man now he would be saved. It was not death that seemed terrible but the loneliness before it. The fear grew in him. He heard how its dark and noiseless voice went round and round in his head ever more rapidly and violently. He ceased to feel the pounding of his heart. He existed only in the cry which raged under his skull. He was sweating profusely. "I shall go mad," he thought. Seized with a panic he could no longer bear, he jumped from the stool.

The two soldiers caught his arms simultaneously. He tried to wrench himself free. Again the blows fell upon him. But he felt no pain. Choking with the blood that filled his throat and his eyes, he went on wrestling with the soldiers, gaining strength from his fear. Finally he succeeded in pushing one of the soldiers away and pulling the other towards the table.

The blond Junker stopped looking out the window, and the lieutenant who was sitting closer slowly reached for his revolver.

Peter fell down on the table, striking it with his head. He tried to get up. His blood blinded him. And before the soldier could tear away his fingers clutching the edge of the table, he stammered out: "I'll tell you, I'll tell you!"

Kaczynski had not had the time to translate when the lieutenant gave a sign to the soldier to fall back. Peter remained alone. Clutching the table with both hands, his forehead leaning on the edge, he sank to his knees. And although he immediately realized his humiliation, he had no strength to rise. Everything became indifferent and unimportant to him. Only one importunate thought rang stubbornly in his mind.

Meanwhile, the lieutenant, gazing with his motionless eyes at Peter, was playing with his revolver. Suddenly he said a few words to Kaczynski. The latter stood, hunched and blinking his protruding eyes. The sound of the revolver thrown from one hand into the other could be heard distinctly in the room. The fly kept buzzing steadily at the window. At last Kaczynski bent over the kneeling man.

"Who?" he asked in a whisper.

Peter seemed not to have heard. He did not move.

"Mr. Ranger!" the shopkeeper said, "He's asking for the name."

The voice reached Peter from a very great distance. He felt that he was losing consciousness. But at the same time he realized that he must at once gather all his strength, to say the needed name. He raised his head. The German's face, shaded by the helmet, could scarcely be seen in the dusk. Only the eyes amid this shadow were visible: very bright, almost transparent eyes.

Peter closed his eyes. The salty taste of blood made him nauseous. Finally a sharp dazzling idea tore itself from the bottom of the soundless darkness. He breathed deeply and through the blood running from his parted lips he whispered:

"Walitzki!"

"Walitzki?" the lieutenant bent over him.

And he looked at the shopkeeper.

"Who is he?"

Kaczynski drew back and wrenching his fingers started mumbling incoherently. The officer rose and motioned him with his finger. The shopkeeper came closer.

"Walitzki?" the lieutenant repeated.

Kaczynski was silent. The German raised his dark brows and looked at him for a while. Suddenly he straightened his arm and across the table hit the standing man in the face. Kaczynski gave a short cry, and covered his head with his arms. He stood thus for a minute, breathing heavily, his mouth wide-open. At last, he spoke haltingly.

Charles Walitzki was a teacher in Rudawica, a kilometer from here. He was the ranger's friend. He lived with his half-paralyzed mother by the schoolhouse.

"Genug!"[10] the lieutenant snapped and looked at his companion with satisfaction.

The latter nodded, stretched his arms lazily, and rose. Kaczynski looked at one then at the other, blinking his red eyelids.

"Raus, raus!"[11] the lieutenant shouted and pushed him toward the door.

---

10. *Genug!* Enough! 11. *Raus, raus!* Out, get out!

After a while Peter remained in the room with only one soldier. It was the same man who had kicked him in the stomach so ferociously a minute before. Now this German lifted him from the floor and sat him on the stool. He looked at him for a moment. Then he went to the hall and drew some water from the pail. Peter took the cup mechanically. As he drank greedily, the soldier looked at him with a feeling of pity mixed with contempt. He said something to Peter, waited a moment, and repeated his words. Seeing, however, that Peter could not understand him, he shrugged his shoulders, brought another stool to the window, and sat down, lighting a cigarette.

The dusk grew thicker and darker. The forest, still bluish, now turned into a formless mist, like a motionless cloud growing out of a greyish-gold earth; and over it an unseen wind blew other steel-like and brown clouds. The two solitary apple trees framed this landscape with their black supple branches. In the stillness, the raucous voices of the German soldiers sounded like mysterious outcries. And from the depths of the dusk, the rumble of the tanks and motorized columns came as if the night was heralding its darkness with an awesome growl.

Peter almost felt good. Only the cold bothered him. He huddled to contain the cold within himself. Again it seemed to him that it was all a dream. And, as it happens in dreams, he began to worry lest he be late for the meeting with Charles. When Charles was leaving for Rudawica he promised he would try to come in again before nightfall, if he could. He came at this time almost daily.

The shortest way from the Ranger's house to Rudawica runs through the forest. Peter crosses the potato-field behind the house, and hastens along the familiar path. He meets Charles mid-way. Charles is hatless as usual, in a heavy, grey jacket and well-worn trousers. They return to the house by a somewhat longer route, for Peter wants to take a look at the

nursery of young spruce. The forest is filled with blue light, in which the brown trunks of slender pines, cut off from the ground and the roots, sway softly with the wind. When it is quiet the pine branches rustle, causing the illusion that the rustling comes from the clouds. Charles goes first. He is whistling a rhythmic, joyous melody, in which Peter immediately recognizes the first bars of *Eine kleine Nachtmusik*.[12]

Charles looks at him.

"Would you like me to put on a record for you? I like it very much."

He stoops over the record album and by the light of the dying candle finds the record he wants. The fire is crackling in the stove. The small orchestra begins to proclaim its joy. Peter listens with closed eyes. When he opens them, he sees Charles' profile in front of him, his low forehead and above it, dark, thick hair. The loneliness of his own life suddenly seems less painful than usual. He thinks that upon his return home he will be alone in an empty house, but he thinks at the same time that he will see his friend again tomorrow. Waiting—does it not soothe one's solitude?

"It's Mozart," Charles explains, when the serenade comes to an end. "Did you like it?"

"Sure," Peter replies.

Then, late in the evening, Charles accompanies Peter back to his house. They go through the forest. A March rain is falling. The earth steams with fresh moisture. The whiff of the wind from the meadows behind Rudawica is mild and warm. High above the cloudy sky, as if belonging to another, more perfect sky, a few timid stars gleam through.

"Look," says Charles, "soon it will be spring."

"It looks that way," Peter assents.

He shivered with cold. He opened his eyes. The room, like the outside, was steeped in blue light. This gave the im-

---

12. *Eine kleine Nachtmusik,* "A Little Night Music."

pression that nothing was separating its interior from the dusk. The glowing cigarette lit up the soldier's face from time to time, absent, immobile in a fixed stare.

Peter moved. The soldier started and turned towards him quickly. After a minute he stood up and came to the prisoner. They looked at each other in silence.

"Zigaretten?" the German asked.

Peter nodded. When the soldier offered him a pack he took one cigarette. The moment he bore it to his mouth he felt how swollen and sore his lips were. But he took the light from the soldier's cigarette and inhaled the smoke. He immediately began choking and coughing. The slightest movement sent a pang of pain through his head and chest. At last the attack ceased but he was afraid to straighten up lest the pain surge up again. The cigarette which had fallen out of his hand lay on the floor, still glowing. The soldier squashed it with his boot. He kept looking at Peter. Finally he said slowly and deliberately:

"Die . . . you want not? No . . . pity . . ."

Peter remained motionless. To die? This word, spoken in a bad and funny accent, seemed empty and meaningless.

"My life isn't at all interesting," says Peter.

Charles is looking at him.

"What do you know about it?"

"Well, who is to know?"

Charles is silent. Only after a while does he speak up with slow reflection:

"We don't always know what is important in our lives."

Peter rises suddenly and stops at the open window.

"But, really, there isn't anything important in my life. I'm not important, that's all."

He gazes into the night. An August star rolls across the sky like a fiery streak. Fog near the forests spreads so evenly as if it were shallow, whitish water. Peter sits on the window sill.

"To be sure, I was liked by many people. But I am not indispensable to any woman or man. Nobody needs me. I can exist or not exist, it's all the same."

He keeps looking at the yard. At a certain moment he hears Charles rising. Now he paces in the room.

"A bat has flown by," Peter observes.

Charles stops. "I think," he says with the previous deliberation, "that indeed it is important to be indispensable to some person. But perhaps it is even more important if another man is indispensable."

Peter leans out and passes his hand over the rough sun-flowers growing under the window.

"I would be afraid of this."

Charles looks at him with astonishment.

"Why?" he repeats.

Peter husks the unripe, soft seeds and throws them through the window, into the green thicket.

"I don't know," he says at last. "But I would be afraid."

Suddenly from the direction of the forest the rumble of an engine reached Peter's ears. At the same time he heard his own voice, pronouncing Charles' name. Before he opened his eyes he understood that the Germans were going to Rudawica to get Charles. The room was murky, and night stood beyond the window. He wanted to get up, to run, and to recant his accusation. But he had no strength. Only his consciousness worked in him ever more intensely and more clearly.

Suddenly, brakes screeched violently, and a car pulled to a stop before the Ranger's house.

The soldier guarding Peter straightened up. Outside somebody shouted out loudly. Peter immediately recognized the lieutenant's voice. Simultaneously the hall was invaded by the stomping of heavy boots. The door was thrown open by a kick and enormous shadows filled the room. A large carbide lantern, swaying in a soldier's hand, brightened the dusk with a yellow gleam.

A flame swept through Peter's chest as he huddled on his stool. His heart froze in him for a moment. Someone grabbed him by his arms, pulled him and forced him to stand. He lifted his head.

Scarcely a step from himself he saw Charles, surrounded by several huge soldiers. He seemed small and frail among them. He was wearing his usual grey jacket. He was pale but calm. When their eyes met, Peter trembled. He understood at once that Charles knew everything. But he found no hatred or condemnation in his eyes. Overcome, he lowered his head. He kept on his feet with the last remnant of his strength. His whole face was smeared with blood, his sunken eyes were cavernous.

"I was scared . . ." he whispered through his swollen lips.

The soldier next to him struck his back with his rifle butt.

"*Maul halten!*"[13] he shouted.

Quick steps were heard in the hall. The soldiers jumped to attention at once.

The tall lieutenant was the first to enter, and following him came the blond Junker, his hands in the pockets of his raincoat. The younger stopped on the threshold, and the other cast a brief glance at the group of men as he was standing in the middle of the room. When he saw Charles he leaped toward him with clenched fists and broke into savage shouting. Hitherto cool, collected and contemptuous, the German turned into a totally different man in the twinkling of an eye.

Charles' pallor deepened, but he didn't take his eyes off the frenzied officer even for a moment. He gazed at him calmly, with an intensity which only Peter noticed. And his friend's calm was imparted to him. He straightened his body.

"I lied," he said aloud. "He had nothing to do with it. Only me."

The lieutenant had not noticed who dared interrupt him and was speechless at the first moment. Realizing that it was Peter, he sank into him his eyes, white from rage.

"*Was?*"[14]

Peter took a deep breath.

"I lied," he repeated. "He's innocent."

"*Raus!*" the lieutenant screamed.

Meanwhile, Kaczynski drew closer to him and stammering began to explain something.

"*Raus!*" the lieutenant howled.

And he hit him without looking. The shopkeeper groaned and reeled towards the wall. The officer suddenly grew calm, stepped back and turned to his companion.

Staggering, Peter made a motion as if to go towards them. Charles stopped him with his eyes.

"Leave it," he said in his quiet and even voice. "It's no use." And he added more softly:

"It's all finished . . ."

Peter hunched his body and almost soundlessly whispered his friend's name. But Charles heard him. His lips quivered and his eyes darkened. But he controlled himself immediately.

"Hold on!" he said dryly.

The soldier at his side pushed his arm. "Shut up!"

At this moment the lieutenant standing at the door turned around and with a short gesture pointed at Peter and Charles.

"Shoot 'em!"

He went out without looking back, and the young Junker followed behind.

A commotion began in the room. One of the soldiers pushed Peter toward the door, another lifted the lantern high, and its light illuminated the dark hall. Peter, bending his head at the threshold from habit, crossed it first and was at once enveloped by the cold air of the October night.

Darkness lay over the earth. When he raised his eyes he saw turbulent clouds hanging low, and above them, in the very distant depths he could see another sky, calm, frozen almost, and starry. A certain memory passed through his mind, but he

13. *Maul halten!* Shut up! 14. *Was?* What?

could not grasp it. He looked back. Behind him Charles was also looking at the sky.

"Charles!" he whispered again.

The soldiers were talking, apparently discussing which of them was to carry out the execution. Suddenly Peter felt Charles' hand on his arm. He was shaken by such pain as he had not known until now. His hand trembled.

"Don't be afraid," Charles whispered, leaning towards him.

Peter had no time to reply, for he was pushed in the back with a rifle butt. Mechanically wiping the blood off his face with his palm, he obediently moved forward. The lantern lit up the way with a narrow streak. But he stumbled on the stones several times. They were being led to the back of the yard. Although he was not looking over his shoulder, Peter knew that Charles was walking behind him.

"Remember," he suddenly heard his muffled voice, "even this can mean hope . . ."

The darkness was still. Among the sounds of stomping iron-shod boots, Peter could distinguish his own steps, and behind him every step Charles made. Suddenly someone behind him began to whistle loudly. Peter stopped instinctively. He was certain he recognized the lieutenant's voice.

"*Schnell, schnell!*" one of the soldiers prodded him on. He stumbled again, but before he moved on, he managed to turn back and to cast a glance at Charles. He was also listening.

The high-pitched whistle penetrated the night with the first bars of Mozart's gentle serenade. Peter lifted his head. Thick clouds were whirling above, but higher, like a pale light in the darkness, still shone a few stars, distant and solitary. "Hope" he thought mechanically, but without the certainty that he had a right to it.

They finally reached the end of the yard, near the fence. Beside them loomed the black hole, in which the arms had been buried. The rustle of the forest flowed here in a dark wave.

"Halt!" one of the soldiers yelled.

They stopped. Another soldier, broad-shouldered and helmeted, took out his revolver and came up behind Charles. The latter straightened himself, and raised his head. In the darkness he now seemed taller. The shot rang out, brief and hollow. Charles staggered and with his hands pressed to his body fell on his face into the darkness.

Before the soldier approached him in turn, Peter managed to look at the sky once more. A single, dying star still burned amid the dark and silent abyss. "Hope" he thought with despair.

THE END

Development

INTERPRETATION

1. The occupation of Poland, which was accomplished in less than a month and triggered the beginning of World War II, was a triumph for the German army's practice of blitzkrieg warfare. What are the resemblances, both psychological and circumstantial, between the forest ranger Peter and Poland?

2. Peter is largely unconscious of what is happening during his interrogation. *(a)* What feeling even more painful than death terrorizes him? *(b)* By what does he feel he could be saved? *(c)* When Peter says, "I'll tell you," does he know what he will tell them? *(d)* Study the description of the idea which inspires Peter's betrayal (page 213, column 2, paragraph 1). Does this indicate conscious or subconcious motivation? Explain.

3. The German guard who brutalizes Peter says, "Die . . . you want not? No . . . pity . . ." If this statement were expanded along the Nazi party line, it might read: You are not, as we are, ready and willing to die? Then you are inferior and haven't the right to power, as we have. It is the duty of the strong to use the weak for the realization of their destiny. Since this is necessary, I have no pity for you. *(a)* Expand Charles' statement, "that perhaps it is even more important if another man is indispensable," in a manner similar to the above explication. *(b)* Why do you think Peter says that he would be afraid to admit another man indispensable? *(c)* In what ways is Charles' statement in opposition to the Nazi philosophy?

4. Charles says, "We don't always know what is important in our lives." In what way is this hypothesis confirmed by the events of Peter's interrogation?

5. Study Charles' interrogation in contrast to Peter's. *(a)* What drastic change comes over the tall Nazi lieutenant when he confronts Charles? *(b)* What effect has Charles' demeanor upon Peter? *(c)* Why is a man like Kaczynski necessary to the functioning of a police state? *(d)* What threat to the police state psychology, exhibited by the tall lieutenant, does Charles pose?

6. *(a)* Why is it both appropriate and unthinkable that the tall Nazi lieutenant whistles the gentle Mozart serenade? *(b)* In what way does this paradox embody the reasons for both hope and despair?

7. Is this story propaganda? Discuss.

TECHNIQUE

1. In the opening paragraphs of "The Trial" Andrzejewski describes the German invasion as "that unseen might which like a flood of iron and steel seemed to trample the earth and life with immensity." Cite the ways Andrzejewski manipulates the structure, tone, and descriptive detail of the story in order to make the reader feel the "immensity" of the Nazi domination.

2. There is a definite motif in this story evolved through a correspondence between Peter's experience and descriptions of the stars. *(a)* Trace this motif through the story, describing the way these descriptions of the stars change according to Peter's situation. *(b)* In what way does the use of this motif amplify the pathos of experiencing simultaneously hope and despair?

EXTENSIONS

1. Of how much value, do you feel, are acts of exemplary resistance, such as the deaths of Peter and Charles, in affecting the movement and direction of history? Explain.

Comparison

1. Zhilin, Pablo, and Peter are all prisoners of war, but there the similarity ends. *(a)* To what extent is each man responsible for his imprisonment? *(b)* What is the main reaction of each man to his captivity? *(c)* In what way is the reaction of each appropriate to that individual's background? *(d)* With which character do you most empathize? *(e)* Is empathy between the reader and the hero essential in some cases and of secondary importance in others? Discuss.

2. *(a)* What is the difference between the attitudes which Pablo and Peter seek out in order to endure their imminent deaths? *(b)* What would you regard as the principal reason that might drive each man to despair? *(c)* Which man, in your opinion, has been more realistic and honest in forging his attitude toward death? Explain.

3. It might be said, sardonically, that the stories in this group are also about the joys of being a captor. *(a)* From what do Abdul, the Falangist officer, and the tall Nazi lieutenant seem to get the most pleasure? *(b)* What in the attitudes of their respective captors might account for the fact that Zhilin and Pablo perform gratuitous acts (i.e., Zhilin argues over a ransom he has no intention of paying while Pablo gives false information for no logical reason)? *(c)* Where would you place each captor, relative to the others, on a scale ranging from credibility to abstraction in characterization? *(d)* What correlations do you find between the individual type of captor and the degree to which each story is romantic, emotional, or philosophical?

4. The prisoner-heroes of these stories are all, as might be expected, somewhat courageous. But a second group of characters, Kostuilin, Juan Mirbal, and the shopkeeper Kaczynski, are varyingly deficient in fortitude. From what you know of each of these characters, give the reasons you think each might use to excuse himself from an accusation of "cowardice."

5. *(a)* What are the instances in these stories of the body betraying the man, either physically or emotionally? *(b)* Is a man's freedom to be the person he wants to be curtailed by his physical vulnerability? Explain your answer with reference to the stories in this unit.

6. The hero in each of these stories can lessen his suffering by implicating or abandoning a comrade. *(a)* In what way does the choice given each man force him to acknowledge what is most important in his life? *(b)* To what extent does each of these acknowledgments lead the individual to re-evaluate the meaning of his life?

7. Compared with "A Prisoner in the Caucasus" and "The Trial," "The Wall" is an unconventional and unsettling story. For an audience it is easier to share Zhilin's fear and triumph, to experience Peter's hope and despair, than it is to embrace Pablo's final, hysterical laugh. In analyzing this peculiar quality of "The Wall," start with a comparison of Zhilin to Tom Steinbock and of Peter to Juan Mirbal. *(a)* What similarities in situation, background, and temperament do you find between Zhilin and Tom, between Peter and Juan? *(b)* What would have been the emotional states of Zhilin and Peter if the authors of their stories had denied the possibility of a Dina and a Charles Walitzki? *(c)* In what way does Sartre use Tom and Juan to undermine the validity of traditional heroes like Zhilin and Peter? *(d)* In what way is Pablo heroic? *(e)* Does the conclusion of "The Wall" reinforce Pablo's heroism, or does it make even that, too, absurd?

MEDITATION by Alexei Jawlensky. Courtesy of Mrs. Sascha Hammid, New York.

The Vulnerable

My Friend Jan

CEZAR PETRESCU [1] / Rumania

(1892 – 1961)

translated from the Rumanian

Instead of a reply, my friend gave me a surprised and sympathetic look.

"What a simpleton!" he was about to say.

But as he was gobbling his food hurriedly he refrained, making instead an eloquent gesture of his hand armed with the knife. Then he thrust his fork into the chicken breast and ripped open the tender white flesh hostilely as he would the breast of a defeated opponent.

Around us the station refreshment room was booming. The waiters were hurrying among the tables; the din of the voices was cut by the shrill whistling of the engines; outside the blizzard was whirling enormous snow drifts at the white windows. A snow plow was hardly able to move along the line; in front of the platform it shut out the light of the windows, like some apocalyptic monster.

So I had long to wait, an hour, maybe two. I was terrified at the thought of the time that would pass so slowly, measured every five minutes by a desperate look at the dial of the watch, on which the hands seem to have stood still forever.

But what a feverish din there was at all the neighboring tables. It was like the uproar at a fair or the bidding at an auction sale. The only thing missing was the accompaniment of drums. The railway line to Bucharest had been cleared; an express train was waiting, ready to start— we could hear the breath of the engine coming from its metal valves, and everywhere, at the tables, on the benches, in the corners, in front of the showcase filled with appetizers and mulled plum brandy, the last-minute advice could be heard:

"Hurry to the ministry before nine!"

"Call on Horovitz; it falls due on Monday!"

"Sixty-five thousand, not a penny less!"

"Don't forget Mr. Tache's letter!"

"Eight wagons . . ."

"Make a note: circular no. 435/16 of September 7."

"My Friend Jan" by Cezar Petrescu from INTRODUCTION TO RUMANIAN LITERATURE, edited by Jacob Steinberg. Copyright © 1964 by Twayne Publishers, Inc.

1. *Petrescu* (pä′ trä sü)

"Look him up at home or at Mrs. Vidopol's. . . ."

The voices crossed each other, grew louder and more hurried; they uttered figures and the names of VIP's in a lower tone, in whispers, to rise again aggressively, turning the bustle of the restaurant into an evermore heated noise, like that of a stock-exchange, a fair, an auction sale.

In a corner a woman wearing a shabby black coat was chewing, much against her liking, a horn-shaped roll with a dry interior.

My friend pushed away the plate he had emptied, drained off his glass of wine, and, choosing a cigarette bearing a gilt inscription from a flat silver cigarette case, turned again to me, now willing to answer: "The oaths we took in the trenches? Who on earth still remembers them today? What's the good of digging up ghosts?"

I looked him straight in the face, fully convinced that he would blush, that all the blood would rush to his face.

The last time we had met was five years ago, in uniforms caked with dry mud, our faces unshaven, our eyes glassy, on a rainy autumn afternoon in a mud hut on the bank of the Siret.[2] A revolutionary wind was sweeping over us. We swore we would turn the world upside down, avenge the dead. From the acrid smoke of tobacco, black and moldy, we would imagine then, in the mud hovel, a purified world which we meant to set up as soon as we cast off our military uniforms. And among all of us, wretched reserve officers collected from all parts of the country, dull men harried by petty worries, all of us "heroes" against our will and quite unpremeditatedly, he was the fiercest, because he had also been the bravest.

That is why I expected he would blush under my gaze; I waited to stir up the remorse of the renegade, of those who disavow and capitulate.

My friend, however, chewed the gilt cardboard end of his cigarette, defying my gaze. I was the first to drop my eyes.

It was only after this victory that he asked me in a voice full of sarcastic reproof: "I hear you've taken up literature now. How much better it would suit you to look after a vineyard. Your vineyard is running wild, Sandu was telling me the other day!"

I felt I was blushing. And I couldn't remember the sharp retort I had prepared for him.

My companion took hold of my hand over the white tablecloth and pressed it gently, his voice suddenly tamer: "What poor devils we are. . . . We're to be pitied. D'you think we're any better or any worse than the others?"

I withdrew my hand from his flabby grip. What did that cheap melodramatic tone mean? He was a fellow in a hurry to rise in the world, that's all! Five years ago his eyes were consumed with an inner fire. Between the barbed wire of the trenches and the posts upset by the cannon balls he had appeared to me transfigured, and I feared he might do something rash. Had we not promised one another that we'd bring our grenades home with us? We did not know very well what we would do with them. We were not prepared to do anything; we had no plan, no solution ready. But many of us did return like that, to throw them away into some backwater, just as we had given up our great resolutions. My friend Jan had been the fiercest of them all.

And now there he sat in front of me, with ruddy cheeks, in a suit cut according to the latest fashion, his costly fur coat thrown over the back of a chair with the supreme negligence of a Croesus.[3] From the very first quarter of an hour he had spoken to me only of "consolidated" shares, "premiums," "payments" and of "locked up bonds"—mysterious, puzzling terms which meant nothing to me except that he was stepping briskly along a road quite different from the former one. Why

---

2. *Siret* (sē′ret), a tributary of the Danube River in eastern Rumania. 3. *Croesus* (krē′səs), a rich king of Lydia from 560-546 B.C.; a rich person.

then this hypocrisy designed to arouse, like a beggar, a sympathy he did not deserve?

But my friend Jan went on with the thread of his story, undisturbed:

"I hesitated only once! Because of Private Ion Ion. . . . We had been home two years. Peace! Victory! Great Rumania! I can remember the day: the last day when I doubted myself and regretted having forgotten the sacred oaths we had taken in the trenches. Ha! Ha! The sacred oaths forgotten and our forgotten duties which you too have started writing about latterly! Everything has proved *I* was right, not you! Now I wouldn't blush even in front of Ion Ion. . . ."

He sat staring vacantly, perceiving in the void and in his memory something I did not know yet. Then with a bitter smile and a contraction of his lips, which I had never seen on his face before, he went on.

"He turned up one morning. I was in a hurry, and the phone had already rung three times impatiently. Just as I was going to put on my overcoat the maid reminded me, 'A man's been waiting for you for an hour. A peasant!'

"I told her to show him in. He looked rather like an apparition than a man. He was very thin, his eyes were sunken, and the skin on his face taut on his cheekbones, his nose pinched – a ghost. Still he clicked his heels with soldier-like energy.

" 'Your servant, sir! I see you no longer remember me.'

"He was right. I still could not remember him. But judging by his 'Your servant, sir' it immediately dawned on me he was some man of my former company. And, not wishing to dishearten him I hurried to answer with a lie: 'Why, I remember you quite well, my lad. The truth is, you've changed a bit. . . .'

"And I tried hard to imagine him dressed as a soldier. But the fellow shook his head; he seemed mistrustful and distressed. He had guessed I was lying.

" 'I see you've forgotten me, sir! I'm Ion Ion, orderly to poor Lieutenant Octav, may God rest his soul.'

"How could I help remembering now I had heard these words? Ion Ion had looked after us in the mud hut for a whole winter; he had become famous in the sector for the tea he made, the wine he mulled with pepper corns and cloves on bitterly cold nights, and for his dog-like devotion and fidelity to poor Octav. And all of a sudden what memories he brought back to my mind! The morning of the attack, the shell that smashed Octav's body to smithereens, scattering the pieces of flesh on the earth, the hot fragments of brain on my face, and the two fingers, white and drained of blood which I found later on in my greatcoat, when I recovered my senses! Everything had been so well buried away, so thoroughly forgotten, sealed up, since life had resumed its old course in the country's capital, since we had again bars, cafés, bands, splendid carriages and horses, motor cars and shop windows full of all kinds of early and expensive fruit and vegetables. Private Ion Ion was carrying me back three years. And the streets, the bars, the crammed shop windows, all the comfort around me in my own house, vanished all of a sudden.

"The memory of that hour alone was still alive. A wave of dark anxiety took possession of my soul.

"I made Private Ion Ion sit down on the edge of a chair and tell me about the troubles that had driven him to come and see me. Now I remembered well that that day we had thought he was killed, and in the evening we put his name down on the list of the missing.

"But Private Ion Ion was not dead. It was only now that I learned what had happened. He had been hit and had fallen down near Octav. In the evening, when we had withdrawn into our trenches after unsuccessful counterattacks, he had come to, his eyes blurred. He felt the joints of his limbs. He was all right, he could move, none of his bones was broken, he had no deep wound through which his blood and his life might have oozed out. . . . All that had happened became quite clear to him now. The firing had ceased. The trenches, their barbed wire torn away, were not very far, and with a little luck he might be able to creep along in the night. First he thought of gathering the pieces of Octav's body, putting them in his greatcoat and bringing them to our trenches to be buried according to time-honored traditions. It was snowing; big flakes were falling slowly. He pressed his forehead against the cold snow to cool himself and pick up strength. He collected the letters found in the lieutenant's pocket, all the small trivial things which death suddenly makes so precious. He crept along on his elbows, from one fragment to another. . . . After that he could not remember anything. A bullet hit him. Maybe it was one from our trenches, maybe from the enemy. He awoke stupefied, much later, in a German ambulance. The first moment he felt glad: it was warm, the bed was soft, a light hand was carefully dressing his wound. The physician spoke to him in a friendly voice, in an unknown language. He did not understand him, but he could see, behind the thick-rimmed glasses, a gentle, kindly look, and all this filled him with wonder. He had expected less compassion. Had the war not accustomed him only to men insanely savage and cruel, to men lost to all sense of humanity? But the doctor and the hospital were but a rare and happy exception.

"The horror began again, for after the hospital came the camp. Days of fierce gnashing of teeth and slavery began. First they had to dig trenches, then mines, then to build new railways at the rear. For three years he was carried in cattle trucks from one line of trenches to another, from one end to the other of the enemy country. He suffered hunger, he was beaten with the rifle butt, he lived on scraps of refuse, lay on the frozen earth,

his teeth chattering with the cold. His eyes sank in; his legs could hardly carry him. Exactly a week, at last, after the negotiations and arrangements of the peace treaty, after being examined by sundry control committees and commissions, a train had brought him home, together with other companions, now only skin and bone, after all their suffering and want. He had hurried home to see his wife, his children, and his cattle. And now he had come to bring me the lieutenant's wallet and letters which he had carried day after day, night after night, at his breast like so many invaluable talismans. He was not very clever; he could hardly read or write, and could not imagine where he could find the lieutenant's lady to deliver to her the things with his own hands. So he wanted me to do it for him.

"Private Ion Ion handed me the 'wallet' and the papers.

"It was a miserable brown pocketbook; its corners had become round with so many mishaps—a wretched talisman of leather discolored by sweat, its inner partitions in pieces, its monogram broken.

" 'I've got the other piece, too!' Private Ion Ion added, producing from a carefully folded hankerchief the other half of the broken silver initials.

"Private Ion Ion considered he had fulfilled his mission. He rose to leave. He stumbled over the carpets. He did not dare to hold out his hand to me.

"Left alone, I realized how futile all the hustle of my morning was. I disconnected the telephone, lest some call should tempt me. I needed to examine my heart.

"How soon had I forgotton poor Octav! And still, at the time, for months on end, the sight had appeared to me cruel and unforgettable. . . . I thought it would accompany me at every step, all my life.

"The night before he was killed, mangled by a shell, we had played cards in the hut, had sung and made merry with silly jokes. Then, with chins resting on the palms of our hands and with elbows on the table, we sat up late, making splendid and absurd plans for our country of tomorrow, the country we would build on returning home. How clearly I remembered now that table made of a door brought by Private Ion Ion, and supported by four stakes stuck in the beaten earthen floor of the hut. Of course none of us suspected what was in store for us the next day. War.

"For a fortnight the firing had ceased in our sector. We were even expecting to be sent to the rear for a rest and recovery. We were making plans. When we finished gambling, when the others had gone off to their dens, we sat and talked for a long time. Private Ion Ion had brought us some boiling hot tea. Tea made of carrots and tree leaves, wartime tea. Poor Octav again talked to me anxiously of his wife Lia, left in Bucharest, beyond the front line, from where he had had no news. He missed her so much. In their one year of married life they had never had any trouble. He knew she had no money now, maybe she had to suffer privations, maybe she was compelled to put up with the impudence and the swaggering airs of some *feldwebel*,[4] according to the old law of wars, in all times. From the same pocketbook that Ion Ion had just brought me, he produced her photo, laid it on his knees, and looked at it for a long while, his chin firmly gripped in his fists, his eyes blurred by tears. . . . And the next day, the same fingers that had laid under my eyes the pale photo, the eyes moist with emotion, the brain in which so many thoughts, hopes, and wants had struggled —everything had been, all of a sudden, savagely torn to pieces, thrown down in the ground, mixed with the dust, changed into a ghastly heap of blood, cartilage and nerve, still according to the old law of wars in all times, beginning with Homer's *Iliad*. How could I forget? How could I go on laughing, talking, joking? How could I listen to bands playing? How could I let my eyes look greedily at a woman? How could I go on making plans,

untroubled, as though nothing had happened, as though all my life I had never budged from my comfortable flat except to engage in the mean tricks and dodges of a lawyer's trade which brought me in the money to keep me in luxury for the two months' holiday I spent in summer, at the seaside or in the mountains.

"So, Private Ion Ion had been a man indeed, but I had not.

"For three long years, amid terrible sufferings, *he had not forgotten*. In his rags, he had carried in his bosom, like an extraordinarily valuable treasure, the last possessions of a man who had been my closest friend. No sooner had he come home, than he got on the train, maybe traveling on the top of a carriage, or had perhaps denied himself food to bring me those souvenirs he prized so highly. . . . So I was a beast, wasn't I? I remembered that in the early days of the war when we had not entered the trenches yet, the horse of one of the company's carts had been killed by a bomb dropped by a plane. We had had to take the horse out of the shafts in order to repair the broken wheels. Well, the other horse, untouched, had trotted away to the edge of the ditch and was grazing quietly as though nothing had happened. He had walked around his dead companion, without even turning to look at him for a moment and was nibbling at the grass, indifferently. And then I had been shocked! All the yarns about the horse being noble proved mere cock-and-bull stories, lies, rot. In my ridiculous fury I couldn't refrain from kicking the unfeeling brute. Was I now less of a brute than the wretched creature satisfying his hunger near his dead companion? Was there really any difference?

"Then I remembered that I had collected in a drawer a lot of sad souvenirs of the war. There lay the handkerchief with which I had wiped poor Octav's blood and brain off my face.

"I felt I had to see it again. I rummaged

---

4. *feldwebel*, in military terms, a sergeant in the infantry.

among the letters and buttons, the fragments of shell, the photo taken in the trenches. I found it. A dirty crumpled ball of linen with blackened stains of blood, of smoke and ashes.

"I felt I would have liked to press it to my lips, to ask forgiveness from Octav's memory. I unrolled it. The bits of brain, gray and dried up, looked like hateful dirt and refuse: it was all that was left of a poor decomposed brain. And suddenly some white moths which had made their nest there flew away through my fingers. I shuddered and dropped the handkerchief. How sad it all was!

"After a long time I put on my overcoat to carry out Private Ion Ion's mission. I took Octav's letters and pocketbook with me.

"On the way I tried to think of extenuating circumstances I might set forth with all my lawyer's tactfulness to explain to the widow why I had forgotten her for such a long time. And I felt another pang of conscience. That woman had suffered. I had found her so often with tearstained eyes; and she never tired of asking me to describe every hour I had spent with Octav, until the very last! Every time I had called on her at the time, their house bore the signs of mourning. No doors were banged; the servants spoke in whispers; everybody walked on tiptoe; the curtains were always drawn. Lia was still wearing mourning and every time she seemed to me paler and more remote from the vain trifles of life. *She* did not forget. And such fidelity, continuing steadfastly beyond death, had touched me. . . . But gradually and instinctively I had from cowardice avoided the house more and more. Life had conquered me again. I needed laughter, smiles, mirth, plans I could speak of aloud; I felt strong and healthy. In the house with curtains always drawn and with the eternal memory of death I felt uncomfortable. Driven by a savage selfishness for which I often reproached myself mercilessly, I had gradually become a stranger to the

'sombre vault of memories' as I called Octav's house to myself. And how was I to tell Lia now, what words was I to use? What grief would the dead man's relics that I was carrying in my pocket revive? And how was I to discover in my heart and mind the wise precepts of life that would allay her pain?

"I opened the little gate of the iron fence with the same anguish I had felt on the morning when I had brought her the news, the first time. The curtains were no longer drawn.

"The appearance of the house seemed in a way to have revived and brightened up. It made me look around with justified surprise. I was even wondering if she had not moved.

"A bright-eyed young girl opened the door for me; that old woman with a funereal air who used to open it had vanished forever. In the vestibule I could hear the sound of a piano. When I took off my coat I cast a look around with the same surprise. There was something changed inside too: flowers, brighter colors, more light. I could hardly recognize the place. And then only, and with great difficulty, did I begin to realize what was such a simple thing: life had conquered here too. Suddenly my task seemed to me more difficult: would I not cruelly and inopportunely revive a wound that was closing?

"Octav's widow received me with unfeigned joy.

"From the very first moment I couldn't take my eyes off her. How astoundingly she had changed. Her cheeks were pink, her lips were red, her eyes shone playfully. Something new and daring had transfigured her gloomy, mournful face which I had avoided instinctively for so long a time, taking a roundabout way in the street lest I should risk meeting her. Then I realized what made her look younger. She had changed the style of her hair—her hair was brushed up, showing her bare forehead; it was like a blind lifted up to let in floods of joyful light.

"I suddenly felt awkward, awkward in a way different from the guilty awkwardness I used to feel. I started with the usual small talk. I tried to slip in the words imperceptibly, slyly, to reach the object of my visit. But Lia asked me in a very simple and offhand way, what new plays were on; she wanted to know about a new singer from La Scala of Milan whose arrival had been announced, and about the horse races that were to begin on the first Sunday, next month.

"My eyes kept searching for Octav's portrait which I used to see multiplied, wherever my eyes turned to, on the walls, on the tables and little tables, over the piano closed forever. . . . The portrait had vanished. And just as I was about to disclose abruptly what had brought me there —to have done with it—the door at the far end of the room opened and in there came, walking steadily as if he were in his own house, a fair giant with a part accurately drawn like a line going to the crown of his head, with placid blue eyes, the eyes of a handsome and empty-minded animal.

"Lia jumped to her feet cheerfully, her cheeks afire. 'My husband! You will forgive us, won't you? We were so flurried, we forgot to send you an invitation. . . . As a matter of fact, we've been abroad. We got back only a week ago.'

"I sat gazing at her foolishly, foolishly and paralyzed.

"Luckily Octav's successor felt it his duty to carry on a polite conversation. He talked to me of the exceptionally fine weather, of the depression of the currency, then again of the horse races, the latest plays, the singer who was expected to arrive. The war and those killed in the war seemed never to have existed anywhere. . . .

"He talked moderately, seeming to pronounce final sentences; he informed me that he was keen only on sports and was expecting to get a new type of car from abroad, by special order.

"'We'll start adventures that'll mark a decisive moment in the history of motoring in our country. What we need is courage; initiative. The country's become larger! There are heaps of picturesque spots that can vie with places abroad. All the same, the war has been of some use! We'll explore every highroad, every mountain, every pass in Great Rumania! Won't we Lia?'

"And he caressed the white hand and put it to his lips and gave it a long kiss as befits a couple who are prolonging their honeymoon.

"Then, before my eyes there suddenly rose the other man, his mangled flesh, the pieces of hot brain on my cheek, the two white bloodless fingers I found in the folds of my greatcoat at the time when Great Rumania was but a dream of the trenches . . . another kind of Great Rumania, in another kind of dream.

"There was no sense in fulfilling my mission now. I rose to leave. Lia asked me to her at-homes on Thursday, from four to seven.

"In the street I stopped undecided. The packet of letters in my pocket seemed to burn me. I thought for a moment of keeping them to put them among the distressing and reproachful treasures of my relics. Then I remembered Octav's sister. I remembered his old father who had mourned for him so long and whose eyes would fill with tears every time I pronounced his son's name.

"Surely *they* had not forgotten him. They would keep those sacred relics stained with the blood of a brother, with the blood of a son, more piously than I would.

"I found Octav's sister standing at the top of the stairs, buttoning her gloves, ready to go out.

"'What a surprise! You've neglected us lately, Jan.'

"The top of the stairs was no place to talk. We walked down the steps together.

"'Papa is at his club, for his usual game!' she explained. 'He's managed well this year! The price of wheat is tremendous and the crop has exceeded all expectations! All the same, the war has been of some use. There's another life in this Rumania, in this Great Rumania!'

"We walked side by side. She was lovely; she had grown taller, and slimmer. The passers-by turned to look at her; she walked with steady springy steps, with the enticing gait of a feline, delightful to the eye, but disquieting at the same time.

"After a few steps she spoke to me of the horse races, of the long expected singer, of the latest plays. It seemed to be contagious. Almost the same phrases! Almost the same words! Almost the same eagerness, the same tribute of gratitude to Great Rumania. She was cheerful, and her trilling laughter bubbled forth resonantly from her white throat, while she kept looking at her little shoes the color of gold, which, I gathered, she was wearing for the first time then.

"She stopped and, smoothing the lapel of my coat with a familiar gesture, she looked into my eyes cajolingly: 'Guess?'

"I didn't know what she meant.

" 'Guess what the girlie's going to tell you?'

"I shrugged my shoulders. I looked at her, from top to toe and could not help admiring her slim waist, her large eyes shining with precocious sensuality, her tiny white teeth, as white as an advertisement for a miraculous tooth paste. How the girl had changed since she used to come and sit on my knees seven years ago, in Octav's study, and get me to teach her to color the maps in her exam copybooks, the map of little Rumania then! Now, Octav's sister was pouting, shocked that I had not been able to guess.

" 'The girlie's getting engaged! A splendid fiancé. You'll love him, won't you? A handsome, athletic fiancé! The very image of Rudolph Valentino!'[5]

"I parted with her abruptly, almost hostilely.

"I felt her eyes were following me, puzzled and distressed. She could not understand. How could she? She too had forgotten. They had all forgotten. The bundle of letters weighed heavier and heavier in my pocket.

"For a time I walked in the streets, aimlessly.

"People were bustling along. The streets were flooded with sunshine. Gipsy women were selling flowers freshly come out from under the snow. Carriages were driving to the Chaussée, at full trot. The town was brimming over with noise. It was one of those first warm spring days when women, in light natty seasonable clothes, worn for the first time, seemed to possess a youthfulness and beauty as inflammatory, destructive, and threatening as a public danger.

"I found myself counting them and identifying them: one had lost a brother, another her husband or her fiancé, there in the mire where flesh and arteries mixed with the earth. Everyone of them had forgotten, everyone of them had forgotten.

"At home I locked up Octav's letters in the drawer. I did not keep my promise to Private Ion Ion. Would you have done otherwise? Say, would you? You who haven't the pluck to scold me . . . But my train's leaving. So long!"

My friend put on his costly fur-lined coat; a waiter with bent back, a napkin over his arm, accompanied him to the door, fawningly. A middleman ran after him as far as the train, hat in hand, begging something of him. The red lips of a woman smiled at him, fascinated by the strong, graceful, lithe appearance of the man who had been my companion in the trenches. I sat on, making bread pellets on the white table cloth, big pellets of the generous white bread of Great Rumania.

Was he only a cynic? Was he a sage? What could I reply from this bitter solitude?

THE END

---

5. *Rudolph Valentino* (1895-1926). Known as "the great lover," Valentino became the most sensational romantic actor of the silent motion pictures.

Development

INTERPRETATION

1. (a) As the story opens, what question do you suppose the narrator has asked Jan? (b) What is the premise on which the narrator bases his thinking as he meets with Jan? (c) Does their conversation strengthen or diminish this premise? Explain.

2. (a) Discuss the character of the narrator as revealed through his conversation with Jan. (b) What is Jan's attitude toward the narrator?

3. (a) Describe the contrast between Jan as a soldier and the same man five years later. (b) Is Jan sincere or does he seem to protest too much in telling his story? Explain.

4. (a) Which of the following characteristics best describes Private Ion Ion: loyalty? sentimentality? goodness? naivete? (b) What is his role in the story?

5. Do any of the characters seem to have a sense of wrongdoing? If so, how is this manifested in the story?

6. (a) What attitudes toward the dead are found in "My Friend Jan"? (b) Discuss the significance of the incident with the horse within the context of the story.

7. Have Jan, Octav's wife, and his sister really forgotten the dead man, Octav? Discuss.

8. (a) What is the meaning of the statement, "All the same, the war has been of some use" (page 228, column 2, lines 6-7)? (b) What motivates Octav's sister and Lia's husband to make this remark? (c) Have they experienced the effects of war? (d) What has the author achieved through inclusion of the statement?

9. As the story concludes, the narrator muses about Jan, "Was he only a cynic? Was he a sage? What could I reply from this bitter solitude?" (a) How do you regard Jan—as cynic, sage, or something else? (b) What is the narrator's "bitter solitude"? (c) Is the narrator naive? Discuss.

TECHNIQUE

1. Cezar Petrescu includes numerous descriptive details in his account. Cite specific details used by the author. What purpose does the use of such details serve?

2. In "My Friend Jan" the author has made use of the frame-story technique, the telling of a story within a story. How does the use of this literary device color your reaction toward the narrator and toward Jan?

EXTENSIONS

1. Is there, or should there be, a middle road between the extremes of continual remembrance and complete forgetfulness of the dead? Discuss.

2. Are the protests and visionary ideals of youth bound to be overcome by the worldly demands of living? Discuss.

At the Fair

ALEXANDER KIELLAND[1] / Norway
(1849—1906)
translated from the Norwegian by William Archer

It was by the merest chance that Monsieur and Madame Tousseau came to Saint-Germain-en-Laye[2] in the early days of September.

Four weeks ago they had been married in Lyons,[3] which was their home; but where they had passed these four weeks they really could not have told you. The time had gone hop-skip-and-jump; a couple of days had entirely slipped out of their reckoning, and, on the other hand, they remembered a little summer-house at Fontainebleau, where they had rested one evening, as clearly as if they had passed half their lives there.

Paris was, strictly speaking, the goal of their wedding-journey, and there they established themselves in a comfortable little *hôtel garni.*[4] But the city was sultry and they could not rest; so they rambled about among the small towns in the neighbourhood, and found themselves, one Sunday at noon, in Saint-Germain.

"Monsieur and Madame have doubtless come to take part in the fête?" said the plump little landlady of the Hôtel Henri Quatre, as she ushered her guests up the steps.

The fête? They knew of no fête in the world except their own wedded happiness; but they did not say so to the landlady.

They soon learned that they had been lucky enough to drop into the very midst of the great and celebrated fair which is held every year, on the first Sunday of September, in the Forest of Saint-Germain.

The young couple were highly delighted with their good hap. It seemed as though Fortune followed at their heels, or rather ran ahead of them, to arrange surprises. After a delicious tête-à-tête dinner behind one of the clipped yew trees in the quaint garden, they took a carriage and drove off to the forest.

In the hotel garden, beside the little fountain in the middle of the lawn, sat a ragged condor[5] which the landlord had bought to amuse his guests. It was attached to its perch by a good strong rope. But when the sun shone upon it with real warmth, it fell a-thinking of the snow-peaks of Peru, of mighty wing-strokes over the deep valleys—and then it forgot the rope.

Two vigorous strokes with its pinions would bring the rope up taut, and it would fall back upon the sward. There it would lie by the hour, then shake itself and clamber up to its little perch again.

When it turned its head to watch the happy pair, Madame Tousseau burst into a fit of laughter at its melancholy mien.

The afternoon sun glimmered through the dense foliage of the interminable straight-ruled avenue that skirts the terrace. The young wife's veil fluttered aloft as they sped through the air, and wound itself right round Monsieur's head. It

"At the Fair" by Alexander Kielland, translated by William Archer from TALES FROM TWO COUNTRIES. Published by Harper and Brothers.
1. *Kielland* (kel′än). **2.** *St. Germain-en-Laye,* a French town on the Seine River located about thirteen miles west of Paris. **3.** *Lyons* (lyôn), a city in southeastern France on the Rhone River. **4.** *hôtel garni,* a furnished room or lodging house. **5.** *condor,* a large vulture with a bare neck and head. Condors live on high mountains in South America and California.

took a long time to put it in order again, and Madame's hat had to be adjusted ever so often. Then came the relighting of Monsieur's cigar, and that, too, was quite a business; for Madame's fan would always give a suspicious little flirt every time the match was lighted; then a penalty had to be paid, and that, again, took time.

The aristocratic English family which was passing the summer at Saint-Germain was disturbed in its regulation walk by the passing of the gay little equipage. They raised their correct gray or blue eyes; there was neither contempt nor annoyance in their look—only the faintest shade of surprise. But the condor followed the carriage with its eyes, until it became a mere black speck at the vanishing-point of the straight-ruled interminable avenue.

"La joyeuse fête des Loges"[6] is a genuine fair, with gingerbread cakes, sword-swallowers, and waffles piping hot. As the evening falls, coloured lamps and Chinese lanterns are lighted around the venerable oak which stands in the middle of the fairground, and boys climb about among its topmost branches with maroons and Bengal lights.[7]

Gentlemen of an inventive turn of mind go about with lanterns on their hats, on their sticks, and wherever they can possibly hang; and the most inventive of all strolls around with his sweetheart under a great umbrella, with a lantern dangling from each rib.

On the outskirts, bonfires are lighted; fowls are roasted on spits, while potatoes are cut into slices and fried in dripping. Each aroma seems to have its amateurs, for there are always people crowding round; but the majority stroll up and down the long street of booths.

Monsieur and Madame Tousseau had plunged into all the fun of the fair. They had gambled in the most lucrative lottery in Europe, presided over by a man who excelled in dubious witticisms. They had seen the fattest goose in the world, and the celebrated flea "Bismarck," who could drive six horses. Furthermore, they had purchased gingerbread, shot at a target for clay pipes and soft-boiled eggs, and finally had danced a waltz in the spacious dancing-tent.

They had never had such fun in their lives. There were no great people there—at any rate, none greater than themselves. As they did not know a soul, they smiled to every one, and when they met the same person twice they laughed and nodded to him.

They were charmed with everything. They stood outside the great circus and ballet marquees and laughed at the shouting buffoons. Scraggy mountebanks[8] performed on trumpets, and young girls with well-floured shoulders smiled alluringly from the platforms.

Monsieur Tousseau's purse was never at rest, but they did not grow impatient of the perpetual claims upon it. On the contrary, they only laughed at the gigantic efforts these people would make to earn—perhaps half a franc, or a few centimes.[9]

Suddenly they encountered a face they knew. It was a young American whom they had met at the hotel in Paris.

"Well, Monsieur Whitmore," cried Madame Tousseau, gaily, "here at last you've found a place where you can't possibly help enjoying yourself."

"For my part," answered the American, slowly, "I find no enjoyment in seeing people who haven't money making fools of themselves to please the people who have."

"Oh, you're incorrigible!" laughed the young wife. "But I must compliment you on the excellent French you are speaking to-day."

---

6. *La joyeuse fête des Loges,* the joyous feast of the Lodges. 7. *maroons and Bengal lights.* A maroon is a loudly exploding firework. Bengal lights are vivid, sustained blue lights. 8. *mountebanks,* those who try to deceive people by tricks, stories, and jokes. 9. *franc . . . centimes.* A franc is a unit of money in France, Belgium, and Switzerland worth about twenty cents. A centime is 1/100 of a franc. A sou, mentioned later in the story, was formerly either of two bronze coins equal to five or ten centimes.

After exchanging a few more words, they lost each other in the crowd; Mr. Whitmore was going back to Paris immediately.

Madame Tousseau's compliment was quite sincere. As a rule the grave American talked deplorable French, but the answer he had made to Madame was almost correct. It seemed as though it had been well thought out in advance—as though a whole series of impressions had condensed themselves into these words. Perhaps that was why his answer sank so deep into the minds of Monsieur and Madame Tousseau.

Neither of them thought it a particularly brilliant remark; on the contrary, they agreed that it must be miserable to take so gloomy a view of things. But, nevertheless, his words left something rankling. They could not laugh so lightly as before, Madame felt tired, and they began to think of getting homewards.

Just as they turned to go down the long street of booths in order to find their carriage, they met a noisy crew coming upward.

"Let us take the other way," said Monsieur.

They passed between two booths, and emerged at the back of one of the rows. They stumbled over the tree-roots before their eyes got used to the uncertain light which fell in patches between the tents. A dog, which lay gnawing at something or other, rose with a snarl, and dragged its prey further into the darkness, among the trees.

On this side the booths were made up of old sails and all sorts of strange draperies. Here and there light shone through the openings, and at one place Madame distinguished a face she knew.

It was the man who had sold her that incomparable gingerbread—Monsieur had half of it still in his pocket.

But it was curious to see the gingerbread-man from this side. Here was something quite different from the smiling obsequiousness which had said so many pretty things to her pretty face, and had been so unwearied in belauding the gingerbread—which really was excellent.

Now he sat crouched together, eating some indescribable mess out of a checked pocket-handkerchief—eagerly, greedily, without looking up.

Further down they heard a muffled conversation. Madame was bent upon peeping in; Monsieur objected, but he had to give in.

An old mountebank sat counting a handful of coppers, grumbling and growling the while. A young girl stood before him, shivering and pleading for pardon; she was wrapped in a long water-proof.

The man swore, and stamped on the ground. Then she threw off the water-proof and stood half naked in a sort of ballet costume. Without saying a word, and without smoothing her hair or preening her finery, she mounted the little steps that led to the stage.

At that moment she turned and looked at her father. Her face had already put on the ballet-expression. The mouth remained fixed, but the eyes tried, for a second, to send him a beseeching smile. The mountebank shrugged his shoulders, and held out his hand with the coppers; the girl turned, ducked under the curtain, and was received with shouts and applause.

Beside the great oak-tree the lottery man was holding forth as fluently as ever. His witticisms, as the darkness thickened, grew less and less dubious. There was a different ring, too, in the laughter of the crowd; the men were noisier, the mountebanks leaner, the women more brazen, the music falser—so it seemed, at least, to Madame and Monsieur.

As they passed the dancing-tent the racket of a quadrille reached their ears. "Great heavens!—was it really there that we danced?" said Madame, and nestled closer to her husband.

They made their way through the rout

as quickly as they could; they would soon reach their carriage, as it was just beyond the circus-marquee. It would be nice to rest and escape from all this hubbub.

The platform in front of the circus-marquee was now vacant. Inside in the dim and stifling rotunda, the performance was in full swing.

Only the old woman who sold the tickets sat asleep at her desk. And a little way off, in the light of her lamp, stood a tiny boy.

He was dressed in tights, green on one side, red on the other; on his head he had a fool's cap with horns.

Close up to the platform stood a woman wrapped in a black shawl. She seemed to be talking to the boy.

He advanced his red leg and his green leg by turns, and drew them back again. At last he took three steps forward on his meagre shanks and held out his hand to the woman.

She took what he had in it, and disappeared into the darkness.

He stood motionless for a moment, then he muttered some words and burst into tears.

Presently he stopped, and said: "Maman m'a pris mon sou!"—and fell to weeping again.

He dried his eyes and left off for a time, but as often as he repeated to himself his sad little history—how his mother had taken his sou from him—he was seized with another and a bitterer fit of weeping.

He stooped and buried his face in the curtain. The stiff, wrinkly oil-painting must be hard and cold to cry into. The little body shrank together; he drew his green leg close up under him, and stood like a stork upon the red one.

No one on the other side of the curtain must hear that he was crying. Therefore he did not sob like a child, but fought as a man fights against a broken heart.

When the attack was over, he blew his nose with his fingers, and wiped them on his tights. With the dirty curtain he had dabbled the tears all over his face until it was streaked with black; and in this guise, and dry eyed, he gazed for a moment over the fair.

Then: "Maman m'a pris mon sou"—and he set off again.

The backsweep of the wave leaves the beach dry for an instant while the next wave is gathering. Thus sorrow swept in heavy surges over the little childish heart.

His dress was so ludicrous, his body so meagre, his weeping was so wofully bitter, and his suffering so great and manlike——

——But at home at the hotel—the Pavillion Henri Quatre, where the Queens of France condescended to be brought to bed—there the condor sat and slept upon its perch.

And it dreamed its dream—its only dream—its dream about the snow-peak of Peru and the mighty wing-strokes over the deep valleys; and then it forgot its rope.

It uplifted its ragged pinions vigorously, and struck two sturdy strokes. Then the rope drew taut, and it fell back where it was wont to fall—it wrenched its claw, and the dream vanished——

——Next morning the aristocratic English family was much concerned, and the landlord himself felt annoyed, for the condor lay dead upon the grass.

THE END

Development

INTERPRETATION

1. (a) What evil situation is mentioned early in the story? (b) Why is it evil? (c) For what other unthinking cruelty in the story does this situation prepare us?

2. (a) Characterize the attitudes displayed by the Tousseaus early in the story. (b) As the story progresses, what change in their attitudes occurs and what causes that change? (c) What circumstances cause the Tousseaus to be particularly vulnerable to disillusionment?

3. Why, in your opinion, might the author have used an American, rather than a European, to call the Tousseaus' attention to the fair's shoddiness?

4. Consider the adults who work in the carnival. Are they victims? victimizers? both? Discuss.

5. (a) What part do the children have in this story? (b) Do you think they will perpetuate the situation which has victimized them? Why or why not?

6. (a) Trace the various appearances of the condor throughout the story. (b) What are its aspirations? (c) Why might one sympathize with the bird and, at the same time, be repulsed by it? (d) What function does the bird have in the total context of the story?

7. Which of the following statements best summarizes the story? Defend your choice.

(a) In "At the Fair" Alexander Kielland is protesting against a situation in which people (the carnival performers) are used solely for the advantage of others (the visitors). He is thus championing the cause of the poor and oppressed who are victimized by the wealthy.

(b) In writing "At the Fair" Alexander Kielland has exposed a problem for which there is no pat solution. Rather, the evil he shows goes full circle involving all those in the story, and in some way making them both victim and victimizer.

(c) In "At the Fair" Alexander Kielland writes sympathetically of a young married couple who have their happiness jarred by the unthinking and depressing comment of an American tourist.

TECHNIQUE

1. (a) Characterize the atmosphere established early in the story, citing details which create it. (b) Does the atmosphere remain the same throughout the narrative? Explain.

2. (a) What does the carnival setting add to the prevailing tone, or mood, of this selection? (b) How might the effect of the story have differed if it had been set in an ordinary town on an ordinary day?

3. Note the author's repeated use of the word *mountebank*. Look up its meaning and discuss the effect of its repetition on your attitude toward the events in the story. Can you find other instances in which Kielland uses repetition to influence attitude?

4. Kielland uses contrasts to suggest that happiness is bordered on all sides by the ugly and depressing. Describe these contrasts and discuss their contributions to the story.

EXTENSIONS

1. Comment on the opinion that all men are in some way vultures preying on the helpless.

2. Do you agree or disagree with the following statement: "Every man is responsible for his situation and is, therefore, capable of raising himself above his environment if he so desires"? Explain.

The Blacksmith's Daughter

HEINZ PIONTEK[1] / GERMANY / 1925—

translated from the German by Michael Hamburger

I had a father
powerful as the post of the well
at Kobnitza,[2]
with eyes of blue iron and sparks in his beard,
5 who limped and knew what the legends mean.

He had a daughter,
lovely as the river in the meadows
near Kobnitza.
In winter she wore her dainty boots,
10 in summer a sash of cotton around her hips.

He dreamed that he was a charcoal-burner
and understood the language of birds.
But a blacksmith he worked in a tumbledown manor-farm
and went in fear of the bailiff.

15 And she, his daughter, would have liked best
to go out riding with an ensign twenty years old,
but a postmaster made her his wife,
bought her rusks[3] and a pair of spectacles.

"The Blacksmith's Daughter" by Heinz Piontek, translated by Michael Hamburger, from MODERN GERMAN POETRY 1910-1960, edited by Michael Hamburger and Christopher Middleton. Reprinted by permission of Grove Press, Inc., Heinz Piontek, and MacGibbon & Kee. Copyright © 1962 by Michael Hamburger and Christopher Middleton.

1. *Piontek* (pē′ ôn tack′). 2. *Kobnitza* (côb′ ñē tzä), geographical name, most probably a fortress. 3. *rusks*, pieces of bread or cake toasted in the oven; a kind of light, soft, sweet biscuit.

My father was lamed by a dapple-gray's kick.
20 His leg kept him out of the forests.
He stoked the fire with small coal:
his heart was a forge gone out.
He drank nine tankards of thin beer
and died of it.

25 I learned that one is never safe
from his memory.
In the mornings I see our little horizon
and in feeble lamplight I write addresses
for the customers.

Development

1. In your own words state the main idea of this poem.

2. Do the blacksmith's and his daughter's disillusionment seem inevitable? Discuss.

3. (a) What does the narrator mean when she says of her father, ". . . his heart was a forge gone out" (line 22)? (b) Discuss the appropriateness of this metaphor.

4. (a) Does the daughter seem to express regret for her unrealized dreams? Explain. (b) Refer to lines 25-26. Why is a person never safe from his own memories? (c) In your opinion, does the girl in the poem create her own unhappiness? Explain.

5. (a) What is the point of view in stanzas 1, 5, and 6? in stanzas 2-4? (b) In each case, why might the author have chosen that particular point of view? (c) Which tends to involve you more deeply in the poem—use of the first or third person? Why?

6. (a) Cite details from the poem which sketch the lives of the blacksmith and his daughter. (b) Does the author's simplicity of language and style add to or detract from the meaning of the work? Explain.

7. Are Longfellow's words, "Life is but an empty dream," a true evaluation of the girl's situation in the poem? Why, or why not?

The Trellis

BIBHUTI BANDYOPADHYAY[1]/ India

(1893 – 1950)

translated from the Bengali by Lila Ray

"Please get me a bowl or pot or some-thing," Sahayhari said to his wife as he stepped into the courtyard. "Uncle Tarak has tapped a palm. I'll bring some of the fresh sap."

His wife was sitting on the porch of the thatched kitchen. The winter morning was chilly and she was digging hardened coconut oil out of a bottle with a straw from the broom. Pinching the oil off the straw, she began rubbing it into her hair. She looked at her husband silently, drew her sari closer about her, but made no move to hand him anything.

"What's the matter?" Sahayhari de-manded, going up to her. "Why do you sit there like that? Hand me a bowl, will you? Ah, where is Kshenti[2] and the others? Now you've started putting oil on your hair. I don't suppose you'll touch a uten-sil now."

Annapurna set the bottle down and studied her husband. "Can you tell me," she began in an unusually quiet voice, "what you are thinking of?"

Sahayhari shuddered at his wife's tone. He recognized it as the lull before the storm, and he awaited the onslaught with trepidation. "Why . . . what . . . this time . . ." he protested feebly.

Annapurna's voice became even quieter. "Now don't start any tricks, I tell you. If you want to play the fool, do it some other time. You never know what's going on. Why don't you ask? I can tell you how it feels to have a man with a marriageable daughter at home waste his time fishing and drinking palm juice. Do you know what the people in the village are saying?"

"What," he asked in surprise, "what are they saying?"

"Go to the Choudhurys' and ask. How can you expect to live with respectable people when you spend all your time with untouchables?[3] You must obey the rules."

"The Trellis" by Bibhuti Bhusan Bandyopadhyay from BROKEN BREAD translated by Lila Ray. Published by M. C. Sarkar & Sons Private, Ltd. Reprinted by permission of the translator.

1. *Bibhuti Bandyopadhyay* (bē bü/ tē bän dô päd/ hē). Banerjee, the anglicized form of the author's name, is frequently used. 2. *Kshenti* (khen/ tē). 3. *untouchables,* persons of the lowest caste in India whose touch supposedly defiles members of higher castes.

The astonished Sahayhari was about to say something, but Annapurna rattled on in the same drumming voice. "You will be ostracised, my love, ostracised. It was all settled at the Choudhurys' yesterday. They talked it over in the temple pavilion. No one is to drink water we have touched. You won't be asked to take part in village activities any more. It's all because our daughter's marriage has not taken place despite the formal blessings. Everyone thinks of her as betrothed. It's all right with you, though. Now you are free to waste your time with your untouchable friends."

"Is that all," Sahayhari answered with contempt. "I thought it was something serious. Ostracism! They've all tried it. So it's Mr. Kalimoi Takur's turn now."

"Why?" Annapurna flared back. "You think it is so difficult to ostracise you? Are you one of the village elders or the headman? You own neither a home nor a fire, and there is no one you can count on for help. And really the girl is getting big."

She lowered her voice suddenly. "She is fifteen. People have eyes. What if we do give out that she is less?" She raised her voice again. "You make no attempt to arrange her marriage. Must I be the one to look for a suitable match?"

Sahayhari knew it would be impossible to get his wife to lower her voice as long as he stayed, so he quickly picked up a brass bowl and made for the back door. But he stopped a few feet away from the door, exclaiming joyfully: "Kshenti, my dear child, where did you get that? Where did you find it? Oh, this is . . ."

A girl of fourteen or fifteen entered, followed in turn by two younger sisters. She was carrying a bundle of pui leaves. The stalks were thick, and with a yellowness that showed someone had thrown them away after thinning out his garden. Happily, the girl had gathered them up. One of the younger girls was carrying something wrapped in pui leaves; the other was empty-handed.

The eldest girl was tall and well-formed.

Her hair was dry and dishevelled, wind-blown, and her face was large, and her eyes, large too, and quiet. The glass bracelets on her wrist were held together by a kind of safety-pin sold at two bronze coins a dozen. It would have been necessary to go back to prehistoric times to determine the age of that pin. The girl's name was Kshenti. She turned quickly, took the small bundle from her sister and held it out.

"Look, father," she said. "Some prawns. I got them on the road from old Gaya. She did not want to give them to me. She said you still owe her a couple of coins from the other day. I told her you weren't going to run away with her money. And the pui. Uncle Ray told me to take them. See how thick the stalks are—"

"Take them away!" Annapurna cried shrilly from her seat. She was more than angry. "What wonderful things they've given you!" she shouted bitterly. "The pui is old and dry as a stick. They would have thrown it away tomorrow. That's why they gave it to you, and you . . . you . . . clean their courtyard for them and bring away these weeds. That saves them the trouble of doing it themselves. Of all the stony-brained idiots come to die on my neck! You're a grown girl. Haven't I told you not to go out of the house? Aren't you ashamed to be seen all over the place? If you were married you would be the mother of four children by now—do you know that? And you are found wherever a few leaves are to be had, or a couple of egg plants. And that fellow—he is always on the lookout for a little palm juice. And what not! Get rid of those stalks, I'm telling you, throw them away!"

The frightened girl looked at her mother, then silently dropped her prize. The bundle of pui fell to the ground. "Radha!" Annapurna ordered. "Go throw that worthless bundle out. Dump it beside the pool in the back. Hurry. And if I ever catch you, Kshenti, trying to leave this house again I'll break your bones."

The bundle lay on the ground. The

youngest girl mechanically picked it up and went towards the back door. She was too small for so large a bundle and a number of the stalks fell as she walked.

Sahayhari tried to object. "The child brought them to eat . . ." he began apologetically. "And you . . . rather . . ."

The child with the bundle stopped and looked back at her mother. "No! no!" Annapurna scolded. "Take it away. It will not be eaten. A girl should not be so greedy. Must she beg for wilted pui? Go on, go! Take it and throw it into the jungle."

Sahayhari looked at his eldest daughter, and saw that her eyes had filled with tears. He felt very sad. Yet, however dear his daughter might have been to him, he did not have the courage to quarrel with his wife in broad daylight over a few stalks of pui. Without a word, he went out the back door.

The hurt expression on her daughter's face came back to Annapurna later while she was busy cooking, and she remembered how Kshenti had pleaded the day before the last festival: "Please, Mother, keep half the pui for me. The others can share the other half."

As no one else was home, Annapurna went out to gather up the stalks scattered around the back door and in the courtyard. Only those on the refuse heap beside the pond, mixed now with garbage, were left alone. Almost furtively, Annapurna made a tasty dish of the pui and the prawns.

When Kshenti sat down to her midday meal and discovered the pui and prawns on her plate, she looked timidly up at her mother. Her large eyes showed both joy and surprise. "Do you want some more, Kshenti? What do you say?" her mother asked after the last trace of pui had disappeared from the girl's plate. Kshenti immediately nodded her head happily. Annapurna choked off the surge of tears, busying herself by taking dried chilies out of a basket in the thatch.

That afternoon Sahayhari was summoned to appear before the village elders at the temple pavilion. The temple belonged to Mr. Kalimoi, and after a few introductory words, Kalimoi turned to Sahayhari. "Times have changed—haven't they, brother?" he broke out excitedly. "Take the case of Kesto Mukherjee. He wouldn't have anyone but a man of good character for his son-in-law. That got him into trouble. In the end he had to save his honor by pleading with Hari's son to marry his daughter. And what kind of character does Hari's son have? Disgraceful. They are just rotten Kshatriyas who have gone to pot in only six or seven generations!" He lowered his voice. "Has society the power it used to have? No! It is shrinking from one day to the next. One doesn't have to look far for an example. Take your thirteen-year-old daughter—"

"On the thirteenth of next Sravan—"[4] Sahayhari broke in.

"Ah! What's the difference between thirteen and sixteen? I ask you? And we are not interested in whether she is thirteen or sixteen or fifty—the count is yours to keep. Why have you refused to go on with the marriage after the formal blessing? Is she not betrothed? A blessing is practically the same as a wedding. Only the Seven Rounds[5] remain—don't they? Don't think we will look on passively while you dally. Unless you want the Brahmins[6] of this village to lose their caste, make immediate arrangements for your daughter's marriage. What are you waiting for—a prince? You know well enough you cannot afford a dowry. You are poor. That is why I selected Srimanta Majumdar's son for you. What if he doesn't know how to read or write? Must one be a judge or magistrate to be a

4. *Sravan,* one of the monsoon months of the year. 5. *Seven Rounds,* part of the traditional Indian marriage ceremony. The bride is carried around the bridegroom seven times. She is then placed in front of him and they look at each other for the first time as man and woman. 6. *Brahmins,* the highest caste in the Hindu social structure who enjoy numerous prerogatives.

man? He has a nice house, a garden and a pond. I've heard that he has planted winter rice on Kunri's land this year, too."

The history of the affair was that Kalimoi had suggested the son of this Majumdar of Manigaon as the son-in-law for Sahayhari. And why should Kalimoi take so much interest in Sahayhari's daughter's marriage to this boy? Gossip had it that Kalimoi was heavily in debt to Majumdar. He had, it was said, not even been able to pay the interest on his debt for a long time, and a complaint was soon to be lodged against him. But there is some doubt about the truth of this rumor. It might have been merely the invention of a malicious enemy. Be that as it may, shortly after the formal blessing Sahayhari discovered that the boy had been confined to bed for some time a few months previously as the result of a severe beating received from relatives of a pot-ter's wife of his own village. Not wanting to give his daughter to such a man, Sahayhari had promptly broken off the engagement.

Several days after the meeting in the temple pavilion, Sahayhari sat smoking contentedly in the warmth of the little sun which made its way through the leaves of the pomelo tree in the courtyard. "Father, won't you come? Mother is bath-ing," said Kshenti, coming up quietly.

Sahayhari glanced towards the ghat next to the house, then answered in a low voice: "Bring me the crow-bar as quick as you can. Go." Once more he cast a nervous eye towards the back door. Kshenti came, carrying a crow-bar so big she had to hold it in both hands. Then father and daughter tiptoed silently out of the door. From their manner one would think they were about to commit a robbery.

Annapurna finished her bath and left the ghat. Changing into dry clothes, she was about to light the fire in the stove when Durga, the Mukherjee's small daughter, came in. "Auntie," she said,

"mother sent me. She will not touch the pot on the altar, and she wants you to come and take it off. She also wants to know if you will help prepare the food for the feast of the rice harvest. Will you come?"

To the left of the path leading to the Mukherjee's lay a thick patch of jungle and scrub. The heavy scent of a wild creeper drifted up from it in the chill of the winter morning. On a hog plum tree a yellow bird with a long tail flitted from branch to branch.

"Auntie, Auntie," cried Durga, pointing at the bird with her finger, "what kind of bird is that?" Turning her attention to the bird, Annapurna noticed something else. Somewhere in the jungle growth a thudding sound came at regular intervals, as though someone were digging. But as soon as Durga spoke, it stopped, sudden-ly. Annapurna stood there for a moment, then went on. When they had gone some distance, the thudding started once again.

It was late when Annapurna finished her work and returned home. She found Kshenti sitting in the sunny courtyard with a bottle of oil. She was letting her hair down. Annapurna glanced sharply at the girl before going into the kitchen to light the stove. "Where have you been all this time?" she asked her daughter. "Why are you so late with your bath?"

"I'm going, mother," the child answered hastily. "I won't be a minute."

Kshenti had just gone to bathe when her father came in carrying a wild potato weighing more than thirty pounds. Unex-pectedly finding himself face to face with his wife, he looked at her apologetically. "The watchman, Moisha, has been asking me to go and see him every day for a long time. My father used to visit him regular-ly. So he said he had planted this potato beside the fence and that I could have it . . ."

Annapurna eyed her husband suspi-ciously. "What were you doing in the Barojpota jungle a little while ago?"

"Me!" Sahayhari acted shocked.

"When? I never . . . I was here . . ." He looked as though he had dropped from the sky the moment before.

"If you must steal," Annapurna's gaze was steady, "don't lie as well. Your days are numbered now. I know all about it. You thought I was in the ghat. But Durga's mother sent for me and on my way to the Mukherjee's I heard digging in the Barojpota jungle. I understood at once. The thudding stopped when Durga spoke and started again as soon as we had passed. You have no thought either for this world or the next! Steal or rob as you like, but why drag the girl into it and turn her head?"

Sahayhari gesticulated in protest, trying to produce proof that he had not been in the Barojpota jungle. But, under his wife's unflinching eyes, words failed him, and he could not discover anything convincing in the arguments that occurred to him.

Half an hour later Kshenti came from her bath. She gave the imposing potato a sidelong glance and hung her sari out to dry with concentrated attention. An innocent expression crossed her face.

"Kshenti, come here a minute," the mother called.

Kshenti's face wilted. Hesitantly she approached her mother. "This potato— you dug it up and brought it home together. Didn't you?" her mother demanded.

Kshenti gave her mother a stealthy look, then glanced at the potato on the ground. She looked at her mother once more, finally turning her eyes to the top of the bamboo clump in front of the house. Beads of sweat stood out on her forehead, but she did not reply.

"Why don't you say something?" Annapurna's voice had become harsh. "Did you bring in this potato?"

Kshenti looked at her mother with stricken eyes. "Yes."

Annapurna spluttered like an egg plant frying in oil. "PAGEE! Fool," she shouted. "I'll break a stick of wood across your back before I finish with you today. Did you go to the Barojpota jungle to steal a wild potato? You're a big girl. You've been marriageable for a long time. That patch of jungle is so lonely tigers lurk there in the daytime. And you go there to dig up somebody else's potato! What if the watchman reports you? Where is a father-in-law to come to your rescue? Eat what you earn and if you don't earn anything, don't eat. Understand? Don't touch anything that belongs to somebody else. What am I to do with such a girl?"

Two or three days later—it was afternoon—Kshenti ran up to her mother with dirt on her hands. "Mother," she called, "Mother, come and see!"

Annapurna found that Kshenti and her little sister had cleared a small plot of ground next to the crumbling wall of the overgrowth of cactus and thorn bushes. Kshenti was enthusiastically turning the soil into a garden. As an augury of the abundance to come, a single pui seedling hung face upwards, tied by a strip of cloth to a stick like a prisoner on the gallows. The rest of the crop existed for the present only in the dreams of the eldest daughter. It had not yet bloomed on this earth.

"Foolish child," Annapurna chided. "Is this the season for planting pui? It grows during the rains. It will die without water."

"I'll water it every day."

"Perhaps then it will live. The night dew is heavy at this time of year."

The weather turned very cold. When Sahayhari woke in the morning, he found his two youngest daughters standing under the jackfruit tree in the courtyard. They were wrapped in a quilt waiting hopefully for the sun to rise. Kshenti, shivering with the cold, came in with a broken basket. She had been gathering cow-dung at the Mukherjee's. "Kshenti," Sahayhari called, "why don't you put something warm on when you get up so early?"

"All right," she answered, "I'll put

something on. But it's not as cold as that—"

"Do it anyway, Kshenti, or you will catch your death," Sahayhari said as he went out, thinking all along that he had not taken a good look at his oldest daughter for a long time. Since when had she become so pretty?

The history of the warm blouse Kshenti should have been wearing is as follows: Many years before Sahayhari had purchased a black serge blouse at the Haripur fair for two and half rupees.[7] It had been mended over and over again. Kshenti had been growing up during this time and the blouse no longer fitted her. Now Sahayhari never concerned himself with such unimportant domestic affairs, while Annapurna was unaware of the present state of the blouse. Kshenti said nothing, but kept the blouse out of sight in her own tin trunk.

In the evening of the last day of Pous (January 14), Annapurna sat kneading rice flour with molasses. A small bowl of oil lay beside her. Kshenti had spread a banana leaf underneath a grater and was shredding coconut. At first Annapurna had not wanted Kshenti's help, for Kshenti was in the habit of sitting anywhere and of playing about in the dirt. Her clothes were always more soiled and disheveled than the ritual prescribed. But she finally gave in to Kshenti's pleas, had her wash and put on clean clothes, and allowed her to grate the coconut.

The dough was ready and Annapurna put the shallow pan on the fire. Her youngest daughter, Lakshmi, put out her hand saying, "Mother, just a little."

Annapurna took a small ball of dough, patted it with her fingers and handed it to the child. The second daughter, Puthie, quickly wiped her hand on her sari and stretched it out. "Mother, a little . . ."

Kshenti looked up hungrily from her grating from time to time, but she said nothing lest her mother scold her for wanting to eat while she was preparing food.

"Bring me the coconut shell," called Annapurna, adding: "Kshenti, let me put a little aside for you."

Kshenti deftly handed her the top half of the coconut shell. Annapurna filled it with a large ball of the mixture.

Puthie announced: "Jataima has ordered a lot of milk. Ranga Didi is boiling it down to make cream. They are going to have all sorts of cakes."

"Are they cooking again this afternoon?" Kshenti asked, lifting her face. "They invited Brahmins to lunch—Uncle Suresh and Tinu's father. They had rice pudding and sweetmeats, and everything."

"Mother," Puthie asked, "can't rice cakes be made without using cream? Khendi says they have to have a cream filling. I said my mother can make them with coconut filling."

Annapurna didn't know how to answer her daughter, not wanting to have to explain to her why she couldn't use cream. She remained silent, dipping the stem of an eggplant in oil and rubbing it around the pan.

"That's just Khendi's talk," broke in Kshenti. "Khendi's mother's not a good cook. Does a little cream fried in butter make a rice cake? The other day their son-in-law came to visit them, and I went to watch. Auntie gave me a couple of her cakes to eat. Oh, my! They smelled burned. A good cake is never burned. And the cream they used didn't make the cakes taste any better."

Kshenti sought out her mother's eyes as she finished her bold statement. "Mother, can I have a little of that grated coconut?"

"Take some, but don't eat it sitting here. The crumbs will drop all over. Take it over there."

Kshenti put some of the grated coconut into half a coconut shell, and moved

---

7. *rupees.* A rupee is a unit of Indian money worth about twenty-one cents.

to the other side of the room. If a face mirrors feeling, there was no doubt at all that Kshenti was experiencing the greatest satisfaction.

An hour or so later, Annapurna called to her children: "Bring your plates and sit down for some hot cakes. Kshenti, some rice is left over from this morning. Take that."

From Kshenti's look it was obvious that her mother's suggestion was not to her liking. "Mother," Puthie suggested, "let Kshenti have the cakes. She likes them so. We can have the rice tomorrow morning."

Radha was unable to eat more than one or two, insisting that she did not like sweet things. Kshenti was still eating after everyone had finished. She ate quietly and spoke very little. Annapurna counted the cakes and found that she had eaten at least eighteen or nineteen.

"Would you like some more?" she asked. Kshenti nodded her head happily. Annapurna gave her a second helping. Kshenti's face and eyes were shining. She looked at her mother and smiled. "They are so good, Mother. You beat the mixture that way . . . that is how . . ." And she went on with her munching.

As she gathered up the utensils, Annapurna looked tenderly at her quiet, innocent child, a child who was just a bit too fond of food. Kshenti would bring much happiness to her future home, she thought to herself. She was so good. No matter how much she was scolded or beaten she never said a word. No one had ever heard her raise her voice.

Kshenti was married early in the summer through the good offices of one of Sahayhari's distant relatives. She was the second wife of her husband. But he was not much more than forty. At first Annapurna did not like the match at all. Still the bridegroom was well-to-do, and he did have a house in town. It was said he made his money dealing in slate, lime and bricks. It was rare good luck finding such a son-in-law.

Annapurna was shy about appearing in front of her new son-in-law—because of his age. But at the reception she took Kshenti's plump little hands and placed them in his. She did not want Kshenti to feel hurt. Tears choked her and she was unable to say anything at all.

Outside the house the bearers, trying to center the weight, set the sedan chair down under the amloki tree. Annapurna saw the tip of Kshenti's cheap red veil hanging out of the sedan chair just where a cluster of the lavender flowers of the medi swung low on the fence. Her heart cried out at the thought of sending this untidy, good-natured, hungry child of hers into a family of strangers. How could they understand her?

Kshenti had tried to console her before she left. "Mother, send for me in the month of Ashar.[8] Send father to get me. It's only two months away."

"Why," bantered an old woman from the neighborhood, "let there be a grandson for him first. Then . . ."

Kshenti blushed. "No," she said obstinately, smiling shyly through the tears coming to her large eyes. "Of course he will come. Just you wait and see whether he comes or not!"

As she gathered up the sheets of mango juice drying on a latticed frame, Annapurna felt a surge of tears come to her eyes. In the dying sun of that late spring afternoon, she thought of her foolish, hungry little girl, and how she was no longer there to come into the kitchen, holding her hand out shamelessly and pleading: "Mother, please, just a little —tear this corner off—just a little bit."

It was more than a year now. The month of Ashar had come again. The rains had set in. Sahayhari sat on the verandah chatting with his neighbor, Vishnu Sarkar. "Take that for granted," he said, filling his pipe. "It is bound to be like that. Can people in our circumstances expect any better?"

---

8. *Ashar,* period of time from June 16 to July 15.

Vishnu Sarkar was sitting cross-legged on a mat, hunched forward so that from a distance one might imagine he was kneading dough. "No," he answered, clearing his throat. "All that . . . I'll give all I have to give in cash. By the way, what was wrong with your daughter?"

"I was told she was taken with small-pox," Sahayhari explained between coughs as he pulled strongly on his pipe. "You see this is the way it happened. They refused to send her home. They insisted that the balance of payments due them—about 250 rupees—be paid first. Then she could come."

"How awful."

"I said I would pay it slowly. I could not send presents worth less than thirty rupees to the Pujahs. I took that into consideration. They said unpleasant things about the girl: that she behaved like the daughter of an ill-bred family, that she was greedy . . . and what not. I went to see her in the month of Pous. But I couldn't bear to look at her."

Sahayhari drew deeply on his pipe, as if unable to go on. For a few moments neither man spoke.

"And then?" Vishnu finally asked in a soft voice.

"My wife was very anxious. She used to cry. So I went to see the girl in the month of Pous. What a state she was in! Her mother-in-law cursed me. 'This is what happens,' she cried, 'when no proper inquiries are made before being tied in a relationship with people of low class. And the father is no better than his daughter. He comes to see her empty-handed.'" He glanced at Vishnu Sarkar, adding: "You know very well whether we are low class or not. There was a time when Parameswar Chatterjee was so influential he could make a lion and a lamb lie beside one another. What if I today . . ." Sahayhari Chatterjee laughed dryly at the vanished glory of his lineage.

Vishnu Sarkar shook his head and grunted in agreement.

"She was taken with smallpox in the spring. Such people they are. As soon as the spots showed, they left her with a distant cousin of mine, a woman they met on an outing to Kalighat. They did not even bother to tell me. Tara sent word. I went—"

"And didn't see her?"

"No! Such people. They took off all her jewelry before sending her to my cousin. Let it go. We should get started. It's getting late. What about the bait? Puffed rice will not do where ants are needed."

The months passed. The rice festival came once more. This year the weather was so cold towards the end of the month of Pous that the old people began to complain they could not remember any like it.

In the evening Annapurna was in the kitchen making dough for long narrow rice cakes. Puthie and Radha sat beside the fire warming themselves.

"Add a little more water, Mother," Radha said. "Why have you made the mixture so thick?"

"Shouldn't you add a little salt?" Puthie asked.

"Look, Mother! See where Radha's jacket is hanging. It will catch fire. . ."

"Move over a little," Annapurna ordered. "Can't you get warm without sitting on top of the fire? Come here."

The rounds of dough were ready. Annapurna put the pan on the fire and pressed the cakes into it. Over the low flame they expanded, rose and crisped softly.

"Give me the first cake, Mother," said Puthie. "We must offer it to the goddess Shasti."[9]

"Don't go alone. Take Radha with you."

The moon was very bright and its light clung to the white clusters of flowers on the creeper hanging over the top of the giant fern behind the house.

As Puthie and Radha opened the back door, a jackal disappeared into the thick brush, rustling the dead leaves. Puthie

_____

9. _Shasti,_ the Indian goddess of children.

hurled the cake with all her strength towards the top of the fern tree. Then, frightened by the silence around them, the hush of the lonely bamboo grove, they backed away, more or less falling through the door, and closed it quickly.

"Did you offer it?" Annapurna asked when they had returned.

"Yes, Mother," answered Puthie. "I threw it at the spot where you got the lemon seedling last year. . . ."

The hour grew late. The cakes were almost ready. Behind the house a woodpecker had been tapping away by the light of the moon for a long time. His tapping was growing drowsy. As the two sisters cut banana leaves for their plates, Puthie grew thoughtful. At last she spoke: "How Kshenti loved cakes. . . ."

For a while no one spoke. Gradually, the mother and the two daughters turned their eyes to the corner of the courtyard. There, enshrining her memory in its spreading branches and rich foliage, the little pui seedling which Kshenti had planted with so much care had grown and grown until a trellis had been required to support it. What with the water in the rainy season and the dew of early winter, the profusion of tender green buds was more than the trellis could hold. And they hung down from the sides, soft and strong, and full of the loveliness of life.

Development

INTERPRETATION

1. (a) In what ways does Kshenti differ from many fifteen-year-old girls? (b) What problems do these differences raise?

2. (a) Discuss Annapurna's attitude toward Kshenti. Cite specific references from the story to support your answer. (b) Why is Annapurna so preoccupied with Kshenti's marriage prospects?

3. (a) What is Sahayhari's attitude toward his wife and family? (b) What type of man is he?

4. Who is responsible for what happens to Kshenti: society? her family? her husband's family? Kshenti herself? all of them?

5. (a) How is the pui seedling symbolic of the girl, Kshenti? (b) How do their patterns of development differ? (c) What is the significance of the trellis mentioned in the title and only once in the story?

6. Though Kshenti possesses the potentialities for growing "soft and strong, and full of the loveliness of life," these possibilities are not realized in her life. (a) In your opinion, if Kshenti had not been afflicted with smallpox, would she have developed into a happy young woman in her husband's home? Why or why not? (b) Is Kshenti to be criticized because she is unable to assume the role which society has placed upon her?

7. Do you agree with the opinion of some Western critics that in "The Trellis" Bandyopadhyay condemns a system which forces a girl into a life not of her own choosing? Why or why not?

TECHNIQUE

1. Select specific details from this selection which help to (a) furnish setting, (b) indicate culture, (c) sketch character.

2. Which devices in "The Trellis" are indicative of the storyteller's technique?

EXTENSIONS

1. (a) What point about a young person's growth and development is the author making in this selection? (b) What factors contribute to a young person's accepting a role thrust upon him rather than chosen by him? In your answer consider not only the individual but also the family, society, and custom.

Comparison

1. Man has been rightly called "the dreamer"; illusions are essential to his existence. The four selections in this group present people who have been robbed of their illusions. *(a)* Have these individuals also been robbed of their happiness? Explain. *(b)* In your opinion, do these people deserve their disillusionment? *(c)* Do you see any way in which their disillusionment could have been avoided? If so, how?

2. *(a)* One reader commenting on this group of selections said that the characters were too unrealistic in their approach to life, thereby preparing the groundwork for their eventual—and inevitable—disillusionment. Do you agree with this statement? Why or why not? *(b)* The results of disillusionment may take many forms: bitterness, cynicism, apathy, acceptance, regret, or further striving to reach an ideal. How do the characters in these selections respond to their situation? Do you notice any similarity in their responses? *(c)* Do they respond as you expect them to? Explain.

3. *(a)* Of the major characters studied in this group of selections, whom do you consider the most vulnerable? the least vulnerable? Why? *(b)* What elements in the make-up of these people are most responsible for their vulnerability or their lack of it? *(c)* In your opinion, is a person to be criticized because he is vulnerable?

4. To some extent all men are vulnerable, but man still has the ability to protect himself from pain through the building of defenses. Consider Jan ("My Friend Jan") and Kshenti ("The Trellis"). Which character has better protected himself against disillusionment? What are his defenses?

5. "The Vulnerable" includes a poem by a German writer and stories by Norwegian, Rumanian, and Indian authors. *(a)* What experiences in the selections may be called universal? *(b)* Which elements reflect a definite local color? *(c)* Which elements predominate—the universal or the regional? Explain.

6. Pathos in literature is that quality which evokes pity, tenderness, or sorrow in the reader. It differs from tragedy in that pathos usually refers to helpless suffering or unmerited grief while tragedy arises from the grandeur, struggle, and terrible justice of the tragic hero. *(a)* Why would the literature presented here tend to be pathetic rather than tragic? *(b)* Which of the selections do you find the most pathetic? the least pathetic? Why? *(c)* Compare selections from this group with a tragedy you have already read, pointing out differences between elements of the pathetic in this group with those of the tragic in the work you have selected.

7. Of the characters presented in this group, whom do you consider the most admirable? Why?

8. *(a)* Which selection seems most inevitable in its outcome? Why? *(b)* Given an opportunity, which ending would you most like to change? What specific changes would you make?

The Hypocrites

THE FOX AND THE WOODCUTTER / AESOP / GREECE

THE POOR / CARLO CASSOLA / ITALY

TORQUEMADA IN THE FLAMES / BENITO PÉREZ GALDÓS / SPAIN

TARTUFFE / MOLIÈRE / FRANCE

TWINS SEVEN-SEVEN: ELEPHANT MAN from Oshogbo, Western Nigeria. Courtesy of the Pall Mall Press, London.

The Fox and the Woodcutter

AESOP / Greece
(620? – 560? B.C.)

translated from the Latin by Denison B. Hull

A fox was fleeing. As she fled
A hunter fast behind her sped.
But being wearied, when she spied
An old man cutting wood, she cried,
5   "By all the gods that keep you well,
Hide me among these trees you fell,
And don't reveal the place, I pray."
He swore that he would not betray
The wily vixen; so she hid,
10 And then the hunter came to bid
The old man tell him if she'd fled,
Or if she'd hidden there. He said,
"I did not see her," but he showed
The place the cunning beast was stowed

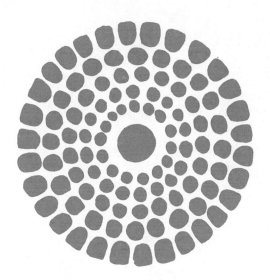

₁₅ By pointing at it with his finger.
But still the hunter did not linger.
He put no faith in leering eye,
But trusting in the words, went by.
Escaped from danger for a while
₂₀ The fox peeked out with coaxing smile.
The old man said to her, "You owe
Me thanks for saving you, you know."
"Most certainly; for I was there
As witness of your expert care.
₂₅ But now farewell. And don't forget,
The god of oaths will catch you yet
For saving with your voice and lips
While slaying with your finger tips."

Development

1. *(a)* Why do you think the wood-cutter attempts to betray the fox? Support your answer. *(b)* Why does he fail?

2. *(a)* "Voice and lips" and "finger tips" are metaphorical expressions. What two kinds of activities do they represent? *(b)* How do they conflict? *(c)* What is the moral of the fable?

3. What effect would each of the following character changes have on the tone and meaning of the fable? *(a)* The "wily vixen" is, instead, an "innocent lamb." *(b)* The "old man cutting wood" is, instead, a "young man whittling wood." *(c)* The "hunter" is, instead, a "farmer."

The Poor

CARLO CASSOLA / Italy

(1917–   )

translated from the Italian by Anthony Rhodes

On arriving at the little flight of steps she stopped for a moment, as if to summon up courage to make the difficult visit ahead. The district of the town extended below, a forest of little red roofs bristling with skylights and gables. On the right, it was bounded by the town walls; on the left, by a large white slope formed from pieces of rejected alabaster up which a footpath ran diagonally.

Before starting her work as a Visitor, the signorina had never set foot here before. Now one might say that not a day passed without her venturing into this labyrinth of narrow streets and small steps. Last winter the surface had been frozen; at this very point where she was now walking, she had fallen and broken her shoulder. The houses were nearly all unplastered, with small square windows which had saucepans and tins of geraniums on the sills.

"Good evening, signorina," said a woman sitting on the steps of a doorway. On her knees she held a small child, aged about five or six

The signorina felt she must stop.

"How's your husband?" she asked.

"What do you expect?" replied the woman. She had a dark complexion and was still young and buxom; she might have been beautiful if her face had not been pock-marked. "He's been out of work six months. How do you expect him to be, with all this?"

"But his health?"

"Oh, his health's all right. He occasionally has a little difficulty breathing at night."

"I shouldn't worry too much about that," said the signorina. "Most alabaster workers seem to have a touch of asthma. The main thing is, he hasn't had any more heart attacks. He hasn't, has he?"

"No, not those," replied the woman.

"I'm glad of that," said the signorina. "Health, you know, is the first thing. For everything else . . . well, God always provides."

"Health is the first thing—but so is work." The woman abruptly put the child aside and got up. "Don't you realize it's been going on for six months now? The only money coming into the house is from the public assistance . . ."

"Yes, yes, I know . . ." the signorina replied hastily.

"He's tried ten places. The same reply from all of them. And you know, my husband—he's not at all demanding. He'll do any work—if it brings in food for the family."

"But surely, the Foresters' Cooperative held out some hope?" said the signorina. "I remember, I spoke to Signor Puccianti, and he promised me . . ."

"Yes; yes, fine hopes they gave him at the Cooperative. First, they said, it's the slack season and there's no question of taking on more hands. We'll wait until the summer's over, they said. And then —we'll think about it again in the autumn. Fine! Yes, and what are we going to eat during the summer? Is that the sort of reply you give the father of a family?" The woman had raised her voice. "How are we going to manage? Do they want people to start stealing in order to get a scrap of bread for the family?"

The signorina had drawn back a little. The mad look in those eyes, that pock-marked face, that strident tone, made her feel uncomfortable, almost frightened. A little woman had appeared in the next doorway, from where she was watching the scene.

"Well, I'm sorry, I must go now," said the signorina at last. "Let's hope your husband soon finds a job."

"Hope! Yes, we've got to hope a lot," said the woman gloomily. The signorina waited anxiously for what she was going to say next. "We must hope for an epidemic. An epidemic to kill us all off. Me—my wretched husband—and this creature here."

The signorina could not help feeling a little relieved; she had feared the woman might come out with a subversive speech. It would not have been the first time people had spoken their minds in this part of the town, where writings of this kind sometimes appeared on the walls. "You shouldn't talk like that," she said. "We must always hope for God's help." And then, employing again her usual authoritative tone, "And tell me, where's Chiorboli? The bricklayer with the sick wife."

"There, down the street." The woman became listless again. "The last house. Go with her, Tatiana!"

"No, it doesn't matter, thank you," parried the signorina; but the child was already at her side. They went off to the right down some small steps, and turned into a blind alley. The child accompanied her as far as the door.

"She's on the second floor," it said, and then turned back briskly.

"Thank you, my dear," said the signorina.

She went up the dark staircase. On the first floor, the door was wide open; she saw an untidy kitchen, with a five- or six-year-old child standing naked on a chair drawn up beside the sink; its mother was washing it and the infant was whining. "They might at least shut the door," thought the signorina. What annoyed her most about the poor was their lack of modesty. She climbed the second flight and found herself standing in front of a door. In the dark she groped for a bell or knocker, but without finding it; she was about to call out, when she realized that the door was only ajar. She pushed it and entered a kitchen, which was in darkness too.

"May I come in?" she said. A voice, or rather a groan answered her. "I'm Signorina Verdi. I've come on behalf of the Visitors."

"Come in, signorina! Come in!" whined the voice.

Groping, the signorina crossed the room and pushed open a door—to be suddenly assailed by an acrid smell of sweat and urine. She went to the window and threw it open. "Ah!" she turned, relieved, to the invalid. "A little fresh air is always a good thing."

The invalid was a fat woman with a large, red sweating face. She was raised in the bed, her back propped up against two cushions without pillowcases.

The signorina gave a glance at the dirty sheets and then addressed the woman.

"How long have you been ill?" she asked.

"A year," replied the woman. "But I've been completely bedridden for a month."

"How do you feel now? A little better?"

"What do you expect, signorina? I seem to lose a little more strength every day. If you looked, you'd see my legs are swollen. If I'm not helped, I can't even get up to pass water."

"Staying in bed makes you weaker, you know. Who's your doctor? Carboni?" The sick woman made an affirmative sign. "What does he say—how long before you get well?"

"Listen. In the first place the doctor doesn't ever come. And secondly, when he does, he's absolutely no use."

The signorina put a few more questions (with her double activity, as nurse and Visitor, she knew by now as much as a doctor); then she picked up a box of injections on the bedside table and examined it for a moment.

"How many of these does he say you're to have? One a day?"

"One every other day," replied the invalid. "A woman comes and gives them to me."

"But who looks after you? Your husband's away at work all day, I suppose. Haven't you anybody else . . . I mean, a sister, a sister-in-law?"

"I've a sister-in-law, my brother's wife. But, you see, she's always away in the country, she has four children. She certainly hasn't time for me. If I need anything, I call the family below. But I'm here all the time alone, signorina! Just think of it! I'm here alone, waiting to die . . ." The woman began crying quietly.

"Now come, you mustn't let yourself get depressed," said the signorina. "Your condition isn't serious. All you need is a bit of company to raise your spirits. I'm sorry I must go now. But I promise to come back soon and see you."

When the signorina arrived at the top of the hundred and thirty steps she heaved a sigh of relief, not only at having finished the climb, but with another kind of relief, spiritual relief, at having finished viewing such misery.

On entering the church she immediately looked round at the first row on the left, where the Marchesa[1] Lastrucci always sat. Yes, she was there, in her little hat and veil. But she saw the Nobildonna[2] Ormanni too; and then she sat down on the first free bench, beside a small red-eyed woman who was mumbling over her rosary. A minute later the priest appeared, and the service began.

On her knees, her face hidden in her hands, the signorina repeated the prayers one after the other; but her thoughts were elsewhere. She was thinking of her poor— and not very kindly. That woman with the out-of-work husband for one, she was all covered with jewellery. "They're like that, they're gypsies. When the husband works and earns, they spend it down to the last farthing. They don't think of saving." As for the invalid—well, there was nothing much she could say about her. But was it really possible that the woman could be left alone like that? No doubt the husband would be off to the tavern when he'd finished work, instead of coming back home. And what about that sister-in-law who hadn't shown a sign of life once, throughout the whole illness?

Outside the church she found the Marchesa, who had got rid of Signora Ormanni. The Marchesa was surprised to see her. "Ah!" she said. "I thought you weren't coming. You see, I thought you were arriving late, because . . ."

"No, no. I was on time. But I saw you with her, there . . ."

"Any news?" interrupted the Marchesa Lastrucci.

"No news, Maria dear," replied the signorina emphatically. "Always the same—poverty, sickness, scenes of moral and physical degradation . . ."

They went on talking for a while and the signorina had the chance of adding a number of similar high-sounding phrases about what she had seen. While they talked she could not help noticing the milk-woman who was standing at the door of her shop; she knew the woman wanted to speak to her, and she knew it was about a favour for her brother-in-law. But this evening she was too tired to listen to her; so, as soon as she saw the milk-woman engaged with a client, she quickly left her friend. They embraced and kissed, as they always did in the evening. Then the Marchesa, supporting herself on her stick, set off laboriously for the piazza. The signorina meanwhile went hurriedly under the big doorway.

Once home she changed and went into

---

1. *Marchesa* (mär kā′ zä), an Italian woman who holds the rank next above a countess. 2. *Nobildonna,* the daughter of a nobleman.

the room which served her as office, workroom, and dining room; it was a small room, certainly no more cheerful than the others, for it gave onto a small courtyard, a veritable well into which the sunlight never fell. It was also the coldest room in the house. In spite of this, the signorina used to spend the day here. The furniture consisted of a writing-desk, a small wicker armchair, another chair, a sideboard and two shelves on which her few books were aligned: *Lives of the Saints* and other volumes of a religious nature, and all the publications of the Touring Club, of which she had been a member for many years. The signorina had never been much of a reader. Travel, yes, she would have liked to travel; but being on her own, she had never been able to satisfy the wish. Her pilgrimages had been particularly valuable for seeing a bit of the world; during the war she had been a nurse in Salonica.

She had time before supper to write a letter. After the meal, she unwrapped the *Osservatore Romano*,[3] which arrived by the evening post. She was reading about the religious persecution in Mexico when the bell rang. "Vittoria!" she cried. Vittoria, who was washing up, was a little deaf and did not hear. With a suffering expression on her face, the signorina went to open the door herself. It was the milk-woman. The signorina's expression of suffering increased.

The milk-woman apologized for having come at this hour of the day, but said that during the daytime she was always busy in the shop. "Just one minute, signorina!" The signorina took her into the small drawing room, but did not ask her to sit down. "I've come on behalf of that brother-in-law of mine," continued the woman. "You know, the one who's an orderly at the hospital." The signorina said she remembered him very well. It was she who had done her best to get him taken on there.

The problem now was that the head orderly had reached the retiring age, and his post on the staff had become vacant. It was just the moment for her brother-in-law to get a permanent job. There was another candidate, less senior and who was, moreover, a bachelor. But—in the opinion of her brother-in-law—this man had the support of the Fascio.[4]

"You realize, signorina, that if my brother-in-law could have a sure job things would be very different. Then the pay would be nearly double, and it would offer security for the future . . . . Because a casual labourer can be dismissed at any moment. All that's needed is a change in management." It was right that her brother-in-law should have the job, not only because he was an older man and had the responsibility of a family, but because he was a worker who had made himself liked at the hospital, as much by the patients as by the nuns. "We certainly aren't asking a favour, signorina. We only want what is just. You've only to ask the sisters if they're pleased with him . . ."

"Is it true that he ill-treats his wife?" said the signorina suddenly. "I've heard he beats her, too!"

The milk-woman looked disconcerted, but she continued immediately:

"It's true that they don't get on very well in the house. But what do you expect? Poverty, that's what's at the bottom of everything. When a man comes home once a fortnight with 125 lire[5] and has to pay the rent with it, the electric light, the coal, and feed four mouths, you'll agree it's not enough. And then of course he gets into a temper. So does she, and it's easy to quarrel like that."

"But you help them a bit?"

"Yes, of course we give them something," said the woman. "After all, it's my sister, and my sister's children. . . . And my husband, he's the first to say,

---

3. *Osservatore Romano,* the official newspaper of the Vatican. 4. *Fascio* (fä′ shē ô), the local branch of the Fascist party at the time of the story. 5. *125 lire* (lir′ ā). The present value of the lira is about 625 to a dollar. Its value was greater during the time of the story, but still a small sum.

Let's help them!—as if they were his own relations . . ."

The signorina promised she would put in a good word for them. "You can find your own way to the door, can't you?" she said, interrupting the thanks of the milk-woman.

She went into the kitchen to have a word with the maid, and then into her bedroom.

It was a small room, whitewashed—unlike the others, simple and unadorned. Franciscan bareness was exactly what she had wanted as inspiration here; she called it "my little cell." From the iron bed rail hung an olive branch; above the chest of drawers a coloured print showed Saint Francis in the act of receiving the Stigmata.[6]

The signorina undressed, took off her scapular,[7] put on her nightdress and then, in front of the mirror on the chest of drawers, let down her long hair which was now grey. She then got into bed and put out the light. While her lips murmured the Pater, the Ave Maria, the Gloria, and the Requiem, and the special prayer composed by the Pope for the Tertiaries,[8] her mind was busy elsewhere. Voices and laughter came up from the alley immediately below, where there was a wine booth. More voices, more laughter—then a resounding oath.

"What beasts they are!" she thought, turning over onto her side. She was half asleep when she remembered that during the same day she had thought and spoken badly of the Ormanni woman. She must bear this in mind at Confession.

THE END

---

6. *St. Francis . . . Stigmata.* St. Francis experienced religious ecstasies wherein he received stigmata, wounds resembling those of the crucified Christ. 7. *scapular,* bands worn about the neck, often used by religious orders. 8. *Tertiaries,* a lay group associated with the Franciscan order.

Development

INTERPRETATION

1. Compare the signorina's professed attitude toward religion with the one revealed in her thoughts and actions.

2. *(a)* What obstacles keep the signorina from being more helpful to the poor than she is? *(b)* In what sense might the signorina herself symbolize an obstacle to improving the lot of the poor?

3. Explain the irony in the last paragraph of the story.

TECHNIQUE

1. Discuss what the following details contribute to the characterization of the signorina and to your attitude toward her: *(a)* She had fallen and broken a shoulder while making her round of visits. *(b)* While reciting prayers, her thoughts are elsewhere. *(c)* She spends her days in the coldest room of the house. *(d)* When the milk-woman arrives, the signorina does not invite her to sit down. *(e)* She does not read or travel much.

EXTENSIONS

1. Ralph Waldo Emerson made the following comment on virtuous acts:

Men do what is called a good action, as some piece of courage or charity, much as they would pay a fine in expiation of daily non-appearance on parade. Their works are done as an apology or extenuation of their living in the world. . . . Their virtues are penances. I do not wish to expiate, but to live.

(a) Does this description apply to the signorina? *(b)* What do you think Emerson means by the last sentence?

Torquemada in the Flames

BENITO PÉREZ GALDÓS / Spain

(1843 – 1920)

translated from the Spanish by Willard Trask

In 1868, the year of the Revolution,[1] Don Francisco Torquemada bought a tenement house in the calle[2] de San Blas—a very useful piece of property with twenty-four small flats, which, not counting the inevitable bankruptcies, repairs, taxes, etc., brought him in thirteen hundred reals[3] a month, equivalent to between seven and seven-and-a-half per cent on his investment. Every Sunday, Don Francisco appeared in person to collect the rents, the receipts in one hand, his staghorn-handled walking stick in the other. By 1874, the year of the Restoration,[4] he had doubled his capital, and the radical political change brought him very pretty opportunities to place it in advances and loans. The brand-new dignitaries, who had to get together wardrobes, and the functionaries, who emerged from obscurity ravenous, made him a good harvest. When, in

1. *1868, the year of the revolution.* In 1868 Queen Isabella II was expelled by the military. Her expulsion was followed by the brief reign of Amedeo of Savoy and by an abortive attempt to make Spain a republic. 2. *calle* (kä′ ye). 3. *real* (rä äl′). A real is a former silver coin of Spain valued at approximately one cent according to present standards. Eight reals are equal in value to one peso ("piece of eight"). 4. *1874, the year of the Restoration.* In order to end domestic strife, the army restored the monarchy in 1874 by proclaiming Isabella's son King Alfons XII.

1881, the Liberals,[5] who had long been out of it, got into the government, Torquemada was again on the crest of the wave: good loans, good payments and here we go! In short, he soon found himself eying another house—not a tenement this time, but a house in a good neighborhood, almost new, fit for decent tenants, and which, if it brought in only three-and-a-half per cent all told, would be much less of a headache, so far as running it and collecting the rents went, than the troublesome object of his Sunday excursions.

Everything was going as smooth as silk for this ferocious ant when heaven suddenly visited a terrible calamity upon him: his wife died. She died of intestinal colic, and it must be said in Torquemada's behalf that he spared no expense to save the poor woman's life. The loss was a cruel blow to Don Francisco, for the couple had lived in virtuous and industrious peace for over twenty years. With Doña Silvia guarding every penny in the house so that it should not get out, and Don Francisco combing the outside so that nothing that passed by should escape, they had made a couple which could serve as a model for all ants, whether above or below ground.

During the first days of his widowhood, Torquemada the Worse, as certain unpublished historians call him, hardly knew what was going on around him. He turned even yellower than usual, and some white appeared in his hair and beard. But time did what it always does, sweetening the bitter, gnawing with unfeeling tooth at the asperities of life; and by the time two years had passed Torquemada seemed to have become consoled—though, to his honor be it said and repeated, he had no desire to marry again.

Two children remained to him: Rufina and Valentín.[6] At the time of my narrative, Rufina had passed twenty-two, Valentín was just twelve. And—to show you what a lucky star this beast of a Don Francisco had—both of his children were, in their different ways, real jewels, almost like divine blessings showered upon him to console him in his loneliness. Rufina had copied all of her mother's domestic virtues and managed the house almost as well. To be sure, she possessed neither the high business sense nor the consummate acumen nor the other half-moral, half-olfactory aptitudes which had characterized that remarkable matron; but in manners, behavior and seemly presence, no girl of her age could outdo her.

If we turn from Rufina to Torquemada's male offspring, we shall find a still better explanation for the vanity which his children caused in him, because (I say it sincerely) I never knew a more beguiling boy than Valentín, nor such extraordinary precocity as his. Despite his resemblance to his father, the lad was as attractive as could be, with such an expression of intelligence that you were stupefied to find it in such a face; with such charms of person and character, and touches of behavior so far beyond his years, that to see him, talk with him, and love him dearly were one and the same thing. And what an enchanting seriousness he had—yet not incompatible with the restlessness that is characteristic of childhood! Tall and lanky, he had thin but well-shaped legs; a head bigger than normal, with some slight malformation in the bony structure. As for his aptitude for study, it was literally prodigious—the terror of his school and the pride and joy of his masters. All I can say is that our Torquemada never deserved such a jewel, and that if he had been a man capable of praising God for the benefits bestowed upon him, he had reason to stand hour after hour, like Moses, with his arms raised to heaven. He did not raise them, because he knew that none of the joys he delighted in would come to him from that direction.

Torquemada was not one of those usurers who spend their lives multiply-

5. *in 1881, the Liberals.* The Liberals came into power just after the conservative Antonio Canovas del Castillo. 6. *Valentín* (val ən tēn′).

ing money for the Platonic pleasure[7] of possessing it. No. Don Francisco could not escape the influence of this second half of the nineteenth century, which has almost made a religion of the decorously material side of life. Misers of the old stamp, who laboriously gathered wealth and lived like beggars and died like dogs on a pallet full of fleas, with bank notes stuffed among the straw, were the mystics or metaphysicians of usury; their egoism concentrated and sublimated itself in the pure idea of business; living in a period which began with the expropriation of monasteries, Torquemada, without comprehending it, underwent the metamorphosis which has changed the nature of usury from metaphysical to positivistic; and if it is true, as history affirms, that from 1851 to 1868, which was his real period of apprenticeship, he went about shabbily dressed and with an affectation of poverty, his face and hands unwashed, constantly scratching his legs and arms as if he had lice, his hat greasy and his coat threadbare; if, again, the neighborhood chronicle states that in his house there was fast-day food all year round and that his wife went out on her errands in a torn kerchief and old shoes that had belonged to her husband, it is equally certain that by 1870, or thereabouts, he was living on quite another footing; that Doña Silvia dressed very well on particular occasions; that Don Francisco changed his shirt more often than once a fortnight; that they ate less mutton and more beef, and on Sundays some chicken giblets were added to the soup; that beans at every meal, with dry bread and sausages now and again, were becoming a thing of the past; that, in short—and lest this enumeration become boring—the whole family began to live as God intended that human beings should.

Well, sir: Doña Silvia ups and dies, Rufina takes over the reins of household government—and the metamorphosis becomes even more marked. New monarchs, new principles. Torquemada—what else could he do?—submitted to the logic of the times. He put up with a clean shirt twice a week; without much protest, he accepted a clean tablecloth in the middle of the week, wine at meals, lamb with peas (in season), and turkey at Christmas; he tolerated a braided jacket, which in him was a refinement of etiquette, and said nothing about the carpet in the drawing room, nor the many other improvements which were gradually smuggled into the house.

And very soon Don Francisco saw that these innovations were good and that his daughter was really very clever, because—it seemed extraordinary, but there it was!—he would go out into the street and feel, in his good clothes, more of a personage than ever before. He walked more vigorously, coughed more vehemently, talked more loudly and spoke up in the discussions at his café, even finding courage to defend his own opinions; whereas before—no doubt as the result of his shabby exterior and his habitual affectation of poverty—he had always been of everyone else's opinion. Little by little he became aware of his vigorous social and financial possibilities; he tapped himself, and the sound told him that he was a landlord with a comfortable income. But vanity never blinded him.

In his character there was something that resisted change. His mannerisms even increased; he was still forever saying that the times were very bad, very bad indeed; forever complaining that his hard work was out of all proportion to his miserable profits; his tones were as honeyed as ever; he kept his habit of making a wry face to show what he thought of life. Except for his clothes, which were improved in quality if not in his manner of wearing them, he was the same: his face the same strange mixture of the soldier and the ecclesiastic, his complexion bilious, his eyes black and a

---

7. *Platonic pleasure,* apparently, the pleasure of holding something (money) as a good in itself rather than as a means to gaining some other good.

little dreary, his gestures and manners expressing hypocrisy and effeminacy in equal degree—the same unctuous, treacherous and repulsive person, always very quick when anyone greeted him to hold out a hand that was sure to be sweaty.

He was so proud of Valentín's precocious intelligence that he could hardly contain himself. To the honor of our usurer be it said that if he thought of himself as physically reproduced in this offspring of his own body, he felt his son's superiority and rejoiced in it more than in having given him life. For little Valentín was the prodigy of prodigies, a sublime fragment of the Divine Being fallen to earth.

Let no one think that there is the least exaggeration in what I say of the boy's unexampled intellectual gifts. Once his infancy was over, he never had to be punished or even scolded. He learned to read miraculously, in a few days, as if he had brought the art with him from his mother's womb. At five he knew many things which other boys can hardly learn at twelve.

Grammar he knew by heart; but geography he mastered like a grown man. Outside of schoolwork, it was amazing to see the assurance of his answers and observations, yet with no trace of childish arrogance. Shy and discreet, he seemed not to realize that there was any value in the talents he revealed, and he was astonished to see them evoke so much attention and applause. No boy outdid him in obedience and modesty, and, that not a perfection should be lacking, he was even as careful as possible not to wear out his clothes.

But his most extraordinary aptitudes had not yet shown themselves: it began when he studied arithmetic. No sooner had he imbibed the first notions of the science of quantities than he added and subtracted two- and even three-digit numbers in his head. His arithmetical sense was infallible, and even his father, who in the course of his reveries had become a wizard at calculating interest due, would often consult him. But it was when he began to study mathematics in secondary school that the full measure of his arithmetical genius was revealed. He did not learn, he already knew; the textbook simply awakened his ideas, made them open, if I may say so, like buds which the warmth of spring brings to flower. One day his teacher called on his father and said: "The boy is beyond explaining, Señor Torquemada. Before long I'll have nothing left to teach him. He is Newton come back to earth."

How Torquemada felt when he heard this, it is easy to understand. From that day on, he was beside himself with pride: he not only loved his son, he even treated him with a certain superstitious respect. He took care of him as if he were a supernatural being, placed in his hands as a special privilege. He watched his diet and became terrified if he showed a lack of appetite; when he saw him studying, he shut the windows to keep out drafts; informed himself of the temperature outside before letting him go out, to determine whether he should wear a muffler, or his greatcoat, or his rubbers; walked on tiptoe when he was asleep; took him out for a stroll, or to the theater, on Sundays, and if the little angel had shown any desire for strange and expensive playthings, Torquemada would have conquered his stinginess to buy them for him. But this prodigy of a boy manifested no liking for anything but books: he read fast and as if it were by magic, mastering the contents of each page as quick as a wink.

At the suggestion of the teacher who had praised him, Valentín was put into the hands of a professor who prepared students for special careers and who, as soon as he sampled the boy's colossal intelligence, was flabbergasted. One day, putting his hands to his head in stupefaction, and running out in search of other professors of higher mathematics, he announced: "I am going to show you the phenomenon of our times." And he exhibited him, and the others were amazed, for the boy went to the blackboard and solved the most difficult problems like someone scribbling to amuse himself and waste chalk.

It really made an interesting picture, and one worthy to figure in the annals of science: four dignified gentlemen in their fifties, bald and half blind from study, silent and perplexed in front of a boy who had to do his figuring on the bottom of the blackboard. One said he was the Antichrist; another picked him up and set him on his shoulder; and all quarreled over which of them should have the honor of finishing the education of this mathematical genius. Valentín looked at them, neither proud nor shy—innocent and master of himself, like the boy Christ among the doctors.[8]

Torquemada was still living in his house in the calle de Tudescos; and there every evening a certain Don José Bailón would call on him to play a game of draughts or cards. This Señor Bailón was a priest who abandoned the cassock in '69, in Málaga, and applied himself to revolution and religious freedom with such furious ardor that he could no longer return to the flock. The first thing the scoundrel did was to let his beard grow, talk nonsense at clubs, write tremendous invectives against those of his profession, and, finally, following the principle of *verbo et gladio*,[9] fling himself on the barricades with a blunderbuss whose mouth was as big as a trumpet.

Defeated and left to his own devices, a few years later our man was to be found living in Chamberí,[10] and, according to the gossip of the quarter, sharing bed and board with a rich widow who owned a flock of goats and a herd of milch asses. What is public knowledge is that the widow died, and that soon after Bailón appeared with money. The dairy and the goats and asses belonged to him. He rented the whole thing out and moved to the center of Madrid, where he set up as a moneylender—and I need say no

more for my reader to u⸻
acquaintance and deal⸻
mada originated, beca⸻
that the latter was his⸻

Bailón was very ta⸻
in limb, with strong f⸻
anatomical study by virtue of his ⸻
lar development. He had gone back to shaving, but he looked neither a priest nor a monk nor a bullfighter. He was more like a degenerate Dante. At the time of my narrative he was fifty.

Torquemada thought highly of him because in his business relations Bailón made a great show of formality and even of a certain delicacy. And since the renegade had such a colorful history and knew how to tell it well, embellishing it with lies, Don Francisco was ravished when he listened to him and regarded him as an oracle on all subjects of an elevated nature. Don José was one of those people who with four ideas and not many more words put them together in a way which dazzles the innocent and ignorant—no one more dazzled than Don Francisco.

On certain evenings the two sharpers would go walking together, conversing endlessly. And if Torquemada was the sibyl in business, in other branches of knowledge there was no greater sibyl than Señor Bailón. In politics especially the renegade priest made a great show of being an expert. They talked a good deal about urban reforms. Public hygiene preoccupied them both; the cleric put the blame for everything on noxious effluvia, and formulated certain biological theories which were something to hear.

But his encyclopedic knowledge nowhere showed to better advantage than in matters of religion. His meditations and studies had enabled him to plumb the great and venturesome problem of our entire destiny.

"What will happen to us when we die? Why, we shall be born again—it's as

---

8. *Christ among the doctors.* Luke 2:46. 9. *verbo et gladio,* by means of word and sword. 10. *Chamberí* (shän bā rē').

is water. I remember," he said, looking hard at his friend and dismaying him by the solemn tone which he gave to his words, "I remember having lived before. As a boy I had a vague recollection of my former life, and now, as the result of meditation, I can see it clearly. I was a priest in Egypt, back I don't know how many years ago . . . yes, Don Francisco, a priest in Egypt. I seem to see myself in a cassock or vestment the color of saffron. They burned me alive, because in the church—I mean the temple—there was a priestess who attracted me . . . . In short, the thing got going, and the goddess Isis and Apis the bull[11] took it in very bad part. . . . What I tell you is as true as that the sun is shining.

"Concentrate, my friend; search your memory; and you too will know that you lived in another age. That boy of yours, prodigy that he is, must once have been Newton or Galileo or Euclid. As for the rest of it, my ideas are perfectly clear. Hell and heaven do not exist—they are sheer symbolic pap. Hell and heaven are here. Here, sooner or later, we pay for whatever we have done; here, if not today then tomorrow, we get our reward. . . . God—oh, the idea of God is very mysterious . . . and to understand it you have to beat your brains as I have beaten mine, read, and then meditate.

"God . . ." (he looked very reverent and spread both his hands in a gesture indicating that he was taking in an immense space) "is Humanity, Humanity— do you understand me?—which does not mean that He ceases to be personal. Mark me well. Personal is what one is. And the great Totality, my dear Don Francisco, is One because there is nothing else, and possesses the attributes of a being infinitely infinite . . . do you understand . . . ?"

Torquemada had not understood a word; but the other had involved himself in a maze from which there was no escape except to stop talking. The only thing Don Francisco got out of the whole rigmarole was that "God is Humanity" and that Humanity is what makes us pay for our skulduggeries and rewards us for our good works. He'd be hanged if he understood the rest.

To tell the truth, none of these theological considerations long occupied our scoundrel's imagination, which was always intent on the base reality of his business. But a day came—or rather a night—when they were to take possession of his mind with a certain tenacity, for a reason which I shall now set forth. One late afternoon in February, Don Francisco returned home, planning what steps he should take the next day, when his daughter, who opened the door for him, addressed him as follows: "Don't be alarmed, Papa, it is nothing. . . . Valentín came home from school sick."

The prodigy's indispositions always upset Don Francisco. This one might be unimportant, as others had been. Yet in Rufina's voice there was a tremor, a strange tone, which left Torquemada cold with anxiety.

"I put him right to bed and sent a note to Dr. Quevedo to come as quickly as possible."

Rousing from his stupor as if he had been slapped, Don Francisco ran to the boy's room and found him in bed, with so many covers over him that he appeared to be suffocating. His face was flushed, his eyes vague. The father put his hand to the innocent prodigy's temples, which were burning.

"That useless Quevedo! May he burst. . . . What is the fool thinking of? Better send for a doctor who knows something."

His daughter tried to calm him but he refused to be comforted. His son was not an ordinary boy, and he could not be sick without the order of the universe changing. The grieving father would not eat; all he did was to pace through the

11. *Isis and Apis the bull.* Isis was the Egyptian goddess of fertility. Apis was a sacred bull who represented Isis' brother-husband Osiris.

house, waiting for the accursed doctor, going again and again from his own room to his son's and from there to the dining room, where each time his heart would be wrenched by the sight of the slate on which Valentín wrote his mathematical problems with chalk.

The problem he had set down that morning was still there, symbols which Torquemada did not understand but which almost made him weep, like sad music: the square-root sign, with letters above and below, and somewhere else a network of lines forming a sort of many-pointed star with little figures at the points.

Finally—God be praised!—the fortune-favored Quevedo appeared. After examining the boy, the doctor did not look very cheerful. Putting both his hands on Torquemada's shoulders, he said: "I don't like this at all; but we must wait until tomorrow to see if some eruption doesn't break out. He has a high fever. I warned you you'd have trouble with your prodigy. So much studying, so much knowledge, an extravagant intellectual development! What you should do with Valentín is put a bell around his neck, turn him loose in the country with a herd of cattle, and not bring him back to Madrid until he is really strong."

Torquemada hated the country and could not conceive that there was anything good about it. But he made up his mind, if the boy recovered, to take him to a dairy farm where he could drink plenty of milk and breathe fresh air. Ah, it was those accursed effluvia Bailón talked about which were to blame for what had happened! Don Francisco was so distraught that if he could have laid hands on an effluvium just then, he would have torn it limb from limb.

The children's room, where Valentín's bed was, adjoined his own bedroom; the boy passed a very restless night; he choked, his skin was on fire, his eyes sparkled, yet seemed not to see, his speech was uncertain, his ideas discon-nected, like the beads of a rosary when the string breaks.

The following day was a day of shocks and anguish. Quevedo concluded that the disease was "inflammation of the meninges" and that the boy was in danger of death. He did not tell this to the father, but to Bailón, who was to try to prepare him. Torquemada had to go out on various errands in connection with his laborious profession, but he kept returning to the house every few minutes, panting, his tongue hanging out, his hat on the back of his head. He came in, took a look, and went out again. He brought in the medicines himself, and told the whole story at the apothecary's . . . "a sudden giddi-ness at school; a terrible fever ever since . . . what good are doctors?"

The night of the second day, Torque-mada, overcome with fatigue, planted himself in an armchair in the sitting room, and there he stayed, turning over a sly idea which had come into his head. "I have sinned against Humanity, and the damned so-and-so is making me pay up now. . . . No: because if God, or whoever it is, takes my son from me, I'll turn even worse! . . . That'll show them! Nobody can play with me.

"But what nonsense am I talking? . . . This saying that I have never done any-one any good is a lie. Let them prove it . . . saying it is not enough. What about all the people I have gotten out of tight corners? Because if they have gone run-ning to Humanity with stories about me . . . I've had too much of this. . . . If I have never done good, I'll do it now—now, because there must be something in the saying that it is never too late to do good. Let me see . . . if I started praying now, what would they say up there? Bailón must be mistaken, I think; Hu-manity can't be God, it must be the Vir-gin. . . . No, no, no . . . Humanity is God, the Virgin and all the saints. . . . Hold on, man, hold on, you're going mad. . . . All I can be certain of is that without good works everything is, so to speak, dung. . . . Oh God, oh God how I suffer! If You make my son well for me, I don't know what I won't do! Things so magnificent, so . . . But who has the impudence to say that I have never done any good works? It's because they want to undo me, want to take away my son, who was born to teach all the scholars and leave them pigmies. And they envy me because I am his father, because that glory of the world came from these bones and this blood. . . . Envy . . . but that hog Humanity is nothing but envy! No, I don't mean Humanity, because that is God . . . I mean men, all of us, we're all scoundrels."

Then he remembered that the next day was Sunday and that he had not written out the receipts for the rents from his tenement house. The following morning, between nine and ten, he went to make the Sunday collection.

He began with the ground floor, and the bricklayer and the two cigarette girls paid without a murmur, only wanting to see the last of the hated Don Francisco. They noticed something unusual and abnormal about him, for he took the money mechanically and without examining it and gloating over it as usual—as if his thoughts were a hundred miles from the important act he was performing.

When he reached the room of the widow Rumalda, the ironing woman—with her mother lying sick on a miserable pallet and three little boys running around the patio with their skin showing through the holes in their clothes—the poor woman, her voice shaking as if she were confessing a terrible crime in court, brought out the regulation phrase: "I can't today, Don Francisco. I'll make it up later." I cannot convey the stupor which descended upon the widow and her two neighbors, who happened to be present, when they heard the usurer say, in the most lachrymose of voices: "No, my dear, if I don't press you . . . if it hasn't entered my head to scold you . . .

how can I put it? The thing is that you are all convinced that I am a man who . . . Where did you get the idea that there is no compassion in me . . . no . . . no charity? Instead of being grateful to me for what I do for you, you slander me. When times are bad, my dears, what can we do but help one another?"

On reaching the next floor, he ran into another tenant, a woman who was always in arrears but who had the courage to stand up to the lion. Seeing him coming, and judging from his face that he was in a worse humor than ever, she took the offensive with these arrogant words:

"Listen, you—don't you come worrying me. You know I haven't got it. My man is out of work. Do you want me to take to the streets? Can't you see that our place is as bare as a poorhouse?"

"And who told you, you foulmouthed so-and-so, that I have come to squeeze you? I'd like to see any of you ill-conditioned hags maintain that I have no humanity. Just any of you dare to say it to my face. . . ."

In the crowd which had collected, nothing was to be seen but open mouths and expressions of stupefaction.

"I tell you—and I tell all of you—that it doesn't matter a peppercorn to me if you pay me today or not! I'd like to know how to put it so that you can understand it! . . . And don't go believing that I'm doing this so that you'll call down blessings on me. Just bear witness that I am not grinding you down; and, so that you can see how goodhearted I am . . . "

He stopped and thought for a moment, putting his hand in his pocket and looking at the floor.

"No—that's all, that's all. Good-bye and God bless you."

At the next three doors, he collected without difficulty.

"Oh, Don Francisco," said the woman in No. 14, "here is your damned fifty reals. To scrape it together, all we've had to eat is two pennyworth of tripe, with dry bread."

"But this is an insult, an injustice; because if I have been hard on you, it was not for the money, but because I like to see people keep their promises . . . so that no one can say . . . Here, you can keep your money. Or better, so that you won't take it too lightly, we'll divide it and you can keep twenty-five reals. You can give them to me some other day. . . . You are all the same—when you ought to admit that I treat you like a father, you accuse me of being inhuman and I don't know what else! No, I assure you one and all that I respect humanity, that I esteem and regard it . . ."

The group followed him, whispering: "Something bad must have happened to him. . . . He's not right in the head. Look at that gallows face of his. Don Francisco showing humanity!"

All the women watched him as he went down the stairs, and across the patio, and out the door, with gestures that made him look like the very Devil crossing himself.

He hastened homeward and, contrary to his habit, took a cab to get there sooner. His heart began telling him that he would find good news, the sick boy better, Rufina smiling when she opened the door; in his insane impatience, the carriage seemed not to be moving, the horse to be stumbling, the coachman not flogging the poor creature enough. "Give him the whip, man!" he screamed. "Can't you see I'm in a hurry!"

As he panted up the stairs, he was justifying his hopes to himself. What a bitter blow to find Rufina's face so sad and to hear the "just the same, Papa," which sounded to his ears like a death bell! He approached his son's bed on tiptoe and looked at him. The poor boy was drowsing, so Don Francisco could observe him with comparative calm. But when he moaned in delirium, Torquemada felt a desire to start running and hide himself and his grief in the farthest corner of the world.

That afternoon Bailón, the butcher from the ground floor, the tailor from the second and the photographer from upstairs, sat with him for a time, all trying to console him with the conventional phrases; but Torquemada, unable to continue talking on so sad a theme, thanked them curtly. All he could do was sigh volubly, stride up and down, gulp mouthfuls of water, and occasionally beat the wall with his fists. . . .

The flower of the world cut down! It was enough to drive anyone mad. A pretty piece of work God, or Humanity, or whoever the big so-and-so was, had done when he invented the world and put us in it! To take that boy, that light of science, and leave all these fools here! Did it make any sense? And what a blow for the father! Because imagine what Don Francisco would be when his son had grown up and begun to shine and confound all the scholars and turn science upside down!

Up there, in the invisible depths of the sky, someone had taken it into his head to hurt Torquemada. But . . . if it were not envy, but punishment? If it had all been arranged to humble the cruel usurer, the tyrannical landlord? Ah, when that idea had its turn, Torquemada was seized by an impulse to run against the nearest wall and smash himself to pieces. But he had an instant reaction. No, it could not be a punishment because he was not wicked, and if he had been, he would reform. He was enviable; they hated him for being the father of such supreme eminence. They wanted to kill his future and take away the joy and opulence of his declining years . . . because his son, if he lived, was bound to make a lot of money, a very great deal of money, and hence the celestial intrigue. But he (he thought it sincerely) would renounce all claim to his son's pecuniary gains. After all, his own business was a competence.

When Bailón was left alone with him, he told him that he must be philosophical, and since Torquemada did not quite understand the meaning and application of the word, the sibyl explained his idea as follows: "We must resign ourselves, considering our littleness before these great evolutions of matter ... or vital substance. We are atoms, my dear Don Francisco, nothing but inane atoms. Let us respect the dispositions of the great All to which we belong, and let trouble come. That is what philosophy is for, or, if you prefer, religion: to give us courage in adversity."

At nightfall Quevedo and the other doctor talked to Torquemada in disconsolate terms. They had little or no hope, though they were afraid to say that they had entirely lost it.

Grief-stricken, Don Francisco went to the half-open door of his son's room and looked timidly in; with the boy's labored breathing, he thought he heard something like the sizzling of his flesh as it grilled in the fire of fever. He listened to the delirious lad's incoherent expressions and heard him say: "x square, minus 1, divided by 2, plus 5 x minus 2, divided by 4, equals x times x plus 2, divided by 12 ... Papa, Papa, the characteristic of the logarithm of a whole number contains as many units minus 1 as ..." No torture of the Inquisition[12] equaled what Torquemada suffered as he heard these words. He fled to the living room and flung himself on the sofa, where he lay for half an hour, holding his head in his hands as if it were trying to get away. Suddenly he rose, frenzied by an idea; he went to his desk, took out a roll of coins, which must have been coppers, and emptying them into his trouser pocket, put on his cape and hat, took the door key, and went out.

After walking for a long time, he stopped at a corner, looked uneasily in all directions, then hurried along the street again with the step of a moneylender tracking down his prey. Each time his right leg swung forward, the coins in his pocket jingled. Great were his impatience and disgust at not finding, on that night, what, on other nights, turned up at every step to annoy and bore him. At last—praise

be to God!—a beggar approached. "Here, take it, man! Where on earth have you all been hiding tonight? When nobody wants you, you're out like flies, and when somebody looks for you to help you—not a trace. ..."

Farther on, an apparition emerged from an alley. It was a woman who begs in the lower part of the calle de la Salud, dressed in black, with a heavy veil shrouding her face. "Here, take it, take it. And now let anyone say that I have never given an alms! Can you imagine what a calumny! Go now, you must have scraped together enough coppers for tonight. Because there are people who say that, begging as you do, and with that veil over your face, you have gotten together a nice little capital. Go now, it's turning very cold ... and pray to God for me."

"Hey lad, are you begging or what are you doing there like a fool?" This was addressed to a boy who stood leaning against a wall with his hands on his shoulders. He held out a hand stiff with cold. "Here, take that. ... Didn't your heart tell you that I would come along and help you? Take more, and go home, if you have a home. I am here to get you out of your difficulties; I mean, to share a loaf of bread with you, because I am poor too, and more unfortunate than you are— if you only knew it. ..." He walked quickly away without looking into the mocking face of his protégé, and went on giving, giving, until there were only a few coins left in his pocket.

Hurrying back home, he stared up at the sky—an action very much out of his normal behavior, because if he had occasionally looked at it to see what the weather promised, never until that night had he contemplated it. What a multitude of stars! And an idea came into the eminent moneylender's head: "When he gets well, he must solve this problem for me: If we turned all the stars in the sky into coins, how much would they produce at

12. *the Inquisition,* a medieval religious court held for the discovery and punishment of heresy.

five per cent compound interest since the time when all this began to exist?"

He reached home about one o'clock, feeling some relief in his torment; he slept without undressing; and the next morning Valentín's fever had gone down considerably. Was there hope?

"Papa," said Rufina, weeping, "pray to the Virgin of Carmen, and forget your Humanities."

"You think I should? I'm willing. But I warn you that without good works there is no use putting faith in the Virgin. And there shall be Christian deeds, cost what it may: that I assure you. I will clothe the naked, visit the sick, console the afflicted. . . . God knows that such is my intention, indeed He knows it. . . . Let us not hear anything later about His not knowing it . . . He knows it, I say. . . ."

The poor boy's legs were on fire with poultices, his head a pitiful sight from the embrocations which had been applied to induce an artificial eruption. More ice had to be bought for the ice bag on his head; then iodoform was needed—errands which Torquemada performed with feverish activity, going in and out every few minutes. Returning home again at nightfall, he encountered an old, tattered beggar wearing army trousers, hatless, with a rag of a jacket over his shoulders, exposing his bare chest. A more venerable face could be found nowhere but among the illustrations of *The Christian Year*. His beard was tangled, his forehead full of wrinkles, like St. Peter's. "Señor, Señor," he said, with the tremor of intense cold, "look at what I have come to!" Torquemada avoided him, then stopped at a little distance; he looked back, hesitated for a moment, and finally went on. An idea had flashed into his mind: "If only I had on my old cape instead of this new one . . ." And, entering the house: "Curse me! I should not have let that Christian act escape me."

He left the medicine he was bringing, and, changing his cape, hurried back into the street. A little while later, Rufina, seeing him come in capeless, said in amazement:

"But Papa, your wits are wandering! . . . Where did you leave your cape?"

"My dear child," the sharper answered, lowering his voice and assuming an expression of great compunction, "you have no conception of what a real act of charity, of humanity, is. . . . My cape? Why, I gave it to a poor old half-naked man who was almost dead with cold. That's how I am; I stop at nothing when I take pity on the poor. . . . I see you are surprised. What is a miserable piece of cloth worth?"

"Was it your new cape?"

"No, the old one."

Nothing more was said on the subject, because graver matters demanded their attention.

Don Francisco felt that he bore his trouble best alone. He sat down in the dining room, his hands on the table, his burning forehead resting on his hands. There he had remained for I do not know how long, when his friend Bailón made him sit up by slapping him on the back and saying: "There is no reason to despair. We must keep a stiff upper lip and never let trouble get us down. . . . In the face of Nature, of the sublime Totality, we are ignorant fragments of atoms."

"Go to the devil with your Totalities and your drivel!" said Torquemada, his eyes flashing.

Bailón did not insist; and, judging that the best thing was to distract his friend from his grief, he began to talk to him about a certain piece of business he had in mind. The lessee of his flocks of asses and goats having voided his contract, Bailón had decided to exploit the business on a large scale, putting up a big modern dairy, with regular home deliveries, moderate prices, an elegant office, telephone, and so on. He had gone into it, and "Believe me, my dear Don Francisco, it is a sure thing, especially if we go into cow's milk too, because in Madrid milk . . ."

"Leave me in peace with your milk and your . . . What have I to do with asses or cows?'' shouted Torquemada, jumping up and looking at him scornfully. "You see the state I am in—by thunder!—half dead with grief, and you come and talk to me about milk, damn it. . . . Talk to me about how we can get God to pay attention when we ask Him for what we need.''

At that moment, Valentín screamed—a harsh, strident scream which left them both tense with terror. It was the "meningeal scream," which resembles the scream of the peacock. This strange encephalic[13] symptom had begun that day, and showed the dangerous and terrifying progress of the poor boy-mathematician's disease. Torquemada would have hidden himself in the center of the earth to avoid hearing that scream: he retired to his office, disregarding Bailón's exhortations and slamming the door in his Dantesque face. From the threshold he was heard to open the drawer of his table, and soon afterward he appeared, carrying something in the inside pocket of his coat. He took his hat and went out without a word.

I will explain what this meant and where the unfortunate Don Francisco was bound that afternoon. The day on which Valentín had been taken ill, his father received a letter from an old and well-plucked client of his, asking for a loan on his household furniture. The relations between the victim and the inquisitor were longstanding, and the latter's profits had been enormous, because the client was in delicate health, a weakling who allowed himself to be skinned, fried and pickled as if he had been born for it. There are such people. Day in and day out, Torquemada went after him, harassed him, put the screws on him and screwed them tight, without succeeding in getting even the past interest. It is easy to imagine the usurer's wrath when he received the letter asking for a new loan. What atrocious insolence!

By now time and occasion had come—precipitated by Valentín's peacock scream. And the sharper had felt a wild impulse. A fiery inspiration had kindled in the sharper's brain, he had taken his hat—and here he is, on the way to see his unfortunate client. The latter was a decent enough man, but with limited abilities, an unlimited family and a wife who aspired to elegance. I don't know what devils possessed the money in that house, to make it be drawn like iron filings to the magnet of the accursed moneylender. The worst of it was that even with the family in hot water up to their necks, the slut of a wife kept charging Paris dresses, inviting her friends to teas or thinking up some other fashionable nonsense in the same style.

Well, sir, here is Don Francisco, off to the house of the gentleman I have described. Suddenly he felt a tug at his cape. He turned . . .

"Isadora!" he exclaimed, looking delighted (a thing which he very seldom did). "Where are you going with that weary body of yours?"

"I was on my way to see you. Have pity on us, Señor Don Francisco. . . . Haven't you even a drop of humanity?"

"My dear child, you misjudge me. What if I told you that I was thinking of you just now . . . that I was remembering the letter you sent me by the concierge's son yesterday?"

"But you don't realize our situation!" said the woman, bursting into tears. "Martín dying, in that freezing garret . . . no bed, no medicines, nothing to make even a miserable stew to give him a cup of something hot! Don Francisco, show some Christianity and do not forsake us. I know we have no credit left, but Martín still has half a dozen very pretty sketches."

"Eh, eh . . . stop crying woman. . . . I am on tenterhooks myself. . . . I have such a grief in my soul, Isadora, that . . . Go home and wait for me there. I'll come in a little while. . . . What—do you doubt my word? You might hold something else against me; but that . . . Go home and stop worrying . . . and until I get there,

13. *encephalic* (en′ sə fal′ ik), of or pertaining to the brain.

pray to God for me with all the fervor you have.''

He soon reached his client's house. While he waited, Torquemada looked at the handsome coat stand and at the splendid living-room curtains, which could be seen through the half-open door, and such magnificence suggested the following reflections: "So far as the furniture goes, it is good enough . . . yes, very good." His friend received him in his office. Torquemada had scarcely asked after the family before he sank into a chair with an appearance of great consternation.

"But what is the matter?" asked the other.

"Don't speak of it, don't speak of it, Señor Don Juan. My soul is hanging on a thread. . . . My son . . . !''

"Poor boy! I heard he is very ill. . . . But have you no hope?"

"No . . . I mean, no real hope . . . I don't know; I am going mad; my head is a volcano!"

"I know what it is," the other remarked sadly. "I lost two sons. They were the joy of my life—one four, the other eleven."

"But your grief cannot be like mine. As a father, I am not like other fathers, because my boy is not like other boys. . . . You'll see, my dear Don Juan. . . . When I received your letter, I couldn't attend to it. . . . My grief would not let me think. . . . But today, although I'm half dead with grief, I remembered you and I said to myself: 'Poor Don Juan! What he must be going through! Being the man I am, I can't leave him in this fix. We must help each other in our afflictions.' And here I am to tell you that, although you owe me seventy-odd thousand reals, which come to more than ninety with the unpaid interest, I have made up my mind to make you the loan you ask on your furniture."

"It is all taken care of," said Don Juan, coldly. "I don't need the loan any longer."

"You don't need it! Consider one thing, Don Juan. I'll do it for you . . . at twelve per cent."

And seeing the other shaking his head,

he rose and readjusting his cape, which was slipping off, took a few steps toward Don Juan, laid his hand on his shoulder, and said:

"It seems you don't want to deal with me because people say I'm hard. I think that twelve per cent . . . Have you ever heard of better terms?"

"I consider the interest very reasonable; but, I repeat, I no longer need the money."

"I take it you have won the grand prize, then," exclaimed Torquemada with crude sarcasm. "Don Juan, don't waste time trying to joke with me. . . . Because, so far as your not needing it goes—you!— who, to say nothing of a trifle like this, could eat up the Mint all by yourself. . . . Don Juan, Don Juan, let me tell you that I have my humanity too, just like anyone else, that I even do favors for those who loathe me. You hate me, Don Juan, you detest me—don't deny it—because you cannot pay me; that is clear. Very well: to show you what I am capable of, I'll give it to you at five . . . at five!"

And as the other began shaking his head again, Torquemada became even more disturbed and raising his arms—at which, of course, his cape fell off—he delivered this tirade:

"Not even at five! But less than five is unheard of! Do you want me to throw in the shirt I have on? How can the fellow suppose . . . If I do it, I am mad. But so that you may see how far my generosity goes: I'll give it to you without interest!"

"Thank you very much, my dear Don Francisco. But the matter is settled. When you did not answer my letter, I went to see a relative of mine, and found the courage to tell him my sad situation. Would that I had done it sooner!"

"Then your relative has got what he deserves! He can say he has thrown his money down the sink. If he does much more of that kind of business. . . . In short, you didn't want to take it from me. You'll be sorry. . . . And now try saying that I haven't a good heart; it is you who haven't a good heart."

"I? You must be out of your head!"

"Yes, you, you!" he said indignantly. "Well, I must be off: I am expected somewhere else where I am very much wanted, where they are waiting for me like manna from heaven. . . ."

He soon reached the other house, where Isadora heard his footsteps and opened the door. Don Francisco found himself in a room whose sloping ceiling descended to the floor on the side opposite the door; overhead, a skylight, with several of its panes broken and stuffed with rags and paper. On the bed, in a confusion of blankets and clothing, lay a man of about thirty—handsome, with a pointed beard, large eyes, and a fine forehead, but wasted by illness, his upper face slightly flushed, greenish hollows in his cheeks, and his ears as transparent as the wax of a votive candle. Torquemada looked at him without answering his greeting, and thought: poor fellow, he is more consumptive than Traviata.[14] What a pity! Such a good painter and such a fool. . . . He could have made a lot of money!

"Well, you see the state I am in, Don Francisco . . . with this damned catarrh. How grateful I am to you."

"There's nothing to be grateful for. . . . What next? Does not God command us to clothe the sick, feed the afflicted, visit the naked? . . . Oh, I've mixed it all up. . . . What a head!"

He looked at the walls, which were almost covered by studies of landscapes, some of them upside down, fastened to the wall or leaning against it.

"Very pretty things, these!"

"As soon as my cold gets better, I shall go to the country," said the sick man, his eyes bright with fever. "I have an idea —what an idea! I think I shall be well in a week, Don Francisco, if you will help me—and then, off to the country . . ."

The graveyard is where you will go, and very soon, my friend, thought Torquemada; and then, aloud: "Yes, it is a matter of days, that's all. Then you can leave here . . . in a carriage. Do you know this attic is very chilly? Do you mind if I wrap up in my cape?"

"And put on your hat—don't stand there bareheaded," said the sick man, sitting up. He was taken with a violent fit of coughing; Isadora ran to support him and piled pillows behind him. The wretched man's eyes seemed to be bursting, his exhausted lungs labored like a broken pair of bellows.

"Talk as little as possible, dear," Isadora advised him. "I will settle matters with Don Francisco; he and I will come to terms—you'll see."

Her smile showed her beautiful teeth, one of the few charms that remained to her. Torquemada, playing the kindly friend, made her sit down beside him and put his hand on her shoulder, saying: "Of course we'll come to terms."

"Don Francisco, have you realized our situation? Martín's studio was attached. Our debts were so heavy that all we were able to save is what you see here. For Martín to get well and be able to go to the country, we need three thousand reals . . . and I do not say four to keep from frightening you."

"Three thousand reals!" said the usurer, assuming the expression of doubtful reflection which he kept for cases of benevolence. "My dear child, consider . . ." And, making a perfect circle with his thumb and forefinger, he presented it for Isadora's contemplation, and continued: "I don't know if I can spare three thousand reals at the moment. In any case, it seems to me that you could do with less. Think it over carefully, and review your accounts. I have made up my mind to look after you until things get better. I will even go so far as to sacrifice myself, to take the bread out of my own mouth, so that you shall not go hungry; but . . . but bear in mind that I must also consider my own interests."

"Make it any interest you please," the

14. *Traviata*, the heroine of the opera *La Traviata* (*The Lost One*), by Giuseppe Verdi. She dies of tuberculosis.

sick man said emphatically; it was obvious that he wanted to get it over with.

"I am not alluding to the materialism of a return on the money, but to my interests, my interests. Of course I expect you to give me some sort of security too. . . . I have it. . . ."

"Yes indeed. My studies. Take as many as you please."

Casting a practiced look around, Torquemada explained himself as follows:

"Very well, my friends; I am going to tell you something that will astound you. Ah! the idea that you have of me! Because once upon a time you owed me a small sum and I kept after you tooth and nail, you think I am made of marble? You don't know me, I assure you, you don't know me. . . . I am so good, so good, that I am obliged to praise myself and be grateful to myself for the good that I do. Now see here . . ."

Again the perfect circle appeared, accompanied by these solemn words: "I shall give you the three thousand reals, and I shall give them to you here and now. . . . But that is not the best of it—I shall give them to you without interest. . . . Now what do you say—is that something, or isn't it something?"

"Don Francisco!" Isadora exclaimed effusively. "Let me give you a kiss!"

"I'll give you another if you will come over here," cried the sick man, trying to get out of bed.

"All the caresses you please," said the usurer, letting them both embrace him. "But don't praise me, because such actions are the duty of everyone who respects Humanity."

Taking the paper which Isadora offered him, he looked at his debtors paternally: "My dear children, no doubt you think that I am going to keep this I O U. . . . You couldn't be more mistaken. I am not lending you three thousand reals, I am giving them to you, just because I like you. Look here . . ."

And he tore up the paper. Isadora and Martín believed it because they saw it.

"Only a great man could have done this," said Isadora, deeply moved.

"The most I will do," said Don Francisco, rising and examining the pictures, "is to accept a few of your studies as a souvenir. . . . This one of the snow-covered mountains, and that one of the donkeys at pasture. And I think, Martín, that, if I may, I will also take this little seascape and the ivy-covered bridge there . . ."

Martín's coughing fit had developed and he was choking. Isadora, hurrying to help him, cast a furtive glance at the selection which the diligent money-lender was making.

"I accept them as a souvenir," he said, setting them aside. "And, if you don't mind, I'll take this other one too. And I'd like to tell you this: if you are afraid these pictures will suffer from being moved around, bring them to my house— I'll keep them there and you can have them back whenever you wish. . . . Isn't that damned cough ever going to stop? Never mind, by next week you won't be coughing at all, not at all. You'll be off to the country. . . . But what am I thinking of—here I am, almost forgetting the three thousand reals. Come here, Isadorita, and pay attention. A hundred-peso bill and another and another . . ." (As he counted them out, he moistened his finger with saliva for each bill so that they should not stick together.) "Seven hundred pesos. I haven't got a fifty-peso bill on me, my child. I'll give it to you another day. There you are—exactly two thousand eight hundred reals . . ."

Night was falling, the unhappy usurer's bedroom had grown dark, when, clear and distinct, he heard the peacock scream which Valentín gave in the paroxysm of his fever. "And they said he was better! Oh, my dear son. . . . They've taken us in. We've been sold!"

Rufina entered the lion's den weeping. "Oh, Papa, he is so much worse, so much worse!"

"That bungler Quevedo!" cried Torquemada, raising his fist to his mouth and biting it furiously. "I'll tear his guts out. . . . He has killed him."

"Papa, for God's sake. You must not rebel against the will of God. . . ."

"I am not rebelling, thunder and lightning! I am not rebelling. It is only that I cannot, I cannot give my son, because he is mine, blood of my blood and bone of my bones."

"Resign yourself, resign yourself, and we will submit together," exclaimed his daughter, weeping unrestrainedly.

"I cannot, I do not want to resign myself. It is sheer robbery. Envy, pure envy. What is there for Valentín in heaven? Nothing, let them say what they please; nothing. . . . God, what a lie, what a fraud! Who can still say there's a heaven, a hell, a purgatory, a God, a Devil, a . . . stuff and nonsense! And Death! A fine fool Death is, forgetting all the scoundrels, all the quacks, all the fools, and wanting my boy, because he is the finest boy in the world! . . . Everything is evil, and the world is a stinking shambles."

Rufina went away, and Bailón entered, wearing an expression of great compunction. He had just visited the sick boy, who was now in his death agony, surrounded by a few neighbors and intimate friends of the household. The pious renegade prepared to comfort the afflicted father, and began by embracing him and saying in muffled tones:

"Courage, my friend, courage! The strong soul rises to such occasions. Remember the great philosopher who died on a cross, consecrating the principles of Humanity."

"Get out of here with your principles and your . . . Will you get out of here, you louse! You are the stupidest, dullest, most nauseating creature I ever saw! Every time I am in trouble, you plague me with your drivel!"

"My dear friend, calm yourself. Before the designs of Nature, of Humanity, of the Supreme All, what can man do? Man! That ant, or even less, that flea . . . and still less again."

"That bugbear . . . or even less, that . . ." Torquemada added with horrible sarcasm, imitating the sibyl's voice and then shaking his fist at him. "Thunder and lightning! If you don't shut up, I'll smash your face in. . . . I care as much about the Supreme All as I do about the Supreme Nothing . . . and the supreme louse who invented it. Get out, leave me alone, or . . ."

Rufina came in again, supported by two women who had taken her away from the agonizing spectacle in the dying boy's room. The poor girl could not stand up. She fell to her knees, sobbing and seeing her father struggling with Bailón, she said:

"Papa, for God's sake, stop. Resign yourself. . . . I am resigned—can't you see? . . . My poor little brother . . . when I went in for a moment, he recovered consciousness. He spoke in a clear voice, and said that he saw the angels calling him."

"Oh my son, oh my dearest son!" Torquemada shouted with all the power of his lungs, in a savage frenzy. "Don't go, don't listen to them; they are trying to put one over on you. . . . Stay here with us . . ."

Then he fell flat on the floor; one leg stretched out stiff, the other, and the corresponding arm, contracted. Bailón, with all his strength, could not control him. At the same time, his tense mouth gave a terrible roar and spat foam.

Valentín had expired. His sister was summoned and went to the room. She gave him countless kisses and then, assisted by her friends, prepared to perform the last duties owed to the unfortunate boy. She was brave, far braver than her father, who, when he came out of his terrifying faint and was able to realize the utter extinction of all his hopes, fell into a profound physical and moral depression. He wept silently and exhaled sighs which could be heard all over the house. After a considerable time, he asked for coffee and half a slice of toast, because he felt horribly weak. The complete loss of hope calmed his nerves and brought an urgent need to repair his exhausted organism. At midnight he had to have a substantial potion, which the sister of the photographer and the wife of the butcher made for him from eggs, sherry and broth.

"I don't know what is happening to me," said Torquemada the Worse, "but I feel as if life were trying to leave me." His deep sighs and silent sobbing continued until almost dawn, when he was attacked by a new paroxysm of grief, crying out that he must see his son, must "bring him back to life, at any cost," and tried to get out of bed against the combined efforts of Bailón, the butcher, and the other friends who tried to hold him down. At last they succeeded in quieting him, a result in no small degree due to the renegade cleric's philosophical admonitions and the wise things which fell from the lips of the butcher, a man of small education but a good Christian.

"You are right," said Don Francisco, exhausted and breathless. "What is left but to submit? Submit! Advice is the cheapest thing in the world! Just see what anyone gets for being as good as an angel and sacrificing himself for the afflicted, and doing good to those who can't bear the sight of us. . . . In short, what I intended to use to help a bunch of scoundrels—wasted money, sure to find its way to pothouses and gambling houses and pawnshops!—I say that I'm going to take it and spend it on giving my son the most magnificent funeral Madrid has ever seen! Oh, what a son, what a prodigy! And I have lost him! He was no son; he was a little god, engendered half by me, half by the Eternal Father. . . . Don't you think I should give him a splendid funeral? It is morning already. Bring me pictures of hearses . . . and black-bordered cards for invitations to all the professors."

Excited by these vainglorious plans, our man was up and dressed by nine o'clock, making arrangements efficiently and serenely. He ate a good breakfast and received the many friends who came to visit him.

And the splendid funeral took place and was attended by a great crowd of eminent personages—all of which induced in Torquemada a satisfaction and pride which were the only balm for his profound torment.

The following morning, Torquemada had no sooner opened his eyes than the fever of business took possession of him. Since Rufina was so broken by sleeplessness and grief that she could not attend to her household duties, the maid and the indefatigable old-clothes woman who called at the house, Tia Roma, took her place as far as possible. And behold— when Tia Roma came in to bring the Grand Inquisitor his morning chocolate, he was already up and sitting at the desk in his office, writing a great many things with feverish hand. And since the old woman was perfectly at ease with the master of the house, and permitted herself to treat him as an equal, she went to him, laid her cold, scrawny hand on his shoulder, and said: "You never learn. . . . Here you are, getting your executioner's tools ready again. You will die an evil death, you God-forsaken fiend, if you don't reform."

Torquemada gave her a look which was absolutely yellow, because in his case, yellow was the color of what, in the majority of human eyes, is white, and he said: "I do exactly as I damn well please, you old gargoyle. A fine thing it would be if I had to ask an ignoramus like you what to do!" For a moment his eyes fell on Valentín's slate and he gave a sigh; then he went on: "If I am getting my tools ready, it is none of your business nor anybody's business, because I know all that is to be known on earth and even in heaven—thunder and lightning! I know you are going to come back at me with the materialism of works of mercy. . . . And I answer you that I tried doing my best and what I got for it was a kick in the jaw. All the mercy I have, they are welcome to bash in my skull with!"

THE END

Development

INTERPRETATION

1. The narrator describes Torquemada and his late wife, Doña Silvia, as ". . . a couple which could serve as a model for all ants, whether above or below ground" (page 258, column 1, paragraph 1). *(a)* What does this imply about their characters? *(b)* Are the two children significantly different from their antlike parents? Discuss.

2. The narrator gives the following interpretation of Torquemada's rising standard of living: ". . . Torquemada, without comprehending it, underwent the metamorphosis which has changed the nature of usury from metaphysical to positivistic" (page 259, column 1, lines 15-18). *(a)* Reread the statement in context and explain its meaning. *(b)* In what way does the statement help to account for Torquemada's increasing concern for the trappings of society? *(c)* How does it help to explain his behavior when his son becomes ill?

3. Discuss the source and nature of Torquemada's sorrow at Valentín's illness.

4. *(a)* Compare Torquemada's reaction to the death of Valentín with Rufina's reaction to it. *(b)* Has Torquemada undergone any basic change by the end of the story? Discuss.

TECHNIQUE

1. *(a)* What sort of person do the details in paragraph 1 reveal Torquemada to be? *(b)* How is this impression qualified by the details in paragraphs 2 and 3? *(c)* What do these latter details foreshadow?

2. *(a)* What three natural divisions does the story fall into? *(b)* Which part is the longest? *(c)* What difference would be likely to occur in your attitude toward Torquemada if parts 1 and 2 were condensed to a summarizing paragraph and part 3 were greatly expanded? If parts 2 and 3 were condensed to a summarizing paragraph and part 1 were greatly expanded?

3. *(a)* How do Rufina and Bailón help increase our understanding of Torquemada's religious dilemma? *(b)* What specific part does Bailón play in advancing the plot of the story?

4. In his last-ditch attempt to save Valentín's life by doing charitable acts, Torquemada makes two visits of "mercy." *(a)* What is ironic about the results of the first visit? *(b)* In the visit to the sick painter, which details suggest the real purpose of Torquemada's gift of three thousand *reals*?

5. The character of Torquemada is named after a fifteenth-century Spanish inquisitor who has become a symbol for religious intolerance and brutal fanaticism. Pérez Galdós' Torquemada is certainly not a religious fanatic; how, then, are we to account for this choice of a name?

EXTENSIONS

1. Consider the following observation about virtue: "Deliberate virtue is never worth much: The virtue of feeling or habit is the thing." Does this quotation express the view of virtue implied in "Torquemada in the Flames"? Discuss.

2. The idea that catastrophes are visited upon individuals as a punishment for sin is a very old one. What does this story have to say about such an idea?

Tartuffe

MOLIÈRE / France

(1622 – 1673)

translated from the French by Richard Wilbur

CHARACTERS

MME PERNELLE (pãr nel′), ORGON's mother
ORGON (ôr gôn′), ELMIRE's husband
ELMIRE (el mēr′), ORGON's wife
DAMIS (dä mēs′), ORGON's son, ELMIRE's stepson
MARIANE (mär yän′), ORGON's daughter, ELMIRE's
    stepdaughter, in love with VALÈRE
VALÈRE (vä lãr′), in love with MARIANE
CLÉANTE (clā änt′), ORGON's brother-in-law
TARTUFFE (tär tüf′), a hypocrite
DORINE (dô rēn′), MARIANE's lady's-maid
M. LOYAL, a bailiff
A POLICE OFFICER
FLIPOTE (flē pōt′), MME PERNELLE's maid

The scene throughout: ORGON's *house in Paris*

Act One

SCENE I. MADAME PERNELLE *and* FLIPOTE,
her maid, ELMIRE, MARIANE,
DORINE, DAMIS, CLÉANTE

MADAME PERNELLE. Come, come,
  Flipote; it's time I left this place.
ELMIRE. I can't keep up, you walk at
  such a pace.
MADAME PERNELLE. Don't trouble,
  child; no need to show me out.
It's not your manners I'm concerned
  about.
5 ELMIRE. We merely pay you the
  respect we owe.
But, Mother, why this hurry? Must you
  go?
MADAME PERNELLE. I must. This house
  appals me. No one in it
Will pay attention for a single minute.
Children, I take my leave much vexed
  in spirit.
10 I offer good advice, but you won't hear it.
You all break in and chatter on and on.
It's like a madhouse with the keeper
  gone.
DORINE. If . . .
MADAME PERNELLE. Girl, you talk too
  much, and I'm afraid
You're far too saucy for a lady's-maid.
15 You push in everywhere and have your
  say.
DAMIS. But . . .
MADAME PERNELLE. You, boy, grow
  more foolish every day.
To think my grandson should be such a
  dunce!
I've said a hundred times, if I've said
  it once,
That if you keep the course on which
  you've started,
20 You'll leave your worthy father broken-
  hearted.
MARIANE. I think . . .
MADAME PERNELLE. And you, his
  sister, seem so pure,
So shy, so innocent, and so demure.
But you know what they say about still
  waters.

I pity parents with secretive daughters.
ELMIRE. Now, Mother . . .
MADAME PERNELLE.   And as for   25
  you, child, let me add
That your behavior is extremely bad,
And a poor example for these children,
  too.
Their dear, dead mother did far better
  than you.
You're much too free with money, and
  I'm distressed
To see you so elaborately dressed.   30
When it's one's husband that one aims
  to please,
One has no need of costly fripperies.
CLÉANTE. Oh, Madam, really . . .
MADAME PERNELLE.   You
  are her brother, Sir,
And I respect and love you; yet if I were
My son, this lady's good and pious   35
  spouse,
I wouldn't make you welcome in my
  house.
You're full of wordly counsels which, I
  fear,
Aren't suitable for decent folk to
  hear.
I've spoken bluntly, Sir; but it behooves
  us
Not to mince words when righteous   40
  fervor moves us.
DAMIS. Your man Tartuffe is full of
  holy speeches . . .
MADAME PERNELLE. And practises
  precisely what he preaches.
He's a fine man, and should be listened
  to.
I will not hear him mocked by fools like
  you.
DAMIS. Good God! Do you expect me   45
  to submit
To the tyranny of that carping hypocrite?
Must we forgo all joys and satisfactions
Because that bigot censures all our
  actions?
DORINE. To hear him talk—and he
  talks all the time—

50 There's nothing one can do that's not a
    crime.
  He rails at everything, your dear Tartuffe.
    MADAME PERNELLE. Whatever he
    reproves deserves reproof.
  He's out to save your souls, and all of
    you
  Must love him, as my son would have
    you do.
55   DAMIS. Ah no, Grandmother, I could
    never take
  To such a rascal, even for my father's
    sake.
  That's how I feel, and I shall not
    dissemble.
  His every action makes me seethe and
    tremble
  With helpless anger, and I have no
    doubt
60 That he and I will shortly have it out.
    DORINE. Surely it is a shame and a
    disgrace
  To see this man usurp the master's
    place—
  To see this beggar who, when first he
    came,
  Had not a shoe or shoestring to his name
65 So far forget himself that he behaves
  As if the house were his, and we his
    slaves.
    MADAME PERNELLE. Well, mark my
    words, your souls would fare far
    better
  If you obeyed his precepts to the letter.
    DORINE. You see him as a saint. I'm
    far less awed;
70 In fact, I see right through him. He's a
    fraud.
    MADAME PERNELLE. Nonsense!
    DORINE. His man Laurent's the same,
    or worse;
  I'd not trust either with a penny purse.
    MADAME PERNELLE. I can't say what
    his servant's morals may be;
  His own great goodness I can guarantee.
75 You all regard him with distaste and fear
  Because he tells you what you're loath
    to hear,
  Condemns your sins, points out your
    moral flaws,

And humbly strives to further Heaven's
    cause.
    DORINE. If sin is all that bothers him,
    why is it
He's so upset when folk drop in to visit? 80
Is Heaven so outraged by a social call
That he must prophesy against us all?
I'll tell you what I think: if you ask me,
He's jealous of my mistress' company.
    MADAME PERNELLE. Rubbish! (*To* 85
    ELMIRE.) He's not alone, child, in
    complaining
Of all your promiscuous entertaining.
Why, the whole neighborhood's upset,
    I know,
By all these carriages that come and go,
With crowds of guests parading in and
    out
And noisy servants loitering about. 90
In all of this, I'm sure there's nothing
    vicious;
But why give people cause to be
    suspicious?
    CLÉANTE. They need no cause; they'll
    talk in any case.
Madam, this world would be a joyless
    place
If, fearing what malicious tongues might 95
    say,
We locked our doors and turned our
    friends away.
And even if one did so dreary a thing,
D'you think those tongues would cease
    their chattering?
One can't fight slander; it's a losing
    battle;
Let us instead ignore their tittle-tattle. 100
Let's strive to live by conscience' clear
    decrees,
And let the gossips gossip as they please.
    DORINE. If there is talk against us, I
    know the source:
It's Daphne and her little husband, of
    course.
Those who have greatest cause for guilt 105
    and shame
Are quickest to besmirch a neighbor's
    name.
When there's a chance for libel, they
    never miss it;

When something can be made to seem
 illicit
They're off at once to spread the joyous
 news,
110 Adding to fact what fantasies they
 choose.
By talking up their neighbor's
 indiscretions
They seek to camouflage their own
 transgressions,
Hoping that others' innocent affairs
Will lend a hue of innocence to theirs,
115 Or that their own black guilt will come
 to seem
Part of a general shady color-scheme.
    MADAME PERNELLE. All that is quite
 irrelevant. I doubt
That anyone's more virtuous and devout
Than dear Orante; and I'm informed
 that she
120 Condemns your mode of life most
 vehemently.
    DORINE. Oh, yes, she's strict, devout,
 and has no taint
Of worldliness; in short, she seems a
 saint.
But it was time which taught her that
 disguise;
She's thus because she can't be
 otherwise.
125 So long as her attractions could enthrall,
She flounced and flirted and enjoyed it
 all,
But now that they're no longer what they
 were
She quits a world which fast is quitting
 her,
And wears a veil of virtue to conceal
130 Her bankrupt beauty and her lost
 appeal.
That's what becomes of old coquettes
 today:
Distressed when all their lovers fall
 away,
They see no recourse but to play the
 prude,
And so confer a style on solitude.
135 Thereafter, they're severe with everyone,
Condemning all our actions, pardoning
 none,

And claiming to be pure, austere, and
 zealous
When, if the truth were known, they're
 merely jealous,
And cannot bear to see another know
The pleasures time has forced them to 140
 forgo.
    MADAME PERNELLE (*initially to*
 ELMIRE). That sort of talk is what
 you like to hear;
Therefore you'd have us all keep still,
 my dear,
While Madam rattles on the livelong day.
Nevertheless, I mean to have my say.
I tell you that you're blest to have 145
 Tartuffe
Dwelling, as my son's guest, beneath
 this roof;
That Heaven has sent him to forestall
 its wrath
By leading you, once more, to the true
 path;
That all he reprehends is reprehensible,
And that you'd better heed him, and be 150
 sensible.
These visits, balls, and parties in which
 you revel
Are nothing but inventions of the Devil.
One never hears a word that's edifying:
Nothing but chaff and foolishness and
 lying,
As well as vicious gossip in which one's 155
 neighbor
Is cut to bits with épée, foil, and saber.
People of sense are driven half-insane
At such affairs, where noise and folly
 reign
And reputations perish thick and fast.
As a wise preacher said on Sunday last, 160
Parties are Towers of Babylon,[1] because
The guests all babble on with never a
 pause;
And then he told a story which, I
 think . . .
    (*To* CLÉANTE.)

---

1. *Babylon,* a reference to the Biblical story in
which God makes the Babylonians speak a number
of different languages as punishment for their
pride in trying to build a tower to reach to heaven.
(Genesis 11: 4-9)

I heard that laugh, Sir, and I saw that
    wink!
165 Go find your silly friends and laugh
    some more!
Enough; I'm going; don't show me to the
    door.
I leave this household much dismayed
    and vexed;
I cannot say when I shall see you next.
    (Slapping FLIPOTE.*)*
Wake up, don't stand there gaping into
    space!
170 I'll slap some sense into that stupid face.
Move, move, you slut.

SCENE II. CLÉANTE, DORINE

CLÉANTE.   I think I'll stay behind;
I want no further pieces of her mind.
How that old lady . . .
    DORINE.   Oh, what wouldn't she say
If she could hear you speak of her that
    way!
175 She'd thank you for the *lady,* but I'm
    sure
She'd find the *old* a little premature.
    CLÉANTE. My, what a scene she made,
    and what a din!
And how this man Tartuffe has taken
    her in!
    DORINE. Yes, but her son is even worse
    deceived;
180 His folly must be seen to be believed.
In the late troubles, he played an able
    part
And served his king with wise and loyal
    heart,[2]
But he's quite lost his senses since he
    fell
Beneath Tartuffe's infatuating spell.
185 He calls him brother, and loves him as
    his life,
Preferring him to mother, child, or
    wife.
In him and him alone will he confide;
He's made him his confessor and his
    guide;
He pets and pampers him with love
    more tender
190 Than any pretty mistress could engender,

Gives him the place of honor when they
    dine,
Delights to see him gorging like a swine,
Stuffs him with dainties till his guts
    distend,
And when he belches, cries "God bless
    you, friend!"
In short, he's mad; he worships him; he 195
    dotes;
His deeds he marvels at, his words he
    quotes,
Thinking each act a miracle, each word
Oracular as those that Moses heard.
Tartuffe, much pleased to find so easy a
    victim,
Has in a hundred ways beguiled and 200
    tricked him,
Milked him of money, and with his
    permission
Established here a sort of Inquisition.
Even Laurent, his lackey, dares to give
Us arrogant advice on how to live;
He sermonizes us in thundering tones 205
And confiscates our ribbons and
    colognes.
Last week he tore a kerchief into pieces
Because he found it pressed in a *Life of
    Jesus:*
He said it was a sin to juxtapose
Unholy vanities and holy prose. 210

SCENE III. ELMIRE, MARIANE, DAMIS,
CLÉANTE, DORINE

ELMIRE *(to* CLÉANTE*).* You did well
    not to follow; she stood in the door
And said *verbatim* all she'd said before.
I saw my husband coming. I think I'd
    best
Go upstairs now, and take a little rest.
    CLÉANTE. I'll wait and greet him here; 215
    then I must go.
I've really only time to say hello.
    DAMIS. Sound him about my sister's
    wedding, please.
I think Tartuffe's against it, and that he's

2. *late troubles . . . heart.* This and later references
indicate that there has been civil strife in the kingdom. The king is Louis XIV.

Been urging Father to withdraw his
blessing.
220 As you well know, I'd find that most
distressing.
Unless my sister and Valère can marry,
My hopes to wed *his* sister will miscarry,
And I'm determined . . .
DORINE.   He's coming.

SCENE IV. ORGON, CLÉANTE, DORINE

ORGON.   Ah, Brother, good-day.
CLÉANTE. Well, welcome back. I'm
sorry I can't stay.
225 How was the country? Blooming, I trust,
and green?
ORGON. Excuse me, Brother; just one
moment.
(To DORINE.*)*
        Dorine . . .
(To CLÉANTE.*)*
To put my mind at rest, I always learn
The household news the moment I
return.
(To DORINE.*)*
Has all been well, these two days I've
been gone?
230 How are the family? What's been going
on?
DORINE. Your wife, two days ago, had
a bad fever,
And a fierce headache which refused
to leave her.
ORGON. Ah. And Tartuffe?
DORINE.   Tartuffe?
Why, he's round and red,
Bursting with health, and excellently
fed.
235 ORGON. Poor fellow!
DORINE.   That night, the
mistress was unable
To take a single bite at the dinner-table.
Her headache-pains, she said, were
simply hellish.
ORGON. Ah. And Tartuffe?
DORINE.   He ate his
meal with relish,
And zealously devoured in her presence
240 A leg of mutton and a brace of pheasants.
ORGON. Poor fellow!

DORINE.   Well, the pains
continued strong,
And so she tossed and tossed the whole
night long,
Now icy-cold, now burning like a flame.
We sat beside her bed till morning came.
ORGON. Ah. And Tartuffe?   245
DORINE.   Why, having
eaten, he rose
And sought his room, already in a doze,
Got into his warm bed, and snored
away
In perfect peace until the break of day.
ORGON. Poor fellow!
DORINE.   After much ado,
we talked her
Into dispatching someone for the doctor.   250
He bled her, and the fever quickly fell.
ORGON. Ah. And Tartuffe?
DORINE.   He bore it
very well.
To keep his cheerfulness at any cost,
And make up for the blood *Madame* had
lost,
He drank, at lunch, four beakers full of   255
port.
ORGON. Poor fellow!
DORINE.   Both are doing
well, in short.
I'll go and tell *Madame* that you've
expressed
Keen sympathy and anxious interest.

SCENE V. ORGON, CLÉANTE

CLÉANTE. That girl was laughing in
your face, and though
I've no wish to offend you, even so   260
I'm bound to say that she had some
excuse.
How can you possibly be such a goose?
Are you so dazed by this man's hocus-
pocus
That all the world, save him, is out of
focus?
You've given him clothing, shelter, food,   265
and care;
Why must you also . . .
ORGON.   Brother, stop
right there.

You do not know the man of whom you
    speak.
    CLÉANTE. I grant you that. But my
    judgment's not so weak
That I can't tell, by his effect on
    others . . .
270   ORGON. Ah, when you meet him, you
    two will be like brothers!
There's been no loftier soul since time
    began.
He is a man who . . . a man who . . . an
    excellent man.
To keep his precepts is to be reborn,
And view this dunghill of a world with
    scorn.
275 Yes, thanks to him I'm a changed man
    indeed.
Under his tutelage my soul's been freed
From earthly loves, and every human
    tie:
My mother, children, brother, and wife
    could die,
And I'd not feel a single moment's pain.
280   CLÉANTE. That's a fine sentiment,
    Brother; most humane.
    ORGON. Oh, had you seen Tartuffe as I
    first knew him,
Your heart, like mine, would have
    surrendered to him.
He used to come into our church each
    day
And humbly kneel nearby, and start to
    pray.
285 He'd draw the eyes of everybody there
By the deep fervor of his heartfelt
    prayer;
He'd sigh and weep, and sometimes with
    a sound
Of rapture he would bend and kiss the
    ground;
And when I rose to go, he'd run before
290 To offer me holy-water at the door.
His serving-man, no less devout than he,
Informed me of his master's poverty;
I gave him gifts, but in his humbleness
He'd beg me every time to give him less.
295 "Oh, that's too much," he'd cry, "too
    much by twice!
I don't deserve it. The half, Sir, would
    suffice."

And when I wouldn't take it back, he'd
    share
Half of it with the poor, right then and
    there.
At length, Heaven prompted me to take
    him in
To dwell with us, and free our souls   300
    from sin.
He guides our lives, and to protect our
    honor
Stays by my wife, and keeps an eye
    upon her;
He tells me whom she sees, and all she
    does,
And seems more jealous than I ever
    was!
And how austere he is! Why, he can   305
    detect
A mortal sin where you would least
    suspect;
In smallest trifles, he's extremely strict.
Last week, his conscience was severely
    pricked
Because, while praying, he had caught
    a flea
And killed it, so he felt, too wrathfully.   310
    CLÉANTE. Good God, man! Have you
    lost your common sense—
Or is this all some joke at my expense?
How can you stand there and in all
    sobriety . . .
    ORGON. Brother, your language savors
    of impiety.
Too much free-thinking's made your   315
    faith unsteady,
And as I've warned you many times
    already,
'Twill get you into trouble before you're
    through.
    CLÉANTE. So I've been told before by
    dupes like you:
Being blind, you'd have all others blind
    as well;
The clear-eyed man you call an infidel,   320
And he who sees through humbug and
    pretense
Is charged, by you, with want of
    reverence.
Spare me your warnings, Brother; I have
    no fear

Of speaking out, for you and Heaven to hear,
325 Against affected zeal and pious knavery.
There's true and false in piety, as in bravery,
And just as those whose courage shines the most
In battle, are the least inclined to boast,
So those whose hearts are truly pure and lowly
330 Don't make a flashy show of being holy.
There's a vast difference, so it seems to me,
Between true piety and hypocrisy:
How do you fail to see it, may I ask?
Is not a face quite different from a mask?
335 Cannot sincerity and cunning art,
Reality and semblance, be told apart?
Are scarecrows just like men, and do you hold
That a false coin is just as good as gold?
Ah, Brother, man's a strangely fashioned creature
340 Who seldom is content to follow Nature,
But recklessly pursues his inclination
Beyond the narrow bounds of moderation,
And often, by transgressing Reason's laws,[3]
Perverts a lofty aim or noble cause.
345 A passing observation, but it applies.
    ORGON. I see, dear Brother, that you're profoundly wise;
You harbor all the insight of the age.
You are our one clear mind, our only sage,
The era's oracle, its Cato[4] too,
350 And all mankind are fools compared to you.
    CLÉANTE. Brother, I don't pretend to be a sage,
Nor have I all the wisdom of the age.
There's just one insight I would dare to claim:
I know that true and false are not the same;
355 And just as there is nothing I more revere
Than a soul whose faith is steadfast and sincere,
Nothing that I more cherish and admire
Than honest zeal and true religious fire,
So there is nothing that I find more base
Than specious piety's dishonest face— 360
Than these bold mountebanks, these histrios
Whose impious mummeries and hollow shows
Exploit our love of Heaven, and make a jest
Of all that men think holiest and best;
These calculating souls who offer prayers 365
Not to their Maker, but as public wares,
And seek to buy respect and reputation
With lifted eyes and sighs of exaltation;
These charlatans, I say, whose pilgrim souls
Proceed, by way of Heaven, toward earthly goals, 370
Who weep and pray and swindle and extort,
Who preach the monkish life, but haunt the court,
Who make their zeal the partner of their vice—
Such men are vengeful, sly, and cold as ice,
And when there is an enemy to defame 375
They cloak their spite in fair religion's name,
Their private spleen and malice being made
To seem a high and virtuous crusade,
Until, to mankind's reverent applause,
They crucify their foe in Heaven's cause. 380
Such knaves are all too common; yet, for the wise,
True piety isn't hard to recognize,
And, happily, these present times provide us
With bright examples to instruct and guide us.

---

3. *to follow Nature ... by transgressing Reason's laws.* These lines reflect the strong belief in the order of the natural world prevalent during the seventeenth and eighteenth centuries: man could perceive this order through reason and find virtue and happiness in following it. 4. *Cato,* refers to Marcus Porcius (95-46 B.C.), Roman statesman, soldier, and Stoic philosopher.

385 Consider Ariston and Périandre;
Look at Oronte, Alcidamas, Clitandre ;
Their virtue is acknowledged; who could
doubt it?
But you won't hear them beat the drum
about it.
They're never ostentatious, never vain,
390 And their religion's moderate and
humane;
It's not their way to criticize and chide:
They think censoriousness a mark of
pride,
And therefore, letting others preach and
rave,
They show, by deeds, how Christians
should behave.
395 They think no evil of their fellow man,
But judge of him as kindly as they can.
They don't intrigue and wangle and
conspire;
To lead a good life is their one desire;
The sinner wakes no rancorous hate in
them;
400 It is the sin alone which they condemn;
Nor do they try to show a fiercer zeal
For Heaven's cause than Heaven itself
could feel.
These men I honor, these men I advocate
As models for us all to emulate.
405 Your man is not their sort at all, I fear:
And, while your praise of him is quite
sincere,
I think that you've been dreadfully
deluded.
  ORGON. Now then, dear Brother, is
your speech concluded?
  CLÉANTE. Why, yes.
  ORGON.   Your servant, Sir.
  (He turns to go.)
  CLÉANTE.   No, Brother; wait.
410 There's one more matter. You agreed of
late

That young Valère might have your
daughter's hand.
  ORGON. I did.
  CLÉANTE.   And set the date, I
understand.
  ORGON. Quite so.
  CLÉANTE.   You've now
postponed it; is that true?
  ORGON. No doubt.
  CLÉANTE.   The match no longer
pleases you?
  ORGON. Who knows?   415
  CLÉANTE.   D'you mean to go
back on your word?
  ORGON. I won't say that.
  CLÉANTE.   Has anything occurred
Which might entitle you to break your
pledge?
  ORGON. Perhaps.
  CLÉANTE.   Why must you hem,
and haw, and hedge?
The boy asked me to sound you in this
affair . . .
  ORGON. It's been a pleasure.   420
  CLÉANTE.   But what
shall I tell Valère?
  ORGON. Whatever you like.
  CLÉANTE.   But what
have you decided?
What are your plans?
  ORGON.   I plan, Sir, to be guided
By Heaven's will.
  CLÉANTE.   Come, Brother, don't
talk rot.
You've given Valère your word; will you
keep it, or not?
  ORGON. Good day.   425
  CLÉANTE.   This looks like
poor Valère's undoing;
I'll go and warn him that there's trouble
brewing.

                  CURTAIN

Act Two

ORGON. Mariane.

MARIANE.   Yes, Father?

ORGON.   A word
with you; come here.

MARIANE. What are you looking for?

ORGON (peering into a small closet).
        Eavesdroppers, dear.
I'm making sure we shan't be overheard.
Someone in there could catch our every
word.

5 Ah, good, we're safe. Now, Mariane, my
child,
You're a sweet girl who's tractable and
mild,
Whom I hold dear, and think most
highly of.

MARIANE. I'm deeply grateful, Father,
for your love.

ORGON. That's well said, Daughter; and
you can repay me

10 If, in all things, you'll cheerfully obey
me.

MARIANE. To please you, Sir, is what
delights me best.

ORGON. Good, good. Now, what d'you
think of Tartuffe, our guest?

MARIANE. I, Sir?

ORGON.   Yes. Weigh your
answer; think it through.

MARIANE. Oh, dear. I'll say whatever
you wish me to.

15 ORGON. That's wisely said, my
Daughter. Say of him, then,
That he's the very worthiest of men,
And that you're fond of him, and would
rejoice
In being his wife, if that should be my
choice.
Well?

MARIANE. What?

ORGON.   What's that?

MARIANE.   I . . .

ORGON.   Well?

MARIANE.   Forgive me, pray.

ORGON. Did you not hear me?   20

MARIANE.   Of whom,
Sir, must I say
That I am fond of him, and would
rejoice
In being his wife, if that should be your
choice?

ORGON. Why, of Tartuffe.

MARIANE.   But, Father,
that's false, you know.
Why would you have me say what isn't
so?

ORGON. Because I am resolved it shall   25
be true.
That it's my wish should be enough for
you.

MARIANE. You can't mean, Father . . .

ORGON.   Yes, Tartuffe shall be
Allied by marriage to this family,
And he's to be your husband, is that
clear?
It's a father's privilege . . .

ORGON (to DORINE).   What are you   30
doing in here?
Is curiosity so fierce a passion
With you, that you must eavesdrop in
this fashion?

DORINE. There's lately been a rumor
going about—
Based on some hunch or chance remark,
no doubt—
That you mean Mariane to wed Tartuffe.   35
I've laughed it off, of course, as just a
spoof.

ORGON. You find it so incredible?

DORINE.   Yes, I do.
I won't accept that story, even from you.

ORGON. Well, you'll believe it when
the thing is done.

DORINE. Yes, yes, of course. Go on and   40
have your fun.

ORGON. I've never been more serious
in my life.

DORINE. Ha!

ORGON.   Daughter, I mean it; you're to be his wife.

DORINE. No, don't believe your father; it's all a hoax.

ORGON. See here, young woman . . .

DORINE.   Come, Sir, no more jokes;
45 You can't fool us.

ORGON.   How dare you talk that way?

DORINE. All right, then: we believe you, sad to say.

But how a man like you, who looks so wise

And wears a moustache of such splendid size,

Can be so foolish as to . . .

ORGON.   Silence, please!
50 My girl, you take too many liberties.

I'm master here, as you must not forget.

DORINE. Do let's discuss this calmly; don't be upset.

You can't be serious, Sir, about this plan.

What should that bigot want with Mariane?
55 Praying and fasting ought to keep him busy.

And then, in terms of wealth and rank, what is he?

Why should a man of property like you

Pick out a beggar son-in-law?

ORGON.   That will do.

Speak of his poverty with reverence.
60 His is a pure and saintly indigence

Which far transcends all worldly pride and pelf.

He lost his fortune, as he says himself,

Because he cared for Heaven alone, and so

Was careless of his interests here below.
65 I mean to get him out of his present straits

And help him to recover his estates—

Which, in his part of the world, have no small fame.

Poor though he is, he's a gentleman just the same.

DORINE. Yes, so he tells us; and, Sir, it seems to me
70 Such pride goes very ill with piety.

A man whose spirit spurns this dungy earth

Ought not to brag of lands and noble birth;

Such worldly arrogance will hardly square

With meek devotion and the life of prayer.

. . . But this approach, I see, has drawn a blank;   75

Let's speak, then, of his person, not his rank.

Doesn't it seem to you a trifle grim

To give a girl like her to a man like him?

When two are so ill-suited, can't you see

What the sad consequence is bound to be?   80

A young girl's virtue is imperilled, Sir,

When such a marriage is imposed on her;

For if one's bridegroom isn't to one's taste,

It's hardly an inducement to be chaste,

And many a man with horns[1] upon his brow   85

Has made his wife the thing that she is now.

It's hard to be a faithful wife, in short,

To certain husbands of a certain sort,

And he who gives his daughter to a man she hates

Must answer for her sins at Heaven's gates.   90

Think, Sir, before you play so risky a role.

ORGON. This servant-girl presumes to save my soul!

DORINE. You would do well to ponder what I've said.

ORGON. Daughter, we'll disregard this dunderhead.

Just trust your father's judgment. Oh, I'm aware   95

That I once promised you to young Valère;

But now I hear he gambles, which greatly shocks me;

---

1. *horns*, a medieval symbol for a husband with an unfaithful wife.

What's more, I've doubts about his
  orthodoxy.
His visits to church, I note, are very few.
100 DORINE. Would you have him go at
  the same hours as you,
And kneel nearby, to be sure of being
  seen?
  ORGON. I can dispense with such
  remarks, Dorine.
  (To MARIANE.*)*
Tartuffe, however, is sure of Heaven's
  blessing,
And that's the only treasure worth
  possessing.
105 This match will bring you joys beyond
  all measure;
Your cup will overflow with every
  pleasure;
You two will interchange your faithful
  loves
Like two sweet cherubs, or two turtledoves.
No harsh word shall be heard, no frown
  be seen,
110 And he shall make you happy as a
  queen.
  DORINE. And she'll make him a
  cuckold, just wait and see.
  ORGON. What language!
  DORINE.   Oh, he's a man of destiny;
He's *made* for horns, and what the stars
  demand
Your daughter's virtue surely can't
  withstand.
115 ORGON. Don't interrupt me further.
  Why can't you learn
That certain things are none of your
  concern?
  DORINE. It's for your own sake that I
  interfere.
  (She repeatedly interrupts ORGON
  *just as he is turning to speak to his
  daughter.)*
  ORGON. Most kind of you. Now, hold
  your tongue, d'you hear?
  DORINE. If I didn't love you . . .
  ORGON.   Spare me your affection.
120 DORINE. I'll love you, Sir, in spite of
  your objection.
  ORGON. Blast!

DORINE.   I can't bear, Sir, for
  your honor's sake,
To let you make this ludicrous mistake.
  ORGON. You mean to go on talking?
  DORINE.   If I didn't protest
This sinful marriage, my conscience
  couldn't rest.
  ORGON. If you don't hold your tongue, 125
  you little shrew . . .
  DORINE. What, lost your temper?
  A pious man like you?
  ORGON. Yes! Yes! You talk and talk.
  I'm maddened by it.
Once and for all, I tell you to be quiet.
  DORINE. Well, I'll be quiet. But I'll be
  thinking hard.
  ORGON. Think all you like, but you   130
  had better guard
That saucy tongue of yours, or I'll . . .
  (Turning back to MARIANE.*)*
            Now, child,
I've weighed this matter fully.
  DORINE *(aside).*   It drives me wild
That I can't speak.
  *(*ORGON *turns his head, and she is
  silent.)*
  ORGON.   Tartuffe is no young
  dandy,
But, still his person . . .
  DORINE *(aside).*   Is as sweet as
  candy.
  ORGON. Is such that, even if you   135
  shouldn't care
For his other merits . . .
  (He turns and stands facing DORINE,
  arms crossed.)
  DORINE *(aside).*   They'll make a
  lovely pair.
If I were she, no man would marry me
Against my inclination, and go scot-free.
He'd learn, before the wedding-day was
  over,
How readily a wife can find a lover.   140
  ORGON *(to* DORINE*).* It seems you treat
  my orders as a joke.
  DORINE. Why, what's the matter?
  'Twas not to you I spoke.
  ORGON. What *were* you doing?
  DORINE.   Talking
  to myself, that's all.

ORGON. Ah! *(Aside.)* One more bit of impudence and gall,

145 And I shall give her a good slap in the face.

(He puts himself in a position to slap her; DORINE, *whenever he glances at her, stands immobile and silent.)*

Daughter, you shall accept, and with good grace,

The husband I've selected . . . Your wedding-day . . .

(To DORINE.*)*

Why don't you talk to yourself?

DORINE.   I've nothing to say.

ORGON. Come, just one word.

DORINE.   No thank you, Sir. I pass.

150 ORGON. Come, speak; I'm waiting.

DORINE.   I'd not be such an ass.

ORGON *(turning to* MARIANE*)*. In short, dear Daughter, I mean to be obeyed,

And you must bow to the sound choice I've made.

DORINE *(moving away)*. I'd not wed such a monster, even in jest.

*(*ORGON *attempts to slap her, but misses.)*

ORGON. Daughter, that maid of yours is a thorough pest;

155 She makes me sinfully annoyed and nettled.

I can't speak further; my nerves are too unsettled.

She's so upset me by her insolent talk,

I'll calm myself by going for a walk.

SCENE III. DORINE, MARIANE

DORINE *(returning)*. Well, have you lost your tongue, girl? Must I play

160 Your part, and say the lines you ought to say?

Faced with a fate so hideous and absurd,

Can you not utter one dissenting word?

MARIANE. What good would it do? A father's power is great.

DORINE. Resist him now, or it will be too late.

165 MARIANE. But . . .

DORINE.   Tell him one cannot love at a father's whim;

That you shall marry for yourself, not him;

That since it's you who are to be the bride,

It's you, not he, who must be satisfied;

And that if his Tartuffe is so sublime,

He's free to marry him at any time.   170

MARIANE. I've bowed so long to Father's strict control,

I couldn't oppose him now, to save my soul.

DORINE. Come, come, Mariane. Do listen to reason, won't you?

Valère has asked your hand. Do you love him, or don't you?

MARIANE. Oh, how unjust of you!   175
What can you mean

By asking such a question, dear Dorine?

You know the depth of my affection for him;

I've told you a hundred times how I adore him.

DORINE. I don't believe in everything I hear;

Who knows if your professions were   180
sincere?

MARIANE. They were, Dorine, and you do me wrong to doubt it;

Heaven knows that I've been all too frank about it.

DORINE. You love him, then?

MARIANE.   Oh, more than I can express.

DORINE. And he, I take it, cares for you no less?

MARIANE. I think so.   185

DORINE.   And you both, with equal fire,

Burn to be married?

MARIANE. That is our one desire.

DORINE. What of Tartuffe, then? What of your father's plan?

MARIANE. I'll kill myself, if I'm forced to wed that man.

DORINE. I hadn't thought of that recourse. How splendid!

Just die, and all your troubles will be   190
ended!

A fine solution. Oh, it maddens me

To hear you talk in that self-pitying key.

MARIANE. Dorine, how harsh you are!
   It's most unfair.
You have no sympathy for my despair.
195 DORINE. I've none at all for people
   who talk drivel
And, faced with difficulties, whine and
   snivel.
   MARIANE. No doubt I'm timid, but it
   would be wrong . . .
   DORINE. True love requires a heart
   that's firm and strong.
   MARIANE. I'm strong in my affection
   for Valère,
200 But coping with my father is his affair.
   DORINE. But if your father's brain has
   grown so cracked
Over his dear Tartuffe that he can retract
His blessing, though your wedding-day
   was named,
It's surely not Valère who's to be blamed.
205 MARIANE. If I defied my father, as you
   suggest,
Would it not seem unmaidenly, at best?
Shall I defend my love at the expense
Of brazenness and disobedience?
Shall I parade my heart's desires, and
   flaunt . . .
210 DORINE. No, I ask nothing of you.
   Clearly you want
To be Madame Tartuffe, and I feel bound
Not to oppose a wish so very sound.
What right have I to criticize the match?
Indeed, my dear, the man's a brilliant
   catch.
215 Monsieur Tartuffe! Now, there's a man
   of weight!
Yes, yes, Monsieur Tartuffe, I'm bound
   to state,
Is quite a person; that's not to be denied;
'Twill be no little thing to be his bride.
The world already rings with his renown;
220 He's a great noble—in his native town;
His ears are red, he has a pink
   complexion,
And all in all, he'll suit you to
   perfection.
   MARIANE. Dear God!
   DORINE.   Oh, how
   triumphant you will feel
At having caught a husband so ideal!

MARIANE. Oh, do stop teasing, and use 225
   your cleverness
To get me out of this appalling mess.
Advise me, and I'll do whatever you say.
   DORINE. Ah no, a dutiful daughter
   must obey
Her father, even if he weds her to an ape.
You've a bright future; why struggle to 230
   escape?
Tartuffe will take you back where his
   family lives,
To a small town aswarm with relatives—
Uncles and cousins whom you'll be
   charmed to meet.
You'll be received at once by the elite,
Calling upon the bailiff's wife, no less— 235
Even, perhaps, upon the mayoress,
Who'll sit you down in the *best* kitchen
   chair.
Then, once a year, you'll dance at the
   village fair
To the drone of bagpipes—two of them,
   in fact—
And see a puppet-show, or an animal act. 240
Your husband . . .
   MARIANE.   Oh, you turn my blood
   to ice!
Stop torturing me, and give me your
   advice.
   DORINE *(threatening to go)*. Your
   servant, Madam.
   MARIANE.   Dorine, I beg of you . . .
   DORINE. No, you deserve it; this
   marriage must go through.
   MARIANE. Dorine!   245
   DORINE.   No.
   MARIANE.   Not Tartuffe! You
   know I think him . . .
   DORINE. Tartuffe's your cup of tea, and
   you shall drink him.
   MARIANE. I've always told you
   everything, and relied . . .
   DORINE. No. You deserve to be
   tartuffified.
   MARIANE. Well, since you mock me
   and refuse to care,
I'll henceforth seek my solace in despair: 250
Despair shall be my counsellor and
   friend,
And help me bring my sorrows to an end.

(She starts to leave.)

DORINE. There now, come back; my
  anger has subsided.
You do deserve some pity, I've decided.

255 MARIANE. Dorine, if Father makes me
  undergo
This dreadful martyrdom, I'll die, I know.

DORINE. Don't fret; it won't be difficult
  to discover
Some plan of action . . . But here's
  Valère, your lover.

SCENE IV. VALÈRE, MARIANE, DORINE

VALÈRE. Madam, I've just received
  some wondrous news
260 Regarding which I'd like to hear your
  views.

MARIANE. What news?

VALÈRE.   You're marrying
  Tartuffe.

MARIANE.   I find
That Father does have such a match in
  mind.

VALÈRE. Your father, Madam . . .

MARIANE.   . . . has just this minute
  said
That it's Tartuffe he wishes me to wed.

265 VALÈRE. Can he be serious?

MARIANE.   Oh, indeed he can;
He's clearly set his heart upon the plan.

VALÈRE. And what position do you
  propose to take,
Madam?

MARIANE. Why—I don't know.

VALÈRE.   For heaven's sake—
You don't know?

MARIANE.   No.

VALÈRE.   Well, well!

MARIANE.   Advise me, do.

270 VALÈRE. Marry the man. That's my
  advice to you.

MARIANE. That's your advice?

VALÈRE.   Yes.

MARIANE.   Truly?

VALÈRE.   Oh, absolutely.
You couldn't choose more wisely, more
  astutely.

MARIANE. Thanks for this counsel; I'll
  follow it, of course.

VALÈRE. Do, do; I'm sure 'twill cost
  you no remorse.

MARIANE. To give it didn't cause your   275
  heart to break.

VALÈRE. I gave it, Madam, only for
  your sake.

MARIANE. And it's for your sake that
  I take it, Sir.

DORINE *(withdrawing to the rear of the
  stage).* Let's see which fool will
  prove the stubborner.

VALÈRE. So! I am nothing to you, and
  it was flat
Deception when you . . .   280

MARIANE.   Please, enough of that.
You've told me plainly that I should
  agree
To wed the man my father's chosen for
  me,
And since you've deigned to counsel
  me so wisely,
I promise, Sir, to do as you advise me.

VALÈRE. Ah, no, 'twas not by me that   285
  you were swayed.
No, your decision was already made;
Though now, to save appearances, you
  protest
That you're betraying me at my behest.

MARIANE. Just as you say.

VALÈRE.   Quite so.
  And I now see
That you were never truly in love with me.   290

MARIANE. Alas, you're free to think
  so if you choose.

VALÈRE. I choose to think so, and
  here's a bit of news:
You've spurned my hand, but I know
  where to turn
For kinder treatment, as you shall
  quickly learn.

MARIANE. I'm sure you do. Your   295
  noble qualities
Inspire affection . . .

VALÈRE.   Forget my qualities,
  please.
They don't inspire you overmuch, I find.
But there's another lady I have in mind
Whose sweet and generous nature will
  not scorn
To compensate me for the loss I've borne.   300

MARIANE. I'm no great loss, and I'm
  sure that you'll transfer
Your heart quite painlessly from me to
  her.
  VALÈRE. I'll do my best to take it in
  my stride.
The pain I feel at being cast aside
305 Time and forgetfulness may put an end
  to.
Or if I can't forget, I shall pretend to.
No self-respecting person is expected
To go on loving once he's been rejected.
  MARIANE. Now, that's a fine, high-
  minded sentiment.
310 VALÈRE. One to which any sane man
  would assent.
Would you prefer it if I pined away
In hopeless passion till my dying day?
Am I to yield you to a rival's arms
And not console myself with other
  charms?
315 MARIANE. Go then: console yourself;
  don't hesitate.
I wish you to; indeed, I cannot wait.
  VALÈRE. You wish me to?
  MARIANE.   Yes.
  VALÈRE.   That's the final straw.
Madam, farewell. Your wish shall be my
  law.
  (He starts to leave, and then returns:
  this repeatedly.)
  MARIANE. Splendid.
  VALÈRE (coming back again). This
  breach, remember, is of your making;
320 It's you who've driven me to the step
  I'm taking.
  MARIANE. Of course.
  VALÈRE (coming back again).
          Remember, too, that I am merely
Following your example.
  MARIANE.   I see that clearly.
  VALÈRE. Enough. I'll go and do your
  bidding, then.
  MARIANE. Good.
  VALÈRE (coming back again). You
  shall never see my face again.
325 MARIANE. Excellent.
  VALÈRE (walking to the door, then
  turning about).   Yes?
  MARIANE.   What?

  VALÈRE.   What's
  that? What did you say?
  MARIANE. Nothing. You're dreaming.
  VALÈRE.   Ah. Well, I'm on my way.
Farewell, *Madame. (He moves slowly away.)*
  MARIANE.   Farewell.
  DORINE (to MARIANE). If you ask me,
Both of you are as mad as mad can be.
Do stop this nonsense, now. I've only
  let you
Squabble so long to see where it would   330
  get you.
Whoa there, Monsieur Valère!
  (She goes and seizes VALÈRE by the
  arm; he makes a great show of re-
  sistance.)
  VALÈRE.   What's this, Dorine?
  DORINE. Come here.
  VALÈRE.   No, no, my heart's
  too full of spleen.
Don't hold me back; her wish must be
  obeyed.
  DORINE. Stop!
  VALÈRE.   It's too late now; my
  decision's made.
  DORINE. Oh, pooh!   335
  MARIANE (aside).   He hates the sight
  of me, that's plain.
I'll go, and so deliver him from pain.
  DORINE (leaving VALÈRE, running after
  MARIANE). And now *you* run away!
  Come back.
  MARIANE.   No, no.
Nothing you say will keep me here. Let
  go!
  VALÈRE (aside). She cannot bear my
  presence, I perceive.
To spare her further torment, I shall   340
  leave.
  DORINE (leaving MARIANE, running
  after VALÈRE). Again! You'll not
  escape, Sir; don't you try it.
Come here, you two. Stop fussing and
  be quiet.
  (She takes VALÈRE by the hand, then
  MARIANE, and draws them together.)
  VALÈRE (to DORINE). What do you
  want of me?
  MARIANE (to DORINE). What is the
  point of this?

DORINE. We're going to have a little
  armistice. *(To* VALÈRE.*)*
345 Now, weren't you silly to get so
    overheated?
  VALÈRE. Didn't you see how badly I
    was treated?
  DORINE *(to* MARIANE*)*. Aren't you a
    simpleton, to have lost your head?
  MARIANE. Didn't you hear the hateful
    things he said?
  DORINE *(to* VALÈRE*)*. You're both
    great fools. Her sole desire, Valère,
350 Is to be yours in marriage. To that I'll
    swear.
    (To MARIANE.*)*
  He loves you only, and he wants no wife
  But you, Mariane. On that I'll stake my
    life.
  MARIANE *(to* VALÈRE*)*. Then why you
    advised me so, I cannot see.
  VALÈRE *(to* MARIANE*)*. On such a
    question, why ask advice of *me?*
355 DORINE. Oh, you're impossible. Give
    me your hands, you two.
    (To VALÈRE.*)*
  Yours first.
  VALÈRE *(giving* DORINE *his hand)*. But
    why?
  DORINE *(to* MARIANE*)*. And now a
    hand from you.
  MARIANE *(also giving* DORINE *her
    hand)*. What are you doing?
  DORINE.   There: a perfect fit.
  You suit each other better than you'll
    admit.
    *(*VALÈRE *and* MARIANE *hold hands
    for some time without looking at
    each other.)*
  VALÈRE *(turning toward* MARIANE*)*.
    Ah, come, don't be so haughty.
    Give a man
360 A look of kindness, won't you, Mariane?
    *(*MARIANE *turns toward* VALÈRE *and
    smiles.)*
  DORINE. I tell you, lovers are
    completely mad!
  VALÈRE *(to* MARIANE*)*. Now come,
    confess that you were very bad
  To hurt my feelings as you did just now.
  I have a just complaint, you must allow.

  MARIANE. *You* must allow that you   365
    were most unpleasant . . .
  DORINE. Let's table that discussion
    for the present;
  Your father has a plan which must be
    stopped.
  MARIANE. Advise us, then; what
    means must we adopt?
  DORINE. We'll use all manner of
    means, and all at once.
    (To MARIANE.*)*
  Your father's addled; he's acting like a 370
    dunce.
  Therefore you'd better humor the old
    fossil.
  Pretend to yield to him, be sweet and
    docile,
  And then postpone, as often as necessary,
  The day on which you have agreed to
    marry.
  You'll thus gain time, and time will turn 375
    the trick.
  Sometimes, for instance, you'll be
    taken sick,
  And that will seem good reason for
    delay;
  Or some bad omen will make you
    change the day—
  You'll dream of muddy water, or you'll
    pass
  A dead man's hearse, or break a looking- 380
    glass.
  If all else fails, no man can marry
    you
  Unless you take his ring and say
    "I do."
  But now, let's separate. If they should
    find
  Us talking here, our plot might be
    divined.
    (To VALÈRE.*)*
  Go to your friends, and tell them what's 385
    occurred,
  And have them urge her father to keep
    his word.
  Meanwhile, we'll stir her brother into
    action,
  And get Elmire, as well, to join our
    faction.
  Good-bye.

VALÈRE (to MARIANE). Though each
  of us will do his best,
390 It's your true heart on which my hopes
  shall rest.
    MARIANE (to VALÈRE). Regardless
  of what Father may decide,
None but Valère shall claim me as
  his bride.
    VALÈRE. Oh, how those words content
  me! Come what will . . .

DORINE. Oh, lovers, lovers! Their
  tongues are never still.
Be off, now.   395
    VALÈRE (turning to go, then turning
  back). One last word . . .
DORINE.   No time to chat:
You leave by this door; and you
  leave by that.
    (DORINE pushes them, by the shoul-
    ders, toward opposing doors.)
                                        CURTAIN

Act Three

SCENE I. DAMIS, DORINE

  DAMIS. May lightning strike me even
    as I speak,
May all men call me cowardly and
  weak,
If any fear or scruple holds me back
From settling things, at once, with
  that great quack!
5   DORINE. Now, don't give way to
    violent emotion.
Your father's merely talked about this
  notion,
And words and deeds are far from
  being one.
Much that is talked about is left undone.
  DAMIS. No, I must stop that
    scoundrel's machinations;
10 I'll go and tell him off; I'm out of
    patience.
  DORINE. Do calm down and be
    practical. I had rather
My mistress dealt with him—and with
  your father.
She has some influence with Tartuffe,
  I've noted.
He hangs upon her words, seems most
  devoted,
15 And may, indeed, be smitten by her
  charm.

Pray Heaven it's true! 'Twould do our
  cause no harm.
She sent for him, just now, to sound
  him out
On this affair you're so incensed about;
She'll find out where he stands, and
  tell him, too,
What dreadful strife and trouble will   20
  ensue
If he lends countenance to your father's
  plan.
I couldn't get in to see him, but his man
Says that he's almost finished with
  his prayers.
Go, now. I'll catch him when he comes
  downstairs.
  DAMIS. I want to hear this conference, 25
    and I will.
  DORINE. No, they must be alone.
  DAMIS.   Oh, I'll keep still.
  DORINE. Not you. I know your temper.
    You'd start a brawl,
And shout and stamp your foot and
  spoil it all.
Go on.
  DAMIS.   I won't; I have a perfect
    right . . .
  DORINE. Lord, you're a nuisance! He's   30
    coming; get out of sight.
    (DAMIS conceals himself in a closet
    at the rear of the stage.)

292   THE HYPOCRITES

SCENE II. TARTUFFE, DORINE

TARTUFFE *(observing* DORINE, *and calling to his manservant offstage).*
Hang up my hair-shirt, put my scourge
  in place,
And pray, Laurent, for Heaven's
  perpetual grace.
I'm going to the prison now, to share
My last few coins with the poor
  wretches there.
35 DORINE *(aside).* Dear God, what
  affectation! What a fake!
TARTUFFE. You wished to see me?
DORINE.   Yes . . .
TARTUFFE *(taking a handkerchief from
  his pocket).*   For mercy's sake,
Please take this handkerchief, before
  you speak.
DORINE. What?
TARTUFFE.   Cover that bosom, girl.
  The flesh is weak,
And unclean thoughts are difficult to
  control.
40 Such sights as that can undermine the
  soul.
DORINE. Your soul, it seems, has very
  poor defenses,
And flesh makes quite an impact on
  your senses.
It's strange that you're so easily
  excited;
My own desires are not so soon ignited,
45 And if I saw you naked as a beast,
Not all your hide would tempt me in the
  least.
TARTUFFE. Girl, speak more modestly;
  unless you do,
I shall be forced to take my leave of you.
DORINE. Oh, no, it's I who must be on
  my way;
50 I've just one little message to convey.
Madame is coming down, and begs you,
  Sir,
To wait and have a word or two with her.
TARTUFFE. Gladly.
DORINE *(aside).*   *That* had a softening
  effect!
I think my guess about him was correct.
55 TARTUFFE. Will she be long?

DORINE.   No: that's her step I hear.
Ah, here she is, and I shall disappear.

SCENE III. ELMIRE, TARTUFFE

TARTUFFE. May Heaven, whose
  infinite goodness we adore,
Preserve your body and soul forevermore,
And bless your days, and answer thus
  the plea
Of one who is its humblest votary.   60
ELMIRE. I thank you for that pious
  wish. But please,
Do take a chair and let's be more at ease.
  (They sit down.)
TARTUFFE. I trust that you are once
  more well and strong?
ELMIRE. Oh, yes: the fever didn't
  last for long.
TARTUFFE. My prayers are too   65
  unworthy, I am sure,
To have gained from Heaven this
  most gracious cure;
But lately, Madam, my every
  supplication
Has had for object your recuperation.
ELMIRE. You shouldn't have troubled
  so. I don't deserve it.
TARTUFFE. Your health is priceless,   70
  Madam, and to preserve it
I'd gladly give my own, in all sincerity.
ELMIRE. Sir, you outdo us all in
  Christian charity.
You've been most kind. I count myself
  your debtor.
TARTUFFE. 'Twas nothing, Madam. I
  long to serve you better.
ELMIRE. There's a private matter I'm   75
  anxious to discuss.
I'm glad there's no one here to hinder us.
TARTUFFE. I too am glad; it floods
  my heart with bliss
To find myself alone with you like this.
For just this chance I've prayed with
  all my power—
But prayed in vain, until this happy hour. 80
ELMIRE. This won't take long, Sir,
  and I hope you'll be
Entirely frank and unconstrained with
  me.

TARTUFFE. Indeed, there's nothing
  I had rather do
Than bare my inmost heart and soul
  to you.
85 First, let me say that what remarks I've
  made
About the constant visits you are paid
Were prompted not by any mean
  emotion,
But rather by a pure and deep devotion,
A fervent zeal . . .
  ELMIRE.   No need for explanation.
90 Your sole concern, I'm sure, was my
  salvation.
  TARTUFFE (taking ELMIRE's hand and
  pressing her fingertips). Quite so;
  and such great fervor do I feel . . .
  ELMIRE. Ooh! Please! You're
  pinching!
  TARTUFFE. 'Twas from excess of zeal.
I never meant to cause you pain, I swear.
I'd rather . . .
  (He places his hand on ELMIRE's
  knee.)
  ELMIRE.   What can your hand be
  doing there?
95 TARTUFFE. Feeling your gown; what
  soft, fine-woven stuff!
  ELMIRE. Please, I'm extremely
  ticklish. That's enough.
  (She draws her chair away; TARTUFFE
  pulls his after her.)
  TARTUFFE (fondling the lace collar of
  her gown). My, my, what lovely
  lacework on your dress!
The workmanship's miraculous, no less.
I've not seen anything to equal it.
100 ELMIRE. Yes, quite. But let's talk
  business for a bit.
They say my husband means to break
  his word
And give his daughter to you, Sir. Had
  you heard?
  TARTUFFE. He did once mention it.
  But I confess
I dream of quite a different happiness.
105 It's elsewhere, Madam, that my eyes
  discern
The promise of that bliss for which I
  yearn.

ELMIRE. I see: you care for nothing
  here below.
TARTUFFE. Ah, well—my heart's not
  made of stone, you know.
ELMIRE. All your desires mount
  heavenward, I'm sure,
In scorn of all that's earthly and impure. 110
  TARTUFFE. A love of heavenly beauty
  does not preclude
A proper love for earthly pulchritude;
Our senses are quite rightly captivated
By perfect works our Maker has created.
Some glory clings to all that Heaven   115
  has made;
In you, all Heaven's marvels are
  displayed.
On that fair face, such beauties have
  been lavished,
The eyes are dazzled and the heart is
  ravished;
How could I look on you, O flawless
  creature,
And not adore the Author of all Nature,   120
Feeling a love both passionate and pure
For you, his triumph of self-portraiture?
At first, I trembled lest that love should
  be
A subtle snare that Hell had laid for me;
I vowed to flee the sight of you,   125
  eschewing
A rapture that might prove my soul's
  undoing;
But soon, fair being, I became aware
That my deep passion could be made
  to square
With rectitude, and with my bounden
  duty.
I thereupon surrendered to your beauty.   130
It is, I know, presumptuous on my part
To bring you this poor offering of my
  heart,
And it is not my merit, Heaven knows,
But your compassion on which my
  hopes repose.
You are my peace, my solace, my   135
  salvation;
On you depends my bliss—or desolation;
I bide your judgment and, as you think
  best,
I shall be either miserable or blest.

ELMIRE. Your declaration is most
    gallant, Sir,
140 But don't you think it's out of character?
You'd have done better to restrain your
    passion
And think before you spoke in such a
    fashion.
It ill becomes a pious man like you . . .
    TARTUFFE. I may be pious, but I'm
    human too:
145 With your celestial charms before his
    eyes,
A man has not the power to be wise.
I know such words sound strangely,
    coming from me,
But I'm no angel, nor was meant
    to be,
And if you blame my passion, you must
    needs
150 Reproach as well the charms on which
    it feeds.
Your loveliness I had no sooner seen
Than you became my soul's unrivalled
    queen;
Before your seraph glance, divinely
    sweet,
My heart's defenses crumbled in defeat,
155 And nothing fasting, prayer, or tears
    might do
Could stay my spirit from adoring you.
My eyes, my sighs have told you in the
    past
What now my lips make bold to say at
    last,
And if, in your great goodness, you will
    deign
160 To look upon your slave, and ease his
    pain,—
If, in compassion for my soul's distress,
You'll stoop to comfort my unworthiness,
I'll raise to you, in thanks for that
    sweet manna,
An endless hymn, an infinite hosanna.
165 With me, of course, there need be no
    anxiety,
No fear of scandal or of notoriety.
These young court gallants, whom all
    the ladies fancy,
Are vain in speech, in action rash and
    chancy;

When they succeed in love, the world
    soon knows it;
No favor's granted them but they
    disclose it   170
And by the looseness of their tongues
    profane
The very altar where their hearts have
    lain.
Men of my sort, however, love discreetly,
And one may trust our reticence
    completely.
My keen concern for my good name   175
    insures
The absolute security of yours;
In short, I offer you, my dear Elmire,
Love without scandal, pleasure without
    fear.
    ELMIRE. I've heard your well-turned
    speeches to the end,
And what you urge I clearly apprehend.   180
Aren't you afraid that I may take a
    notion
To tell my husband of your warm
    devotion,
And that, supposing he were duly told,
His feelings toward you might grow
    rather cold?
    TARTUFFE. I know, dear lady, that   185
    your exceeding charity
Will lead your heart to pardon my
    temerity;
That you'll excuse my violent affection
As human weakness, human
    imperfection;
And that—O fairest!—you will bear in
    mind
That I'm but flesh and blood, and am   190
    not blind.
    ELMIRE. Some women might do
    otherwise, perhaps,
But I shall be discreet about your lapse;
I'll tell my husband nothing of what's
    occurred
If, in return, you'll give your solemn
    word
To advocate as forcefully as you can   195
The marriage of Valère and Mariane,
Renouncing all desire to dispossess
Another of his rightful happiness,
And . . .

SCENE IV. DAMIS, ELMIRE, TARTUFFE

DAMIS *(emerging from the closet where he has been hiding)*. No! We'll not hush up this vile affair;
200 I heard it all inside that closet there,
Where Heaven, in order to confound the pride
Of this great rascal, prompted me to hide.
Ah, now I have my long-awaited chance
To punish his deceit and arrogance,
205 And give my father clear and shocking proof
Of the black character of his dear Tartuffe.

ELMIRE. Ah no, Damis; I'll be content if he
Will study to deserve my leniency.
I've promised silence—don't make me break my word;
210 To make a scandal would be too absurd.
Good wives laugh off such trifles, and forget them;
Why should they tell their husbands, and upset them?

DAMIS. You have your reasons for taking such a course,
And I have reasons, too, of equal force.
215 To spare him now would be insanely wrong.
I've swallowed my just wrath for far too long
And watched this insolent bigot bringing strife
And bitterness into our family life.
Too long he's meddled in my father's affairs,
220 Thwarting my marriage-hopes, and poor Valère's.
It's high time that my father was undeceived,
And now I've proof that can't be disbelieved—
Proof that was furnished me by Heaven above.
It's too good not to take advantage of.
225 This is my chance, and I deserve to lose it
If, for one moment, I hesitate to use it.

ELMIRE. Damis . . .

DAMIS.   No, I must do what I think right.
Madam, my heart is bursting with delight,
And, say whatever you will, I'll not consent
To lose the sweet revenge on which I'm 230 bent.
I'll settle matters without more ado;
And here, most opportunely, is my cue.

SCENE V. ORGON, DAMIS, TARTUFFE, ELMIRE

DAMIS. Father, I'm glad you've joined us. Let us advise you
Of some fresh news which doubtless will surprise you.
You've just now been repaid with interest 235
For all your loving-kindness to our guest.
He's proved his warm and grateful feelings toward you;
It's with a pair of horns he would reward you.
Yes, I surprised him with your wife, and heard
His whole adulterous offer, every word. 240
She, with her all too gentle disposition,
Would not have told you of his proposition;
But I shall not make terms with brazen lechery,
And feel that not to tell you would be treachery.

ELMIRE. And I hold that one's 245 husband's peace of mind
Should not be spoilt by tattle of this kind.
One's honor doesn't require it: to be proficient
In keeping men at bay is quite sufficient.
These are my sentiments, and I wish, Damis,
That you had heeded me and held your 250 peace.

SCENE VI. ORGON, DAMIS, TARTUFFE

ORGON. Can it be true, this dreadful thing I hear?

TARTUFFE. Yes, Brother, I'm a wicked man, I fear:
A wretched sinner, all depraved and twisted,
The greatest villain that has ever existed.
255 My life's one heap of crimes, which grows each minute;
There's naught but foulness and corruption in it;
And I perceive that Heaven, outraged by me,
Has chosen this occasion to mortify me.
Charge me with any deed you wish to name;
260 I'll not defend myself, but take the blame.
Believe what you are told, and drive Tartuffe
Like some base criminal from beneath your roof;
Yes, drive me hence, and with a parting curse:
I shan't protest, for I deserve far worse.
265 ORGON (to DAMIS). Ah, you deceitful boy, how dare you try
To stain his purity with so foul a lie?
DAMIS. What! Are you taken in by such a bluff?
Did you not hear . . . ?
ORGON. Enough, you rogue, enough!
TARTUFFE. Ah, Brother, let him speak: you're being unjust.
270 Believe his story; the boy deserves your trust.
Why, after all, should you have faith in me?
How can you know what I might do, or be?
Is it on my good actions that you base
Your favor? Do you trust my pious face?
275 Ah, no, don't be deceived by hollow shows;
I'm far, alas, from being what men suppose;
Though the world takes me for a man of worth,
I'm truly the most worthless man on earth.
(To DAMIS.)

Yes, my dear son, speak out now: call me the chief
Of sinners, a wretch, a murderer, a thief; 280
Load me with all the names men most abhor;
I'll not complain; I've earned them all, and more;
I'll kneel here while you pour them on my head
As a just punishment for the life I've led.
ORGON (to TARTUFFE). This is too much, 285
dear Brother.
(To DAMIS.) Have you no heart?
DAMIS. Are you so hoodwinked by this rascal's art . . . ?
ORGON. Be still, you monster.
(To TARTUFFE.)
Brother, I pray you, rise.
(To DAMIS.) Villain!
DAMIS. But . . .
ORGON. Silence!
DAMIS. Can't you realize . . . ?
ORGON. Just one word more, and I'll tear you limb from limb.
TARTUFFE. In God's name, Brother, 290
don't be harsh with him.
I'd rather far be tortured at the stake
Than see him bear one scratch for my poor sake.
ORGON (to DAMIS). Ingrate!
TARTUFFE. If I must beg you, on bended knee,
To pardon him . . .
ORGON (falling to his knees, addressing TARTUFFE). Such goodness cannot be!
(To DAMIS.)
Now, there's true charity! 295
DAMIS. What, you . . . ?
ORGON. Villain, be still!
I know your motives; I know you wish him ill:
Yes, all of you—wife, children, servants, all—
Conspire against him and desire his fall,
Employing every shameful trick you can
To alienate me from this saintly man. 300

Ah, but the more you seek to drive him
    away,
The more I'll do to keep him. Without
    delay,
I'll spite this household and confound
    its pride
By giving him my daughter as his bride.

305   DAMIS. You're going to force her to
    accept his hand?

  ORGON. Yes, and this very night, d'you
    understand?
I shall defy you all, and make it clear
That I'm the one who gives the orders
    here.
Come, wretch, kneel down and clasp
    his blessed feet,

310 And ask his pardon for your black deceit.
  DAMIS. I ask that swindler's pardon?
    Why, I'd rather . . .

  ORGON. So! You insult him, and defy
    your father!
A stick! A stick! *(To* TARTUFFE.*)* No,
    no—release me, do.
    (To DAMIS.*)*
Out of my house this minute! Be off
    with you,

315 And never dare set foot in it again.
  DAMIS. Well, I shall go, but . . .
  ORGON.   Well, go quickly, then.
I disinherit you; an empty purse
Is all you'll get from me—except my
    curse!

SCENE VII.   ORGON, TARTUFFE

  ORGON. How he blasphemed your
    goodness! What a son!

320   TARTUFFE. Forgive him, Lord, as I've
    already done. *(To* ORGON.*)*
You can't know how it hurts when
    someone tries
To blacken me in my dear Brother's eyes.
  ORGON. Ahh!
  TARTUFFE.   The mere thought of such
    ingratitude
Plunges my soul into so dark a mood . . .

325 Such horror grips my heart . . . I gasp
    for breath,
And cannot speak, and feel myself near
    death.

  ORGON *(he runs, in tears, to the door
    through which he has just driven
    his son).* You blackguard! Why did
    I spare you? Why did I not
Break you in little pieces on the spot?
Compose yourself, and don't be hurt,
    dear friend.

  TARTUFFE. These scenes, these   330
    dreadful quarrels, have got to end.
I've much upset your household, and I
    perceive
That the best thing will be for me to
    leave.
  ORGON. What are you saying!
  TARTUFFE.   They're
    all against me here;
They'd have you think me false and
    insincere.
  ORGON. Ah, what of that? Have I   335
    ceased believing in you?
  TARTUFFE. Their adverse talk will
    certainly continue,
And charges which you now repudiate
You may find credible at a later date.
  ORGON. No, Brother, never.
  TARTUFFE.   Brother, a
    wife can sway
Her husband's mind in many a subtle   340
    way.
  ORGON. No, no.
  TARTUFFE.   To leave at once is the
    solution;
Thus only can I end their persecution.
  ORGON. No, no, I'll not allow it; you
    shall remain.
  TARTUFFE. Ah, well; 'twill mean much
    martyrdom and pain,
But if you wish it . . .   345
  ORGON.   Ah!
  TARTUFFE.   Enough; so be
    it.
But one thing must be settled, as I see it.
For your dear honor, and for our
    friendship's sake,
There's one precaution I feel bound to
    take.
I shall avoid your wife, and keep
    away . . .
  ORGON. No, you shall not, whatever   350
    they may say.

It pleases me to vex them, and for spite
I'd have them see you with her day and
    night.
What's more, I'm going to drive them
    to despair
By making you my only son and heir;
355 This very day, I'll give to you alone
Clear deed and title to everything I own.
A dear, good friend and son-in-law-to-be

Is more than wife, or child, or kin to me.
Will you accept my offer, dearest son?
    TARTUFFE. In all things, let the will   360
    of Heaven be done.
    ORGON. Poor fellow! Come, we'll go
    draw up the deed.
Then let them burst with disappointed
    greed!

                    CURTAIN

Act Four

SCENE I. CLÉANTE, TARTUFFE

    CLÉANTE. Yes, all the town's
    discussing it, and truly,
Their comments do not flatter you
    unduly.
I'm glad we've met, Sir, and I'll give my
    view
Of this sad matter in a word or two.
5 As for who's guilty, that I shan't discuss;
Let's say it was Damis who caused the
    fuss;
Assuming, then, that you have been
    ill-used
By young Damis, and groundlessly
    accused,
Ought not a Christian to forgive, and
    ought
10 He not to stifle every vengeful thought?
Should you stand by and watch a father
    make
His only son an exile for your sake?
Again I tell you frankly, be advised:
The whole town, high and low, is
    scandalized;
15 This quarrel must be mended, and my
    advice is
Not to push matters to a further crisis.
No, sacrifice your wrath to God above,
And help Damis regain his father's love.
    TARTUFFE. Alas, for my part I should
    take great joy

In doing so. I've nothing against the boy. 20
I pardon all, I harbor no resentment;
To serve him would afford me much
    contentment.
But Heaven's interest will not have it so:
If he comes back, then I shall have to go.
After his conduct—so extreme, 25
    so vicious—
Our further intercourse would look
    suspicious.
God knows what people would think!
    Why, they'd describe
My goodness to him as a sort of bribe;
They'd say that out of guilt I made
    pretense
Of loving-kindness and benevolence— 30
That, fearing my accuser's tongue, I
    strove
To buy his silence with a show of love.
    CLÉANTE. Your reasoning is badly
    warped and stretched,
And these excuses, Sir, are most
    far-fetched.
Why put yourself in charge of Heaven's 35
    cause?
Does Heaven need our help to enforce
    its laws?
Leave vengeance to the Lord, Sir; while
    we live,
Our duty's not to punish, but forgive;
And what the Lord commands, we
    should obey

Without regard to what the world may
    say.
What! Shall the fear of being
    misunderstood
Prevent our doing what is right and good?
No, no; let's simply do what Heaven
    ordains,
And let no other thoughts perplex our
    brains.
    TARTUFFE. Again, Sir, let me say
    that I've forgiven
Damis, and thus obeyed the laws of
    Heaven;
But I am not commanded by the Bible
To live with one who smears my name
    with libel.
    CLÉANTE. Were you commanded, Sir,
    to indulge the whim
Of poor Orgon, and to encourage him
In suddenly transferring to your name
A large estate to which you have no
    claim?
    TARTUFFE. 'Twould never occur to
    those who know me best
To think I acted from self-interest.
The treasures of this world I quite
    despise;
Their specious glitter does not charm
    my eyes;
And if I have resigned myself to taking
The gift which my dear Brother insists
    on making,
I do so only, as he well understands,
Lest so much wealth fall into wicked
    hands,
Lest those to whom it might descend in
    time
Turn it to purposes of sin and crime,
And not, as I shall do, make use of it
For Heaven's glory and mankind's
    benefit.
    CLÉANTE. Forget these trumped-up
    fears. Your argument
Is one the rightful heir might well resent;
It *is* a moral burden to inherit
Such wealth, but give Damis a chance
    to bear it.
And would it not be worse to be accused
Of swindling, than to see that wealth
    misused?

I'm shocked that you allowed Orgon to
    broach
This matter, and that you feel no
    self-reproach;
Does true religion teach that lawful heirs
May freely be deprived of what is theirs?
And if the Lord has told you in your
    heart
That you and young Damis must dwell
    apart,
Would it not be the decent thing to beat
A generous and honorable retreat,
Rather than let the son of the house be
    sent,
For your convenience, into banishment?
Sir, if you wish to prove the honesty
Of your intentions . . .
    TARTUFFE.   Sir, it is half-past
    three.
I've certain pious duties to attend to,
And hope my prompt departure won't
    offend you.
    CLÉANTE (*alone*). Damn.

SCENE II. ELMIRE, MARIANE, CLÉANTE,
    DORINE

    DORINE.   Stay, Sir, and
    help Mariane, for Heaven's sake!
She's suffering so, I fear her heart will
    break.
Her father's plan to marry her off tonight
Has put the poor child in a desperate
    plight.
I hear him coming. Let's stand together,
    now,
And see if we can't change his mind,
    somehow,
About this match we all deplore and fear.

SCENE III. ORGON, ELMIRE, MARIANE,
    CLÉANTE, DORINE

    ORGON. Hah! Glad to find you all
    assembled here.
    (*To* MARIANE.)
This contract, child, contains your
    happiness,
And what it says I think your heart can
    guess.

MARIANE *(falling to her knees)*. Sir,
     by that Heaven which sees me
     here distressed,
And by whatever else can move your
     breast,
Do not employ a father's power, I pray
     you,
To crush my heart and force it to obey
     you,
Nor by your harsh commands oppress
     me so
100 That I'll begrudge the duty which I
     owe—
And do not so embitter and enslave me
That I shall hate the very life you
     gave me.
If my sweet hopes must perish, if you
     refuse
To give me to the one I've dared to
     choose,
105 Spare me at least—I beg you, I implore—
The pain of wedding one whom I abhor;
And do not, by a heartless use of force,
Drive me to contemplate some desperate
     course.
     ORGON *(feeling himself touched by
     her)*. Be firm, my soul. No human
     weakness, now.
110 MARIANE. I don't resent your love for
     him. Allow
Your heart free rein, Sir; give him your
     property,
And if that's not enough, take mine from
     me;
He's welcome to my money; take it, do,
But don't, I pray, include my person too.
115 Spare me, I beg you; and let me end the
     tale
Of my sad days behind a convent veil.
     ORGON. A convent! Hah! When crossed
     in their amours,
All lovesick girls have the same thought
     as yours.
Get up! The more you loathe the man,
     and dread him,
120 The more ennobling it will be to wed
     him.
Marry Tartuffe, and mortify your flesh!
Enough; don't start that whimpering
     afresh.

DORINE. But why . . . ?
ORGON.   Be still, there.
     Speak when you're spoken to.
Not one more bit of impudence out of
     you.
     CLÉANTE. If I may offer a word of   125
     counsel here . . .
     ORGON. Brother, in counseling you
     have no peer;
All your advice is forceful, sound, and
     clever;
I don't propose to follow it, however.
     ELMIRE *(to ORGON)*. I am amazed, and
     don't know what to say;
Your blindness simply takes my breath   130
     away.
You are indeed bewitched, to take no
     warning
From our account of what occurred this
     morning.
     ORGON. Madam, I know a few plain
     facts, and one
Is that you're partial to my rascal son;
Hence, when he sought to make Tartuffe   135
     the victim
Of a base lie, you dared not contradict
     him.
Ah, but you underplayed your part, my
     pet;
You should have looked more angry,
     more upset.
     ELMIRE. When men make overtures,
     must we reply
With righteous anger and a battle-cry?   140
Must we turn back their amorous
     advances
With sharp reproaches and with fiery
     glances?
Myself, I find such offers merely
     amusing,
And make no scenes and fusses in
     refusing;
My taste is for good-natured rectitude,   145
And I dislike the savage sort of prude
Who guards her virtue with her teeth
     and claws,
And tears men's eyes out for the
     slightest cause:
The Lord preserve me from such honor
     as that,

150 Which bites and scratches like an
    alley-cat!
I've found that a polite and cool rebuff
Discourages a lover quite enough.
    ORGON. I know the facts, and I shall
    not be shaken.
    ELMIRE. I marvel at your power to
    be mistaken.
155 Would it, I wonder, carry weight with
    you
If I could *show* you that our tale was
    true?
    ORGON. Show me?
    ELMIRE.   Yes.
    ORGON.   Rot.
    ELMIRE.   Come, what
    if I found a way
To make you see the facts as plain as
    day?
    ORGON. Nonsense.
    ELMIRE.   Do answer me; don't
    be absurd.
160 I'm not now asking you to trust our
    word.
Suppose that from some hiding-place
    in here
You learned the whole sad truth by
    eye and ear—
What would you say of your good friend,
    after that?
    ORGON. Why, I'd say . . . nothing, by
    Jehoshaphat!
165 It can't be true.
    ELMIRE.   You've been too long
    deceived,
And I'm quite tired of being disbelieved.
Come now: let's put my statements to
    the test,
And you shall see the truth made
    manifest.
    ORGON. I'll take that challenge. Now
    do your uttermost.
170 We'll see how you make good your
    empty boast.
    ELMIRE (to DORINE). Send him to me.
    DORINE.   He's crafty; it may be hard
To catch the cunning scoundrel off
    his guard.
    ELMIRE. No, amorous men are gullible.
    Their conceit

So blinds them that they're never hard
    to cheat.
Have him come down. (*To* CLÉANTE *and*   175
    MARIANE.) Please leave us, for a bit.

SCENE IV. ELMIRE, ORGON

    ELMIRE. Pull up this table, and get
    under it.
    ORGON. What?
    ELMIRE.   It's essential that you be
    well-hidden.
    ORGON. Why there?
    ELMIRE.   Oh, Heavens! Just
    do as you are bidden.
I have my plans; we'll soon see how
    they fare.
Under the table, now; and once you're   180
    there,
Take care that you are neither seen nor
    heard.
    ORGON. Well, I'll indulge you, since I
    gave my word
To see you through this infantile charade.
    ELMIRE. Once it is over, you'll be glad
    we played.
    (*To her husband, who is now under
    the table.*)
I'm going to act quite strangely, now,   185
    and you
Must not be shocked at anything I do.
Whatever I may say, you must excuse
As part of that deceit I'm forced to use.
I shall employ sweet speeches in the
    task
Of making that imposter drop his   190
    mask;
I'll give encouragement to his bold
    desires,
And furnish fuel to his amorous fires.
Since it's for your sake, and for his
    destruction,
That I shall seem to yield to his
    seduction,
I'll gladly stop whenever you decide   195
That all your doubts are fully satisfied.
I'll count on you, as soon as you have
    seen
What sort of man he is, to intervene,
And not expose me to his odious lust

200 One moment longer than you feel you
    must.
    Remember: you're to save me from my
        plight
    Whenever . . . He's coming! Hush! Keep
        out of sight!

SCENE V. TARTUFFE, ELMIRE, ORGON

TARTUFFE. You wish to have a word
    with me, I'm told.
ELMIRE. Yes. I've a little secret to
    unfold.
205 Before I speak, however, it would be wise
    To close that door, and look about for
        spies.
        (TARTUFFE goes to the door, closes it,
        and returns.)
    The very last thing that must happen
        now
    Is a repetition of this morning's row.
    I've never been so badly caught off
        guard.
210 Oh, how I feared for you! You saw how
        hard
    I tried to make that troublesome Damis
    Control his dreadful temper, and hold
        his peace.
    In my confusion, I didn't have the sense
    Simply to contradict his evidence;
215 But as it happened, that was for the best,
    And all has worked out in our interest.
    This storm has only bettered your
        position;
    My husband doesn't have the least
        suspicion,
    And now, in mockery of those who do,
220 He bids me be continually with you.
    And that is why, quite fearless of
        reproof,
    I now can be alone with my Tartuffe,
    And why my heart—perhaps too quick
        to yield—
    Feels free to let its passion be revealed.
225 TARTUFFE. Madam, your words
        confuse me. Not long ago,
    You spoke in quite a different style,
        you know.
ELMIRE. Ah, Sir, if that refusal made
    you smart,

It's little that you know of woman's
    heart,
Or what the heart is trying to convey
When it resists in such a feeble way!   230
Always, at first, our modesty prevents
The frank avowal of tender sentiments;
However high the passion which
    inflames us,
Still, to confess its power somehow
    shames us.
Thus we reluct, at first, yet in a tone   235
Which tells you that our heart is
    overthrown,
That what our lips deny, our pulse
    confesses,
And that, in time, all noes will turn
    to yesses.
I fear my words are all too frank and
    free,
And a poor proof of woman's modesty;   240
But since I'm started, tell me, if you
    will—
Would I have tried to make Damis be
    still,
Would I have listened, calm and
    unoffended,
Until your lengthy offer of love was
    ended,
And been so very mild in my reaction,   245
Had your sweet words not given me
    satisfaction?
And when I tried to force you to undo
The marriage-plans my husband has in
    view,
What did my urgent pleading signify
If not that I admired you, and that I   250
Deplored the thought that someone
    else might own
Part of a heart I wished for mine alone?
TARTUFFE. Madam, no happiness is so
    complete
As when, from lips we love, come words
    so sweet;
Their nectar floods my every sense, and   255
    drains
In honeyed rivulets through all my veins.
To please you is my joy, my only goal;
Your love is the restorer of my soul;
And yet I must beg leave, now, to
    confess

Some lingering doubts as to my
  happiness.
Might this not be a trick? Might not
  the catch
Be that you wish me to break off the
  match
With Mariane, and so have feigned to
  love me?
I shan't quite trust your fond opinion
  of me
Until the feelings you've expressed so
  sweetly
Are demonstrated somewhat more
  concretely,
And you have shown, by certain kind
  concessions,
That I may put my faith in your
  professions.
  ELMIRE *(she coughs, to warn her hus-
  band).* Why be in such a hurry?
  Must my heart
Exhaust its bounty at the very start?
To make that sweet admission cost
  me dear,
But you'll not be content, it would
  appear,
Unless my store of favors is disbursed
To the last farthing, and at the very
  first.
  TARTUFFE. The less we merit, the less
  we dare to hope,
And with our doubts, mere words can
  never cope.
We trust no promised bliss till we
  receive it;
Not till a joy is ours can we believe it.
I, who so little merit your esteem,
Can't credit this fulfillment of my dream,
And shan't believe it, Madam, until I
  savor
Some palpable assurance of your favor.
  ELMIRE. My, how tyrannical your love
  can be,
And how it flusters and perplexes me!
How furiously you take one's heart in
  hand,
And make your every wish a fierce
  command!
Come, must you hound and harry me
  to death?

Will you not give me time to catch my
  breath?
Can it be right to press me with such
  force,
Give me no quarter, show me no
  remorse,
And take advantage, by your stern
  insistence,
Of the fond feelings which weaken my
  resistance?
  TARTUFFE. Well, if you look with favor
  upon my love,
Why, then, begrudge me some clear
  proof thereof?
  ELMIRE. But how can I consent
  without offense
To Heaven, toward which you feel
  such reverence?
  TARTUFFE. If Heaven is all that holds
  you back, don't worry.
I can remove that hindrance in a hurry.
Nothing of that sort need obstruct our
  path.
  ELMIRE. Must one not be afraid of
  Heaven's wrath?
  TARTUFFE. Madam, forget such fears,
  and be my pupil,
And I shall teach you how to conquer
  scruple.
Some joys, it's true, are wrong in
  Heaven's eyes;
Yet Heaven is not averse to compromise;
There is a science, lately formulated,
Whereby one's conscience may be
  liberated,
And any wrongful act you care to
  mention
May be redeemed by purity of intention.
I'll teach you, Madam, the secrets of
  that science;
Meanwhile, just place on me your full
  reliance.
Assuage my keen desires, and feel no
  dread:
The sin, if any, shall be on my head.
  *(ELMIRE coughs, this time more
  loudly.)*
You've a bad cough.
  ELMIRE.   Yes, yes. It's bad
  indeed.

TARTUFFE *(producing a little paper bag)*. A bit of licorice may be what you need.

315 ELMIRE. No, I've a stubborn cold, it seems. I'm sure it
Will take much more than licorice to cure it.

TARTUFFE. How aggravating.

ELMIRE.   Oh, more than I can say.

TARTUFFE. If you're still troubled, think of things this way:
No one shall know our joys, save us alone,
320 And there's no evil till the act is known;
It's scandal, Madam, which makes it an offense,
And it's no sin to sin in confidence.

ELMIRE *(having coughed once more)*.
Well, clearly I must do as you require,
And yield to your importunate desire.
325 It is apparent, now, that nothing less
Will satisfy you, and so I acquiesce.
To go so far is much against my will;
I'm vexed that it should come to this; but still,
Since you are so determined on it, since you
330 Will not allow mere language to convince you,
And since you ask for concrete evidence, I
See nothing for it, now, but to comply.
If this is sinful, if I'm wrong to do it,
So much the worse for him who drove me to it.
335 The fault can surely not be charged to me.

TARTUFFE. Madam, the fault is mine, if fault there be,
And . . .

ELMIRE. Open the door a little, and peek out;
I wouldn't want my husband poking about.

TARTUFFE. Why worry about the man? Each day he grows
340 More gullible; one can lead him by the nose.
To find us here would fill him with delight,
And if he saw the worst, he'd doubt his sight.

ELMIRE. Nevertheless, do step out for a minute
Into the hall, and see that no one's in it.

SCENE VI. ORGON, ELMIRE

ORGON *(coming out from under the table)*. That man's a perfect monster, 345 I must admit!
I'm simply stunned. I can't get over it.

ELMIRE. What, coming out so soon? How premature!
Get back in hiding, and wait until you're sure.
Stay till the end, and be convinced completely;
We mustn't stop till things are proved 350 concretely.

ORGON. Hell never harbored anything so vicious!

ELMIRE. Tut, don't be hasty. Try to be judicious.
Wait, and be certain that there's no mistake.
No jumping to conclusions, for Heaven's sake!
(She places ORGON *behind her, as* TARTUFFE *re-enters.)*

SCENE VII. TARTUFFE, ELMIRE, ORGON

TARTUFFE *(not seeing* ORGON*)*. Madam, 355 all things have worked out to perfection;
I've given the neighboring rooms a full inspection;
No one's about; and now I may at last . . .

ORGON *(intercepting him)*. Hold on, my passionate fellow, not so fast!
I should advise a little more restraint.
Well, so you thought you'd fool me, my 360 dear saint!
How soon you wearied of the saintly life—
Wedding my daughter, and coveting my wife!

I've long suspected you, and had a
  feeling
That soon I'd catch you at your
  double-dealing.
365 Just now, you've given me evidence
  galore;
It's quite enough; I have no wish for
  more.
  ELMIRE (to TARTUFFE). I'm sorry to
    have treated you so slyly,
But circumstances forced me to be wily.
  TARTUFFE. Brother, you can't think . . .
  ORGON.   No more talk from you;
370 Just leave this household, without more
  ado.
  TARTUFFE. What I intended . . .
  ORGON.   That seems fairly clear.
Spare me your falsehoods and get out of
  here.
  TARTUFFE. No, I'm the master, and
    you're the one to go!
This house belongs to me, I'll have
  you know,
375 And I shall show you that you can't
  hurt *me*
By this contemptible conspiracy,
That those who cross me know not what
  they do,

And that I've means to expose and
  punish you,
Avenge offended Heaven, and make you
  grieve
That ever you dared order me to leave. 380

SCENE VIII. ELMIRE, ORGON

ELMIRE. What was the point of all that
  angry chatter?
ORGON. Dear God, I'm worried. This is
  no laughing matter.
ELMIRE. How so?
ORGON.   I fear I understood
  his drift.
I'm much disturbed about that deed of
  gift.
ELMIRE. You gave him . . . ?   385
ORGON.   Yes, it's
  all been drawn and signed.
But one thing more is weighing on my
  mind.
ELMIRE. What's that?
ORGON.   I'll tell you; but
  first let's see if there's
A certain strong-box in his room
  upstairs.
                            CURTAIN

Act Five

SCENE I. ORGON, CLÉANTE

CLÉANTE. Where are you going so
  fast?
ORGON. God knows!
CLÉANTE.   Then wait;
Let's have a conference, and deliberate
On how this situation's to be met.
ORGON. That strong-box has me utterly
  upset;
5 This is the worst of many, many shocks.
CLÉANTE. Is there some fearful mystery
  in that box?

ORGON. My poor friend Argas brought
  that box to me
With his own hands, in utmost secrecy;
'Twas on the very morning of his
  flight.
It's full of papers which, if they came   10
  to light,
Would ruin him—or such is my
  impression.
CLÉANTE. Then why did you let it out
  of your possession?
ORGON. Those papers vexed my
  conscience, and it seemed best

To ask the counsel of my pious guest.
15 The cunning scoundrel got me to agree
To leave the strong-box in his custody,
So that, in case of an investigation,
I could employ a slight equivocation
And swear I didn't have it, and thereby,
20 At no expense to conscience, tell a lie.
    CLÉANTE. It looks to me as if you're
    out on a limb.
Trusting him with that box, and offering
    him
That deed of gift, were actions of a kind
Which scarcely indicate a prudent mind.
25 With two such weapons, he has the
    upper hand,
And since you're vulnerable, as matters
    stand,
You erred once more in bringing him to
    bay.
You should have acted in some subtler
    way.
  ORGON. Just think of it: behind that
    fervent face,
30 A heart so wicked, and a soul so base!
I took him in, a hungry beggar, and
    then . . .
  Enough, by God! I'm through with
    pious men:
Henceforth I'll hate the whole false
    brotherhood,
And persecute them worse than Satan
    could.
35   CLÉANTE. Ah, there you go—
    extravagant as ever!
Why can you not be rational? You
    never
Manage to take the middle course, it
    seems,
But jump, instead, between absurd
    extremes.
You've recognized your recent grave
    mistake
40 In falling victim to a pious fake;
Now, to correct that error, must you
    embrace
An even greater error in its place,
And judge our worthy neighbors as a
    whole
By what you've learned of one corrupted
    soul?

Come, just because one rascal made you   45
    swallow
A show of zeal which turned out to be
    hollow,
Shall you conclude that all men are
    deceivers,
And that, today, there are no true
    believers?
Let atheists make that foolish inference;
Learn to distinguish virtue from pretense,   50
Be cautious in bestowing admiration,
And cultivate a sober moderation.
Don't humor fraud, but also don't
    asperse
True piety; the latter fault is worse,
And it is best to err, if err one must,   55
As you have done, upon the side of
    trust.

SCENE II. DAMIS, ORGON, CLÉANTE

    DAMIS. Father, I hear that scoundrel's
    uttered threats
Against you; that he pridefully forgets
How, in his need, he was befriended
    by you,
And means to use your gifts to crucify   60
    you.
    ORGON. It's true, my boy, I'm too
    distressed for tears.
    DAMIS. Leave it to me, Sir; let me trim
    his ears.
Faced with such insolence, we must
    not waver.
I shall rejoice in doing you the favor
Of cutting short his life, and your   65
    distress.
    CLÉANTE. What a display of young
    hotheadedness!
Do learn to moderate your fits of rage.
In this just kingdom, this enlightened
    age,
One does not settle things by violence.

SCENE III. MADAME PERNELLE, MARIANE,
    ELMIRE, DORINE, DAMIS, ORGON,
    CLÉANTE

    MADAME PERNELLE. I hear strange   70
    tales of very strange events.

ORGON. Yes, strange events which these two eyes beheld.
The man's ingratitude is unparalleled.
I save a wretched pauper from starvation,
House him, and treat him like a blood relation,
75 Shower him every day with my largesse,
Give him my daughter, and all that I possess;
And meanwhile the unconscionable knave
Tries to induce my wife to misbehave;
And not content with such extreme rascality,
80 Now threatens me with my own liberality,
And aims, by taking base advantage of
The gifts I gave him out of Christian love,
To drive me from my house, a ruined man,
And make me end a pauper, as he began.
DORINE. Poor fellow!
85 MADAME PERNELLE. No, my son, I'll never bring
Myself to think him guilty of such a thing.
ORGON. How's that?
MADAME PERNELLE. The righteous always were maligned.
ORGON. Speak clearly, Mother. Say what's on your mind.
MADAME PERNELLE. I mean that I can smell a rat, my dear.
90 You know how everybody hates him, here.
ORGON. That has no bearing on the case at all.
MADAME PERNELLE. I told you a hundred times, when you were small,
That virtue in this world is hated ever;
Malicious men may die, but malice never.
95 ORGON. No doubt that's true, but how does it apply?
MADAME PERNELLE. They've turned you against him by a clever lie.

ORGON. I've told you, I was there and saw it done.
MADAME PERNELLE. Ah, slanderers will stop at nothing, Son.
ORGON. Mother, I'll lose my temper . . . For the last time,
I tell you I was witness to the crime. 100
MADAME PERNELLE. The tongues of spite are busy night and noon,
And to their venom no man is immune.
ORGON. You're talking nonsense. Can't you realize
I saw it; saw it; saw it with my eyes?
Saw, do you understand me? Must I shout it 105
Into your ears before you'll cease to doubt it?
MADAME PERNELLE. Appearances can deceive, my son. Dear me,
We cannot always judge by what we see.
ORGON. Drat! Drat!
MADAME PERNELLE. One often interprets things awry;
Good can seem evil to a suspicious eye. 110
ORGON. Was I to see his pawing at Elmire
As an act of charity?
MADAME PERNELLE. Till his guilt is clear,
A man deserves the benefit of the doubt.
You should have waited, to see how things turned out.
ORGON. Great God in Heaven, what 115
more proof did I need?
Was I to sit there, watching, until he'd . . .
You drive me to the brink of impropriety.
MADAME PERNELLE. No, no, a man of such surpassing piety
Could not do such a thing. You cannot shake me.
I don't believe it, and you shall not make 120
me.
ORGON. You vex me so that, if you weren't my mother,
I'd say to you . . . some dreadful thing or other.
DORINE. It's your turn now, Sir, not to be listened to;

You'd not trust us, and now she won't
    trust you.
125   CLÉANTE. My friends, we're wasting
    time which should be spent
In facing up to our predicament.
I fear that scoundrel's threats weren't
    made in sport.
    DAMIS. Do you think he'd have the
    nerve to go to court?
    ELMIRE. I'm sure he won't: they'd
    find it all too crude
130 A case of swindling and ingratitude.
    CLÉANTE. Don't be too sure. He won't
    be at a loss
To give his claims a high and righteous
    gloss;
And clever rogues with far less valid
    cause
Have trapped their victims in a web of
    laws.
135 I say again that to antagonize
A man so strongly armed was most
    unwise.
    ORGON. I know it; but the man's
    appalling cheek
Outraged me so, I couldn't control my
    pique.
    CLÉANTE. I wish to Heaven that we
    could devise
140 Some truce between you, or some
    compromise.
    ELMIRE. If I had known what cards
    he held, I'd not
Have roused his anger by my little plot.
    ORGON (*To* DORINE, *as* M. LOYAL *enters*).
What is that fellow looking for? Who
    is he?
Go talk to him—and tell him that I'm
    busy.

SCENE IV. MONSIEUR LOYAL, MADAME PER-
    NELLE, ORGON, DAMIS, MARIANE,
    DORINE, ELMIRE, CLÉANTE

---

145   MONSIEUR LOYAL. Good day, dear
    sister. Kindly let me see
Your master.
    DORINE.   He's involved with
    company,

And cannot be disturbed just now, I
    fear.
    MONSIEUR LOYAL. I hate to intrude; but
    what has brought me here
Will not disturb your master, in any
    event.
Indeed, my news will make him most   150
    content.
    DORINE. Your name?
    MONSIEUR LOYAL.   Just say that I
    bring greetings from
Monsieur Tartuffe, on whose behalf I've
    come.
    DORINE (*to* ORGON). Sir, he's a very
    gracious man, and bears
A message from Tartuffe, which he
    declares,
Will make you most content.   155
    CLÉANTE.   Upon my word.
I think this man had best be seen, and
    heard.
    ORGON. Perhaps he has some
    settlement to suggest.
How shall I treat him? What manner
    would be best?
    CLÉANTE. Control your anger, and if
    he should mention
Some fair adjustment, give him your   160
    full attention.
    MONSIEUR LOYAL. Good health to you,
    good Sir. May Heaven confound
Your enemies, and may your joys
    abound.
    ORGON (*aside, to* CLÉANTE). A gentle
    salutation: it confirms
My guess that he is here to offer terms.
    MONSIEUR LOYAL. I've always held   165
    your family most dear;
I served your father, Sir, for many a
    year.
    ORGON. Sir, I must ask your pardon; to
    my shame,
I cannot now recall your face or name.
    MONSIEUR LOYAL. Loyal's my name; I
    come from Normandy,
And I'm a bailiff, in all modesty.   170
For forty years, praise God, it's been
    my boast
To serve with honor in that vital post,
And I am here, Sir, if you will permit

The liberty, to serve you with this
    writ . . .
175 ORGON. To—*what?*
    MONSIEUR LOYAL. Now, please, Sir,
      let us have no friction:
It's nothing but an order of eviction.
You are to move your goods and family
    out
And make way for new occupants,
    without
Deferment or delay, and give the keys . . .
180 ORGON. I? Leave this house?
    MONSIEUR LOYAL.   Why yes,
    Sir, if you please.
This house, Sir, from the cellar to the
    roof,
Belongs now to the good Monsieur
    Tartuffe,
And he is lord and master of your
    estate
By virtue of a deed of present date,
185 Drawn in due form, with clearest legal
    phrasing . . .
    DAMIS. Your insolence is utterly
      amazing!
    MONSIEUR LOYAL. Young man, my
      business here is not with you,
But with your wise and temperate
    father, who,
Like every worthy citizen, stands in awe
190 Of justice, and would never obstruct
    the law.
    ORGON. But . . .
    MONSIEUR LOYAL. Not for a million,
      Sir, would you rebel
Against authority; I know that well.
You'll not make trouble, Sir, or interfere
With the execution of my duties here.
195 DAMIS. Someone may execute a smart
    tattoo
On that black jacket of yours, before
    you're through.
    MONSIEUR LOYAL. Sir, bid your son
    be silent. I'd much regret
Having to mention such a nasty threat
Of violence, in writing my report.
200 DORINE *(aside).* This man Loyal's a
    most disloyal sort!
    MONSIEUR LOYAL. I love all men of
    upright character,

And when I agreed to serve these papers,
    Sir,
It was your feelings that I had in mind.
I couldn't bear to see the case assigned
To someone else, who might esteem   205
    you less
And so subject you to unpleasantness.
    ORGON. What's more unpleasant than
    telling a man to leave
His house and home?
    MONSIEUR LOYAL.   You'd like a short
    reprieve?
If you desire it, Sir, I shall not press you,
But wait until tomorrow to dispossess   210
    you.
Splendid. I'll come and spend the
    night here, then,
Most quietly, with half a score of men.
For form's sake, you might bring me,
    just before
You go to bed, the keys to the front
    door.
My men, I promise, will be on their best   215
Behavior, and will not disturb your
    rest.
But bright and early, Sir, you must be
    quick
And move out all your furniture, every
    stick:
The men I've chosen are both young
    and strong,
And with their help it shouldn't take   220
    you long.
In short, I'll make things pleasant and
    convenient,
And since I'm being so extremely
    lenient,
Please show me, Sir, a like consideration,
And give me your entire cooperation.
    ORGON *(aside).* I may be all but   225
    bankrupt, but I vow
I'd give a hundred louis,[1] here and now,
Just for the pleasure of landing one
    good clout
Right on the end of that complacent
    snout.
    CLÉANTE. Careful; don't make things
    worse.

---

1. *louis* (lü′ i), a gold coin.

DAMIS. My bootsole itches
To give that beggar a good kick in the
breeches.

DORINE. Monsieur Loyal, I'd love to
hear the whack
Of a stout stick across your fine broad
back.

MONSIEUR LOYAL. Take care: a woman
too may go to jail if
She uses threatening language to a
bailiff.

CLÉANTE. Enough, enough, Sir. This
must not go on.
Give me that paper, please, and then
begone.

MONSIEUR LOYAL. Well, *au revoir.* God
give you all good cheer!

ORGON. May God confound you, and
him who sent you here!

SCENE V. ORGON, CLÉANTE, MARIANE,
ELMIRE, MADAME PERNELLE,
DORINE, DAMIS

ORGON. Now, Mother, was I right or
not? This writ
Should change your notion of Tartuffe
a bit.
Do you perceive his villainy at last?

MADAME PERNELLE. I'm thunderstruck.
I'm utterly aghast.

DORINE. Oh, come, be fair. You
mustn't take offense
At this new proof of his benevolence.
He's acting out of selfless love, I know.
Material things enslave the soul, and so
He kindly has arranged your liberation
From all that might endanger your
salvation.

ORGON. Will you not ever hold your
tongue, you dunce?

CLÉANTE. Come, you must take some
action, and at once.

ELMIRE. Go tell the world of the low
trick he's tried.
The deed of gift is surely nullified
By such behavior, and public rage will
not
Permit the wretch to carry out his
plot.

SCENE VI. VALÈRE, ORGON, CLÉANTE,
ELMIRE, MARIANE, MADAME
PERNELLE, DAMIS, DORINE

VALÈRE. Sir, though I hate to bring
you more bad news,
Such is the danger that I cannot choose.
A friend who is extremely close to me
And knows my interest in your family
Has, for my sake, presumed to violate
The secrecy that's due to things of state,
And sends me word that you are in a
plight
From which your one salvation lies in
flight.
That scoundrel who's imposed upon you
so
Denounced you to the King an hour ago
And, as supporting evidence, displayed
The strong-box of a certain renegade
Whose secret papers, so he testified,
You had disloyally agreed to hide.
I don't know just what charges may be
pressed,
But there's a warrant out for your arrest;
Tartuffe has been instructed,
furthermore,
To guide the arresting officer to your
door.

CLÉANTE. He's clearly done this to
facilitate
His seizure of your house and your
estate.

ORGON. That man, I must say, is a
vicious beast!

VALÈRE. Quick, Sir; you mustn't tarry
in the least.
My carriage is outside, to take you hence;
This thousand louis should cover all
expense.
Let's lose no time, or you shall be
undone;
The sole defense, in this case, is to run.
I shall go with you all the way, and
place you
In a safe refuge to which they'll never
trace you.

ORGON. Alas, dear boy, I wish that I
could show you
My gratitude for everything I owe you.

But now is not the time; I pray the Lord
That I may live to give you your reward.
Farewell, my dears; be careful . . .

CLÉANTE.   Brother, hurry.
We shall take care of things; you needn't
worry.

SCENE VII. THE OFFICER, TARTUFFE, ORGON,
VALÈRE, MADAME PERNELLE,
ELMIRE, MARIANE, CLÉANTE,
DORINE, DAMIS

TARTUFFE. Gently, Sir, gently; stay
right where you are.
No need for haste; your lodging isn't far.
You're off to prison, by order of the
Prince.

ORGON. This is the crowning blow,
you wretch; and since
It means my total ruin and defeat,
Your villainy is now at last complete.

TARTUFFE. You needn't try to provoke
me; it's no use.
Those who serve Heaven must expect
abuse.

CLÉANTE. You are indeed most patient,
sweet, and blameless.

DORINE. How he exploits the name of
Heaven! It's shameless.

TARTUFFE. Your taunts and mockeries
are all for naught;
To do my duty is my only thought.

MARIANE. Your love of duty is most
meritorious,
And what you've done is little short of
glorious.

TARTUFFE. All deeds are glorious,
Madam, which obey
The sovereign prince who sent me here
today.

ORGON. I rescued you when you were
destitute;
Have you forgotten that, you thankless
brute?

TARTUFFE. No, no, I well remember
everything;
But my first duty is to serve my King.
That obligation is so paramount
That other claims, beside it, do not
count;

And for it I would sacrifice my wife,
My family, my friend, or my own life.

ELMIRE. Hypocrite!

DORINE.   All that we most
revere, he uses
To cloak his plots and camouflage his
ruses.

CLÉANTE. If it is true that you are
animated
By pure and loyal zeal, as you have
stated,
Why was this zeal not roused until
you'd sought
To make Orgon a cuckold, and been
caught?
Why weren't you moved to give your
evidence
Until your outraged host had driven you
hence?
I shan't say that the gift of all his treasure
Ought to have damped your zeal in any
measure;
But if he is a traitor, as you declare,
How could you condescend to be his
heir?

TARTUFFE (to the OFFICER). Sir, spare
me all this clamor; it's growing
shrill.
Please carry out your orders, if you
will.

OFFICER. Yes, I've delayed too long,
Sir. Thank you kindly.
You're just the proper person to remind
me.
Come, you are off to join the other
boarders
In the King's prison, according to his
orders.

TARTUFFE. Who? I, Sir?

OFFICER.   Yes.

TARTUFFE.   To prison?
This can't be true!

OFFICER. I owe an explanation, but not
to you.
(To ORGON.)
Sir, all is well; rest easy, and be grateful.
We serve a Prince to whom all sham is
hateful,
A Prince who sees into our inmost
hearts,

And can't be fooled by any trickster's
    arts.
His royal soul, though generous and
    human,
Views all things with discernment and
    acumen;
His sovereign reason is not lightly
    swayed,
340 And all his judgments are discreetly
    weighed.
He honors righteous men of every kind,
And yet his zeal for virtue is not blind,
Nor does his love of piety numb his wits
And make him tolerant of hypocrites.
345 'Twas hardly likely that this man could
    cozen
A King who's foiled such liars by the
    dozen.
With one keen glance, the King
    perceived the whole
Perverseness and corruption of his soul,
And thus high Heaven's justice was
    displayed:
350 Betraying you, the rogue stood
    self-betrayed.
The King soon recognized Tartuffe as one
Notorious by another name, who'd done
So many vicious crimes that one could
    fill
Ten volumes with them, and be writing
    still.
355 But to be brief: our sovereign was
    appalled
By this man's treachery toward you,
    which he called
The last, worst villainy of a vile career,
And bade me follow the impostor here
To see how gross his impudence could
    be,
360 And force him to restore your property.
Your private papers, by the King's
    command,
I hereby seize and give into your hand.
The King, by royal order, invalidates
The deed which gave this rascal your
    estates,
365 And pardons, furthermore, your grave
    offense

In harboring an exile's documents.
By these decrees, our Prince rewards you
    for
Your loyal deeds in the late civil war,
And shows how heartfelt is his
    satisfaction
In recompensing any worthy action, 370
How much he prizes merit, and how he
    makes
More of men's virtues than of their
    mistakes.
    DORINE. Heaven be praised!
    MADAME PERNELLE.   I breathe
    again, at last.
    ELMIRE. We're safe.
    MARIANE.   I can't believe the
    danger's past.
    ORGON (to TARTUFFE). Well, traitor,
    now you see . . .   375
    CLÉANTE.   Ah, Brother, please,
Let's not descend to such indignities.
Leave the poor wretch to his unhappy
    fate,
And don't say anything to aggravate
His present woes; but rather hope that
    he
Will soon embrace an honest piety,   380
And mend his ways, and by a true
    repentance
Move our just King to moderate his
    sentence.
Meanwhile, go kneel before your
    sovereign's throne
And thank him for the mercies he has
    shown.
    ORGON. Well said: let's go at once and, 385
    gladly kneeling,
Express the gratitude which all are
    feeling.
Then, when that first great duty has been
    done,
We'll turn with pleasure to a second
    one,
And give Valère, whose love has proven
    so true,
The wedded happiness which is his
    due.   390
                              CURTAIN

Development

INTERPRETATION

1. *(a)* What are Orgon's professed reasons for allowing Tartuffe to rule his family? *(b)* What other reasons are implied through the reactions of the other characters? through Orgon's own words and behavior?

2. *(a)* At what point in the play does Tartuffe's mask of hypocrisy drop? *(b)* Why does it drop? *(c)* Is Tartuffe more sympathetic or more contemptible at this point? Discuss.

3. Dorine is typical of the female-servant-confidante found in many seventeenth-century dramas. As a stock character with a particular function to perform, she is necessarily one-sided, an animated quality rather than a complex person. *(a)* Describe the quality she expresses. *(b)* What does she contribute to the comic expression of the play's theme of hypocrisy?

4. Molière's play came into a great deal of criticism during his own time. The author himself has summarized this criticism:

> *"Tartuffe,* they say, is a play that offends piety: it is filled with abominations from beginning to end, and nowhere is there a line that does not deserve to be burned."

But, he argues in his own defense, "I have used all the art and skill that I could to distinguish the character of the hypocrite from that of the truly devout man."

(a) Elaborate on Molière's defense by citing and explaining some of the ways he makes this distinction. *(b)* How else might you defend the play against the charge of being offensive to religion?

TECHNIQUE

1. Goethe has said that the opening scene of *Tartuffe* contains some of the greatest exposition ever written. *(a)* What information is furnished in the first part of this scene? *(b)* What characteristics of Madame Pernelle come through in the first part? *(c)* What conflict is established between Madame Pernelle and the other characters? *(d)* What theme and technique are introduced in the dialogue between Madame Pernelle and Dorine on gossiping neighbors?

2. Reread Act Two, Scene III; Act Three, Scene IV; and Act Four, Scene I. *(a)* Who is the normative character in each scene, that is, the character who provides a standard for judging the other(s)? *(b)* Explain the connection between each of these scenes and the theme of reason and unreason in the play. *(c)* Explain the way in which each normative character is particularly right for the function he performs in his scene. *(d)* How does each scene serve to advance the plot?

3. *(a)* Discuss the effect of delaying Tartuffe's entrance on your attitude toward him when he finally appears. *(b)* How does placing Madame Pernelle at the beginning and at the end of the play affect its structural feeling?

EXTENSIONS

1. Assume that someone has just voiced the following thought: "If people would just learn to talk to each other—I mean really talk to each other—most of the world's problems would cease to exist." How might you use *Tartuffe* in order to illustrate to the speaker that his idea is oversimple and naive?

2. Discuss the following observation: "Hypocrisy is impossible in our own time, for there is no longer a stable concept of self that can be falsified."

Comparison

1. Unlike Tartuffe and the woodcutter, Torquemada and the signorina are not totally aware of the lies their actions represent. *(a)* Are they self-deluded to the same extent about their hypocrisy? Discuss. *(b)* Compare the source of the hypocrisy in all four characters.

2. The Aesop fable provides us with a very simple description of the hypocrite: one who says one thing, but does another. Can this definition be applied to each of the other three characters? Discuss.

3. Comment on the following statement: "The theme of *Tartuffe* is that common sense and honesty are always rewarded; while the theme of 'Torquemada in the Flames' is that nothing is ever rewarded."

4. *(a)* Compare your reaction to the character of Tartuffe with your reaction to the character of Torquemada. *(b)* Explain the reasons for the difference in your reactions, referring to devices of characterization, plot, and style.

5. Read the following interpretation of "The Poor":

> Cassola's "The Poor" is a story of an institution-bound society in which petrified forms take control of human life, and even the word *charity* describes a cold and useless gesture of giving. In such a society hypocrisy is inescapable. Unlike the old classic *Tartuffe,* where the hypocrite becomes a social outcast when he is unmasked by characters of good sense, in Cassola's story the hypocrite cannot be unmasked, as he is sanctioned by society as a defender of the *status quo.*

(a) Summarize the conflict the critic sets up between the society of *Tartuffe* and the society of "The Poor." *(b)* According to the critic, why is hypocrisy inescapable in the society of "The Poor"? Discuss the validity of this conclusion.

(c) What reason does he give for the fact that Tartuffe is exposed for his hypocrisy while the signorina is not? Is it a sound reason? Are there other possibilities? Discuss.

6. Like the fox in the Aesop fable, Orgon finds himself at the mercy of a hypocrite who is prepared to take advantage of his apparently helpless situation. *(a)* What, in each case, saves the victim? *(b)* Is Orgon a more sympathetic figure than the fox? Discuss.

7. Compare the encounter between the signorina and the sick woman with that between Torquemada and the sick painter, noting the following points: *(a)* the attitude of the visitor toward the person visited; *(b)* the degree of sympathy the reader feels for Torquemada and for the signorina on the one hand, and for the sick painter and woman on the other; *(c)* the nature of the hypocrisy expressed in each scene.

8. Generally speaking, a realistic character is one who is neither all bad nor all good, but one whose character includes elements of both. *(a)* Does the signorina fulfill this definition? *(b)* Does Torquemada? *(c)* Compare the good and/or the bad you find in each of them.

9. Unlike Tartuffe, who only pretends to be pious, the signorina does indeed sacrifice her time and physical comfort in pursuit of a holy life. With this in mind, discuss whether or not Molière's defense of his play against the critics who found it anti-religious could also be applied to Cassola's story (See *Tartuffe,* INTERPRETATION question 4).

10. *(a)* Which of these stories includes the "trickster tricked" as one of its themes? *(b)* How does the inclusion of this theme affect the moral tone of the story in each case?

OUR CONTEMPORARY COUNTENANCE by David Alfaro Siqueiros. Courtesy of the Instituto Nacional de Bellas Artes, Mexico.

The Opportunists

THE STORY OF MIDAS / OVID / ROME

THE DEVIL / GUY DE MAUPASSANT / FRANCE

PROPERTY / GIOVANNI VERGA / ITALY

The Story of Midas[1]

OVID / ROME / 43 B.C. — 17 or 18 A.D.

translated from the Latin by Rolfe Humphries

And even this was not enough for Bacchus.[2]
He left those fields, and with a worthier band
He sought the vineyards of his own Timolus
And Pactolus,[3] a river not yet gold
5 Nor envied for its precious sands. The throng
He always had surrounded him, the satyrs,
The Bacchanals[4]; Silenus,[5] though, was missing.
The Phrygian rustics found him, staggering
Under the weight of years, and maybe also
10 From more than too much wine, bound him with wreaths
And led him to King Midas. Now this king
Together with the Athenian Eumolpus[6]
Had learned the rites of Bacchic lore from Orpheus.
And therefore, since he recognized a comrade,
15 A brother in the lodge, he gave a party
For ten long days and nights, and then, rejoicing,
Came to the Lydian fields and gave Silenus
Back to his precious foster son. And Bacchus,
Happy and grateful, and meaning well, told Midas
20 To make his choice of anything he wanted.
And Midas, never too judicious, answered:
"Grant that whatever I touch may turn to gold!"
Bacchus agreed, gave him the ruinous gift,
Sorry the monarch had not chosen better.
25 So Midas went his cheerful way, rejoicing
In his own bad luck, and tried to test the promise
By touching this and that. It all was true,
He hardly dared believe it! From an oak-tree
He broke a green twig loose: the twig was golden.

---

1. *Midas.* In mythology Midas, the king of Phrygia, an ancient country in western Asia Minor, was given the power to turn objects to gold. **2.** *this . . . Bacchus* (bak′ əs). Prior to this story, a group of women, in a mad fury, had killed Orpheus. Bacchus, the mythological god of wine, changed them into trees. Orpheus, mentioned later in the poem, was a musician who played the lyre so sweetly that animals and even trees followed him. **3.** *Timolus . . . Pactolus.* Timolus was a mountain in Phrygia through which the river Pactolus flowed. **4.** *satyrs . . . Bacchanals.* The satyrs, also called Bacchanals because they followed Bacchus, were Greek deities of the woods, part man and part beast. **5.** *Silenus* (sī lē′ nəs), the foster father of Bacchus and leader of the satyrs. His chief characteristic was drunkenness. **6.** *Eumolpus* (yū mol′ pəs), a flute player in classical mythology.

30 He picked a stone up from the ground; the stone
Paled with light golden color; he touched a clod,
The clod became a nugget. Awns[7] of grain
Were a golden harvest; if he picked an apple
It seemed a gift from the Hesperides.[8]
35 He placed his fingers on the lofty pillars
And saw them gleam and shine. He bathed his hands
In water, and the stream was golden rain
Like that which came to Danae.[9] His mind
Could scarcely grasp his hopes—all things were golden,
40 Or would be, at his will! A happy man,
He watched his servants set a table before him
With bread and meat. He touched the gift of Ceres[10]
And found it stiff and hard; he tried to bite
The meat with hungry teeth, and where the teeth
45 Touched food they seemed to touch on golden ingots.
He mingled water with the wine of Bacchus;
It was molten gold that trickled through his jaws.

Midas, astonished at his new misfortune,
Rich man and poor man, tries to flee his riches
50 Hating the favor he had lately prayed for.
No food relieves his hunger; his throat is dry
With burning thirst; he is tortured, as he should be,
By the hateful gold. Lifting his hands to Heaven,
He cries: "Forgive me, father! I have sinned.
55 Have mercy upon me, save me from this loss
That looks so much like gain!" The gods are kind,
And Bacchus, since he owned his fault, forgave him,
Took back the gift. "You need not be forever
Smeared with that foolish color: go to the stream
60 That flows by Sardis, take your way upstream
Into the Lydian hills, until you find
The tumbling river's source. There duck your head
And body under the foaming white of the fountain,
And wash your sin away." The king obeyed him,
65 And the power of the golden touch imbued the water,
So that even now the fields grow hard and yellow
If that vein washes over them to flood
Their fields with the water of the touch of gold.

---

7. *Awns,* the bristly hairs forming the beard on a head of barley, oats, etc. 8. *Hesperides* (hes per′ ə dēz). The golden apples of Hera were guarded by nymphs called Hesperides. 9. *Danae* (dan′ ā ē). In classical mythology Danae was visited by Jupiter in the form of golden rain. 10. *gift of Ceres,* grain; it is used here metaphorically to mean bread. Ceres was the Roman goddess of agriculture.

The Devil

GUY DE MAUPASSANT[1] / France

(1850–1893)

translated from the French by Artine Artiman

The peasant was standing opposite the doctor, by the bedside of the dying old woman, and she, calmly resigned and quite lucid, looked at them and listened to their talking. She was going to die and she did not rebel at it, for her life was over—she was ninety-two.

The July sun streamed in at the window and through the open door and cast its hot flames onto the uneven brown clay floor which had been stamped down by four generations of clodhoppers.[2] The smell of the fields came in also, driven by the brisk wind and parched by the noontide heat. The grasshoppers chirped themselves hoarse, filling the air with their shrill noise, like that of the wooden crickets which are sold to children at fair time.

The doctor raised his voice and said: "Honoré,[3] you cannot leave your mother in this state; she may die at any moment." And the peasant, in great distress, replied: "But I must get in my wheat, for it has been lying on the ground a long time, and the weather is just right for it; what do you say about it, Mother?" And the dying woman, still possessed by her Norman avariciousness,[4] replied yes with her eyes and her forehead and so urged her son to get in his wheat and to leave her to die alone.

But the doctor got angry and, stamping his foot, he said: "You are no better than a brute; do you hear? And I will not allow you to do it. Do you understand? And if you must get in your wheat today, go and fetch Rapet's[5] wife and make her look after your mother. I *will* have it. And if you do not obey me I will let you die

like a dog when you are ill in your turn; do you hear me?"

The peasant, a tall thin fellow with slow movements who was tormented by indecision, by his fear of the doctor and his keen love for saving, hesitated, calculated and stammered out: "How much does La Rapet charge for attending sick people?"

"How should I know?" the doctor cried. "That depends upon how long she is wanted for. Settle it with her, by Jove! But I want her to be here within an hour; do you hear?"

So the man made up his mind. "I will go for her," he replied; "don't get angry, Doctor." And the latter left, calling out as he went: "Take care, you know, for I do not joke when I am angry!" And as soon as they were alone the peasant turned to his mother and said in a resigned voice: "I will go and fetch La Rapet, as the man will have it. Don't go off while I am away."

And he went out in his turn.

La Rapet, who was an old washerwoman, watched the dead and the dying of the neighborhood, and then as soon as she had sewn her customers into that linen cloth from which they would

1. *Maupassant* (mō pä saN′). 2. *clodhoppers*, large, heavy shoes. 3. *Honoré* (on ə rā′). His last name, mentioned later in the story, is *Bontemps* (bôn tän′). 4. *Norman avariciousness*. Maupassant often used this trait to characterize the Norman peasants. 5. *Rapet* (rä pā′). She is usually referred to as La Rapet, which signifies "the Rapet woman."

emerge no more, she went and took up her irons to smooth the linen of the living. Wrinkled like a last year's apple, spiteful, envious, avaricious with a phenomenal avarice, bent double, as if she had been broken in half across the loins by the constant movement of the iron over the linen, one might have said that she had a kind of monstrous and cynical affection for a death struggle. She never spoke of anything but of the people she had seen die, of the various kinds of deaths at which she had been present, and she related, with the greatest minuteness, details which were always the same, just like a sportsman talks of his shots.

When Honoré Bontemps entered her cottage he found her preparing the starch for the collars of the village women, and he said: "Good evening; I hope you are pretty well, Mother Rapet."

She turned her head round to look at him and said: "Fairly well, fairly well, and you?"

"Oh, as for me, I am as well as I could wish, but my mother is very sick."

"Your mother?"

"Yes, my mother!"

"What's the matter with her?"

"She is going to turn up her toes; that's what's the matter with her!"

The old woman took her hands out of the water and asked with sudden sympathy: "Is she as bad as all that?"

"The doctor says she will not last till morning."

"Then she certainly is very bad!" Honoré hesitated, for he wanted to make a few preliminary remarks before coming to his proposal, but as he could hit upon nothing, he made up his mind suddenly.

"How much are you going to ask to stop with her till the end? You know that I am not rich, and I cannot even afford to keep a servant girl. It is just that which has brought my poor mother to this state, too much work and fatigue! She used to work for ten, in spite of her ninety-two years. You don't find any made of that stuff nowadays!"

La Rapet answered gravely: "There are two prices: forty sous by day and three francs[6] by night for the rich, and twenty sous by day and forty by night for the others. You shall pay me the twenty and forty." But the peasant reflected, for he knew his mother well. He knew how tenacious of life, how vigorous and unyielding she was. He knew, too, that she might last another week, in spite of the doctor's opinion, and so he said resolutely: "No, I would rather you would fix a price until the end. I will take my chance one way or the other. The doctor says she will die very soon. If that happens, so much the better for you and so much the worse for me, but if she holds out till tomorrow or longer, so much the better for me and so much the worse for you!"

The nurse looked at the man in astonishment, for she had never treated a death as a speculative job, and she hesitated, tempted by the idea of the possible gain. But almost immediately she suspected that he wanted to juggle her. "I can say nothing until I have seen your mother," she replied.

"Then come with me and see her."

She washed her hands and went with him immediately. They did not speak on the road; she walked with short, hasty steps, while he strode on with his long legs, as if he were crossing a brook at every step. The cows lying down in the fields, overcome by the heat, raised their heads heavily and lowed feebly at the two passers-by, as if to ask them for some green grass.

When they got near the house Honoré Bontemps murmured: "Suppose it is all over?" And the unconscious wish that it might be so showed itself in the sound of his voice.

But the old woman was not dead. She was lying on her back on her wretched bed, her hands covered with a pink cotton

---

6. *sous . . . francs.* A franc is a French coin worth about twenty cents. A sou was formerly a bronze coin worth about a cent.

counterpane, horribly thin, knotty paws, like some strange animal's or like crabs' claws, hands closed by rheumatism, fatigue and the work of nearly a century which she had accomplished.

La Rapet went up to the bed and looked at the dying woman, felt her pulse, tapped her on the chest, listened to her breathing and asked her questions so as to hear her speak; then, having looked at her for some time longer, she went out of the room, followed by Honoré. His decided opinion was that the old woman would not last out the night, and he asked: "Well?" And the sick nurse replied: "Well, she may last two days, perhaps three. You will have to give me six francs, everything included."

"Six francs! Six francs!" he shouted. "Are you out of your mind? I tell you that she cannot last more than five or six hours!" And they disputed angrily for some time, but as the nurse said she would go home as the time was slipping away, and as his wheat would not come to the farmyard of its own accord, he agreed to her terms at last.

"Very well then, that is settled; six francs, including everything, until the corpse is taken out."

"That is settled, six francs."

And he went away with long strides to the wheat which was lying on the ground under the hot sun which ripens the grain, while the sick nurse returned to the house.

She had brought some work with her, for she worked without stopping by the side of the dead and dying, sometimes for herself, sometimes for the family who employed her as seamstress also, paying her rather more in that capacity. Suddenly she asked:

"Have you received the last sacrament, Mother Bontemps?"

The old peasant woman said no with her head, and La Rapet, who was very devout, got up quickly. "Good heavens, is it possible? I will go and fetch the curé," and she rushed off to the parsonage so

quickly that the urchins in the street thought some accident had happened when they saw her trotting off like that.

The priest came immediately in his surplice, preceded by a choirboy, who rang a bell to announce the passage of the Host through the parched and quiet country. Some men, working at a distance, took off their hats and remained motionless until the white vestment had disappeared behind some farm buildings; the women who were making up the sheaves stood up to make the sign of the cross; the frightened black hens ran away along the ditch until they reached a well-known hole through which they suddenly disappeared, while a foal, which was tied up in a meadow, took fright at the sight of the surplice and began to gallop round at the length of its rope, kicking violently. The choirboy, in his red cassock, walked quickly, and the priest, the square biretta on his bowed head, followed him, muttering some prayers. Last of all came La Rapet, bent almost double, as if she wished to prostrate herself; she walked with folded hands, as if she were in church.

Honoré saw them pass in the distance, and he asked: "Where is our priest going to?" And his man, who was more acute, replied: "He is taking the sacrament to your mother, of course!"

The peasant was not surprised and said: "That is quite possible," and went on with his work.

Mother Bontemps confessed, received absolution and extreme unction, and the priest took his departure, leaving the two women alone in the suffocating cottage. La Rapet began to look at the dying woman and to ask herself whether it could last much longer.

The day was on the wane, and a cooler air came in stronger puffs, making a view of Epinal,[7] which was fastened to the wall by two pins, flap up and down. The scanty window curtains, which had

---

7. *Epinal* (ā pē näl′), a city in northeastern France.

formerly been white but were now yellow and covered with flyspecks, looked as if they were going to fly off and seemed to struggle to get away, like the old woman's soul.

Lying motionless, with her eyes open, the old mother seemed to await the death which was so near and which yet delayed its coming, with perfect indifference. Her short breath whistled in her throat. It would stop altogether soon, and there would be one woman less in the world, one whom nobody would regret.

At nightfall Honoré returned, and when he went up to the bed and saw that his mother was still alive he asked: "How is she?" just as he had done formerly when she had been sick. Then he sent La Rapet away, saying to her: "Tomorrow morning at five o'clock without fail." And she replied: "Tomorrow at five o'clock."

She came at daybreak and found Honoré eating his soup, which he had made himself, before going to work.

"Well, is your mother dead?" asked the nurse.

"She is rather better, on the contrary," he replied with a malignant look out of the corners of his eyes. Then he went out.

La Rapet was seized with anxiety and went up to the dying woman, who was in the same state, lethargic and impassive, her eyes open and her hands clutching the counterpane. The nurse perceived that this might go on thus for two days, four nights, eight days, even, and her avaricious mind was seized with fear. She was excited to fury against the cunning fellow who had tricked her and against the woman who would not die.

Nevertheless, she began to sew and waited with her eyes fixed on the wrinkled face of Mother Bontemps. When Honoré returned to breakfast he seemed quite satisfied and even in a bantering humor, for he was carrying in his wheat under very favorable circumstances.

La Rapet was getting exasperated; every passing minute now seemed to her so much time and money stolen from her.

She felt a mad inclination to choke this old ass, this headstrong old fool, this obstinate old wretch—to stop that short, rapid breath, which was robbing her of her time and money, by squeezing her throat a little. But then she reflected on the danger of doing so, and other thoughts came into her head, so she went up to the bed and said to her: "Have you ever seen the devil?"

Mother Bontemps whispered: "No."

Then the sick nurse began to talk and to tell her tales likely to terrify her weak and dying mind. "Some minutes before one dies the devil appears," she said, "to all. He has a broom in his hand, a saucepan on his head, and he utters loud cries. When anybody has seen him all is over, and that person has only a few moments longer to live"; and she enumerated all those to whom the devil had appeared that year: Josephine Loisel, Eulalie Ratier, Sophie Padagnau, Séraphine Grospied.

Mother Bontemps, who was at last most disturbed in mind, moved about, wrung her hands and tried to turn her head to look at the other end of the room. Suddenly La Rapet disappeared at the foot of the bed. She took a sheet out of the cupboard and wrapped herself up in it; then she put the iron pot onto her head so that its three short, bent feet rose up like horns, took a broom in her right hand and a tin pail in her left, which she threw up suddenly so that it might fall to the ground noisily.

Certainly when it came down it made a terrible noise. Then, climbing onto a chair, the nurse showed herself, gesticulating and uttering shrill cries into the pot which covered her face, while she menaced the old peasant woman, who was nearly dead, with her broom.

Terrified, with a mad look on her face, the dying woman made a superhuman effort to get up and escape; she even got her shoulders and chest out of bed; then she fell back with a deep sigh. All was over, and La Rapet calmly put everything back into its place; the broom into the corner by the cupboard, the sheet inside it, the pot onto the hearth, the pail onto the floor and the chair against the wall. Then with a professional air she closed the dead woman's enormous eyes, put a plate on the bed and poured some holy water into it, dipped the twig of boxwood into it and, kneeling down, she fervently repeated the prayers for the dead, which she knew by heart, as a matter of business.

When Honoré returned in the evening, he found her praying. He calculated immediately that she had made twenty sous out of him, for she had only spent three days and one night there, which made five francs altogether, instead of the six which he owed her.

THE END

Development

INTERPRETATION

1. *(a)* What was your response to the last two sentences of the story? *(b)* Is the tone of these sentences justified by what Maupassant wanted to say about his characters and their lives? Discuss.

2. *(a)* What type of person is the peasant Honoré? *(b)* As Maupassant depicts him, is he a one-dimensional character? Explain. *(c)* Is Honoré totally indifferent to his mother and her illness? Explain.

3. What elements in the character of La Rapet make her impersonation of the devil not only possible but believable?

4. *(a)* What do you learn about the mother from the narrator's comments and the words and actions of Honoré and La Rapet? *(b)* The dying woman speaks only one word in the entire story. What prompts her to speak at this point and not before? *(c)* What does this single outburst reveal about her beliefs?

5. *(a)* What attitudes do Honoré, his mother, and La Rapet share toward life and death? *(b)* What factors in their lives may have caused these attitudes?

6. Who is the devil of the title? Explain.

TECHNIQUE

1. *(a)* The province of Normandy is a setting Maupassant often chose for his short stories and novels. What do the details in paragraph 2, particularly those which appeal to the senses, contribute to the story? *(b)* Which other details in "The Devil" highlight the setting and reveal characteristics of the people?

2. Find examples from this story which illustrate Maupassant's concern with accuracy of detail, objectivity, and conciseness in his writing.

3. Consult a French dictionary for the meaning of the names *Honoré, Bontemps,* and the closest equivalent to *La Rapet.* What effect does Maupassant achieve through use of these particular names?

EXTENSIONS

1. *(a)* Which of the following statements most aptly applies to "The Devil"? Why?

Avarice is the spur of industry. (David Hume)

Avarice destroys honor, integrity, and all other noble qualities. (Sallust)

(b) In your opinion, would Maupassant agree with your choice? Would the peasants of the area?

Property

GIOVANNI VERGA[1] / Italy
(1840-1922)
translated from the Italian by D. H. Lawrence

The traveler passing along by the Lake of Lentini, stretched out there like a piece of dead sea, and by the burnt-up stubble fields of the Plain of Catania, and the evergreen orange trees of Francofonte, and the gray cork trees of Resecone, and the deserted pasture lands of Passanetto and of Passanitello,[2] if ever he asked, to while away the tedium of the long dusty road, under the sky heavy with heat in the hour when the litter bells ring sadly in the immense campagna,[3] and the mules let their heads and tails hang helpless, and the litter driver sings his melancholy song so as not to be overcome by the malaria sleep, "Whom does the place belong to?" was bound to get for answer, "To Mazzarò."[4] And passing near to a farmstead as big as a village, with store barns that looked like churches, and crowds of hens crouching in the shade of the big well, and the women putting their hands over their eyes to see who was going by:—"And this place?" —"To Mazzarò."—And you went on and on, with the malaria weighing on your eyes, and you were startled by the unexpected barking of a dog, as you passed an endless, endless vineyard, which stretched over hill and plain, motionless, as if the dust upon it were weighing it down, and the watchman stretched out face downward with his gun beneath him, beside the valley, raised his head sleepily to see who it might be. "To Mazzarò."— Then came an olive grove thick as a wood, under which the grass never grew, and the olive gathering went on until March. They were the olive trees belonging to Mazzarò. And toward evening, as the sun sank red as fire, and the countryside was veiled with sadness, you met the long files of Mazzarò's plows coming home softly, wearily from the fallow land, and the oxen slowly crossing the ford, with their muzzles in the dark water; and you saw on the far-off grazing land of Canziria, on naked slope, the immense whitish blotches of the flocks of Mazzarò; and you heard the shepherd's pipe resounding through the gullies, and the bell of the ram sometimes ringing and sometimes not, and the solitary singing lost in the valley.

All Mazzarò's property. It seemed as if even the setting sun and the whirring cicadas belonged to Mazzarò, and the birds which went on a short, leaping flight to nestle behind the clods, and the crying of the horned owl in the wood. It was as if Mazzarò had become as big as the world, and you walked upon his belly. Whereas he was an insignificant little fellow, said the litter driver, and you wouldn't have thought he was worth a *baiocco*,[5] to look at him, with no fat on him except his paunch, and it was a marvel how ever he filled that in, for he never ate anything more than a crust of bread, for

1. *Verga* (vär′ ga). 2. *Lentini . . . Passanitello.* All the places mentioned in this paragraph are regions of eastern Sicily. 3. *campagna* (käm pan′ yə), any flat open plain. 4. *Mazzarò* (mät sar′ ô). 5. *baiocco* (bä yôk′ kō), a former Italian coin worth a small sum.

all that he was rich as a pig, but he had a head on his shoulders that was keen as a diamond, that man had.

In fact, with that head as keen as a diamond he had got together all that property, whereas previously he had to work from morning till night hoeing, pruning, mowing, in the sun and rain and wind, with no shoes to his feet, and not a rag of a cloak to his back; so that everybody remembered the days when they used to give him kicks in the backside, and now they called him *Excellency,* and spoke to him cap in hand. But for all that he hadn't got stuck-up, now that all the Excellencies of the neighborhood were in debt to him, for he said *Excellency* meant poor devil and bad payer; he still wore the peasant's stocking cap, only his was made of black silk, which was his only grandeur, and lately he had started wearing a felt hat, because it cost less than the long silk stocking cap. He had possessions as far as the eye could reach, and he was a long-sighted man—everywhere, right and left, before and behind, in mountain and plain. More than five thousand mouths, without counting the birds of the air and the beasts of the earth, fed upon his lands, without counting his own mouth, that ate less than any of them, and was satisfied with a crust of bread and a bit of cheese, gulped down as fast as he could, standing in a corner of the store barn big as a church, or in the midst of the wheat dust, so that you could hardly see him, while his peasants were emptying the sacks, or leaning against a straw stack, when the wind swept the frozen country, in the time of the sowing of the seed, or with his head inside a basket, in the hot days of harvest time. He didn't drink wine, and he didn't smoke, he didn't take snuff, although indeed he grew plenty of tobacco in his fields beside the river, broad-leaved and tall as a boy, the sort that is sold at ninety-five lire. He hadn't the vice of gaming, nor of women. As for women, he'd never had to bother with any one of them save his mother, who had cost him

actually twelve *tari*[6] when he'd had her carried to the cemetery.

And he had thought about it and thought about it times enough, all that property means, when he went with no shoes to his feet, to work on the land that was now his own, and he had experienced what it was to earn his three *tari* in the month of July, to work with your back bent for fourteen hours, with the foreman on horseback behind you, laying about you with a stick if you stood up to straighten yourself for a minute. Therefore he had not let a minute of his whole life pass by that wasn't devoted to the acquiring of property; and now his plows were as many as the long strings of crows that arrive in November; and other strings of mules, endless, carried the seed; the women who were kept squatting in the mire, from October to March, picking up his olives, you couldn't count them, as you can't count the magpies that come to steal the olives; and in vintage time whole villages came to his vineyards, so that as far as ever you could hear folks singing, in the countryside, it was at Mazzarò's vintage. And then at harvest time Mazzarò's reapers were like an army of soldiers, so that to feed all those folks, with crackers in the morning and bread and a bitter orange at midday, and an afternoon snack, and homemade noodles in the evening, it took shoals of money, and they dished up the noodles in kneading troughs as big as washtubs. For that reason, when nowadays he went on horseback along the long line of his reapers, his whip in his hand, he didn't miss a single one of them with his eye, and kept shouting, "Bend over it, boys!" He had to have his hand in his pocket all the year round, spending, and simply for the land tax the King[7] took so much from him that Mazzarò went into a fever every time.

However, every year all those store

---

6. *lire . . . tari.* Lira, the standard monetary unit of Italy, and the tari, a former Sicilian coin, are individually worth small sums. 7. *King.* Italy was a monarchy until 1946, when it became a republic.

barns as big as churches were filled up with grain so that you had to raise up the roof to get it all in; and every time Mazzarò sold his wine it took over a day to count the money, all silver twelve-*tarì* pieces, for he didn't want any of your dirty paper in payment for his goods, and he went to buy dirty paper only when he had to pay the King, or other people; and at the cattle fairs the herds belonging to Mazzarò covered all the fairground, and choked up the roads, till it took half a day to let them go past, and the saint in procession with the band had at times to turn down another street, to make way for them.

And all that property he had got together himself, with his own hands and his own head, with not sleeping at night, with catching fever from worry or malaria, with slaving from dawn till dark, and going round in the sun and rain, and wearing out his boots and his mules— wearing out everything except himself, thinking of his property, which was all he had in the world, for he had neither children nor grandchildren, nor relations of any sort; he had nothing but his property. And when a man is made like that, it just means he is made for property.

And property was made for him. It really seemed as if he had a magnet for it, because property likes to stay with those who know how to keep it, and don't squander it like that baron who had previously been Mazzarò's master, and had taken him out of charity, naked and ignorant, to work on his fields; and the baron had been owner of all those meadows, and all those woods, and all those vineyards, and all those herds, so that when he came down to visit his estates on horseback, with his keepers behind him, he seemed like a king, and they got ready his lodging and his dinner for him, the simpleton, so that everybody knew the hour and the minute when he was due to arrive, and naturally they didn't let themselves be caught with their hands in the sack.

"That man absolutely asks to be robbed!" said Mazzarò, and he almost burst himself laughing when the baron kicked his behind, and he rubbed his rear with his hand, muttering, "Fools should stay at home. Property doesn't belong to those that have got it, but to those that know how to acquire it." He, on the contrary, since he had acquired his property, certainly didn't send to say whether he was coming to superintend the harvest, or the vintage, and when and in what way, but he turned up unexpectedly on foot or on muleback, without keepers, with a piece of bread in his pocket, and he slept beside his own sheaves, with his eye open and the gun between his legs.

And in that way Mazzarò little by little became master of all the baron's possessions; and the latter was turned out, first from the olive groves, then from the vineyards, then from the grazing land, and then from the farmsteads and finally from his very mansion, so that not a day passed but he was signing stamped paper, and Mazzarò put his own brave cross underneath. Nothing was left to the baron but the stone shield that used to stand over his entrance door— which was the only thing he hadn't wanted to sell, saying to Mazzarò, "There's only this, out of everything I've got, which is no use for you." And that was true; Mazzarò had no use for it, and wouldn't have given two *baiocchi* for it. The baron still said *thou*[8] to him, but he didn't kick his behind any longer.

"Ah, what a fine thing, to have Mazzarò's good fortune!" folks said, but they didn't know what it had taken to make that fortune, how much thinking, how much struggling, how many lies, how much danger of being sent to jail, and how that head that was sharp as a diamond had worked day and night, better than a mill wheel, to get all that property

---

8. *thou*, a familiar form of address used by master to servant or with implications of contempt.

together. If the owner of a piece of land with a dam adjoining his land persisted in not giving it up to him, and wanted to take Mazzarò by the throat, Mazzarò had to find some stratagem to force him to sell, to make him fall, in spite of the peasant's shrewdness. He went to him, for example, boasting about the fertility of a holding which wouldn't even produce lupines, and kept on till he made him believe it was the promised land, till the poor devil let himself be persuaded into leasing it, to speculate with it, and then he lost the lease, his house, and his dam, which Mazzarò got hold of—for a bit of bread. And how many annoyances Mazzarò had to put up with! His share tenants coming to complain of the bad seasons, his debtors always sending their wives in a procession to tear their hair and beat their breasts trying to persuade him not to turn them out and put them in the street, by seizing their mule or their donkey, so that they'd not have anything to eat.

"You see what I eat," he replied. "Bread and onion! and I've got all those store barns cram full, and I'm owner of all that stuff." And if they asked him for a handful of beans from all that stuff, he said:

"What, do you think I stole them? Don't you know what it costs, to sow them, and hoe them, and harvest them?" And if they asked him for a *soldo*[9] he said he didn't have one, which was true, he didn't have one. He never had twelve *tarì* in his pocket; it took all his money to make that property yield and increase, and money came and went like a river through the house. Besides, money didn't matter to him; he said it wasn't property, and as soon as he'd got together a certain sum he immediately bought a piece of land; because he wanted to get so that he had as much land as the King, and be better than the King, because the King can neither sell his land nor say it is his own.

Only one thing grieved him, and that was that he was beginning to get old, and he had to leave the earth there behind him. This was an injustice on God's part, that after having slaved one's life away getting property together, when you've got it, and you'd like some more, you have to leave it behind you. And he remained for hours sitting on a small basket, with his chin in his hands, looking at his vineyards growing green beneath his eyes, and his fields of ripe wheat waving like a sea, and the olive groves veiling the mountains like a mist, and if a half-naked boy passed in front of him, bent under his load like a tired ass, he threw his stick at his legs, out of envy, and muttered, "Look at him with his length of days in front of him; him who's got nothing to bless himself with!"

So that when they told him it was time for him to be turning away from his property, and thinking of his soul, he rushed out into the courtyard like a madman, staggering, and went around killing his own ducks and turkeys, hitting them with his stick and screaming, "You're my own property, you come along with me!"

THE END

Development

INTERPRETATION

1. *(a)* Did the amassing of property increase or diminish the stature of Mazzarò as a person? Explain. *(b)* Did Mazzarò's acquisition of property result in greater freedom for him? Why or why not?

2. *(a)* What is Mazzarò's reaction to any young boy who passes him? *(b)* What does Mazzarò mean in saying, ". . . him who's got nothing to bless himself with!" (page 328, column 2, lines 18-19)?

---

9. *soldo,* a former Italian coin worth about one fourth of a cent.

3. (a) Account for Mazzarò's violent reaction to the prospects of old age and death. (b) Given the character and situation of Mazzarò, could the story have ended other than as it does? Why?

4. One reader has commented that while Mazzarò may be pitied, it is not possible to feel compassion for him. Do you agree or disagree with the above statement? Explain.

TECHNIQUE

1. Verga shapes readers' attitudes toward Mazzarò long before the landowner enters the story. (a) What is the feeling Verga creates? (b) How is it created? (c) Does that feeling change later? Discuss.

2. (a) Contrast the opening and closing paragraphs of this story. In your discussion consider the tone and style of each paragraph. (b) What two aspects of Mazzarò's character do these paragraphs reflect?

EXTENSIONS

1. What fault in Mazzarò's values leaves the reader with the impression that neither money nor property is of permanence in a man's life? In your opinion, what, then, is of permanence?

Comparison

1. (a) In your opinion, what are the characteristics of an opportunist? (b) In what sense are Midas, Mazzarò, and Honoré opportunists?

2. (a) What is the essential irony underlying each selection in this group? (b) What function does the ironical element serve in each case? (c) Does the use of irony in any way affect your overall reaction to the selections? If so, how?

3. (a) Compare and contrast the styles of writing found in "The Devil" and "Property." (b) Would it make a difference to the effectiveness of the stories if the two styles were interchanged? Explain.

4. What do you learn of the nature of greed from these selections? In your discussion consider the causes and effects of greed as outlined in the stories.

5. An author has power to direct the feelings of his readers. How might the authors have led us as readers to scorn or to sympathize more deeply with the characters?

6. Greed, personified in Christopher Marlowe's *The Tragical History of Doctor Faustus*, exclaims:

> I am Covetousness begotten of an old churl in an old leathren bag; and, might I have my wish, I would desire that this house and all the people in it were turned to gold, that I might lock you up in my gold chest. O my sweet gold!

(a) What characteristics of greed cause people to regard it as such a heinous thing? (b) Do you think that men are responsible for their greed? If so, why? If not, who or what is responsible? (c) From your own experience and observation, would you say that greed exists in all men? Explain.

7. What indications do you find that the characters will or will not continue to be opportunists?

8. On the basis of your reading, defend or refute the following statements:

> No wealth can satisfy the covetous desire of wealth. (Jeremy Taylor)

> He who covets everything soon loses everything. (Richard Bonier)

9. The selections in this group deal with opportunists all the way from Midas to nineteenth-century peasants obsessed by avarice. Now create your own version of a twentieth-century American opportunist. Sketch his main characteristics, his interests, his work, and his reactions to those around him.

LA BASTILLE by Antonio Recalcati. Owned by artist, Milan.

The Alienated

Anguish

ALBERTO MORAVIA[1] / Italy

(1907 –   )

translated from the Italian by Angus Davidson

Lorenzo stopped the car and turned towards the youth. "Well then, are you coming up or d'you want to stay here?"

He saw him shrug his shoulders, with an expression of arrogant laziness. "Who's going up? I'm not, not even dead."

Lorenzo looked at him for a moment, without speaking. The handsome, depraved face, very dark, with its black, moist eyes of feminine size and shape, its short, sensual nose, its fleshy, glossy, swelling lips, was repugnant to him and, even more, surprised him: how had his parents failed to notice anything? It was a face that spoke. Lorenzo, annoyed, said: "Lionello,[2] if you're going to take it like this, it would have been better not to come to me."

"But, *avvocato*,[3] how ought I to take it?"

"D'you realize you may end up in prison?"

The boy looked at him, settled himself back on the cushions of the car, half lying down, his head thrown back and his neck rising round and strong above his summer jersey; but he said nothing. It was his way of answering embarrassing questions. Lorenzo insisted. "May one at least know why you did it?"

Again silence. The look in the boy's eyes, filtering downwards through his long lashes, irritated Lorenzo. "Why did you come to me, then?" he asked.

This time Lionello decided to speak, slowly and disdainfully. "I came to you because I thought you were more understanding. But if you ask me these questions, then it means that I made a mistake and did wrong."

"Did wrong in doing what?"

"In coming to you."

Lorenzo jumped out of the car and slammed the door hard. "All right, then,

"Anguish" by Alberto Moravia, translated by Angus Davidson from ITALIAN SHORT STORIES edited by Raleigh Trevelyan. Copyright © 1965 by Penguin Books Ltd. Reprinted by permission of Penguin Books Ltd.
1. *Moravia* (mō rä′ vē ə; *It.* mô rä′ vyä). 2. *Lionello* (lē ô nel′ lō). 3. *avvocato* (äv′ vō kä′ tō), lawyer. [*Italian*]

332   THE ALIENATED

stay here, I'll go up." But just as he was walking past the car, he saw the boy make a languid gesture of appeal with his hand, without, however, modifying his listless, lounging position. He stopped and inquired irritably: "And now what d'you want?"

"Cigarettes."

"Here you are." Lorenzo threw the packet into the boy's face and then went into the entrance hall. As he stood in front of the lift he noticed, out of the tail of his eye, a female figure, outside in the street, approach the car and speak to Lionello. He recognized her at once; it was the boy's sister, Gigliola.[4] While Lionello had the face and the manners—whether cultivated or spontaneous, it was impossible to be sure—of a young hooligan from the suburbs, Gigliola, on her side, with her supple body that swayed too much from the hips, her flat, foreheadless face, her eyes that were too large and her mouth that was too wide, had much of the corresponding female type. Lorenzo lingered on purpose beside the lift so as to allow her to come up with him. Finally, indeed, he saw her approach, walking across the shining marble of the spacious hall, half naked in her little dress which looked as though cut out of a handkerchief and which left her shoulders uncovered, as well as her arms, the upper part of her bosom and her legs up to above her knees. Lorenzo noticed that her fashionable hairstyle, in the form of a tall oval crest, confirmed and emphasized the extraordinary lowness of her forehead, not more than two fingers high, and the breadth and animal-like robustness of the lower part of her face. Gigliola entered the lift and, without greeting him, asked Lorenzo: "What's wrong with Lionello? Why won't he come upstairs? And why is he hiding in your car?"

Lorenzo, in turn, entered the lift and said, as he closed the door: "Lionello is in trouble."

"He's got himself into a mess, has he?"

"A very bad mess."

"But what's he done?"

"Clever girl. If I told you, the whole of Rome would get to know at once."

"I think I can make a pretty good guess, all the same. Lionello and the other boys were always saying they wanted to do something to break the monotony of life." She uttered these words as though quoting them from memory, with an ingenuous, blunt seriousness which made Lorenzo smile almost against his will. "Ah, they said that, did they?"

"Yes, and they also said they would do something for which all the newspapers would talk about them. I wanted to go in with them but they wouldn't have me. They said such things were not for women."

The lift came to a stop and they got out on to a landing which, no less than the hall, was glossy with marble. Lorenzo turned towards the girl and took her by the arm. "Now mind what I say: if you love your brother, the things you've just told me, you mustn't mention to anybody."

"I won't say anything if you tell me what Lionello has done. Otherwise—"

She did not finish, for Lorenzo seized her by both arms, exclaiming: "Don't play the fool. You mustn't say anything, and that's that."

He gripped her tightly and saw her look at him with an expression that was not in the least offended. Then she said, in an almost flattered tone of voice: "What a way to behave!"; and at the same time she made a slight forward movement, a provoking movement, with her belly. At that, he let go of her immediately and said hurriedly: "On the whole, Lionello is less compromised than the others. If you don't talk, he may even get away with it. And stop playing the fool."

"What a way to talk! The family lawyer!" mocked the girl. The door opened and a manservant in a white jacket ushered them into the ante-room.

---

4. *Gigliola* (jē′ lyô lä).

"Good-bye, *avvocato*," said Gigliola, and went off, humming and dancing along, into the darkness of a corridor. The manservant showed Lorenzo into the drawing-room.

Lionello's mother, Giulia,[5] was wandering round the room with a little bald man who held a measure in his hand. She shook Lorenzo's hand in passing, saying: "Forgive me, I have to discuss the question of summer chair-covers for a moment with the upholsterer. I'll come in a minute." Lorenzo wondered whether it was advisable for him to speak to Giulia before seeing her husband; in the end he decided that it might be useful: in that house everything depended, fundamentally, on Giulia. Meanwhile he had sat down in an armchair and was watching her as she discussed matters with the tradesman. She was tall, thin, narrow, dressed in grey and black, with the lifeless elegance characteristic of many women who are very rich and very domesticated. In her carefully arranged brown hair there were already a few white threads; her blue eyes, small and deepset, had in them a disquieting sparkle; her face, of a perfect oval shape, looked slightly swollen, on account perhaps of the smallness of her nose.

Giulia finally dismissed the upholsterer, came and sat down beside Lorenzo and began talking to him, as usual, about her family, to which she devoted herself tirelessly and which gave her, in her own words, worry enough to kill her. She spoke in great haste, linking up one sentence precipitately with another, even when the sense did not require it, rather like one of those frenzied smokers who light a fresh cigarette from the butt of the preceding one. One would have thought she was afraid that Lorenzo might interrupt her, and that she knew in advance that he had something disagreeable to tell her. Several times Lorenzo attempted to insinuate the phrase which lay on the tip of his tongue: "Listen, Giulia; on the subject of your children, I must speak to you about Lionello . . . "; but each time he came up against a wall of words that was at the same time both mobile and impassable. Strangely, thought Lorenzo, whereas in her conversation there was apparent the complacency of one who has a conscience at rest and nothing to reproach herself with, the haste, the frenzy almost, with which she talked seemed to indicate a profound, though perhaps unconscious, anguish. She had started by talking about the summer covers for the furniture; from the covers she had gone on to holidays at the seaside and in the mountains; from holidays she had enlarged upon the fashion for yachts, or, as she called them, boats; from boats she had slipped to the subject of her two children, who for her were "my babies," and who had actually both been invited on to one of these boats; and now, without any connexion or any interruption, she had begun describing, in all its minutest details, a small party which Gigliola and Lionello had given, some evenings before, for their friends, on the roof terrace of the house: "They even did variety turns.[6] But they turned us out, Federico and me, saying: 'Not suitable for adults. Only for minors of eighteen years old.' Witty, wasn't it?"

The door opened and Federico, the husband, came in slowly, with the exhausted step of one who is emerging from a long, forced immobility. He was tall, athletic, but with slightly bent shoulders; his face, with its handsome, symmetrical features, could be seen to be closely marked, all round the blue eyes and the still youthful mouth, with fine wrinkles; his brow, at first sight, appeared ample and luminous, but if you looked more carefully you became aware that it was simply bald. Unlike Giulia who was unable to restrain her own chatter, Federico, as Lorenzo knew, restrained himself all too much, reducing conversation to a series of half-sentences and head-shakings that seemed to betray

5. *Giulia* (jül′ yä). 6. *variety turns,* impromptu dramatic sketches or routines.

an anguish which, fundamentally, was not very different from that of his wife. Federico went up to Lorenzo and, as though making a show of ignoring his wife, greeted him with a cordiality that appeared to cost him a painful effort. Lorenzo looked at him and realized that his friend must have passed, as usual, a bad night: he suffered from insomnia and, as he himself expressed it, his nervous system was all to bits. Federico said briefly, in a subdued voice: "Let's go on the terrace, shall we?"

They went out on to the spacious terrace which was, in truth, a real roof garden poised in front of the panorama of the city. It was hot, and the summer sun scorched the brick paving between the brief shadows of shrubs in boxes. Federico went towards a corner of the parapet from which one had a view over the Tiber and over Monte Mario. He walked with long steps and moved his head this way and that, jerkily, like a man who feels himself suffocating and seeks in vain for air. As soon as they were far enough away from the drawing-room, Lorenzo said: "Listen, I must speak to you."

Federico was now looking down; he seemed to be staring straight at Lorenzo's car standing beside the pavement, small and solitary in the middle of a big, grey space of asphalt. Turning, he said: "Speak to me? I'm sorry, but this morning it's not possible."

Lorenzo opened his eyes wide in surprise: "It's not possible? And why?"

He saw Federico's whole face contract, as if with cramp or some other sudden pain. Then Federico answered: "It's impossible. My mind is not calm enough. I haven't closed an eye all night in spite of sleeping-draughts, and, in short, I don't feel well." He said yet other things of the same kind; and both the drawn, shrunken face and the tone of voice, all spasmodic and jerky, were those of a man who is really suffering. This suffering made Lorenzo think that, perhaps, it would not be prudent to speak to him of his son. He persisted, nevertheless: "Mind you, it's a question of something that cannot be put off."

Federico again cast a glance at the car down in the street, in which Lionello was waiting; and he replied: "There are no things that cannot be postponed. They seem always so urgent and then . . . I beg you, come back tomorrow, come tomorrow morning, even; I shall have slept, we shall be able to talk calmly."

"But it's a thing that is really important."

"Just because it's important, I don't wish to know it. I couldn't occupy myself now with an important thing."

"Then you really don't want to?"

"Please don't insist."

He had put his hand on Lorenzo's shoulder and, imperceptibly, was pushing him across the terrace, towards the drawing-room. Lorenzo had noticed that, each time he spoke, Federico's face was contracted by a sort of spasm, and in the end he decided, secretly, not to tell him anything. He would do what he could for Lionello; Giulia and Federico who, each in their own way, did not wish to know anything, would learn their son's misdeeds from the newspapers, or would not learn them at all. He declined a bland invitation to lunch from Federico, said good-bye to him, then went and shook Giulia's hand and passed on into the ante-room.

As though she had been waiting for him, there was Gigliola, emerging from the shadows. "Well," she said, "did you speak to Papa and Mamma?"

"No; and, in fact, please don't tell them anything."

"But who's saying anything? However, you ought to be convinced."

"Of what?"

"That the only person to whom one can tell everything, in this house, is myself."

"Perhaps you're right." Lorenzo closed the doors of the lift. The cage started on its way down.

THE END

Development

INTERPRETATION

1. Moravia fails to state what crime Lionello has committed. *(a)* In doing so, has he written an obscure story? *(b)* Why do you think he might have held back this information?

2. *(a)* In what way does Lionello answer embarrassing questions? *(b)* What is Federico's response to problems? *(c)* Will a good night's sleep make a new man of Federico? Will getting his name in the papers release Lionello from the monotony of his life? Explain your opinions. *(d)* What do you think has caused both father and son to be alienated in a similar way?

3. *(a)* Why is Lorenzo unable to talk to Giulia? *(b)* Why does he distrust Gigliola? *(c)* Do you feel that either Giulia or Gigliola expresses a genuine concern for their family? Why or why not? *(d)* In light of the attitudes of Lionello and Federico, do you feel that mother and daughter are justified in assuming dominant roles? Why or why not?

4. *(a)* Which characters in "Anguish" try to exploit the generation gap? *(b)* Why do you think they do it? *(c)* Why is it significant that only Lorenzo tries to talk to everyone? *(d)* Why does he fail in his attempts to communicate?

5. *(a)* What traditional beliefs about family responsibility run counter to the experience of this story? *(b)* Do you feel that as documentation of a social tendency this story has any validity? Why or why not?

6. Moravia has said that whatever social criticism there is in his work is unintentional, for his main concern is the creation of living fictional characters. Does this statement alter your interpretation of "Anguish"? Why or why not?

TECHNIQUE

1. Look at the first and last sentences of "Anguish." *(a)* What action is described in each? *(b)* In what way do these acts suggest the *milieu* or environment of this story? *(c)* In what way does this environment relate to the theme?

2. Each of the following qualities is associated with a different character in "Anguish": a "lifeless elegance"; an "arrogant laziness"; "an animal-like robustness"; and "a forced immobility." *(a)* Match each phrase with its appropriate character. *(b)* What details does Moravia employ to develop these qualities in the corresponding characters?

EXTENSIONS

1. Assume that you are the fiction editor of a popular magazine and that you receive "Anguish" in manuscript form. It is your job to read the story and pass it on to the editor with a recommendation for or against publication. What would be your decision? Why?

2. The family lawyer is probably a more familiar figure in Italy than in America. *(a)* If "Anguish" were reset in America, what social figure might take the place of the family lawyer? *(b)* In what ways might his attitude be different from Lorenzo's?

3. Moravia's stories have supplied the inspiration for a number of Italian films. *(a)* What do you notice about the style and content of "Anguish" that might readily lend itself to cinematic treatment? *(b)* If you were making a film that went on from the end of the short story, what would be your next scene? *(c)* Which themes from "Anguish" would you want to develop further in your film?

A Hunger Artist

FRANZ KAFKA / Austria-Hungary
(1883 – 1924)
translated from the German by Willa and Edwin Muir

During these last decades the interest in professional fasting has markedly diminished. It used to pay very well to stage such great performances under one's own management, but today that is quite impossible. We live in a different world now. At one time the whole town took a lively interest in the hunger artist; from day to day of his fast the excitement mounted; everybody wanted to see him at least once a day; there were people who bought season tickets for the last few days and sat from morning till night in front of his small barred cage; even in the nighttime there were visiting hours, when the whole effect was heightened by torch flares; on fine days the cage was set out in the open air, and then it was the children's special treat to see the hunger artist; for their elders he was often just a joke that happened to be in fashion, but the children stood open-mouthed, holding each other's hands for greater security, marveling at him as he sat there pallid in black tights, with his ribs sticking out so prominently, not even on a seat but down among straw on the ground, sometimes giving a courteous nod, answering questions with a constrained smile, or perhaps stretching an arm through the bars so that one might feel how thin it was, and then again withdrawing deep into himself, paying no attention to anyone or anything, not even to the all-important striking of the clock that was the only piece of furniture in his cage, but merely staring into vacancy with half-shut eyes, now and then taking a sip from a tiny glass of water to moisten his lips.

Besides casual onlookers there were also relays of permanent watchers selected by the public, usually butchers, strangely enough, and it was their task to watch the hunger artist day and night, three of them at a time, in case he should have some secret recourse to nourishment. This was nothing but a formality, instituted to reassure the masses, for the initiates knew well enough that during his fast the artist would never in any circumstances, not even under forcible compulsion, swallow the smallest morsel of food; the honor of his profession forbade it. Not every watcher, of course, was capable of understanding this, there were often groups of night watchers who were very lax in carrying out their duties and deliberately huddled together in a retired corner to play cards with great absorption, obviously intending to give the hunger artist the chance of a little refreshment, which they supposed he could draw from some private hoard. Nothing annoyed the artist more than such watchers; they made him miserable; they made his fast seem unendurable; sometimes he mastered his feebleness sufficiently to sing during their watch for as long as he could keep going, to show them how unjust their suspicions were. But that was of little use; they only wondered at his cleverness in being able to fill his mouth even while singing. Much more to his taste were the watchers who sat close up to the bars, who were not content with the dim night lighting of the hall but focused him in the full glare of the electric pocket torch given them by the impresario.[1] The harsh light did not trouble him at all, in any case he could never sleep properly, and he could always drowse a little, whatever the light, at any hour, even when the hall was thronged with noisy onlookers. He was quite happy at the prospect of spending a sleepless night with such watchers; he was ready to exchange jokes with them, to tell them stories out of his nomadic life, anything at all to keep them awake and demonstrate to them again that he had no eatables in his cage and that he was fasting as not one of them could fast. But his happiest moment was when the morning came and an enormous breakfast was brought them, at his expense, on which they flung themselves with the keen appetite of healthy men after a weary night of wakefulness. Of course there were people who argued that this breakfast was an unfair attempt to bribe the watchers, but that was going rather too far, and when they were invited to take on a night's vigil without a breakfast, merely for the sake of the cause, they made themselves scarce, although they stuck stubbornly to their suspicions.

Such suspicions, anyhow, were a necessary accompaniment to the profession of fasting. No one could possibly watch the hunger artist continuously, day and night, and so no one could produce firsthand evidence that the fast had really been rigorous and continuous; only the artist himself could know that, he was therefore bound to be the sole completely satisfied spectator of his own fast. Yet for other reasons he was never satisfied; it was not perhaps mere fasting that had brought him to such skeleton thinness that many people had regretfully to keep away from his exhibitions, because the

sight of him was too much for them, perhaps it was dissatisfaction with himself that had worn him down. For he alone knew, what no other initiate knew, how easy it was to fast. It was the easiest thing in the world. He made no secret of this, yet people did not believe him, at the best they set him down as modest, most of them, however, thought he was out for publicity or else was some kind of cheat who found it easy to fast because he had discovered a way of making it easy, and then had the impudence to admit the fact, more or less. He had to put up with all that, and in the course of time had got used to it, but his inner dissatisfaction always rankled, and never yet, after any term of fasting—this must be granted to his credit—had he left the cage of his own free will. The longest period of fasting was fixed by his impresario at forty days, beyond that term he was not allowed to go, not even in great cities, and there was good reason for it, too. Experience had proved that for about forty days the interest of the public could be stimulated by a steadily increasing pressure of advertisement, but after that the town began to lose interest, sympathetic support began notably to fall off; there were of course local variations as between one town and another or one country and another, but as a general rule forty days marked the limit. So on the fortieth day the flower-bedecked cage was opened, enthusiastic spectators filled the hall, a military band played, two doctors entered the cage to measure the results of the fast, which were announced through a megaphone, and finally two young ladies appeared, blissful at having been selected for the honor, to help the hunger artist down the few steps leading to a small table on which was spread a carefully chosen invalid repast. And at this very moment the artist always turned stubborn. True, he would entrust his bony arms to the outstretched helping hands of the ladies bending over him, but stand up

1. *impresario* (im′ prə sä′ rē ō), one who manages and promotes an artist or performing company.

he would not. Why stop fasting at this particular moment, after forty days of it? He had held out for a long time, an illimitably long time; why stop now, when he was in his best fasting form, or rather, not yet quite in his best fasting form? Why should he be cheated of the fame he would get for fasting longer, for being not only the record hunger artist of all time, which presumably he was already, but for beating his own record by a performance beyond human imagination, since he felt that there were no limits to his capacity for fasting? His public pretended to admire him so much, why should it have so little patience with him; if he could endure fasting longer, why shouldn't the public endure it? Besides, he was tired, he was comfortable sitting in the straw, and now he was supposed to lift himself to his full height and go down to a meal the very thought of which gave him a nausea that only the presence of the ladies kept him from betraying, and even that with an effort. And he looked up into the eyes of the ladies who were apparently so friendly and in reality so cruel, and shook his head, which felt too heavy on its strengthless neck. But then there happened yet again what always happened. The impresario came forward, without a word—for the band made speech impossible—lifted his arms in the air above the artist, as if inviting Heaven to look down upon its creature here in the straw, this suffering martyr, which indeed he was, although in quite another sense; grasped him round the emaciated waist, with exaggerated caution, so that the frail condition he was in might be appreciated; and committed him to the care of the blenching ladies, not without secretly giving him a shaking so that his legs and body tottered and swayed. The artist now submitted completely; his head lolled on his breast as if it had landed there by chance; his body was hollowed out; his legs in a spasm of self-preservation clung close to each other at the knees, yet scraped on the ground as if it were not really solid ground, as if they

were only trying to find solid ground; and the whole weight of his body, a featherweight after all, relapsed onto one of the ladies, who, looking round for help and panting a little—this post of honor was not at all what she had expected it to be—first stretched her neck as far as she could to keep her face at least free from contact with the artist, then finding this impossible, and her more fortunate companion not coming to her aid but merely holding extended on her own trembling hand the little bunch of knucklebones that was the artist's, to the great delight of the spectators burst into tears and had to be replaced by an attendant who had long been stationed in readiness. Then came the food, a little of which the impresario managed to get between the artist's lips, while he sat in a kind of half-fainting trance, to the accompaniment of cheerful patter designed to distract the public's attention from the artist's condition; after that, a toast was drunk to the public, supposedly prompted by a whisper from the artist in the impresario's ear; the band confirmed it with a mighty flourish, the spectators melted away, and no one had any cause to be dissatisfied with the proceedings, no one except the hunger artist himself, he only, as always.

So he lived for many years, with small regular intervals of recuperation, in visible glory, honored by the world, yet in spite of that troubled in spirit, and all the more troubled because no one would take his trouble seriously. What comfort could he possibly need? What more could he possibly wish for? And if some good-natured person, feeling sorry for him, tried to console him by pointing out that his melancholy was probably caused by fasting, it could happen, especially when he had been fasting for some time, that he reacted with an outburst of fury and to the general alarm began to shake the bars of his cage like a wild animal. Yet the impresario had a way of punishing these outbreaks which he rather enjoyed putting into operation.

He would apologize publicly for the artist's behavior, which was only to be excused, he admitted, because of the irritability caused by fasting; a condition hardly to be understood by well-fed people; then by natural transition he went on to mention the artist's equally incomprehensible boast that he could fast for much longer than he was doing; he praised the high ambition, the good will, the great self-denial undoubtedly implicit in such a statement; and then quite simply countered it by bringing out photographs, which were also on sale to the public, showing the artist on the fortieth day of a fast lying in bed almost dead from exhaustion. This perversion of the truth, familiar to the artist though it was, always unnerved him afresh and proved too much for him. What was a consequence of the premature ending of his fast was here presented as the cause of it! To fight against this lack of understanding, against a whole world of non-understanding, was impossible. Time and again in good faith he stood by the bars listening to the impresario, but as soon as the photographs appeared he always let go and sank with a groan back on to his straw, and the reassured public could once more come close and gaze at him.

A few years later when the witnesses of such scenes called them to mind, they often failed to understand themselves at all. For meanwhile the aforementioned change in public interest had set in; it seemed to happen almost overnight; there may have been profound causes for it, but who was going to bother about that; at any rate the pampered hunger artist suddenly found himself deserted one fine day by the amusement seekers, who went streaming past him to other more favored attractions. For the last time the impresario hurried him over half Europe to discover whether the old interest might still survive here and there; all in vain; everywhere, as if by secret agreement, a positive revulsion from professional fasting was in evidence. Of course it could not really have sprung up so suddenly as all that, and many premonitory symptoms which had not been sufficiently remarked or suppressed during the rush and glitter of success now came retrospectively to mind, but it was now too late to take any countermeasures. Fasting would surely come into fashion again at some future date, yet that was no comfort for those living in the present. What, then, was the hunger artist to do? He had been applauded by thousands in his time and could hardly come down to showing himself in a street booth at village fairs, and as for adopting another profession, he was not only too old for that but too fanatically devoted to fasting. So he took leave of the impresario, his partner in an unparalleled career, and hired himself to a large circus; in order to spare his own feelings he avoided reading the conditions of his contract.

A large circus with its enormous traffic in replacing and recruiting men, animals and apparatus can always find a use for people at any time, even for a hunger artist, provided of course that he does not ask too much, and in this particular case anyhow it was not only the artist who was taken on but his famous and long-known name as well, indeed considering the peculiar nature of his performance, which was not impaired by advancing age, it could not be objected that here was an artist past his prime, no longer at the height of his professional skill, seeking a refuge in some quiet corner of a circus, on the contrary, the hunger artist averred that he could fast as well as ever, which was entirely credible, he even alleged that if he were allowed to fast as he liked, and this was at once promised him without more ado, he could astound the world by establishing a record never yet achieved, a statement which certainly provoked a smile among the other professionals, since it left out of account the change in public opinion, which the hunger artist in his zeal conveniently forgot.

He had not, however, actually lost his

sense of the real situation and took it as a matter of course that he and his cage should be stationed, not in the middle of the ring as a main attraction, but outside, near the animal cages, on a site that was after all easily accessible. Large and gaily painted placards made a frame for the cage and announced what was to be seen inside it. When the public came thronging out in the intervals to see the animals, they could hardly avoid passing the hunger artist's cage and stopping there for a moment, perhaps they might even have stayed longer had not those pressing behind them in the narrow gangway, who did not understand why they should be held up on their way towards the excitements of the menagerie, made it impossible for anyone to stand gazing quietly for any length of time. And that was the reason why the hunger artist, who had of course been looking forward to these visiting hours as the main achievement of his life, began instead to shrink from them. At first he could hardly wait for the intervals; it was exhilarating to watch the crowds come streaming his way, until only too soon—not even the most obstinate self-deception, clung to almost consciously, could hold out against the fact— the conviction was borne in upon him that these people, most of them, to judge from their actions, again and again, without exception, were all on their way to the menagerie. And the first sight of them from the distance remained the best. For when they reached his cage he was at once deafened by the storm of shouting and abuse that arose from the two contending factions, which renewed themselves continuously, of those who wanted to stop and stare at him—he soon began to dislike them more than the others—not out of real interest but only out of obstinate self-assertiveness, and those who wanted to go straight on to the animals. When the first great rush was past, the stragglers came along, and these, whom nothing could have prevented from stopping to look at him as long as they had

breath, raced past with long strides, hardly even glancing at him, in their haste to get to the menagerie in time. And all too rarely did it happen that he had a stroke of luck, when some father of a family fetched up before him with his children, pointed a finger at the hunger artist and explained at length what the phenomenon meant, telling stories of earlier years when he himself had watched similar but much more thrilling performances, and the children, still rather uncomprehending, since neither inside nor outside school had they been sufficiently prepared for this lesson —what did they care about fasting?—yet showed by the brightness of their intent eyes that new and better times might be coming. Perhaps, said the hunger artist to himself many a time, things would be a little better if his cage were set not quite so near the menagerie. That made it too easy for people to make their choice, to say nothing of what he suffered from the stench of the menagerie, the animals' restlessness by night, the carrying past of raw lumps of flesh for the beasts of prey, the roaring at feeding times, which depressed him continually. But he did not dare to lodge a complaint with the management; after all, he had the animals to thank for the troops of people who passed his cage, among whom there might always be one here and there to take an interest in him, and who could tell where they might seclude him if he called attention to his existence and thereby to the fact that, strictly speaking, he was only an impediment on the way to the menagerie.

A small impediment, to be sure, one that grew steadily less. People grew familiar with the strange idea that they could be expected, in times like these, to take an interest in a hunger artist, and with this familiarity the verdict went out against him. He might fast as much as he could, and he did so; but nothing could save him now, people passed him by. Just try to explain to anyone the art of fasting! Anyone who has no feeling for it cannot be made to understand it. The fine placards grew dirty and illegible, they were torn down; the little notice board telling the number of fast days achieved, which at first was changed carefully every day, had long stayed at the same figure, for after the first few weeks even this small task seemed pointless to the staff; and so the artist simply fasted on and on, as he had once dreamed of doing, and it was no trouble to him, just as he had always foretold, but no one counted the days, no one, not even the artist himself, knew what records he was already breaking, and his heart grew heavy. And when once in a time some leisurely passer-by stopped, made merry over the old figure on the board and spoke of swindling, that was in its way the stupidest lie ever invented by indifference and inborn malice, since it was not the hunger artist who was cheating, he was working honestly, but the world was cheating him of his reward.

Many more days went by, however, and that too came to an end. An overseer's eye fell on the cage one day and he asked the attendants why this perfectly good cage should be left standing there unused with dirty straw inside it; nobody knew, until one man, helped out by the notice board, remembered about the hunger artist. They poked into the straw with sticks and found him in it. "Are you still fasting?" asked the overseer, "when on earth do you mean to stop?" "Forgive me, everybody," whispered the hunger artist; only the overseer, who had his ear to the bars, understood him. "Of course," said the overseer, and tapped his forehead with a finger to let the attendants know what state the man was in, "we forgive you." "I always wanted you to admire my fasting," said the hunger artist. "We do admire it," said the overseer, affably. "But you shouldn't admire it," said the hunger artist. "Well then we don't admire it," said the overseer, "but why shouldn't we admire it?" "Because I have to fast, I can't help it," said the hunger artist. "What a fellow you are," said the overseer, "and why can't you help it?" "Because," said the hunger artist, lifting his head a little and speaking, with his lips pursed, as if for a kiss, right into the overseer's ear, so that no syllable might be lost, "because I couldn't find the food I liked. If I had found it, believe me, I should have made no fuss and stuffed myself like you or anyone else." These were his last words, but in his dimming eyes remained the firm though no longer proud persuasion that he was still continuing to fast.

"Well, clear this out now!" said the overseer, and they buried the hunger artist, straw and all. Into the cage they put a young panther. Even the most insensitive felt it refreshing to see this wild creature leaping around the cage that had so long been dreary. The panther was all right. The food he liked was brought him without hesitation by the attendants; he seemed not even to miss his freedom; his noble body, furnished almost to the bursting point with all that it needed, seemed to carry freedom around with it too; somewhere in his jaws it seemed to lurk; and the joy of life streamed with such ardent passion from his throat that for the onlookers it was not easy to stand the shock of it. But they braced themselves, crowded round the cage, and did not want ever to move away.

THE END

Development

INTERPRETATION

1. *(a)* What forces Kafka's protagonist to become a hunger artist? *(b)* Why is it important for him to have the public's admiration? *(c)* In what way does the cage symbolize his condition?

2. *(a)* Why won't the impresario let the hunger artist fast beyond forty days? *(b)* What reason does the hunger artist give for wanting to continue his fast? *(c)* Why is this only a half-truth? *(d)* Why is the hunger artist so sensitive to accusations of fraud?

3. *(a)* What is your opinion of fasting as an art? *(b)* Why do you think the public is interested in the hunger artist's act? *(c)* Do you think it out of character for them to be interested in the menagerie? Why or why not?

4. *(a)* What is the circus overseer's attitude toward the hunger artist during his confession? *(b)* Why is the persuasion in the dying hunger artist's eyes "firm though no longer proud"? *(c)* Do you feel that at his death the hunger artist has attained a degree of self-fulfillment? Why or why not? *(d)* Does the irony of the revelation in this final scene seem satiric or tragic? Explain.

5. *(a)* What impression is created by the contrast between the panther and the hunger artist? *(b)* If "freedom" and "the joy of life" emanate from the panther, what qualities might the hunger artist be said to express? *(c)* Do you feel that ceaseless striving has ennobled or degraded the hunger artist? Why? *(d)* What is signified by the triumph of the menagerie?

TECHNIQUE

1. *(a)* In what ways is Kafka's narrator taken in by the hunger artist? *(b)* Does this involvement of the narrator with the hunger artist make the story seem more convincing? Why or why not? *(c)* Why might an author write a story from the point of view of a man who never fully understands what is happening?

2. Look at the paragraph describing the hunger artist's initiation into the circus (page 340, column 2, paragraph 1). *(a)* What is unusual about the structure of this paragraph? *(b)* How many different points of view can you find within the paragraph? *(c)* What about Kafka's style facilitates the great transitions he makes from one thought to another?

EXTENSIONS

1. The hunger artist tries to adapt, tries to excel, and ultimately feels he must beg forgiveness for having tried at all. *(a)* Why do you think rejection by society is liable to produce feelings of guilt such as the hunger artist experiences? *(b)* Can a man protect himself against such self-destructive feelings? Explain your view.

2. The hunger artist has been interpreted as a symbol for the religious mystic, for the spiritual element in man, and for the artist in society. Defend or criticize each interpretation in accordance with what you feel is the best way to read the story.

3. The hunger artist devotes his entire life to an enterprise which an inexplicable change in the world renders meaningless. *(a)* What particular significance has this situation for men in the twentieth century? *(b)* What effect might this type of uncertainty have upon a society's values? *(c)* Do you feel that adapting oneself completely to every change is the best way to cope with the world? Why or why not?

Foursome

EUGENE IONESCO[1] / France
(1912–   )

translated from the French by Donald M. Allen

CHARACTERS

DUPONT, costumed like Durand
DURAND, costumed like Dupont
MARTIN, costumed in the same fashion
THE PRETTY LADY, wearing a hat, dress, shoes, cape or furs, and gloves, and carrying a handbag etc., at least on her entrance

First and only scene
The entrance is to the Left. Stage Center, there is a table, and on it three potted plants are lined up side by side. Elsewhere, an armchair or a sofa.

> *(As the curtain rises an agitated* DU-
> PONT, *his hands behind his back, is pacing around the table.* DURAND, *doing the same business, moves in the contrary direction. When* DUPONT *and* DURAND *meet and collide, they about-face and move in opposite directions.)*

DUPONT. . . . No . . .

DURAND. Yes . . .

DUPONT. No . . .

DURAND. Yes . . .

DUPONT. No . . .

DURAND. Yes . . .

DUPONT. I tell you no . . . Look out for the potted plants . . .

DURAND. I tell you yes . . . Look out for the potted plants . . .

DUPONT. And I tell you no . . .

DURAND. And I tell you yes . . . and I repeat to you yes . . .

DUPONT. You don't need to keep on saying yes to me. For it's no, no and no, thirty-two times no.

DURAND. Dupont, look out for the potted plants . . .

DUPONT. Durand, look out for the potted plants . . .

DURAND. You're pigheaded. My god, how pigheaded can you be . . .

DUPONT. Who, me? You're the one that's pigheaded, pigheaded, pigheaded . . .

DURAND. You don't know what you're talking about. Why do you say that I'm

1. *Ionesco* (yə nes′ kō)

pigheaded? Look out for the potted plants. I am not pigheaded at all.

DUPONT. Do you still want to know why you're pigheaded . . . Oh, you do bug me, you know.

DURAND. I don't know whether I bug you or not. Maybe I do bug you. But I'd really like to know why you say I'm pigheaded. Because, in the first place, I'm not pigheaded . . .

DUPONT. Not pigheaded? Not pigheaded, when you refuse, when you deny, when you resist, when you insist, in short, after I've made it all perfectly clear to you . . .

DURAND. Perfectly unclear . . . you haven't convinced me. You're the one who's pigheaded. As for me, I'm not pigheaded.

DUPONT. Yes, you are pigheaded . . .

DURAND. No.

DUPONT. Yes.

DURAND. No.

DUPONT. Yes.

DURAND. I tell you no.

DUPONT. I tell you yes.

DURAND. But I just told you no.

DUPONT. And I just told you yes.

DURAND. You don't need to keep on saying yes to me, it's no, no . . . NO.

DUPONT. You are pigheaded, you can see very well that you are pigheaded . . .

DURAND. You're reversing our roles, my friend . . . Don't knock over the potted plants . . . You're reversing our roles. If you are acting in good faith, you ought very well to realize that you're the one who's being pigheaded.

DUPONT. How could I be pigheaded? Nobody's pigheaded when he's in the right. And as you will come to see, I am right, that's all, I'm just plain right . . .

DURAND. You can't be right because I am right . . .

DUPONT. I beg your pardon, I am.

DURAND. No, I am.

DUPONT. No, I am.

DURAND. No, I am.

DUPONT. No, I.

DURAND. No, I.

DUPONT. No.

DURAND. No.

DUPONT. No.

DURAND. No.

DUPONT. No.

DURAND. No.

DUPONT. No.

DURAND. No. Look out for the potted plants.

DUPONT. Look out for the potted plants.

MARTIN (entering). Ah, at last you have come to an agreement.

DUPONT. Oh, no, far from it . . . I am not at all in agreement with him . . . (He points at DURAND.)

DURAND. I'm not at all in agreement with him. (He points at DUPONT.)

DUPONT. He denies the truth.

DURAND. He denies the truth.

DUPONT. He does.

DURAND. He does.

MARTIN. Oh . . . stop being so stupid . . . And look out for the potted plants. Characters in a play don't always have to be even more stupid than in real life.

DURAND. We're doing the best we can.

DUPONT (to MARTIN). In the first place, you bug me, you and your big cigar.

MARTIN. And you think you two don't bug me, pacing around like this, with your hands behind your backs, neither one of you willing to make the least concession . . . You'll end up by making me dizzy and by knocking over the potted plants . . .

DURAND. Well, you and your disgusting smoking are going to make me vomit . . . It's absurd to go around smoking like a chimney all day long.

MARTIN. Chimneys aren't the only things that smoke.

DUPONT (to MARTIN). You smoke like a chimney that's not been cleaned out.

MARTIN (to DUPONT). What a banal comparison . . . You've got no imagination.

DURAND (to MARTIN). It's certainly true that Dupont has no imagination. But as for you, you haven't got any either . . .

DUPONT (to DURAND). And neither do you, my dear Durand.

MARTIN (to DUPONT). Nor do you, my dear Dupont.

DUPONT (*to* MARTIN). Nor do you, my dear Martin.

DURAND (*to* DUPONT). Nor do you, my dear Dupont. And don't call me my dear Durand anymore, I'm not your dear Durand.

DUPONT (*to* DURAND). Nor do you, my dear Durand, you've got no imagination. And don't call me my dear Dupont.

MARTIN (*to* DUPONT *and* DURAND). Don't call me your dear Martin, I'm not your dear Martin.

DUPONT (*to* MARTIN, *overlapping* DURAND). Don't call me your dear Durand, I'm not your dear Dupont.

DURAND (*to* MARTIN, *overlapping* DUPONT). Don't call me your dear Durand, I'm not your dear Durand.

MARTIN. In the first place, my cigar couldn't possibly bug you because I haven't got a cigar . . . Gentlemen, permit me to tell you that you both exaggerate. You exaggerate. I'm outside whatever is bothering you. So I can judge objectively.

DURAND. Good, judge . . .

DUPONT. Judge, then. Go ahead.

MARTIN. Permit me to tell you, freely, that you are not going about it in a way that will get you anywhere. Try to agree on one thing—find at least some basis for discussion, to make a dialogue possible.

DURAND (*to* MARTIN). No dialogue is possible with Monsieur (*He points at* DUPONT.), under these conditions. The conditions he proposes are not admissible.

DUPONT (*to* MARTIN). I'm not trying to get somewhere, at any cost. These are the conditions of Monsieur (*He points at* DURAND.) and they're dishonorable . . .

DURAND. Oh! what nerve . . . To pretend that my conditions are dishonorable . . .

MARTIN (*to* DUPONT). Let him explain.

DUPONT (*to* DURAND). Go ahead and explain.

MARTIN. Look out for the potted plants.

DUPONT. I shall explain. But I don't know if anyone will really listen to me, nor do I know if anyone will really understand me. However, understand me well, for if we're to understand each other, we have to understand each other, this is what Monsieur Durand doesn't manage to comprehend, and he's famous for his incomprehension.

DURAND (*to* DUPONT). You dare speak of my famous incomprehension. You know very well that it's your incomprehension that's famous. You're the one who has always refused to comprehend me.

DUPONT (*to* DURAND). Now you're going too far. Your bad faith is 'self-evident. A child of three months would understand me, that is if it were a baby in good faith.

DUPONT (*to* MARTIN). You heard him, huh? You heard that . . .

DURAND (*to* DUPONT). That's going too far . . . You're the one who doesn't want to comprehend. (*To* MARTIN.) Did you hear what he had the nerve to claim?

MARTIN. Gentlemen, my friends, let's not waste time. Let's get down to it, you're talking but you're not saying anything.

DUPONT (*to* MARTIN). Who, me? I'm talking without saying anything?

DURAND (*to* MARTIN). What, you dare say that I'm talking without saying anything?

MARTIN. Excuse me, I didn't mean to say exactly that you were talking without saying anything, no, no, it wasn't entirely that.

DUPONT (*to* MARTIN). How could you say that we were talking without saying anything, when you are the one who has just said that there was talking without saying anything, although it is absolutely impossible to talk without saying anything inasmuch as every time one says something, one talks and contrariwise every time one talks one says something.

MARTIN (*to* DUPONT). Let's grant that I said what I said about your talking without saying anything, now this doesn't mean that you always talk without saying anything. There are times, however, when one says more in saying nothing and when one says nothing in talking too much. This depends on the situation and on the people involved. Now just how much have you actually said during the last few minutes? Nothing, absolutely nothing. No matter who says so.

DURAND (*interrupting* MARTIN). Dupont's the one who talks without saying anything, not me.

DUPONT (*to* DURAND). You're the one.

DURAND (*to* DUPONT). You're the one.

MARTIN (*to* DUPONT *and* DURAND). You're the ones.

DUPONT (*to* DURAND *and* MARTIN). You're the ones.

MARTIN. No.

DUPONT. Yes.

DURAND (*to* DUPONT *and* MARTIN). You're talking without saying anything.

DUPONT. I, I'm talking without saying anything?

MARTIN (*to* DURAND *and* DUPONT). Yes, exactly, you're talking without saying anything.

DUPONT (*to* DURAND *and* MARTIN). You too, you're talking without saying anything.

MARTIN (*to* DUPONT *and* DURAND). You're the one who's talking without saying anything . . .

DURAND (*to* DUPONT *and* MARTIN). You're the one who's talking without saying anything . . .

DUPONT (*to* DURAND *and* MARTIN). You're the one who's talking without saying anything.

MARTIN (*to* DURAND). It's you.

DURAND (*to* MARTIN). It's you.

DUPONT (*to* DURAND). It's you.

DURAND (*to* DUPONT). It's you.

DUPONT (*to* MARTIN). It's you.

MARTIN (*to* DURAND *and* DUPONT). ⎤ You!
DURAND (*to* MARTIN *and* DUPONT). ⎬ You!
DUPONT (*to* MARTIN *and* DURAND). ⎦ You!

(*Exactly at this moment, the* PRETTY LADY *enters.*)

THE LADY. Good day, gentlemen . . . Look out for the potted plants. (*The three men halt suddenly and turn toward her.*) What are you squabbling about? (*She simpers.*) Come now, gentlemen . . .

DUPONT. Oh, dear lady, here you are at last and now you're going to rescue us from this impasse.

DURAND. Oh, dear lady, you're going to see where bad faith has brought us . . .

MARTIN (*interrupting* DURAND). Oh, dear lady, let me tell you just what's happened.

DUPONT (*to the two other men*). I'm the one who will tell her what's happened, for this lovely lady is my fiancée . . .

(*The* PRETTY LADY *remains standing and smiling.*)

DURAND (*to the other two men*). This lovely lady is my fiancée.

MARTIN (*to the other two men*). This lovely lady is my fiancée.

DUPONT (*to the* PRETTY LADY). My dear, tell these gentlemen that you are my fiancée.

MARTIN (*to* DUPONT). You're mistaken, she is my fiancée.

DURAND (*to the* PRETTY LADY). Dear lady, tell these gentlemen that you are really . . .

DUPONT (*to* DURAND, *interrupting*). You're mistaken, she is mine.

MARTIN (*to the* LADY). Dear lady, please tell . . .

DURAND (*to* MARTIN). You're mistaken, she's mine.

DUPONT (*to the* LADY). Dear lady . . .

DUPONT (*to* MARTIN). You're mistaken, she's mine.

DURAND (*to the* LADY). Dear lady . . .

DUPONT (*to* MARTIN). You're mistaken, she's mine.

MARTIN (*to the* LADY). Dear lady, please say that . . .

DURAND (*to* DUPONT). You're mistaken, she's mine.

DUPONT (*to the* PRETTY LADY, *violently pulling her toward him by her arm*). Oh, dear lady . . .

(*The* PRETTY LADY *loses a shoe.*)

DURAND (*violently pulling the* LADY *by her other arm*). Let me embrace you.

(*The* LADY *loses her other shoe, and one glove comes off in* DUPONT'S *hands.*)

MARTIN (*who has gone to pick up a potted plant, making the* LADY *turn toward him*). Please accept this bouquet.

(*He sticks the potted plant in her arms.*)

THE LADY. Oh, thank you.

DUPONT (*turning the* LADY *toward him and putting another potted plant in her arms*). Do take these pretty flowers. (*The* LADY *is jostled and loses her hat.*)

THE LADY. Thank you, thank you . . .

DURAND (*same business as* DUPONT). These flowers belong to you, just as my heart belongs to you . . .

THE LADY. I'm delighted . . . (*Her arms are loaded down with the potted plants and she's dropped her purse.*)

MARTIN (*violently pulling her toward him and shouting*). Embrace me, embrace me . . . (*The* LADY *loses her cape and furs.*)

DURAND (*same business*). Embrace me.

DUPONT (*same business*). Embrace me. (*They continue this business for several moments; the* LADY *drops the flowers, her skirt comes undone, and her clothes are rumpled. The three men alternatively tear her from each other's arms as they move about the table.*)

THE LADY. Oh, damn . . . Leave me alone.

DUPONT (*to* MARTIN). Leave her alone.

MARTIN (*to* DURAND). Leave her alone.

DURAND (*to* DUPONT). Leave her alone.

EACH OF THE MEN (*to the other two*). It's you she's telling to leave her alone.

THE LADY (*to the three men*). Leave me alone, all of you.

DURAND, DUPONT, MARTIN (*astonished*). Me? me? me?

(*All movement stops. The* LADY, *rumpled, unhooked, winded, half undressed, moves down to the footlights.*)

THE LADY. Ladies and gentlemen, I agree with you entirely. This is completely idiotic.

CURTAIN

Development

INTERPRETATION

1. Ionesco has commented that his theater is not an exercise in absurdity but rather a realistic denunciation of our decaying language. *(a)* What evidence is there in *Foursome* of the failure of language to communicate? *(b)* What are some of the more familiar clichés or slogans that the characters use? *(c)* Is Ionesco talking without saying anything?

2. There are a number of references in *Foursome* to states of "good faith" and "bad faith." *(a)* What do these phrases mean in everyday usage? *(b)* What relevance have they to the problems of language and communication? *(c)* Is there any indication that they still have a meaning in *Foursome*? Explain.

3. Ionesco has said that the obtrusive presence of objects in his plays implies a spiritual absence. *(a)* Are "potted plants" an appropriate symbol for materialism? Explain. *(b)* Why do you think all the characters in *Foursome* worry about knocking over the potted plants? *(c)* What is ironic in the offer of a potted plant as a bouquet? *(d)* Do you feel that The Pretty Lady is above the level of the potted plants? Why or why not?

4. *Foursome* concludes with the lines: "Ladies and gentlemen, I agree with you entirely. This is completely idiotic." *(a)* To what things might the pronoun *this* refer? *(b)* In what ways does the conclusion dramatize the meaning of the word *alienation*?

5. Throughout his career Ionesco has denounced the tendency of men to divide themselves into ideological camps, a division which, he feels, forces them to become boring, didactic, inquisitorial, and, ultimately, dictatorial, violent, and inhuman. *(a)* What tendencies in *Foursome* might well lead to violence? *(b)* In what way does the division into opposing factions seem to dehumanize the characters? *(c)* Do you think The Pretty Lady might be said to represent unideological man? Why or why not?

TECHNIQUE

1. How has Ionesco made Dupont, Durand, and Martin interesting in spite of the fact that their speeches are largely interchangeable and nonsensical?

2. Ionesco has written that his plays are dramatic progressions in which the stages of development are different states of mind that become increasingly intense. *(a)* Locate the progressive stages of development in *Foursome*. *(b)* At what point does each stage become most intense? *(c)* In what way is the impact of the conclusion dependent upon this progressive structure? Explain.

EXTENSIONS

1. *(a)* If you were directing a production of *Foursome,* at what points would you work to amuse your audience? *(b)* How would you utilize the movements, manners, or expressions of your actors, the props, costumes, or the set in order to enliven your production?

2. One interpretation of *Foursome* might be that, given the nature of the characters and their circumstances, any resolution of their disagreement is highly improbable. *(a)* What situation are you familiar with that might be compared to this one? *(b)* What are the similarities and/or differences between the two?

The Guest

ALBERT CAMUS[1] / France

(1913–1960)

translated from the French by Justin O'Brien

The schoolmaster was watching the two men climb toward him. One was on horseback, the other on foot. They had not yet tackled the abrupt rise leading to the schoolhouse built on the hillside. They were toiling onward, making slow progress in the snow, among the stones, on the vast expanse of the high, deserted plateau. From time to time the horse stumbled. Without hearing anything yet, he could see the breath issuing from the horse's nostrils. One of the men, at least, knew the region. They were following the trail although it had disappeared days ago under a layer of dirty white snow. The schoolmaster calculated that it would take them half an hour to get onto the hill. It was cold; he went back into the school to get a sweater.

He crossed the empty, frigid classroom. On the blackboard the four rivers of France, drawn with four different colored chalks, had been flowing toward their estuaries for the past three days. Snow had suddenly fallen in mid-October after eight months of drought without the transition of rain, and the twenty pupils, more or less, who lived in the villages scattered over the plateau had stopped coming. With fair weather they would return. Daru now heated only the single room that was his lodging, adjoining the classroom and giving also onto the plateau to the east. Like the class windows, his window looked to the south too. On that side the school was a few kilo-

meters from the point where the plateau began to slope toward the south. In clear weather could be seen the purple mass of the mountain range where the gap opened onto the desert.

Somewhat warmed, Daru returned to the window from which he had first seen the two men. They were no longer visible. Hence they must have tackled the rise. The sky was not so dark, for the snow had stopped falling during the night. The morning had opened with a dirty light which had scarcely become brighter as the ceiling of clouds lifted. At two in the afternoon it seemed as if the day were merely beginning. But still this was better than those three days when the thick snow was falling amidst unbroken darkness with little gusts of wind that rattled the double door of the classroom. Then Daru had spent long hours in his room, leaving it only to go to the shed and feed the chickens or get some coal. Fortunately the delivery truck from Tadjid,[2] the nearest village to the north, had brought his supplies two days before the blizzard. It would return in forty-eight hours.

1. *Camus* (kä mü⁄). 2. *Tadjid* (tä⁄ jid), a city in the plateau region of Algeria between the Mediterranean Sea to the north and the Sahara Desert to the south.

Besides, he had enough to resist a siege, for the little room was cluttered with bags of wheat that the administration left as a stock to distribute to those of his pupils whose families had suffered from the drought. Actually they had all been victims because they were all poor. Every day Daru would distribute a ration to the children. They had missed it, he knew, during these bad days. Possibly one of the fathers or big brothers would come this afternoon and he could supply them with grain. It was just a matter of carrying them over to the next harvest. Now shiploads of wheat were arriving from France and the worst was over. But it would be hard to forget that poverty, that army of ragged ghosts wandering in the sunlight, the plateaus burned to a cinder month after month, the earth shriveled up little by little, literally scorched, every stone bursting into dust under one's foot. The sheep had died then by thousands and even a few men, here and there, sometimes without anyone's knowing.

In contrast with such poverty, he who lived almost like a monk in his remote schoolhouse, nonetheless satisfied with the little he had and with the rough life, had felt like a lord with his white-washed walls, his narrow couch, his unpainted shelves, his well, and his weekly provision of water and food. And suddenly this snow, without warning, without the foretaste of rain. This is the way the region was, cruel to live in, even without men—who didn't help matters either. But Daru had been born here. Everywhere else, he felt exiled.

He stepped out onto the terrace in front of the schoolhouse. The two men were now halfway up the slope. He recognized the horseman as Balducci,[3] the old gendarme[4] he had known for a long time. Balducci was holding on the end of a rope an Arab who was walking behind him with hands bound and head lowered. The gendarme waved a greeting to which Daru did not reply, lost as he was in contemplation of the Arab dressed in a faded blue jellaba,[5] his feet in sandals but covered with socks of heavy raw wool, his head surmounted by a narrow, short chèche.[6] They were approaching. Balducci was holding back his horse in order not to hurt the Arab, and the group was advancing slowly.

Within earshot, Balducci shouted: "One hour to do the three kilometers from El Ameur!" Daru did not answer. Short and square in his thick sweater, he watched them climb. Not once had the Arab raised his head. "Hello," said Daru when they got up onto the terrace. "Come in and warm up." Balducci painfully got down from his horse without letting go the rope. From under his bristling mustache he smiled at the schoolmaster. His little dark eyes, deep-set under a tanned forehead, and his mouth surrounded with wrinkles made him look attentive and studious. Daru took the bridle, led the horse to the shed, and came back to the two men, who were now waiting for him in the school. He led them into his room. "I am going to heat up the classroom," he said. "We'll be more comfortable there." When he entered the room again, Balducci was on the couch. He had undone the rope tying him to the Arab, who had squatted near the stove. His hands still bound, the chèche pushed back on his head, he was looking toward the window. At first Daru noticed only his huge lips, fat, smooth, almost Negroid; yet his nose was straight, his eyes were dark and full of fever. The chèche revealed an obstinate forehead and, under the weathered skin now rather discolored by the cold, the whole face had a restless and rebellious look that struck Daru when the Arab, turning his face toward him, looked him straight in the eyes. "Go into the other room," said the schoolmaster, "and I'll make you some mint tea." "Thanks," Balducci said. "What a nui-

---

3. *Balducci* (bal dü′ chē). **4.** *gendarme* (zhän′-därm), policeman. [*French*] **5.** *jellaba* (jə la′ bə), a hooded, loose-fitting robe worn in North Africa. **6.** *chèche* (shāsh′ ya), a round, close-fitting cap with a tassel or tuft on top.

sance! How I long for retirement." And addressing his prisoner in Arabic: "Come on, you." The Arab got up and, slowly, holding his bound wrists in front of him, went into the classroom.

With the tea, Daru brought a chair. But Balducci was already enthroned on the nearest pupil's desk and the Arab had squatted against the teacher's platform facing the stove, which stood between the desk and the window. When he held out the glass of tea to the prisoner, Daru hesitated at the sight of his bound hands. "He might perhaps be untied." "Certainly," said Balducci. "That was for the journey." He started to get to his feet. But Daru, setting the glass on the floor, had knelt beside the Arab. Without saying anything, the Arab watched him with his feverish eyes. Once his hands were free, he rubbed his swollen wrists against each other, took the glass of tea, and sucked up the burning liquid in swift little sips.

"Good," said Daru. "And where are you headed?"

Balducci withdrew his mustache from the tea. "Here, my boy."

"Odd pupils! And you're spending the night?"

"No. I'm going back to El Ameur. And you will deliver this fellow to Tinguit. He is expected at police headquarters."

Balducci was looking at Daru with a friendly little smile.

"What's this story?" asked the schoolmaster. "Are you pulling my leg?"

"No, my boy. Those are the orders."

"The orders? I'm not . . ." Daru hesitated, not wanting to hurt the old Corsican. "I mean, that's not my job."

"What! What's the meaning of that? In wartime[7] people do all kinds of jobs."

"Then I'll wait for the declaration of war!"

Balducci nodded.

"O.K. But the orders exist and they concern you too. Things are brewing, it appears. There is talk of a forthcoming revolt. We are mobilized, in a way."

Daru still had his obstinate look.

"Listen, my boy," Balducci said. "I like you and you must understand. There's only a dozen of us at El Ameur to patrol throughout the whole territory of a small department[8] and I must get back in a hurry. I was told to hand this man over to you and return without delay. He couldn't be kept there. His village was beginning to stir; they wanted to take him back. You must take him to Tinguit tomorrow before the day is over. Twenty kilometers shouldn't worry a husky fellow like you. After that, all will be over. You'll come back to your pupils and your comfortable life."

Behind the wall the horse could be heard snorting and pawing the earth. Daru was looking out the window. Decidedly, the weather was clearing and the light was increasing over the snowy plateau. When all the snow was melted, the sun would take over again and once more would burn the fields of stone. For days, still, the unchanging sky would shed its dry light on the solitary expanse where nothing had any connection with man.

"After all," he said, turning around toward Balducci, "what did he do?" And, before the gendarme had opened his mouth, he asked: "Does he speak French?"

"No, not a word. We had been looking for him for a month, but they were hiding him. He killed his cousin."

"Is he against us?"

"I don't think so. But you can never be sure."

"Why did he kill?"

"A family squabble, I think. One owed the other grain, it seems. It's not at all clear. In short, he killed his cousin with a billhook. You know, like a sheep, *kreezk!*"

Balducci made the gesture of drawing a blade across his throat and the Arab, his attention attracted, watched him with a sort of anxiety. Daru felt a sudden wrath

---

7. *wartime,* a reference to the state of continual crisis and revolt from 1954 until Algeria gained its independence from France in 1962. 8. *department,* an administrative district in the French system of government.

against the man, against all men with their rotten spite, their tireless hates, their blood lust.

But the kettle was singing on the stove. He served Balducci more tea, hesitated, then served the Arab again, who, a second time, drank avidly. His raised arms made the jellaba fall open and the schoolmaster saw his thin, muscular chest.

"Thanks, my boy," Balducci said. "And now, I'm off."

He got up and went toward the Arab, taking a small rope from his pocket.

"What are you doing?" Daru asked dryly.

Balducci, disconcerted, showed him the rope.

"Don't bother."

The old gendarme hesitated. "It's up to you. Of course, you are armed?"

"I have my shotgun."

"Where?"

"In the trunk."

"You ought to have it near your bed."

"Why? I have nothing to fear."

"You're mad. If there's an uprising, no one is safe, we're all in the same boat."

"I'll defend myself. I'll have time to see them coming."

Balducci began to laugh, then suddenly the mustache covered the white teeth.

"You'll have time? O.K. That's just what I was saying. You have always been a little cracked. That's why I like you, my son was like that."

At the same time he took out his revolver and put it on the desk.

"Keep it; I don't need two weapons from here to El Ameur."

The revolver shone against the black paint of the table. When the gendarme turned toward him, the schoolmaster caught the smell of leather and horse-flesh.

"Listen, Balducci," Daru said suddenly, "every bit of this disgusts me, and most of all your fellow here. But I won't hand him over. Fight, yes, if I have to. But not that."

The old gendarme stood in front of him and looked at him severely.

"You're being a fool," he said slowly. "I don't like it either. You don't get used to putting a rope on a man even after years of it, and you're even ashamed—yes, ashamed. But you can't let them have their way."

"I won't hand him over," Daru said again.

"It's an order, my boy, and I repeat it."

"That's right. Repeat to them what I've said to you: I won't hand him over."

Balducci made a visible effort to reflect. He looked at the Arab and at Daru. At last he decided.

"No, I won't tell them anything. If you want to drop us, go ahead; I'll not denounce you. I have an order to deliver the prisoner and I'm doing so. And now you'll just sign this paper for me."

"There's no need. I'll not deny that you left him with me."

"Don't be mean with me. I know you'll tell the truth. You're from hereabouts and you are a man. But you must sign, that's the rule."

Daru opened his drawer, took out a little square bottle of purple ink, the red wooden penholder with the "sergeant-major" pen he used for making models of penmanship, and signed. The gendarme carefully folded the paper and put it into his wallet. Then he moved toward the door.

"I'll see you off," Daru said.

"No," said Balducci. "There's no use being polite. You insulted me."

He looked at the Arab, motionless in the same spot, sniffed peevishly, and turned away toward the door. "Good-by, son," he said. The door shut behind him. Balducci appeared suddenly outside the window and then disappeared. His footsteps were muffled by the snow. The horse stirred on the other side of the wall and several chickens fluttered in fright. A moment later Balducci reappeared outside the window leading the horse by the bridle. He walked toward the little rise without turning around and disappeared from sight with the horse following him.

A big stone could be heard bouncing down. Daru walked back toward the prisoner, who, without stirring, never took his eyes off him. "Wait," the schoolmaster said in Arabic and went toward the bedroom. As he was going through the door, he had a second thought, went to the desk, took the revolver, and stuck it in his pocket. Then, without looking back, he went into his room.

For some time he lay on his couch watching the sky gradually close over, listening to the silence. It was this silence that had seemed painful to him during the first days here, after the war. He had requested a post in the little town at the base of the foothills separating the upper plateaus from the desert. There, rocky walls, green and black to the north, pink and lavender to the south, marked the frontier of eternal summer. He had been named to a post farther north, on the plateau itself. In the beginning, the solitude and the silence had been hard for him on these wastelands peopled only by stones. Occasionally, furrows suggested cultivation, but they had been dug to uncover a certain kind of stone good for building. The only plowing here was to harvest rocks. Elsewhere a thin layer of soil accumulated in the hollows would be scraped out to enrich paltry village gardens. This is the way it was: bare rock covered three quarters of the region. Towns sprang up, flourished, then disappeared; men came by, loved one another or fought bitterly, then died. No one in this desert, neither he nor his guest, mattered. And yet, outside this desert neither of them, Daru knew, could have really lived.

When he got up, no noise came from the classroom. He was amazed at the unmixed joy he derived from the mere thought that the Arab might have fled and that he would be alone with no decision to make. But the prisoner was there. He had merely stretched out between the stove and the desk. With eyes open, he was staring at the ceiling. In that position, his thick lips were particularly noticeable, giving him a pouting look. "Come," said Daru. The Arab got up and followed him. In the bedroom, the schoolmaster pointed to a chair near the table under the window. The Arab sat down without taking his eyes off Daru.

"Are you hungry?"

"Yes," the prisoner said.

Daru set the table for two. He took flour and oil, shaped a cake in a frying-pan, and lighted the little stove that functioned on bottled gas. While the cake was cooking, he went out to the shed to get cheese, eggs, dates, and condensed milk. When the cake was done he set it on the window sill to cool, heated some condensed milk diluted with water, and beat up the eggs into an omelet. In one of his motions he knocked against the revolver stuck in his right pocket. He set the bowl down, went into the classroom and put the revolver in his desk drawer. When he came back to the room, night was falling. He put on the light and served the Arab. "Eat," he said. The Arab took a piece of the cake, lifted it eagerly to his mouth, and stopped short.

"And you?" he asked.

"After you. I'll eat too."

The thick lips opened slightly. The Arab hesitated, then bit into the cake determinedly.

The meal over, the Arab looked at the schoolmaster. "Are you the judge?"

"No, I'm simply keeping you until tomorrow."

"Why do you eat with me?"

"I'm hungry."

The Arab fell silent. Daru got up and went out. He brought back a folding bed from the shed, set it up between the table and the stove, at right angles to his own bed. From a large suitcase which, upright in a corner, served as a shelf for papers, he took two blankets and arranged them on the camp bed. Then he stopped, felt useless, and sat down on his bed. There was nothing more to do or to get ready. He had to look at this man. He looked at him, therefore, trying to imagine his face bursting with rage. He couldn't do so. He could see nothing but the dark yet shining eyes and the animal mouth.

"Why did you kill him?" he asked in a voice whose hostile tone surprised him.

The Arab looked away.

"He ran away. I ran after him."

He raised his eyes to Daru again and they were full of a sort of woeful interrogation. "Now what will they do to me?"

"Are you afraid?"

He stiffened, turning his eyes away.

"Are you sorry?"

The Arab stared at him openmouthed. Obviously he did not understand. Daru's annoyance was growing. At the same time he felt awkward and self-conscious with his big body wedged between the two beds.

"Lie down there," he said impatiently. "That's your bed."

The Arab didn't move. He called to Daru:

"Tell me!"

The schoolmaster looked at him.

"Is the gendarme coming back tomorrow?"

"I don't know."

"Are you coming with us?"

"I don't know. Why?"

The prisoner got up and stretched out on top of the blankets, his feet toward the window. The light from the electric bulb shone straight into his eyes and he closed them at once.

"Why?" Daru repeated, standing beside the bed.

The Arab opened his eyes under the blinding light and looked at him, trying not to blink.

"Come with us," he said.

In the middle of the night, Daru was still not asleep. He had gone to bed after undressing completely; he generally slept naked. But when he suddenly realized that he had nothing on, he hesitated. He felt vulnerable and the temptation came to him to put on his clothes again. Then he shrugged his shoulders; after all, he wasn't a child and, if need be, he could break his adversary in two. From his bed he could observe him, lying on his back, still motionless with his eyes closed under the harsh light. When Daru turned out the light, the darkness seemed to coagulate all of a sudden. Little by little, the night came back to life in the window where the starless sky was stirring gently. The schoolmaster soon made out the body lying at his feet. The Arab still did not move, but his eyes seemed open. A faint wind was prowling around the schoolhouse. Perhaps it would drive away the clouds and the sun would reappear.

During the night the wind increased. The hens fluttered a little and then were silent. The Arab turned over on his side with his back to Daru, who thought he heard him moan. Then he listened for his guest's breathing, which had become heavier and more regular. He listened to that breath so close to him and mused without being able to go to sleep. In this room where he had been sleeping alone for a year, this presence bothered him. But it bothered him also by imposing on him a sort of brotherhood he knew well but refused to accept in the present circumstances. Men who share the same rooms, soldiers or prisoners, develop a strange alliance as if, having cast off their armor with their clothing, they fraternized every evening, over and above their differences, in the ancient community of dream and fatigue. But Daru shook himself; he didn't like such musings, and it was essential to sleep.

A little later, however, when the Arab stirred slightly, the schoolmaster was still not asleep. When the prisoner made a second move, he stiffened, on the alert. The Arab was lifting himself slowly on his arms with almost the motion of a sleepwalker. Seated upright in bed, he waited motionless without turning his head toward Daru, as if he were listening attentively. Daru did not stir; it had just occurred to him that the revolver was still in the drawer of his desk. It was better to act at once. Yet he continued to observe the prisoner, who, with the same slithery motion, put his feet on the ground, waited again, then began to stand up slowly. Daru was about to call out to him when the Arab began to walk, in a quite natural but extraordinarily silent way. He was heading toward the door at the end of the room that opened into the shed. He lifted the latch with precaution and went out, pushing the door behind him but without shutting it. Daru had not stirred. "He is running away," he merely thought. "Good riddance!" Yet he listened attentively. The hens were not fluttering; the guest must be on the plateau. A faint sound of water reached him, and he didn't know what it was until the Arab again stood framed in the doorway, closed the door carefully, and came back to bed without a sound. Then Daru turned his back on him and fell asleep. Still later he seemed, from the depths of his sleep, to hear furtive steps around the schoolhouse. "I'm dreaming! I'm dreaming!" he repeated to himself. And he went on sleeping.

When he awoke, the sky was clear; the loose window let in a cold, pure air. The Arab was asleep, hunched up under the blankets now, his mouth open, utterly relaxed. But when Daru shook him, he started dreadfully, staring at Daru with wild eyes as if he had never seen him and such a frightened expression that the schoolmaster stepped back. "Don't be afraid. It's me. You must eat." The Arab nodded his head and said yes. Calm had returned to his face, but his expression was vacant and listless.

The coffee was ready. They drank it seated together on the folding bed as they munched their pieces of the cake. Then Daru led the Arab under the shed and showed him the tap where he washed. He went back into the room, folded the blankets and the bed, made his own bed and put the room in order. Then he went through the classroom and out onto the terrace. The sun was already rising in the blue sky; a soft, bright light was bathing the deserted plateau. On the ridge the

snow was melting in spots. The stones were about to reappear. Crouched on the edge of the plateau, the schoolmaster looked at the deserted expanse. He thought of Balducci. He had hurt him, for he had sent him off in a way as if he didn't want to be associated with him. He could still hear the gendarme's farewell and, without knowing why, he felt strangely empty and vulnerable. At that moment, from the other side of the schoolhouse, the prisoner coughed. Daru listened to him almost despite himself and then, furious, threw a pebble that whistled through the air before sinking into the snow. That man's stupid crime revolted him, but to hand him over was contrary to honor. Merely thinking of it made him smart with humiliation. And he cursed at one and the same time his own people who had sent him this Arab and the Arab too who had dared to kill and not managed to get away. Daru got up, walked in a circle on the terrace, waited motionless, and then went back into the schoolhouse.

The Arab, leaning over the cement floor of the shed, was washing his teeth with two fingers. Daru looked at him and said: "Come." He went back into the room ahead of the prisoner. He slipped a hunting-jacket on over his sweater and put on walking-shoes. Standing, he waited until the Arab had put on his *chèche* and sandals. They went into the classroom and the schoolmaster pointed to the exit, saying: "Go ahead." The fellow didn't budge. "I'm coming," said Daru. The Arab went out. Daru went back into the room and made a package of pieces of rusk, dates, and sugar. In the classroom, before going out, he hesitated a second in front of his desk, then crossed the threshold and locked the door. "That's the way," he said. He started toward the east, followed by the prisoner. But, a short distance from the schoolhouse, he thought he heard a slight sound behind them. He retraced his steps and examined the surroundings of the house; there was no one there. The

Arab watched him without seeming to understand.

"Come on," said Daru.

They walked for an hour and rested beside a sharp peak of limestone. The snow was melting faster and faster and the sun was drinking up the puddles at once, rapidly cleaning the plateau, which gradually dried and vibrated like the air itself. When they resumed walking, the ground rang under their feet. From time to time a bird rent the space in front of them with a joyful cry. Daru breathed in deeply the fresh morning light. He felt a sort of rapture before the vast familiar expanse, now almost entirely yellow under its dome of blue sky. They walked an hour more, descending toward the south. They reached a level height made up of crumbly rocks. From there on, the plateau sloped down, eastward, toward a low plain where there were a few spindly trees and, to the south, toward outcroppings of rock that gave the landscape a chaotic look.

Daru surveyed the two directions. There was nothing but the sky on the horizon. Not a man could be seen. He turned toward the Arab, who was looking at him blankly. Daru held out the package to him. "Take it," he said. "There are dates, bread, and sugar. You can hold out for two days. Here are a thousand francs too." The Arab took the package and the money but kept his full hands at chest level as if he didn't know what to do with what was being given him. "Now look," the schoolmaster said as he pointed in the direction of the east, "there's the way to Tinguit. You have a two-hour walk. At Tinguit you'll find the administration and the police. They are expecting you." The Arab looked toward the east, still holding the package and the money against his chest. Daru took his elbow and turned him rather roughly toward the south. At the foot of the height on which they stood could be seen a faint path. "That's the trail across the plateau. In a day's walk from here you'll find pasturelands and the first nomads. They'll take you in and shelter you according to their law." The Arab had now turned toward Daru and a sort of panic was visible in his expression. "Listen," he said. Daru shook his head: "No, be quiet. Now I'm leaving you." He turned his back on him, took two long steps in the direction of the school, looked hesitantly at the motionless Arab, and started off again. For a few minutes he heard nothing but his own step resounding on the cold ground and did not turn his head. A moment later, however, he turned around. The Arab was still there on the edge of the hill, his arms hanging now, and he was looking at the schoolmaster. Daru felt something rise in his throat. But he swore with impatience, waved vaguely, and started off again. He had already gone some distance when he again stopped and looked. There was no longer anyone on the hill.

Daru hesitated. The sun was now rather high in the sky and was beginning to beat down on his head. The schoolmaster retraced his steps, at first somewhat uncertainly, then with decision. When he reached the little hill, he was bathed in sweat. He climbed it as fast as he could and stopped, out of breath, at the top. The rock-fields to the south stood out sharply against the blue sky, but on the plain to the east a steamy heat was already rising. And in that slight haze, Daru, with heavy heart, made out the Arab walking slowly on the road to prison.

A little later, standing before the window of the classroom, the schoolmaster was watching the clear light bathing the whole surface of the plateau, but he hardly saw it. Behind him on the blackboard, among the winding French rivers, sprawled the clumsily chalked-up words he had just read: "You handed over our brother. You will pay for this." Daru looked at the sky, the plateau, and, beyond, the invisible lands stretching all the way to the sea. In this vast landscape he had loved so much, he was alone.

THE END

Development

INTERPRETATION

1. *(a)* Describe the region where Daru lives. *(b)* What perspective does this setting give to the lives of human beings? *(c)* Why do you think that self-interest seems to rule the land? *(d)* What bond holds Daru and the Arab to this region?

2. *(a)* What does Balducci mean when he says that Daru has "always been a little cracked"? *(b)* Describe the attitude that underlies Balducci's argument that Daru should just deliver the prisoner and then come back to his pupils and his comfortable life. *(c)* Why does Balducci feel that Daru has insulted him?

3. *(a)* Why doesn't Daru want to admit the existence of a bond between himself and the Arab? *(b)* In what ways do Daru's actions acknowledge such a brotherhood? *(c)* Do you think that the Arab also feels committed to Daru? Explain.

4. *(a)* Why do you think Daru feels "empty and vulnerable" (page 356, column 2, line 10)? *(b)* Would you agree that handing the Arab over is "contrary to honour"? Explain your opinion. *(c)* Is Daru's vulnerability heroic? Why or why not?

5. Daru gives the Arab his freedom and a choice of clearly marked paths. *(a)* Which path does the Arab choose? *(b)* Why do you think he makes that choice? *(c)* How do you interpret Daru's emotion when he discovers the path the Arab has chosen? *(d)* Do you feel that, in terms of the story, there is either a right or a wrong way for the Arab to go? Explain.

6. "The Guest" ends very quietly. *(a)* Describe exactly what you think Daru is feeling in the final scene. *(b)* What are the ironies of his fate? *(c)* If Daru survives the immediate threat to his life, do you think he will have the strength to endure his alienation? Why or why not?

TECHNIQUE

1. Trace the course of the changing weather throughout "The Guest." In what way is it related to the dramatic conflict?

2. In what way does Camus use each of the following details to supply us with information about Daru's attitudes and character: *(a)* the bags of wheat; *(b)* the Arab's manacle of rope; *(c)* the guns; and *(d)* the food and drink?

EXTENSIONS

1. There are some who believe that only a profound commitment to a cause can save a man's life from becoming futile and absurd. *(a)* Is Daru's alienation the result of his refusal to commit himself to a cause? Why or why not? *(b)* Can one man do for another more than Daru has done for the Arab? Explain your opinion.

2. Daru's attitude toward life is an ambivalent one, compounded of love for the physical world and disgust for the brutality of man. *(a)* Do you feel that his evaluation of human nature stems from immaturity, cynicism, or insight? Explain. *(b)* Is a purely emotional attachment to life, such as Daru's, bound to be superficial? Why or why not?

3. Camus said that if a man simply says who he is, he will help himself and others to live; but that if he is silent or lies, everything around him will be condemned to disaster. Daru has not been afraid to say who he is, yet everything around him seems condemned. Do you feel that, ultimately, Daru's protest has helped himself and others? Why or why not?

Comparison

1. Some of the characters in this unit might sympathize with the narrator of "A Hunger Artist" when he says, "To fight against this lack of understanding, against a whole world of non-understanding, was impossible." In these selections, the impossibility seems to result not because people are unable to understand but because they don't want to. *(a)* Choose a character or group from each selection and explain why you feel each doesn't want to understand. *(b)* Compare your four choices and discuss what you find as the main similarities and/or differences in their motivations.

2. *(a)* Describe the view of man that emerges from each selection. *(b)* What are the similarities and/or differences in the tone of each appraisal? *(c)* Do you feel it is unfortunate or admirable to be alienated from the society described by each author? Explain.

3. Reading the selections in this unit, one can feel fairly confident that he understands the attitudes and intentions of Moravia and Camus, but is apt to be less sure of Kafka and Ionesco. *(a)* What is different in the approach to literature characterized by these two groups? *(b)* Do you feel that this difference in approach was instrumental in determining which selection you liked most and least in this unit? Explain.

4. The public's fascination for the panther in "A Hunger Artist" might well exemplify a trend toward dehumanization. If this fascination were to become fanatical, what characters from the other stories might be recruited to a cult of pantherism? Explain your reasoning.

5. The popular classification of personalities as introverts and extroverts seems to carry over into these stories of the alienated. *(a)* What similarities in behavior do you find among the hunger artist, Federico, and Daru as introverts? *(b)* What have the impresario, Giulia, and Dupont-Durand in common as extroverts? *(c)* Does either type of behavior seem a satisfactory cure for alienation? Why or why not?

6. The wasteland has become a prominent symbol in twentieth-century literature. *(a)* What are the human potentialities in these selections that seem, literally, wasted? *(b)* Do these treatments of futility imply that there is some dignity within man that deserves a better fate? Explain.

7. By the end of *Foursome* we recognize the irony of Martin's claim: "I'm outside whatever is bothering you. So I can judge objectively." *(a)* Is the judgment The Pretty Lady makes at the end of the play an objective one? Why or why not? *(b)* What do you think keeps the hunger artist, Lorenzo, and Daru from taking The Pretty Lady's way out? *(c)* Why do the characters in these selections find it so difficult to make judgments?

8. The selections in this group contain a number of objects and images which have a symbolic value in the modern world. *(a)* Choose one item from each selection and explain the way it is symbolic as a cause or effect of alienation. *(b)* Consider your four choices as a group and determine whether they help to explain why alienation is so prevalent a theme in the twentieth century.

9. The selections in this group attest to a profound isolation current in our world. None of them generates much hope for an eventual community of understanding among men. Do you feel that an author's ability to illuminate the experience of alienation is of value if he gives us no solution? Why or why not?

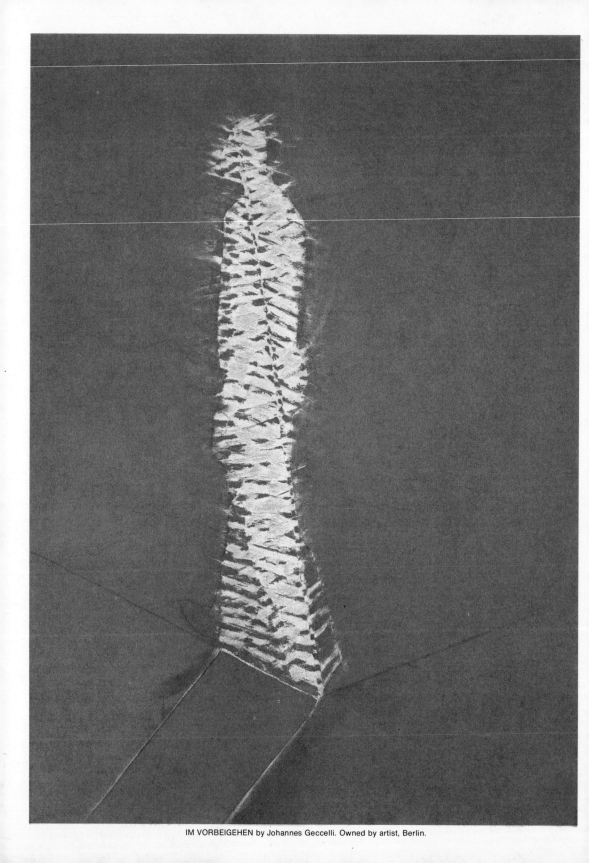

IM VORBEIGEHEN by Johannes Geccelli. Owned by artist, Berlin.

The Bound Man

The Bound Man

ILSE AICHINGER[1] / Austria
(1921 –   )

translated from the German by Eric Mosbacher

Sunlight on his face woke him, but made him shut his eyes again; it streamed unhindered down the slope, collected itself into rivulets, attracted swarms of flies, which flew low over his forehead, circled, sought to land, and were overtaken by fresh swarms. When he tried to whisk them away, he discovered that he was bound. A thin rope cut into his arms. He dropped them, opened his eyes again, and looked down at himself. His legs were tied all the way up to his thighs; a single length of rope was tied round his ankles, criss-crossed up his legs, and encircled his hips, his chest and his arms. He could not see where it was knotted. He showed no sign of fear or hurry, though he thought he was unable to move, until he dis-covered that the rope allowed his legs some free play and that round his body it was almost loose. His arms were tied to each other but not to his body, and had some free play too. This made him smile, and it occurred to him that perhaps children had been playing a practical joke on him.

He tried to feel for his knife, but again the rope cut softly into his flesh. He tried again, more cautiously this time, but his pocket was empty. Not only his knife,

1. *Aichinger* (i′ kin gr).

but the little money that he had on him, as well as his coat, were missing. His shoes had been pulled from his feet and taken too. When he moistened his lips he tasted blood, which had flowed from his temples down his cheeks, his chin, his neck, and under his shirt. His eyes were painful; if he kept them open for long he saw reddish stripes in the sky.

He decided to stand up. He drew his knees up as far as he could, rested his hands on the fresh grass and jerked himself to his feet. An elder-branch stroked his cheek, the sun dazzled him, and the rope cut into his flesh. He collapsed to the ground again, half out of his mind with pain, and then tried again. He went on trying until the blood started flowing from his hidden weals. Then he lay still again for a long while and let the sun and the flies do what they liked.   .

When he awoke for the second time the elder-bush had cast its shadow over him, and the coolness stored in it was pouring from between its branches. He must have been hit on the head. Then they must have laid him down carefully, just as a mother lays her baby behind a bush when she goes to work in the fields.

His chances all lay in the amount of free play allowed him by the rope. He dug his elbows into the ground and tested it. As soon as the rope tautened he stopped, and tried again more cautiously. If he had been able to reach the branch over his head he could have used it to drag himself to his feet, but he could not reach it. He laid his head back on the grass, rolled over, and struggled to his knees. He tested the ground with his toes, and then managed to stand up almost without effort.

A few paces away lay the path across the plateau, and in the grass were wild pinks and thistles in bloom. He tried to lift his foot to avoid trampling on them, but the rope round his ankles prevented him. He looked down at himself.

The rope was knotted at his ankles, and ran round his legs in a kind of playful pattern. He carefully bent and tried to loosen it, but, loose though it seemed to be, he could not make it any looser. To avoid treading on the thistles with his bare feet he hopped over them like a bird.

The cracking of a twig made him stop. People in this district were very prone to laughter. He was alarmed by the thought that he was in no position to defend himself. He hopped on until he reached the path. Bright fields stretched far below. He could see no sign of the nearest village, and if he could move no faster than this, night would fall before he reached it.

He tried walking, and discovered that he could put one foot before another if he lifted each foot a definite distance from the ground and then put it down again before the rope tautened. In the same way he could actually swing his arms a little.

After the first step he fell. He fell right across the path, and made the dust fly. He expected this to be a sign for the long-suppressed laughter to break out, but all remained quiet. He was alone. As soon as the dust had settled he got up and went on. He looked down and watched the rope slacken, grow taut, and then slacken again.

When the first glow-worms appeared he managed to look up. He felt in control of himself again, and his impatience to reach the nearest village faded.

Hunger made him light-headed, and he seemed to be going so fast that not even a motorcycle could have overtaken him; alternatively he felt as if he were standing still and that the earth was rushing past him, like a river flowing past a man swimming against the stream. The stream carried branches which had been bent southward by the north wind, stunted young trees, and patches of grass with bright, long-stalked flowers. It ended by submerging the bushes and the young trees, leaving only the sky and the man above water-level. The moon had risen, and illuminated the bare, curved summit of the plateau, the path, which was overgrown with young grass, the bound man making his way along it with quick, measured steps, and two hares, which ran across the hill just in front of him and vanished down the slope. Though the nights were still cool at this time of the year, before midnight the bound man lay down at the edge of the escarpment and went to sleep.

In the light of morning the animal-tamer who was camping with his circus in the field outside the village saw the bound man coming down the path, gazing thoughtfully at the ground. The bound man stopped and bent down. He held out one arm to help keep his balance and with the other picked up an empty wine-bottle. Then he straightened himself and stood erect again. He moved slowly, to avoid being cut by the rope, but to the circus proprietor what he did suggested the voluntary limitations of an enormous swiftness of movement. He was enchanted by its extraordinary gracefulness, and while the bound man looked about for a stone on which to break the bottle, so that he could use the splintered neck to cut the rope, the animal-tamer walked across the field and approached him. The first leaps of a young panther had never filled him with such delight.

"Ladies and gentlemen, the bound man!" His very first movements let loose a storm of applause, which out of sheer excitement caused the blood to rush to the cheeks of the animal-tamer standing at the edge of the arena. The bound man rose to his feet. His surprise whenever he did this was like that of a four-footed animal which has managed to stand on its hind-legs. He knelt, stood up, jumped, and turned cart-wheels. The spectators found it as astonishing as if they had seen a bird which voluntarily remained earthbound, and confined itself to hopping.

The bound man became an enormous draw. His absurd steps and little jumps, his elementary exercises in movement, made the rope-dancer superfluous. His fame grew from village to village, but the motions he went through were few and always the same; they were really quite ordinary motions, which he had con-

tinually to practice in the daytime in the half-dark tent in order to retain his shackled freedom. In that he remained entirely within the limits set by his rope he was free of it, it did not confine him, but gave him wings and endowed his leaps and jumps with purpose; just as the flights of birds of passage have purpose when they take wing in the warmth of summer and hesitantly make small circles in the sky.

All the children of the neighborhood started playing the game of "bound man." They formed rival gangs, and one day the circus people found a little girl lying bound in a ditch, with a cord tied round her neck so that she could hardly breathe. They released her, and at the end of the performance that night the bound man made a speech. He announced briefly that there was no sense in being tied up in such a way that you could not jump. After that he was regarded as a comedian.

Grass and sunlight, tent-pegs driven into the ground and then pulled up again, and on to the next village. "Ladies and gentlemen, the bound man!" The summer mounted toward its climax. It bent its face deeper over the fish-ponds in the hollows, taking delight in its dark reflection, skimmed the surface of the rivers, and made the plain into what it was. Everyone who could walk went to see the bound man. Many wanted a close-up view of how he was bound. So the circus proprietor announced after each performance that anyone who wanted to satisfy himself that the knots were real and the rope not made of rubber was at liberty to do so. The bound man generally waited for the crowd in the area outside the tent. He laughed or remained serious, and held out his arms for inspection. Many took the opportunity to look him in the face, others gravely tested the rope, tried the knots on his ankles, and wanted to know exactly how the lengths compared with the length of his limbs. They asked him how he had come to be tied up like that, and he answered patiently, always saying the same thing. Yes, he had been tied up, he said, and when he awoke he found that he had been robbed as well. Those who had done it must have been pressed for time, because they had tied him up somewhat too loosely for someone who was not supposed to be able to move and somewhat too tightly for someone who was expected to be able to move. But he did move, people pointed out. Yes, he replied, what else could he do?

Before he went to bed he always sat for a time in front of the fire. When the circus proprietor asked him why he didn't make up a better story he always answered that he hadn't made up that one, and blushed. He preferred staying in the shade.

The difference between him and the other performers was that when the show was over he did not take off his rope. The result was that every movement that he made was worth seeing, and the villagers used to hang about the camp for hours, just for the sake of seeing him get up from in front of the fire and roll himself in his blanket. Sometimes the sky was beginning to lighten when he saw their shadows disappear.

The circus proprietor often remarked that there was no reason why he should not be untied after the evening performance and tied up again next day. He pointed out that the rope-dancers, for instance, did not stay on their rope overnight. But no one took the idea of untying him seriously.

For the bound man's fame rested on the fact that he was always bound, that whenever he washed himself he had to wash his clothes too and vice versa, and that his only way of doing so was to jump in the river just as he was every morning when the sun came out, and that he had to be careful not to go too far out for fear of being carried away by the stream.

The proprietor was well aware that what in the last resort protected the bound man from the jealousy of the other performers was his helplessness; he deliberately left them the pleasure of watching him groping painfully from stone to stone

on the river bank every morning with his wet clothes clinging to him. When the proprietor's wife pointed out that even the best clothes would not stand up indefinitely to such treatment (and the bound man's clothes were by no means of the best), he replied curtly that it was not going to last forever. That was his answer to all objections—it was for the summer season only. But when he said this he was not being serious; he was talking like a gambler who has no intention of giving up his vice. In reality he would have been prepared cheerfully to sacrifice his lions and his rope-dancers for the bound man.

He proved this on the night when the rope-dancers jumped over the fire. Afterward he was convinced that they did it, not because it was midsummer's day, but because of the bound man, who as usual was lying and watching them with that peculiar smile that might have been real or might have been only the effect of the glow on his face. In any case no one knew anything about him because he never talked about anything that had happened to him before he emerged from the wood that day.

But that evening two of the performers suddenly picked him up by the arms and legs, carried him to the edge of the fire and started playfully swinging him to and fro, while two others held out their arms to catch him on the other side. In the end they threw him, but too short. The two men on the other side drew back— they explained afterward that they did so the better to take the shock. The result was that the bound man landed at the very edge of the flames and would have been burned if the circus proprietor had not seized his arms and quickly dragged him away to save the rope which was starting to get singed. He was certain that the object had been to burn the rope. He sacked the four men on the spot.

A few nights later the proprietor's wife was awakened by the sound of footsteps on the grass, and went outside just in time to prevent the clown from playing his last practical joke. He was carrying a pair of scissors. When he was asked for an explanation he insisted that he had had no intention of taking the bound man's life, but only wanted to cut his rope because he felt sorry for him. He was sacked too.

These antics amused the bound man because he could have freed himself if he had wanted to whenever he liked, but perhaps he wanted to learn a few new jumps first. The children's rhyme: "We travel with the circus, we travel with the circus" sometimes occurred to him while he lay awake at night. He could hear the voices of spectators on the opposite bank who had been driven too far downstream on the way home. He could see the river gleaming in the moonlight, and the young shoots growing out of the thick tops of the willow trees, and did not think about autumn yet.

The circus proprietor dreaded the danger that sleep involved for the bound man. Attempts were continually made to release him while he slept. The chief culprits were sacked rope-dancers, or children who were bribed for the purpose. But measures could be taken to safeguard against these. A much bigger danger was that which he represented to himself. In his dreams he forgot his rope, and was surprised by it when he woke in the darkness of morning. He would angrily try to get up, but lose his balance and fall back again. The previous evening's applause was forgotten, sleep was still too near, his head and neck too free. He was just the opposite of a hanged man—his neck was the only part of him that was free. You had to make sure that at such moments no knife was within his reach. In the early hours of the morning the circus proprietor sometimes sent his wife to see whether the bound man was all right. If he was asleep she would bend over him and feel the rope. It had grown hard from dirt and damp. She would test the amount of free play it allowed him, and touch his tender wrists and ankles.

The most varied rumors circulated about the bound man. Some said he had tied himself up and invented the story of having been robbed, and toward the end of the summer that was the general opinion. Others maintained that he had been tied up at his own request, perhaps in league with the circus proprietor. The hesitant way in which he told his story, his habit of breaking off when the talk got round to the attack on him, contributed greatly to these rumors. Those who still believed in the robbery-with-violence story were laughed at. Nobody knew what difficulties the circus proprietor had in keeping the bound man, and how often he said he had had enough and wanted to clear off, for too much of the summer had passed.

Later, however, he stopped talking about clearing off. When the proprietor's wife brought him his food by the river and asked him how long he proposed to remain with them, he did not answer. She thought he had got used, not to being tied up, but to remembering every moment that he was tied up—the only thing that anyone in his position could get used to. She asked him whether he did not think it ridiculous to be tied up all the time, but he answered that he did not. Such a variety of people—clowns, freaks, and comics, to say nothing of elephants and tigers —traveled with circuses that he did not see why a bound man should not travel with a circus too. He told her about the movements he was practicing, the new ones he had discovered, and about a new trick that had occurred to him while he was whisking flies from the animals' eyes. He described to her how he always anticipated the effect of the rope and always restrained his movements in such a way as to prevent it from ever tautening; and she knew that there were days when he was hardly aware of the rope, when he jumped down from the wagon and slapped the flanks of the horses in the morning as if he were moving in a dream. She watched him vault over the bars almost without touching them, and saw the sun on his face, and he told her that sometimes he felt as if he were not tied up at all. She answered that if he were prepared to be untied, there would never be any need for him to feel tied up. He agreed that he could be untied whenever he felt like it.

The woman ended by not knowing whether she was more concerned with the man or with the rope that tied him. She told him that he could go on traveling with the circus without his rope, but she did not believe it. For what would be the point of his antics without his rope, and what would he amount to without it? Without his rope he would leave them, and the happy days would be over. She would no longer be able to sit beside him on the stones by the river without arousing suspicion, and she knew that his continued presence, and her conversations with him, of which the rope was the only subject, depended on it. Whenever she agreed that the rope had its advantages, he would start talking about how troublesome it was, and whenever he started talking about its advantages, she would urge him to get rid of it. All this seemed as endless as the summer itself.

At other times she was worried at the thought that she was herself hastening the end by her talk. Sometimes she would get up in the middle of the night and run across the grass to where he slept. She wanted to shake him, wake him up and ask him to keep the rope. But then she would see him lying there; he had thrown off his blanket, and there he lay like a corpse, with his legs outstretched and his arms close together, with the rope tied round them. His clothes had suffered from the heat and the water, but the rope had grown no thinner. She felt that he would go on traveling with the circus until the flesh fell from him and exposed the joints. Next morning she would plead with him more ardently than ever to get rid of his rope.

The increasing coolness of the weather gave her hope. Autumn was coming, and he would not be able to go on jumping into the river with his clothes on much longer. But the thought of losing his rope, about which he had felt indifferent earlier in the season, now depressed him.

The songs of the harvesters filled him with foreboding. "Summer has gone, summer has gone." But he realized that soon he would have to change his clothes, and he was certain that when he had been untied it would be impossible to tie him up again in exactly the same way. About this time the proprietor started talking about traveling south that year.

The heat changed without transition into quiet, dry cold, and the fire was kept going all day long. When the bound man jumped down from the wagon he felt the coldness of the grass under his feet. The stalks were bent with ripeness. The horses dreamed on their feet and the wild animals, crouching to leap even in their sleep, seemed to be collecting gloom under their skins which would break out later.

On one of these days a young wolf escaped. The circus proprietor kept quiet about it, to avoid spreading alarm, but the wolf soon started raiding cattle in the neighborhood. People at first believed that the wolf had been driven to these parts by the prospect of a severe winter, but the circus soon became suspect. The proprietor could not conceal the loss of the animal from his own employees, so the truth was bound to come out before long. The circus people offered the burgomasters of the neighboring villages their aid in tracking down the beast, but all their efforts were in vain. Eventually the circus was openly blamed for the damage and the danger, and spectators stayed away.

The bound man went on performing before half-empty seats without losing anything of his amazing freedom of movement. During the day he wandered among the surrounding hills under the thin-beaten silver of the autumn sky, and, whenever he could, lay down where the sun shone longest. Soon he found a place which the twilight reached last of all, and when at last it reached him he got up most unwillingly from the withered grass. In coming down the hill he had to pass through a little wood on its southern slope, and one evening he saw the gleam of two little green lights. He knew that they came from no church window, and was not for a moment under any illusion about what they were.

He stopped. The animal came toward him through the thinning foliage. He could make out its shape, the slant of its neck, its tail which swept the ground, and its receding head. If he had not been bound, perhaps he would have tried to run away, but as it was he did not even feel fear. He stood calmly with dangling arms and looked down at the wolf's bristling coat under which the muscles played like his own underneath the rope. He thought the evening wind was still between him and the wolf when the beast sprang. The man took care to obey his rope.

Moving with the deliberate care that he had so often put to the test, he seized the wolf by the throat. Tenderness for a fellow-creature arose in him, tenderness for the upright being concealed in the four-footed. In a movement that resembled the drive of a great bird (he felt a sudden awareness that flying would be possible only if one were tied up in a special way) he flung himself at the animal and brought it to the ground. He felt a slight elation at having lost the fatal advantage of free limbs which causes men to be worsted.

The freedom he enjoyed in this struggle was having to adapt every movement of his limbs to the rope that tied him—the freedom of panthers, wolves, and the wild flowers that sway in the evening breeze. He ended up lying obliquely down the slope, clasping the animal's hind-legs between his own bare feet and its head between his hands. He felt the gentleness of the faded foliage stroking the backs of his hands, and he felt his own grip

almost effortlessly reaching its maximum, and he felt too how he was in no way hampered by the rope.

As he left the wood light rain began to fall and obscured the setting sun. He stopped for a while under the trees at the edge of the wood. Beyond the camp and the river he saw the fields where the cattle grazed, and the places where they crossed. Perhaps he would travel south with the circus after all. He laughed softly. It was against all reason. Even if he continued to put up with the sores that covered his joints and opened and bled when he made certain movements, his clothes would not stand up much longer to the friction of the rope.

The circus proprietor's wife tried to persuade her husband to announce the death of the wolf without mentioning that it had been killed by the bound man. She said that even at the time of his greatest popularity people would have refused to believe him capable of it, and in their present angry mood, with the nights getting cooler, they would be more incredulous than ever. The wolf had attacked a group of children at play that day, and nobody would believe that it had really been killed; for the circus proprietor had many wolves, and it was easy enough for him to hang a skin on the rail and allow free entry. But he was not to be dissuaded. He thought that the announcement of the bound man's act would revive the triumphs of the summer.

That evening the bound man's movements were uncertain. He stumbled in one of his jumps, and fell. Before he managed to get up he heard some low whistles and catcalls, rather like birds calling at dawn. He tried to get up too quickly, as he had done once or twice during the summer, with the result that he tautened the rope and fell back again. He lay still to regain his calm, and listened to the boos and catcalls growing into an uproar. "Well, bound man, and how did you kill the wolf?" they shouted, and: "Are you the man who killed the wolf?" If he had been one of them, he would not have believed it himself. He thought they had a perfect right to be angry: a circus at this time of year, a bound man, an escaped wolf, and all ending up with this. Some groups of spectators started arguing with others, but the greater part of the audience thought the whole thing a bad joke. By the time he had got to his feet there was such a hubbub that he was barely able to make out individual words.

He saw people surging up all round him, like faded leaves raised by a whirlwind in a circular valley at the center of which all was yet still. He thought of the golden sunsets of the last few days; and the sepulchral light which lay over the blight of all that he had built up during so many nights, the gold frame which the pious hang round dark, old pictures, this sudden collapse of everything, filled him with anger.

They wanted him to repeat his battle with the wolf. He said that such a thing had no place in a circus performance, and the proprietor declared that he did not keep animals to have them slaughtered in front of an audience. But the mob stormed the ring and forced them toward the cages. The proprietor's wife made her way between the seats to the exit and managed to get round to the cages from the other side. She pushed aside the attendant whom the crowd had forced to open a cage door, but the spectators dragged her back and prevented the door from being shut.

"Aren't you the woman who used to lie with him by the river in the summer?" they called out. "How does he hold you in his arms?" She shouted back at them that they needn't believe in the bound man if they didn't want to, they had never deserved him. Painted clowns were good enough for them.

The bound man felt as if the bursts of laughter were what he had been expecting ever since early May. What had smelled so sweet all through the summer now stank. But, if they insisted, he was ready to take on all the animals in the circus. He had never felt so much at one with his rope.

Gently he pushed the woman aside. Perhaps he would travel south with them after all. He stood in the open doorway of the cage, and he saw the wolf, a strong young animal, rise to its feet, and he heard the proprietor grumbling again about the loss of his exhibits. He clapped his hands to attract the animal's attention, and when it was near enough he turned to slam the cage door. He looked the woman in the face. Suddenly he remembered the proprietor's warning to suspect of murderous intentions anyone near him who had a sharp instrument in his hand. At the same moment he felt the blade on his wrists, as cool as the water of the river in autumn, which during the last few weeks he had been barely able to stand. The rope curled up in a tangle beside him while he struggled free. He pushed the woman back, but there was no point in anything he did now. Had he been insufficiently on his guard against those who wanted to release him, against the sympathy in which they wanted to lull him? Had he lain too long on the river bank? If she had cut the cord at any other moment it would have been better than this.

He stood in the middle of the cage, and rid himself of the rope like a snake discarding its skin. It amused him to see the spectators shrinking back. Did they realize that he had no choice now? Or that fighting the wolf now would prove nothing whatever? At the same time he felt all his blood rush to his feet. He felt suddenly weak.

The rope, which fell at its feet like a snare, angered the wolf more than the entry of a stranger into its cage. It crouched to spring. The man reeled, and grabbed the pistol that hung ready at the side of the cage. Then, before anyone could stop him, he shot the wolf between the eyes. The animal reared, and touched him in falling.

On the way to the river he heard the footsteps of his pursuers—spectators, the rope-dancers, the circus proprietor, and the proprietor's wife, who persisted in the chase longer than anyone else. He hid in a clump of bushes and listened to them hurrying past, and later on streaming in the opposite direction back to the camp. The moon shone on the meadow; in that light its color was both of growth and of death.

When he came to the river his anger died away. At dawn it seemed to him as if lumps of ice were floating in the water, and as if snow had fallen, obliterating memory.

THE END

Development

INTERPRETATION

1. *(a)* What is the initial fantastic situation on which the story is based? *(b)* Is this situation to be taken literally? Explain. *(c)* How does Miss Aichinger make the bound man's condition seem natural?

2. *(a)* What parallels between the bound man's condition and that of a newborn are either stated or implied in the opening paragraphs? *(b)* Trace the pattern of the bound man's "growth" within his ropes.

3. *(a)* Discuss the relationship between the bound man and the circus proprietor's wife. *(b)* Why is it significant that she is the one to cut his ropes?

4. *(a)* What are the advantages and disadvantages of the ropes for the bound man? *(b)* In what way does the first fight with a wolf enhance the function of the ropes?

5. *(a)* What is the central conflict in

this story? *(b)* What is the resolution? *(c)* What theme—or themes—arise out of the conflict and its resolution?

6. Given below are four interpretations of "The Bound Man"; explore their possibilities and discuss the validity of each.

(a) "The Bound Man" deals with the animal and spiritual nature of man, and in this story the animal wins. Within his ropes the bound man achieves the security of a caged animal's existence. When his ropes are cut, thereby freeing him from his animal-like orientation toward life, he becomes an object to be feared and hunted down by a dehumanized society.

(b) The story explodes the myth that man can live in total freedom. All men, says Aichinger, have their limitations and to exist in society each man must recognize his own. When a man is stripped of his confinements, he becomes a forlorn creature wandering in a desolate and wintry isolation.

(c) Aichinger leads us to see that the freedom permitted by society is little more than the self-controlled movement of a circus performer. The ropes emphasize the infantile character of man in his dependence upon society. The cutting of the ropes represents man's growth to true maturity and independence. In effect, the story is a lament that so many accept man's infantile dependence as normal when it is in reality a grotesque distortion of the natural.

(d) This story can be interpreted as a comment on the artist in society. So long as the artist's audience is not puzzled by his art, they accept him as a figure to both marvel at and scorn; and they allow their children to attempt to imitate him. But when he brings his art to perfection, thus achieving something out of the realm of ordinary men, his audience, which is too limited both intellectually and emotionally to understand his talent, ostracizes him from their company.

TECHNIQUE

1. *(a)* What is the tone of the story and how is it created? *(b)* Show how the tone stresses the conflict between reality and fantasy in the story.

2. What is the significance for both atmosphere and symbolism of the season in which most of the story is set?

EXTENSIONS

1. At the story's end, the bound man has completed a full circle in his life: he has moved from a confused and helpless state into one over which he has almost complete control, only to be thrown into a condition which is frightening in its seeming incomprehensibility. *(a)* In allegorical terms, what might this cycle represent? *(b)* Aichinger's ending, or her lack of one, leaves us not knowing what will become of the man in his unbound state. What kind of existence do you feel is suggested for the man in the closing paragraph of the story?

2. *(a)* Can man become so dependent on his limitations that the thought of total freedom fills him with dread? Discuss. *(b)* Does man ever live in total freedom? Explain.

The Tight Frock-Coat

LUIGI PIRANDELLO / Italy
(1867 – 1936)

translated from the Italian by Robert A. Hall, Jr.

Usually Professor Gori was very patient with the old housemaid, who had been his servant for around twenty years. On that day, however, for the first time in his life, he had to put on a frock-coat, and was in a state of total rage.

Just the mere thought that a matter of so little importance could excite a mind like his, which was foreign to all frivolity and burdened by so many serious intellectual cares, was enough to irritate him. Then his irritation grew, considering that with this mind of his, he could lower himself to putting on that garb required by a foolish custom for certain gala occasions with which life deludes itself that it is indulging in a feast or an amusement.

And then, good Heavens, with that huge body like a hippopotamus, like an antediluvian monster . . .

And the professor was puffing and glaring at the housemaid, who, small and plump like a bale of cotton, was in ecstasies at the sight of her huge master in that unaccustomed parade dress, without realizing, poor thing, what mortification this must have caused to all the honest old workaday furniture around and the poor books in the little half-darkened, disordered room.

That frock-coat, of course, did not belong to Professor Gori. He was hiring it. The clerk of a nearby shop had brought up an armful to him at home, for him to choose from; and now, with the manner of a highly skilled judge of fashion, with his eyes half-closed and on his lips a little smile of complacent superiority, he was scrutinizing him, having him turn this way and that, saying *Pardon me! Pardon me!*, and then concluding, shaking his forelock:

"It won't do."

The professor would puff once more and wipe off the sweat.

He had tried eight, nine, no telling how many. Each one tighter than the last. And that collar in which he felt strangled! and that shirt-front which was bulging, already rumpled, out of his waistcoat! and that dangling starched white tie, in which he still had to make a knot, and did not know how to!

In the end the clerk condescended to say:

"There, this one will do. We couldn't find anything better, believe me, sir."

Professor Gori first glared again at the housemaid, to keep her from repeating "Perfect! Perfect!"; then he looked at the frock-coat, on account of which, undoubtedly, the clerk was calling him "sir"; then he turned to the clerk:

"You have no others with you?"

"I brought up twelve of them, sir!"

"And this would be the twelfth?"

"The twelfth, at your service."

"Very good, then!"

It was tighter than the others. The young man, somewhat resentfully, conceded:

"It is a trifle tight, but it will be all right. If you would be so kind as to look at yourself in the mirror . . ."

"No, thank you!" yelped the professor. "I am already offering enough of a spectacle to you and to this lady, my housemaid."

The young man, then, full of dignity, scarcely nodded his head, and departed with the other eleven frock-coats.

"But can you believe it?" the professor burst out with a groan of rage, as he tried to lift his arms.

He went over to look at the perfumed invitation on the dresser, and puffed again. The time of meeting was set for eight, at the bride's home in Via Milano. A twenty-minutes' walk; and it was already a quarter past seven.

The old housemaid, who had gone to the door with the clerk, came back into the little room.

"Quiet!" the professor ordered her immediately. "Try, if you can, to finish the job of strangling me with this tie."

"Take it easy . . . the collar . . ." the old housemaid urged him. And after cleaning her trembling hands carefully with a handkerchief, she set about the job.

Silence prevailed for five minutes; the professor and the whole surrounding room seemed to be suspended, as if waiting for the Last Judgment.

"Finished?"

"Eh . . ." she sighed.

Professor Gori leaped to his feet, shouting:

"Stop! I'll try! I can't stand it any longer!"

But, as soon as he got in front of the mirror, he burst out in such expressions of rage, that the poor woman was terrified. First of all, he made a clumsy bow to himself; but, as he bowed, seeing the two coat-tails open and immediately close again, he turned around like a cat that feels something tied to its tail; and, as he turned around, *r-r-rip!*, the frock-coat split open under his armpit.

He was beside himself with rage.

"It's unsewed! It's just come unsewed!" the old housemaid reassured him, hurrying up immediately. "Take it off and I'll re-sew it for you!"

"But I haven't any time left!" the professor roared exasperatedly. "I shall go like this, as a punishment! Like this . . . It means I won't shake hands with anybody. Let me go!"

He furiously knotted his tie, hid the shame of that frock-coat under his top-coat, and away he went.

In the last analysis, however, he ought to have been glad, what the deuce! That morning they were holding the wedding of a former student of his, who was very dear to him: Cèsara Reis, who, through his aid, was reaping by that marriage the reward of so many sacrifices which she had made during her endless years of school.

Professor Gori, as he went along, began to think of the strange coincidence by which this marriage had come about. Yes; but what, in the meanwhile, was the name of the groom, that rich widower who, one day, had come to him at the Teachers' College to ask him to suggest a girl to tutor his daughters?

"Grimi? Griti? No, Mitri! Ah, yes, that's it: Mitri, Mitri."

That had been the origin of that marriage. Miss Reis, poor girl, had been left an orphan at fifteen years of age, and had heroically taken care of her own and her aged mother's upkeep, working a little as a seamstress, and a little by giving private lessons; and she had succeeded in getting a teacher's diploma. He, admiring such constancy and such strength of character, had, by begging and by intriguing, been able to get her a place at Rome, in the supplementary schools. When that Mr. Griti had asked him . . .

"Griti, Griti, that's it! His name is Griti. It's not Mitri at all!" . . . he had suggested Miss Reis to him. A few days later he [Griti] had come back upset and embarrassed. Cèsara Reis had not been willing to take the position as tutor, on account of her age, her rank, her old mother whom she could not leave alone, and especially people's readiness to gossip. And who knows with what tone of voice, with what expression the little rascal had said these things to him!

Beautiful, that Reis girl: and with that kind of beauty which he liked most; with a beauty on which diuturnal[1] sorrows (not for nothing was Gori a professor of Italian: he said it just that way, "diuturnal sorrows"), with a beauty on which diuturnal sorrows had conferred the grace of a very gentle sadness, a sweet and lovable nobility.

Certainly that Mr. Grimi . . .

"I'm very much afraid that his name really is Grimi, now that I think of it!"

Certainly that Mr. Grimi, from the very first time he saw her, had fallen madly in love with her. Just one of those things, apparently. And three or four times, although without hope, he had come back and insisted, in vain; in the end, he had asked him, Professor Gori—in fact, he had begged him—to intervene, to ask Miss Reis, who was so beautiful, so modest, so virtuous, to become, if not the tutor, the second mother of his girls. And why not? Professor Gori had been very glad to intervene, and Miss Reis had accepted; and now the wedding was being held, in spite of the relatives of Mr. . . . Grimi or Griti or Mitri, who had opposed it bitterly:

"And the devil take the whole crowd of them!" concluded the fat professor, puffing once again.

In the meanwhile he had to bring the bride a little bouquet of flowers. She had begged him so insistently to serve as a witness; but the professor had pointed out to her that, as a witness, he ought then to have given her a wedding present suitable to the high social standing of the groom, and he wasn't able to; in all conscience, he wasn't able to. The sacrifice of the frock-coat was enough. But a bouquet, yes, he could. And Professor Gori went, with great hesitation and embarrassment, into a flower-shop, where they put together for him a large bunch of greenery with very few flowers and at great cost.

When he arrived at Via Milano, he saw at the end, in front of the gate of the apartment house at which Miss Reis lived, a knot of idlers. He imagined he must be late; that the carriages for the wedding procession must already be in the courtyard, and that all those people were there to watch the parade. He quickened his step. But why were all those idlers looking at him in that way? The frock-coat was hidden by the overcoat. Perhaps . . . the coat-tails? He looked in back of himself. No: they were not visible. Well, then? What had happened? Why was the gate half-closed?

The concierge,[2] with a mournful air, asked him:

---

1. *diuturnal* (di yü tər′ nl), of long continuance, as opposed to *diurnal*, of daily occurrence. 2. *concierge* (kon sē érzh′; *French* kôn syerzh′), doorkeeper, building superintendent.

"Are you going upstairs for the wedding?"

"Yes, sir. A guest."

"But . . . you know, the wedding is off."

"What?"

"The poor lady . . . the mother . . ."

"Dead?" exclaimed Gori, in amazement, looking at the door.

"Last night, unexpectedly."

The professor stood there stock-still.

"Is it possible? The mother? Mrs. Reis?"

And he glanced around the group gathered there, as if to read in their eyes the confirmation of the incredible news. The bouquet fell from his hand. He bent to pick it up, but felt the torn seam of the frock-coat grow larger under his armpit. Oh, Heavens! the frock-coat! . . . indeed! The frock-coat for the wedding, purified thus to appear now in the presence of death. What should he do? Go on up, decked out in this way? Go back?—He picked up the bouquet, then, as if dazed, handed it to the concierge.

"Do me a favor; you keep it for me."

And he entered. He tried to go up the stairs two at a time, but succeeded only for the first flight. At the top floor—curses on his fat paunch!—he was completely out of breath. When he had been shown into the parlor, he noted in the people who were gathered there a certain embarrassment, a quickly repressed confusion, as if someone, at his entry, had hurried away, or as if an intimate and very lively conversation had suddenly been cut short.

Professor Gori, already embarrassed on his own account, stopped a little beyond the entrance; he looked around in perplexity; he felt lost, almost as if in the middle of an enemy camp. They were all very high-class people; relatives and friends of the groom. That old woman there was perhaps his mother; those two others, who seemed to be old maids, were perhaps sisters or cousins. He bowed awkwardly. (Oh Heavens, the frock-coat again . . .) And, bent over, as if pulled from within, he looked around again, as if to discover whether anyone had noticed the tearing noise of that accursed unstitched seam under the armpit. No one replied to his bow, as if the mourning and the seriousness of the occasion did not allow even a slight nod of the head. Some (perhaps close friends of the family) were standing in consternation around a gentleman, in whom Gori, on looking carefully, thought he recognized the groom. He heaved a sigh of relief and went up to him, full of concern.

"Mr. Grimi . . ."

"Migri, please."

"Ah yes, Migri . . . I've been thinking of it for an hour, believe me! I was saying Grimi, Mitri, Griti . . . and I didn't think of Migri! Excuse me . . . I am Professor Fabio Gori, you will remember . . . although now you see me in . . ."

"A pleasure, but . . ." the man said, looking at him with cold hauteur; then, as if remembering: "Ah, Gori . . . yes! You must be the man . . . yes, I mean, the author . . . the author, if we want to put it that way, of the marriage, indirectly! My brother has told me . . ."

"What, what? I beg your pardon, are you the brother?"

"Carlo Migri, at your service."

"Excuse me, please. You look exactly like him, by Jove! Excuse me, Mr. Gri . . . oh yes, Migri, but . . . but this bolt from the blue . . . Yes! Unfortunately I . . . that is to say, not unfortunately; I have nothing to blame myself for, shall we say . . . but yes, indirectly, by chance, shall we say, I have contributed . . ."

Migri interrupted him with a gesture, and stood up.

"Allow me to introduce you to my mother."

"I should be very much honored, of course."

He was led in front of the old lady, who filled half the sofa with her enormous bulk, dressed in black, with a kind of cap, also black, on her woolly hair that surrounded her flat, yellowish, almost parchment-like face.

"Mother, this is Professor Gori. You know? The one who had arranged Andrea's marriage."

The old lady somnolently raised her heavy eyelids, showing, with one more opened and the other less so, her muddy, egg-shaped eyes, with almost no look in them.

"As a matter of fact," the professor corrected him, bowing this time with hesitant concern for the torn frock-coat, "as a matter of fact, it is this way . . . not *arranged;* that would not . . . would not be the right word . . . I simply . . ."

". . . wanted to provide a tutor for my grandchildren," the old lady finished the sentence, with a cavernous voice. "Excellent! That, in fact, would have been the right thing."

"That's it, yes . . ." said Professor Gori. "Recognizing the merits and the modesty of Miss Reis."

"Ah, an excellent girl, no one denies it," the old lady admitted immediately, lowering her eyelids. "And we, believe me, are extremely sorry today . . ."

"What a misfortune! Yes indeed! So suddenly!" exclaimed Gori.

"As if it were not really God's will," concluded the old lady.

Gori looked at her.

"A cruel stroke of fate . . ."

Then, looking around the room, he asked:

"And Mr. Andrea?"

The brother answered him, pretending indifference:

"But . . . I don't know; he was here a short time ago. Perhaps he may have gone to get ready."

"Ah!" Gori exclaimed then, suddenly cheering up. "The wedding will be held all the same, then?"

"No! What are you saying?" burst out the old woman, amazed, offended. "Good Lord in Heaven! With the dead woman in the house! O-oh!"

"O-o-o-o-oh!" yowled the two old maids, echoing her, with horror.

"To get ready to leave," Migri explained.

"He was to leave today with his bride for Turin. We have our papermills up there at Valsangone, where he is needed so badly."

"And . . . and he will leave . . . like that?" Gori asked.

"Of necessity. If not today, then tomorrow. We persuaded him, in fact we urged him, poor fellow. Here, you understand, it is not prudent or suitable for him to remain any longer."

"On account of the girl . . . who is now alone . . ." the mother added with her cavernous voice. "Gossiping tongues . . ."

"Yes indeed," the brother continued. "And then, business . . . It was a marriage . . ."

"An over-hasty marriage!" one of the old maids burst forth.

"Let us say improvised," Migri said, trying to tone it down. "Now this serious misfortune has intervened as a stroke of fate, as if . . . yes, to give time, that's it. A postponement is necessary . . . on account of the mourning . . . And in that way, both parties can think the matter over . . ."

Professor Gori remained silent for a while. The irritating embarrassment that he was caused by that speech, so completely suspended in prudent reticence, was exactly the same as that which he was caused by his frock-coat, which was tight and unsewed beneath the armpit. It was unsewed in the same way that that speech seemed to him to be, and needed to be treated with the same care because of the secret disjointedness with which it had been uttered. If you forced matters a little, and did not keep it so composed and suspended, with all due concern, there was a danger that, just as the sleeve of the frock-coat would come off, so too the hypocrisy of all those high-class people would be opened up and laid bare.

He felt for a moment the need of getting away from that oppression and also from the displeasure with which, in the stupefaction into which he had fallen, he was affected by the white lace that edged the neck of the old lady's black jacket. Every time he saw a piece of white lace like that, there came to his memory, Lord only knows why, the picture of a certain Pietro Cardella, a haberdasher in his distant home town, who was afflicted with an enormous cyst on the nape of his neck. He felt like puffing; he restrained himself in time, and sighed stupidly:

"Oh yes . . . poor girl!"

In answer there arose a chorus of expressions of sympathy for the bride. Professor Gori suddenly felt as if he were lashed by this, and asked, in very great irritation:

"Where is she? Might I see her?"

Migri showed him a door in the parlor: "In there; please go ahead . . ."

And Professor Gori went off that way in fury.

On the little white bed, stretched out in rigor mortis, was the body of the mother, wearing on her head a cap with starched brims.

At first Professor Gori did not see anything else as he came in. Under the influence of that growing irritation which, in his daze and annoyance he could not exactly account for, with his head already in a whirl, instead of being moved at the sight, he felt irritated at it, as if at something truly absurd: a stupidly cruel and insolent trick of fate which—no, by Jove, it should not be allowed to pass at any cost!

All that rigidity of the dead woman seemed to him a show, as if that poor old woman had of her own accord stretched herself out there, on that bed, with that enormous starched cap in order to take over for herself, by foul play, the festival prepared for her daughter; and Professor Gori was nearly tempted to shout:

"Get up, get up, my dear old lady! This is not the moment to play tricks of that kind!"

Cèsara Reis was kneeling on the floor; and all huddled, now, near the little bed on which her mother's body was lying, she was no longer weeping, but seemed suspended in a solemn and empty bewilderment. Among her disheveled black hair she had some locks still twisted up in curl-papers from the evening before.

And yet, instead of feeling pity, Professor Gori felt almost contempt for her. An imperious urge arose in him to pull her up from the floor, to shake her out of that bewilderment. She ought not to give in to destiny, which was so unfairly favoring the hypocrisy of all those upper-class people gathered in the other room! No, no; everything was all prepared, all ready; those people had come in frock-coats, as he had, for the wedding: well, all that was needed was an assertion of will-power on someone's part; to force that poor girl, who had fallen there on the floor, to get up; to lead her, drag her, even half bewildered like that, to carry through that wedding and to save her from ruin.

But that act of will-power, which would so obviously have been contrary to the wishes of all those relatives, was reluctant to arise in him. As Cèsara, however, without moving her head, without batting an eyelash, barely raised a hand to point to her mother stretched out there, saying to him: "You see, professor?"—the professor suddenly moved, and said:

"Yes, my dear, yes!" he answered her with an almost rancorous excitement, which amazed his former student. "But you, get up! Do not make me bend down, because I cannot bend down. Get up by yourself! Immediately, hurry! Up, up, please!"

Without wanting to, forced by that excitement, the young woman shook herself out of her dejection and looked, almost frightened, at the professor:

"Why?" she asked him.

"Because, my girl . . . but first get up! I tell you that I cannot bend down, in Heaven's name!" Gori answered her.

Cèsara got up. However, on seeing again her mother's body on the little bed, she covered her face with her hands and burst into violent sobs. She did not expect to feel herself seized by the arms and shaken and shouted at by the professor, more excited than ever: "No! no! no! Don't weep now! Be patient, my dear girl! Listen to me!"

She looked at him again, almost terrified this time, with her tears stopped in her eyes, and said:

"But how do you expect me not to weep?"

"You must not weep, because this is not a time to weep, for you!" the professor cut her short. "You have been left alone, my dear girl, and must help yourself! Do you understand that you have to help yourself? *Now,* yes, *now!* Take all your courage in your hands; clench your teeth and do what I tell you!"

"What, professor?"

"Nothing. Take off, first of all, those pieces of paper from your hair."

"Oh, Heavens!" groaned the girl, remembering them, and immediately putting her trembling hands to her hair.

"That's right!" urged the professor. "Then go in there and put on your school dress; put on your little hat, and come with me!"

"Where? What are you saying?"

"To the City Hall, my dear girl!"

"Professor, what are you saying?"

"I say, to the City Hall, to the registry office, and then to the church! Because this marriage has to be performed, has to be performed right now; or you are ruined! Do you see what a state I am in on your account? In a frock-coat! And I shall be one of the witnesses, as you desired! Leave your poor mother here; don't think any more about her for a moment, and don't consider it a sacrilege! She herself, your mother, wants you to! Listen to me: go and get dressed! I shall arrange everything out there for the ceremony: right now!"

"No . . . no . . . how could I?" cried Cèsara, falling back again on her mother's bed and burying her head in her arms, in desperation. "It is impossible, professor! It's all up with me, I know! He will go away, will never come back, will abandon me . . . but I can't . . . I can't . . . ."

Gori did not give in; he bent down to lift her up, to pull her away from that bed; but as he stretched out his arms, he angrily stamped his foot, shouting:

"I don't care in the slightest! I will even act as a witness with only one sleeve, but this wedding will be performed today! Do you understand . . . look me in the eyes! . . . you understand, don't you? that if you let this moment escape you, you are lost? How will you keep going, without your position, with no one left? Do you want to blame your mother for your ruin? Didn't the poor lady desire this marriage of yours so eagerly? And do you want it to come to nothing, on her account? What harm are you doing? Courage, Cèsara! I am here; leave to me the responsibility for what you are doing! Go, go and get dressed, go and get dressed, my girl, without losing any more time . . . ."

And as he said this, he led the girl to the door of her room, supporting her by the shoulders. Then he went back through the room of death, closed the door, and went back like a warrior into the parlor.

"Has the groom not come yet?"

The relatives and guests turned around to look at him, surprised by the authoritative tone of his voice; and Migri asked with pretended concern:

"Is the young lady feeling badly?"

"She is feeling excellent!" the professor answered him with a fierce glare. "On the contrary, I have the pleasure of announcing to you, ladies and gentlemen, that I have been fortunate enough to persuade her to dominate her feelings for a moment and to stifle her grief. We are all here; everything is ready; it will be enough— let me speak!—it will be enough for one of you . . . you, for example, will be so kind," he added, turning to one of the guests, "you will do me the favor of hastening in a carriage to the City Hall and of forewarning the officials of the registry office, that . . . ."

A chorus of vigorous protests interrupted the professor at this point. Scandal, amazement, horror, indignation!

"Let me explain!" shouted Professor Gori, dominating all with his presence. "Why should this marriage not be performed? Because of the grief of the bride, isn't that so? Now, if the bride herself . . ."

"But I shall never permit," shouted the old lady, louder than he, interrupting him, "I shall never permit my son . . ."

". . . to do his duty and perform a good deed?" Gori quickly asked, and he was the one to finish the sentence this time.

"Just stop interfering!" Migri came up and said to him, pale and trembling with anger, in defense of his mother.

"I beg your pardon! I am interfering," Gori retorted immediately, "because I know that you are a gentleman, my dear Mr. Grimi . . ."

"Migri, please!"

"Migri, Migri, and you will understand that it is neither permissible nor honorable to refuse to meet the imperative obligations of a situation like this. We must be stronger than the misfortune which has stricken this poor girl, and save her! Can she remain alone, like this, without aid and without any position left? You tell me! No; this wedding will be held in spite of the calamity, and in spite of the . . . please be patient!"

He broke off, furious and puffing; he put a hand under the sleeve of his overcoat, grasped the sleeve of the frock-coat and with a violent jerk pulled it out and hurled it in the air. They all laughed, against their will, at that strange kind of unexpected comic touch, whilst the professor, with a great sigh of liberation, continued:

"And in spite of this sleeve which has been torturing me until now!"

"You are joking!" Migri retorted, regaining his composure.

"No, sir; it had come unsewed."

"You are joking! Your outbursts are uncalled for."

"They are called for by the situation."

"Or by personal interest! I tell you that it is not possible, under these conditions . . ."

Fortunately the groom arrived.

"No! No! Andrea, no!" several voices immediately called to him, from one side and another.

But Gori overwhelmed them, advancing towards Migri.

"You decide! Let me speak! This is what is at stake: I have induced Miss Reis in there to muster her courage; to pull herself together, in view of the seriousness of the situation in which you, my dear sir, have placed her and would leave her. If you are willing, Mr. Migri, we could, without any pomp, very quietly, in a closed carriage, hasten to the City Hall and celebrate the wedding immediately . . . You will not, I trust, refuse. But speak, yourself . . ."

Andrea Migri, taken by surprise in this way, looked first at Gori, then at the others, and finally answered hesitantly:

"But . . . so far as I am concerned, if Cèsara is willing . . ."

"She is willing! She is willing!" shouted Gori, overwhelming with his loud voice the others' expressions of disapproval. "Here, finally, is a word that comes from the heart! You, therefore, come, kind sir, and hasten to the City Hall!"

He took by the arm that guest to whom he had spoken the first time, and went with him as far as the door. In the entrance hall he saw a great number of magnificent baskets of flowers, which had come as wedding presents, and appeared at the door of the parlor to call the groom and free him from his infuriated relatives, who were already surrounding him.

"Mr Migri, Mr. Migri, one request! Look . . ."

Migri hastened up.

"Let us interpret the feelings of the poor girl. All these flowers, to the dead woman . . . Help me!"

He took two baskets, and went back with them into the parlor; carrying them in triumph, he went into the room of death. The groom followed him, contritely, with two more baskets. There was an immediate change in the party.

More than one person hastened to the entrance hall, to take more baskets and to carry them in a procession.

"Take the flowers to the dead woman; excellent, the flowers to the dead woman!"

Soon thereafter, Cèsara came into the parlor, very pale, in her modest black school dress, with her hair barely tidied, and trembling from the effort she was exerting to maintain her composure. Immediately the groom ran to meet her and took her in his arms with compassion. All were silent. Professor Gori, with his eyes shining with tears, requested three of the gentlemen to accompany the bride and groom with him, to serve as witnesses. They set out in silence.

The mother, the brother, the old maids and the guests who had remained in the parlor immediately began again to vent their indignation, which had been restrained for a moment on the appearance of Cèsara. It was fortunate that the poor old mother, out there in the midst of the flowers, was no longer able to hear these fine people who had been proclaiming their great indignation at such a lack of reverence on the occasion of her death.

But Professor Gori, during the trip, thought of what people must certainly, at that moment, be saying about him in that parlor, and remained in a daze so that when he arrived at the City Hall, he seemed drunk—so much so that, no longer remembering that he had torn off the sleeve of his frock-coat, he took off his overcoat like the others.

"Professor!"

"Ah, yes! By Jove!" he exclaimed, and put it back on in a hurry.

Even Cèsara smiled at this. But Gori, who had to a certain extent consoled himself by telling himself that, after all, he wouldn't go back among those people again, could not laugh at the occurrence; now he had of necessity to go back there again, to get that sleeve and return it together with the frock-coat to the shopkeeper from whom he had rented it. The signature? What signature? Ah, yes! of course, he had to put down his signature as a witness. Where?

When the other ceremony, in church, had been quickly gotten over with, the bride and groom and the four witnesses returned home.

They were received in the same icy silence.

Gori, trying to appear as small as possible, looked around the parlor and, turning to one of the guests, with his finger on his lips, asked:

"Quietly . . . Could you please tell me what happened to that sleeve from my frock-coat, which I threw in the air a short while ago?"

And wrapping it up soon afterwards inside a newspaper and slipping away on the sly, he began to reflect that, after all, he owed his fine victory over destiny that day only to the sleeve of that tight frock-coat, because, if the frock-coat, with its sleeve that had come unstitched under his armpit, had not aroused such irritation in him, he, in the familiar roominess of his comfortable and worn-out everyday garments, would certainly have yielded, like an imbecile, to mere emotion and to inactive regret for the unhappy fate of that poor girl. In a state of total fury on account of that tight frock-coat, he had found, on the other hand, in his irritation, the courage and the strength to rebel against it and to triumph over it.

THE END

Development

INTERPRETATION

1. (a) What effect does the donning of the frock-coat have upon Professor Gori's normal behavior? (b) What character traits does Gori exhibit before his arrival at the wedding?

2. After learning that the marriage is to be postponed, Professor Gori wishes that someone would demand that the wedding take place immediately. (a) Why does he feel so strongly about this? (b) What moves Gori from merely desiring that Cèsara be married to actually acting on her behalf?

3. (a) Describe the change in Gori after he decides to help Cèsara. (b) Why does Gori pull off the sleeve of the frock-coat? (c) What has the coat come to symbolize for him?

4. What are the things against which Gori is rebelling?

5. As the story concludes, Professor Gori is musing over "his fine victory over destiny that day." (a) In what way has he been victorious? (b) How has the frock-coat proven to be an unexpected advantage? (c) What inhibitions has Gori shed in his triumph?

6. At the end of the story, is Gori permanently changed? Discuss.

TECHNIQUE

1. In "The Tight Frock-Coat" Pirandello has used a comic situation to make a serious comment. (a) What are some of the comic elements in the story? (b) What is Pirandello's serious comment? (c) Do the comic elements strengthen or weaken Pirandello's theme? Explain.

2. What function is served by the minor characters in "The Tight Frock-Coat"?

EXTENSIONS

1. In an interview, Pirandello once stated, "Society is necessarily formal, and in this sense I am anti-social, but only in the sense that I am opposed to social hypocrisies and conventions. . . ." (a) Do you agree with the opinion that hypocrisy is an integral part of society? Explain. (b) What types of social hypocrisies and conventions are presented in "The Tight Frock-Coat"? (c) Through what characters does Pirandello convey this hypocrisy?

2. If a man finds that he is limited by social conventions and customs, should he ignore those conventions and proceed unhampered? Discuss.

Episode in Malay Camp

PETER ABRAHAMS / South Africa
(1919–   )

The warmth had gone out of the air, and slowly winter had come to Malay Camp, to Vrededorp, to Johannesburg.[1] The days were cold now, and the nights were bitterly so. People wrapped themselves up warmly and snuggled closer to their fires. People slept close together to be warmer. Particularly in Malay Camp and Vrededorp.

Xuma had been in the city three months now. It was Saturday night and in spite of the cold the streets were crowded. He went up the street and walked in the direction of the heart of Johannesburg. He passed a couple under the lamplight. The man had his arms round the woman. The woman was laughing into the man's face. He looked away and hurried past. And everywhere he saw couples. They walked close together to keep out the cold. And they all seemed so happy. Only he walked alone.

His shoes were thin and the cold came through. His toes began to ache. But there were others who passed him who did not even have shoes. And many without coats and one could see it in their eyes, so it was not so bad. But even those whose eyes showed how cold they were were not alone. Most of them walked with a woman. Others had men friends. Only he walked alone.

He neared the heart of Johannesburg and the people grew fewer. There were more white people now and they were different. They did not walk or look like his people and it was as if they were not really there. He stepped aside for them to pass and he heard their voices, but they were strangers. He did not look at them or watch them carefully to see what they said and how their eyes looked and whether there was love in the eyes of the woman who hung on the arm of the man. They were not his people so he did not care.

He passed the window of a restaurant.

From MINE BOY, by Peter Abrahams. Alfred A. Knopf, Inc., (1955). Reprinted by permission of Alfred A. Knopf, Inc., and Curtis Brown Ltd.

1. *Malay Camp . . . Johannesburg.* Malay Camp and Vrededorp are locations where blacks are required to live on the outskirts of Johannesburg, the largest city in South Africa.

Inside white people sat eating and talking and smoking and laughing at each other. It looked warm and comfortable and inviting. He looked away quickly. In another window there were cakes. He stopped and looked at them. He felt a tap on his shoulder and turned. It was a policeman. Without a word he fished his pass from his pocket and gave it to the policeman. The policeman looked at it, looked him up and down, and returned the pass to him. Xuma could see he was a kind one.

"Where are you going, Xuma?"

"I'm just walking."

"Ah, hah! Why not go home and sit in front of the fire with your beer?"

Xuma smiled, "You want me to go to jail?"

The policeman laughed, "All right, but behave yourself."

Xuma watched him go. Not a bad one at that. Maybe he's new. He carried on up the street and turned down Eloff Street. This was the heart of the city and the crowd was thick. It was difficult to move among all these white people. One had to keep stepping aside and to watch out for the motor cars that shot past.

Xuma smiled bitterly. The only place where he was completely free was underground in the mines. There he was a master and knew his way. There he did not even fear his white man, for his white man depended on him. He was the *boss boy*. He gave the orders to the other mine boys. They would do for him what they would not do for his white man or any other white man. He knew that, he had found it out. And underground his white man respected him and asked him for his opinion before he did anything. It was so, and he was at home and at ease underground.

His white man had even tried to make friends with him because the other mine boys respected him so much. But a white man and a black man cannot be friends. They work together. That's all. He smiled. He did not want the things of the white man. He did not want to be friends with the white man. Work for him, yes, but that's all.

Xuma crossed the street and wended his way back to Malay Camp. Gradually he left the heart of the city behind him. The white people thinned out. And more and more he saw only his people. And more and more the feeling of watchfulness and alertness to step out of the way left him. Now he rubbed against people and did not step out of the way. He bumped against them and felt their warmth and softness. It was all right here. This was Malay Camp. And the few white people here were Syrians who sold wine to the black people and colored people.[2] And one did not treat them like white people. They were all right. He turned down Jeppe Street. Lower down the street a crowd of people stood. They were looking upward. He hurried down. When he got to the people he stopped and looked up. There was nothing to see.

"What is it?" he asked a man beside him.

"I don't know," the man said.

Xuma edged away, still looking at the rooftops. He bumped into a woman.

"What is it?"

"There is a man up there," the woman said, "and the police are chasing him."

"Where?"

The woman pointed. He looked closely. Yes, there he was! He was crawling along a slanting roof, and close behind him was a policeman. Xuma held his breath. The roof sloped steeply. One wrong move and the man would plunge down, either to death or a broken body. And for the policeman it was the same too.

A yell of fear rose from the crowd. The man had lost his hold and was slowly sliding down the sloping roof. Down he came. Down. Down. Now he was at the edge of the roof. If he could not stop himself he would plunge to the ground. One

2. *black people and colored people.* As distinguished from black Africans, the colored people are the mixed-blood descendants of native peoples who mingled with the first white settlers.

leg came over the side of the roof. Then the other. He was going to fall.

Xuma held his breath. His heart pounded furiously.

The man got hold of the edge of the roof with his hands and swung there. A tremble of fear passed through the crowd. The policeman edged nearer.

There was a bustle in the crowd and a slender, well-dressed man pushed his way to the fore. He was dressed in the clothes of the white people and behaved like the white people. He pushed people out of the way. Unwillingly the people shifted their gaze from the man swinging on the side of the roof and looked at the man. "Who is he?" they asked one another. "And what does he think he is?" yet others asked.

And someone whispered to his neighbor, "That is the doctor. Doctor Mini." And the whisper was carried along and passed around the crowd. Xuma looked at the doctor.

The doctor stared up at the swinging man. "Who is he?"

No one answered the doctor.

Again the doctor spoke in his sharp, thin voice:

"What has he done? Did anyone see?"

"He was playing dice," a ragged man said sullenly.

A woman cried out. The policeman who was edging nearer had been joined by another. Both were edging nearer. Carefully and slowly. But it was not that that had made the woman cry out. She had seen one of the man's hands slip. He was now holding on by one hand only. The crowd was tense. This was the kill. Automatically they moved forward in a body. The doctor was in the lead. Xuma pushed forward.

Then the man up there, hanging between the sky and the earth, let go his grip as though he were tired. There was a space. Then with a dull thud he was on the ground. For a minute he lay still where he had dropped. The crowd was rooted to where it stood.

Then the man moved. The crowd became individuals again. The doctor ran forward and knelt beside the man. The crowd pressed around.

"Give him air," the doctor said.

Xuma pushed the crowd back. "Give him air," he repeated.

The doctor felt the man's body all over.

"It's all right, only his arm is broken."

The doctor looked at Xuma.

"Help me get away," the man whispered.

Suddenly the crowd parted and moved back. Policemen pushed through.

"Stand back," the foremost shouted.

Xuma moved back with the crowd. Only the doctor remained.

"You!" the policeman said to the doctor. "Didn't you hear?"

The doctor got up and looked at the policeman.

"I'm Doctor Mini."

The policeman laughed. Another behind him pushed forward and smacked the doctor in the face. Xuma bunched his fist and took a deep breath.

"You'll hear about this," the doctor said.

The second policeman again raised his hand.

"You'd better not," another policeman said and stepped forward. "He is a doctor."

The other two looked at the older policeman. There was disbelief in their eyes.

"It's true," the older policeman said.

"I want to take this man with me," the doctor said, looking at the older policeman. "His arm is badly broken and he's got to be looked after."

"No bloody fear," the first policeman said. "He's going where he belongs, in jail."

The doctor took out a card and gave it to the older policeman. "I'm attached to the General Hospital, and this is my home address if you want me."

The policemen looked at each other nonplussed. There was an obstinate look in the eyes of the first. Fear was showing in the eyes of the second. The older man looked tired and weary. He took the card from the doctor's hand and nodded. The first one opened his mouth. The second one shook his head. The first one kept silent.

"Will someone help me carry him to my car?" the doctor said.

The first policeman swung round and looked at the crowd. There was a threat in his eyes. He held his club menacingly. The crowd remained where it was.

The doctor tried to lift the man but could not.

Xuma took a deep breath, bunched his fists, and stepped forward. The policeman tightened his grip on his club and waved it from side to side. He stared hard at Xuma. Xuma returned the stare and kept going forward. He pushed past the policeman. The doctor looked up and smiled.

"Lift him but be careful of that arm."

"Just a minute," the first policeman said and prodded Xuma with his club.

Xuma got up. His body trembled. His fists bunched into hard balls.

"Where's your pass? Let me see it."

Xuma took out his pass and gave it to the policeman. The policeman looked at it for a long time then returned it.

Xuma picked up the wounded man. The crowd made a passage. The doctor led the way through. Xuma followed him. The doctor opened the door of his car and helped Xuma to ease the man gently on to the back seat.

"Can you come with me to help carry him in?"

Xuma nodded.

"Get in there beside him and hold him so that his arm does not bump against anything."

The doctor shut the door then got into the front and started the car. Before the car moved off the doctor turned his eyes and looked to where the crowd had been. Xuma looked too. The crowd was scattering in all directions. The two policemen were chasing them. Only the older one stood where they had left him. Stood with that weary look on his face.

The car moved off, slowly and carefully.

The doctor took out a cigarette and handed the packet to Xuma.

"What's your name?"

"Xuma."

"Been in the city long?"

"Three months."

"I see."

For the rest of the way they drove in silence. Xuma kept looking from the man by his side to the man in front. They were both his people but they were so different. For the one by his side, he didn't have much respect. There were so many like him. They drank and they fought and they gambled. And there were so many like that in the city. He had watched them. He knew them. But this other one was different. Different from all the other people who had stood around there. Even the white people saw the difference and treated him differently. No one Xuma knew could have done what this one had done. And yet this was one of his people.

At the other end of Malay Camp the doctor pulled up. Between them they carried the man into a house.

A colored woman who was almost white and who was dressed like the white people, met them at the door. And inside the house was even more beautiful than the place of the Red One.[3] There were all the things he had seen in the Red One's place and even more.

They carried the man into the surgery. The woman helped the doctor to take off his coat and gave him a thin, white one.

Quickly, deftly, carefully the doctor worked on the man's arm. And all the while the woman was there, giving him things and helping him and talking to him. Xuma sat on a little chair and watched.

---

3. *the place of the Red One.* Xuma had recently visited and been impressed by the apartment of his mine boss, Paddy O'Shea, called "the Red One" because of his mass of red hair.

Maybe the woman is his wife, Xuma thought.

And when they had finished bandaging the man and the doctor had washed his hands and the woman kissed him, Xuma knew she was his wife.

"There!" the doctor said and smiled at Xuma.

The woman smiled too. Maybe I should go now, Xuma thought.

Another woman, a black one, came into the room with a glass. She made the wounded one drink out of it. The wounded one sat up.

"Thank you, Doctor," he said. "Maybe I can go now."

"No, not yet. I told the police to come in an hour. I don't think they will come, but it's best to wait and see. You lie down and get some of your strength back."

"But they will arrest me."

"If they do I will charge the policeman who assaulted me. But if I let you go I'll get into trouble."

The wounded man looked round the room but said nothing.

"Perhaps you will wait too, Xuma, then you can be my witness. You saw everything."

Xuma nodded.

The colored woman put a blanket over the wounded man.

"Come, Xuma, we will have some tea," the doctor said.

They went out and left only the wounded one behind. In the other room there was a big fire. And there was a radio too, and light that one put on by pressing a little thing in the wall. No oil lamp and candles. Xuma looked round the room. The doctor followed his gaze and smiled. Xuma looked at him and saw the smile. He felt as he had felt in the place of the Red One. As though he did not belong there and it was wrong for him to be there.

The doctor saw the shadow pass over his face.

"What is it?"

"This is like the white people's place."

The doctor and his wife laughed.

"No, Xuma," the doctor said. "Not like the white people's place. Just a comfortable place. You are not copying the white man when you live in a place like this. This is the sort of place a man should live in because it is good for him. Whether he is white or black does not matter. A place like this is good for him. It is the other places that are the white people's. The places they make you live in."

"Doctor! Doctor!"

The black woman came into the room. There was distress and agitation on her face.

"What is it, Emily?"

"The one you were bandaging has gone, Doctor. He has gone out through the window."

"Oh . . ."

Xuma watched the doctor's face. For a minute there was sadness and hopelessness in it. Like the faces of the men who had worked on the pile of fine, wet, white sand that would not grow less. It was there for a minute, then it was gone, and his face was again cold and calm and hard to make out.

The doctor got up and went to the surgery. The others followed him. The blanket was on the floor. The window was open. A cool breeze blew in. The man had gone.

The colored woman took the doctor's arm. Emily went and shut the window.

"You can go now, Xuma," the doctor said harshly without looking at him.

Xuma felt hurt. He had done nothing. He had stayed because the doctor had asked him, and now, because the other man had gone, the doctor spoke to him in a hard voice. He was angry, but more than the anger he felt the hurt.

He turned abruptly and walked to the door. The doctor's wife followed him. She held out her hand and smiled at him.

"Thank you very much," she said.

Xuma took her hand. It was soft and small like a white woman's.

THE END

Development

INTERPRETATION

1. We are told that for Xuma "The only place where he was completely free was underground in the mines." (a) How do you account for this apparent contradiction—that Xuma felt free only in the confines of the mine? (b) Find details in the story which reveal Xuma's feelings of freedom or confinement.

2. (a) What is the dominant characteristic of the crowd watching the police chase? (b) At what point does Xuma differ from the other observers in the crowd? How does he differ?

3. Doctor Mini was a native black, yet Xuma observes that he "behaved like the white people" (page 384, column 1, paragraph 3). Is this comment to be interpreted as one of scorn or of awe? Explain.

4. (a) Why is Xuma so in awe of the doctor's home? (b) Explain the doctor's comment that: "This is the sort of place a man should live in because it is good for him. . . . It is the other places that are the white people's. The places they make you live in."

5. At the end of the story, Doctor Mini dismisses Xuma abruptly. (a) Why does the doctor speak so harshly? (b) What does his attitude indicate about the problems of the society in which they live?

6. Consider Xuma's reaction to the various people he meets. (a) In what situations is understanding evident? (b) In which is there an apparent lack of understanding? (c) Which understandings or misunderstandings are based upon differences in race? (d) What other differences result in misunderstandings?

TECHNIQUE

1. (a) Describe the prevailing atmosphere in the first paragraphs of this selection as Xuma walks through the white section of Johannesburg. (b) Does this atmosphere remain the same or does it change in the course of the story? Explain. (c) How does the atmosphere established early in the story prepare the reader for later events?

2. Peter Abrahams presents this story as seen and understood by Xuma. (a) In your opinion, does this point of view strengthen or weaken the impact of the story? Explain. (b) Briefly suggest differences which would have resulted if "Episode in Malay Camp" had been told from the point of view of one of the policemen or of Dr. Mini.

3. Point out the contrasts in "Episode in Malay Camp." What ideas in the story do these contrasts reinforce?

4. What effect is achieved in the last paragraph: "Xuma took her hand. It was soft and small like a white woman's"?

EXTENSIONS

1. (a) Who are the "bound men" of this selection? (b) How are they bound? (c) Is their bondage inevitable or is it one from which they can escape? Explain.

2. In his book *The Fire Next Time*, James Baldwin writes, "The fear I heard in my father's voice . . . when he realized that I really believed I could do anything a white boy could do, and had every intention of proving it, was . . . a fear that the child, in challenging the white world's assumptions, was putting himself in the path of destruction."[1] (a) Discuss the relevance of this statement to the selection you have just read. (b) Who in the story is in the position of placing himself in the "path of destruction"—Xuma? Dr. Mini? the accused man? Explain.

---

1. From THE FIRE NEXT TIME by James Baldwin. Published by The Dial Press, Inc.

To B. Akhmadulina[1]

ANDREI VOZNESENSKY[2] / RUSSIA / 1933–
translated from the Russian by Stanley Kunitz

We are many. Four, perhaps, altogether,
spinning along in our car devil-may-care.
The girl at the wheel flaunts her orange hair,
the sleeves of her jacket yanked up to the elbow.

5 Ah, Bela,[3] though your driving leaves me limp,
you look angelic, out of this world;
your marvelous porcelain profile
glows like a white lamp . . .

In hell they bang their frying pans
10 and send their scouts up to the gate to watch,
when you, as the speedometer runs wild,
lift both hands off the wheel to strike a match.

How I love it, when stepping on the gas
in your transparent tones you say,
15 "What a mess!
they've taken my license away . . .

"I swear they got me wrong!
     You'd think I was a reckless driver!
          Why! I was just poking along . . ."

20 Forget it, Bela. To argue with a cop,
you know, is a losing proposition.
He can't appreciate your lyric speed—
it's past the power of his transmission.

A poet owes it to himself
25 not to be trapped in miles-per-hour;
let him resound at the speed of light
like angels choiring in the stratosphere.

1. *B. Akhmadulina* (ak′ ma dū lēn′ ə), the Russian poet to whom Voznesensky dedicates this poem. **2.** *Voznesensky* (vōz′ nə sen′ skē). **3.** *Bela* (byā′ lä).

No matter, taking light-years as our measure,
if we should vanish like a radiant star,
30   with not a creature left behind to earn the prize.
We were the first to crack the sound-barrier.

Step on it, Bela, heavenly friend!
Who cares if we're smashed to bits in the end?
Long live the speed of poetry,
35   the most lethal of all speeds!

What if the maps ahead are enigmatical?
We are only a few. Four, perhaps, altogether;
hurtling along—and you are a Goddess!
That makes a majority, after all.

Development

1. In what sense has Voznesensky made use of an extended metaphor in "To B. Akhmadulina"?

2. (a) Describe Bela from the poet's portrayal of her. (b) What parallels can be drawn between Bela as driver and Bela as poet? (c) Explain the meaning of lines 38-39, ". . . and you are a Goddess!/That makes a majority, after all."

3. (a) What qualities does Voznesensky attribute to poetry and the poet? (b) In conveying these qualities, what images does the poet use?

4. Trace the use of the basic image of the car speeding along. How many parallels to the writing of poetry can you discover?

5. According to the poet, from what bonds must a poet be free?

6. (a) Which best describes the poet's diction in "To B. Akhmadulina"—formal, informal, colloquial, slangy? Explain. (b) The tone of a poet's work results, in part, from his choice of diction. What tone is established in this poem?

7. Discuss the meaning of the line, "Long live the speed of poetry,/the most *lethal* of all speeds" (lines 34-35). In your discussion consider the importance of the word *lethal*.

8. What does line 37, "We are only a few," imply about the role of the poet as described by Voznesensky?

9. Many of Voznesensky's poems are concerned with the poet as prophet, rebel, witness, and martyr. Which one of these aspects of the poet does Voznesensky emphasize in "To B. Akhmadulina"?

The Exile

KAY CICELLIS [1] / Greece
(1926 –   )

originally written in English

It was a harsh cold day, mid-winter, so the boy couldn't pretend he was a tourist. Even in summer, very few tourists came here. Then the long fighting on the mainland made traveling for pleasure even more improbable. But peacetime or wartime, there had never been much to see here. The big holiday ships kept away. The harbor was extremely shallow, and the voyage was too long anyway. But obedient to his instructions, the boy wandered up and down the pier; he gazed at the houses, admired the seaview from the jetty; he tried to look leisurely, even bored. It was difficult, for he felt excited and impatient.

At lunch-time he gave a sigh of relief, he could make his first move. He walked along the waterfront slowly to see which restaurant was most crowded, so that his presence in it would not be too conspicuous. It took him some time to find out. The restaurants were undistinguishable, at first glance, from the other shops and establishments; the windows were as dirty, difficult to see through; the walls were the same dingy color, the signs above the entrance small, obscure, with no intention to advertise, only inform; the chairs and tables, which in summer would have been under an awning outside and might have guided him, had all been moved indoors.

He finished by singling out the restaurants eventually; there were only two of them. Neither was very crowded. In a place like this people only ate in a restaurant out of necessity, having nowhere else to go; there were a few bachelors, a few widowers, several drunks. Even the strangers who had come to work here (the schoolteacher, the harbor master, the police sergeant) had brought over their wives or got themselves wives, and made a home, because it was more economical.

The boy sat down at a table in the center, and nodded all around two or three

1. *Cicellis* (cə cel′ lis).

times. He had a nice face, he was not too well-dressed, so the people at the other tables soon spoke to him. They didn't ask him at once what he was doing on the island. But there was something ruthless in their set faces, encircling him, watching, that meant they intended finding out sooner or later. He didn't make them wait. He must not appear mysterious. He said he'd come to inquire about a relative of his who had once been a political prisoner on the island.

"We haven't heard from him for some months. We inquired at the Ministry, but they were very vague. They can't be bothered at a time like this."

"What was his name?" said one of the closed, sallow faces.

"That one!" several voices cried out when they heard the name. "That one has been dead over a year now." Some of them laughed. It was rather a joke; ignorance of any kind made them laugh. A man at a corner table explained to a drunk: "No, he had no idea—he's come all this way looking for a man who's dead!" He spoke loudly as one speaks to a deaf person.

The boy composed a sad face, not too sad, while the laughing frittered away. Then he asked:

"Are there no more political exiles left on the island?"

"There's one left. Just one. Way up in the hills."

"He's been there two years."

Their faces turned serious.

"What's his name?" asked the boy.

"We call him the Commander."

Another man put in: "Commander Rigas."[2]

"We just call him the Commander. I don't think Rigas is his real name."

"Perhaps he can tell me some more about my relative," said the boy. "Perhaps they lived together up in the hills."

"Perhaps. But this one keeps very much to himself."

"Doesn't he come down here to the village at all?"

"Oh, once in a while. He buys tobacco. He buys a lot of tobacco. So as not to have to come down often."

"The other one, your relative, he was here all the time. He went round the cafés, every day. . . ."

They laughed again, the joke was still alive.

"Perhaps it's his back—it's the Commander I'm talking about. He was wounded in the war. When they brought him here he was still very bad. Perhaps he doesn't like walking."

"No, no," one of the men said impatiently, "it's not the wound, he likes to keep to himself. He can walk all right. People have seen him climbing where even the goats won't go. He doesn't talk much either."

"He's a character," someone said in a low voice, meditatively.

"But how does he live," asked the boy, "how does he feed himself?"

"He's got a gun. He's a good shot."

"A good shot," they nodded, several of them.

"But do they allow him to carry a gun? A prisoner?" said the boy, looking surprised.

They shrugged. "It's only a small caliber. For birds. Perhaps a hare. There's not much he can do up there."

"Isn't he even guarded?"

"Guarded! Why should they guard him? He can't get away; everybody knows his face, if he tried to get on the ship. There's not much he can do. That's why they chose our island for political exiles, because it's so far away from the mainland, from other islands. Besides, all these exiles, usually they don't want to get away. It's quiet here, it's cheap, they've had enough, they don't want to get mixed up in all that mess again, on the mainland. Glad they're out of it.

"But you know him; you know about him. You know more than us. What was he before they sent him here? That's what

2. *Rigas* (rē′ gəs).

I want to know. He was something big, wasn't he? Not just a commander. A general?"

"He was something in the war. It was before my time. Not a general, I don't think so. Didn't the police sergeant tell you why they sent him here? You should be the ones to know, not me."

"The sergeant! He doesn't know anything. He says they're all communists. He says all the political exiles that are sent here are communists."

"Does he look old?"

"Not very. Middle-aged. He has iron-colored hair, an iron-colored moustache. He looks very proud. And worried; always frowning. . . ."

"Worried? There shouldn't be much to worry him up there in the hills. I thought he would have a calm look, very calm. . . ."

"Who knows? Perhaps it was only an impression."

"Do you think, perhaps, he's gone a bit mad up there all on his own?"

"Who knows?" one of the men said. "I wouldn't be surprised. But who knows? I never see him. It makes me angry; the only thing that ever happens here, the only thing this damned place is known for, is the political exiles. And we never see them. . . ."

Something was worrying him. He frowned.

"You say you don't know him personally," he said to the boy. "But at least you've heard things, you know more than us—it's certain, isn't it, that he was something big? A great man?"

"Yes. He was a great man."

After a silence, someone asked: "And how's the fighting going on over there?"

"It's still going strong, up in the North," said the boy. "There are still a lot of guerillas hiding in the mountains. They say it'll take some time to clear the mountains."

The faces were dubious, sullen; indifferent at heart, but they liked to appear interested in politics, in the Situation.

"You haven't got yesterday's paper, have you?"

The boy gave them the two papers he carried in his pocket. Shuffling and whispering, a clinking of glasses; attention gradually fell away from him. Before it had quite gone, he reached out tentatively: "Perhaps I could go and see the Commander? He might be able to tell me something about my relative," he reminded them. "Something I can tell his mother. You know."

"I suppose you could go," said the waiter who came to take his plate. "I shouldn't think the police sergeant would mind. But it's a long way off. Three or four hours' walk. . . ."

"Do you think I might get lost?"

"There's only the one path."

"Well, perhaps I'll go tomorrow," said the boy.

The boy came within sight of the hut in the hills towards evening. It had been a difficult journey. His uneasiness had grown as he progressed. What right had he to be here? The trees were a very dark green, tall and stern, the sky was grey. Complete silence followed him all the way, except for the knock of his boots against the rocky path. As he climbed higher the trees became sparser; there were just a few isolated ones, mutilated by the wind, and a great deal of grey rock interspersed with short, prickly bushes. The path was steeper, so that now his horizon was studded with sharp profiles—tree-profiles and rock-profiles, great lonely shapes against the void of the sky. The boy longed for the sight of the hut; at the same time he did not expect any real warmth from it. It would be part of this hostile nature, it belonged to this alien world.

The hut seemed empty when he reached it; windows and door were closed. A low wall, like a fence, encircled it. The boy walked slowly round the house. At the back he found the man he was looking for. He was sitting on the wall with his legs hanging over the outer side. His back was a bit hunched, his hands clasped between his knees. He was absolutely motionless.

He did not hear the boy, who was able to walk up almost to his side; he was even able to see part of the man's face. The expression on it was completely vacant. At last the boy spoke. The man gave a great start. Then he stared at the boy in anguish.

"What are you doing here?" he cried roughly. Then, quieter: "You are not from the village. You are a stranger. You've just arrived on the ship . . ." An uncertain eagerness crept into his face.

The boy said: "I have been sent by Apergis."[3]

The eagerness did not quite leave the man's face; only it became coupled to an incongruous, superimposed sarcasm as he replied: "I thought they had forgotten all about me."

"I will try to explain," said the boy falteringly.

"Explain!" he laughed. "What can you know about it? Only what they told you. Let's go into the house. It's horrible out here. Or are you impressed by the view?" He was sarcastic again. He did not wait for the boy's answer but led him to the house.

Once in the house he became feverishly active. He lit a storm lamp, then a small rusty paraffin stove. He fetched a chair, swept a few old, hard crumbs from the table with his palm. Then he hurried to a cupboard to fetch a bottle of yellowish wine, half a loaf of bread, and white cheese that still had some goat's hair in it. Before he sat down, he went to the windows to check if they were properly shut.

He drew up a stool, looked at the boy searchingly: "All right now? Are you comfortable?"

The boy was embarrassed by the fuss. He didn't know how to take it; he had been full of humbleness and wanted to be allowed to use it.

"Please let me talk to you," he stammered. "I've been waiting for this moment—I'm not as ignorant as you think.

I know what happened. I know they betrayed you."

"But it couldn't be helped, isn't that it?" the man said with a short loud laugh, a bark of a laugh.

"Perhaps it couldn't be helped, I can't tell," said the boy with vehemence. Then softly: "I also know they wouldn't have done it—they couldn't have done it—if the Chief had been still alive. The Chief loved you very much, didn't he? You were his right hand."

"Yes," said the man, with a bitter smile.

"I know," the boy said. "Still you can't expect the same thing from the others. They are not the same type of men. They are more—practical. And then things didn't go so well. But all the same I know that Apergis respects you. I know that for sure." He swallowed hard, then tried to add nonchalantly:

"Apergis wants you back. He needs you."

The man flushed violently. He was silent, his eyes fixed. It was some time before he spoke. "What on earth would Apergis need me for?" He tried to laugh again.

He suddenly got up and went to the door. He opened it and leaned forward, his hands gripping the low lintel above his head.

The boy was left alone again and full of awe in the dark presence of this man, the dark hunched back which concealed anger and grief, anger hurled out silently into the great night outside. But he continued bravely:

"They need you, Apergis' guerilla-band is falling to pieces. The men are demoralized. They don't trust Apergis the way they trusted the Chief. He's a good leader, he is brave and very clever, but it's no longer the same. If you came back, things might change—you were the Chief's best friend. You knew all his secrets, all his thoughts." The boy hesitated a little: "And you have his memoirs, his last in-

---

3. *Apergis* (ə par′ gis).

structions, the ones he wrote before he was killed. Apergis believes there might be something there to give the men faith again. It's enough that they are the Chief's words. The effect on their morale may be incalculable, Apergis says."

The man suddenly swung round from the door. A secret excitement twitched in his face:

"And how do you know I still have the papers?" he asked. "When I was sent here, everything was finished. . . . The Chief, and me, and the papers—all that belonged to the past. Finished . . . done away with. Rubbish. And what do you do with rubbish? You throw it away."

"You destroyed the papers?" whispered the boy.

"Who knows," said the man thoughtfully, "who knows?"

The boy did not insist, but watched him without speaking.

The silent hills of the daytime had found a voice now; there were owls, there was a fitful undecided wind coming through the open door. The hut creaked a little. In the room where they sat there was a continuous wheezing sound; the boy couldn't tell if it was the stove or the lamp. He grew thoughtful too. Now the lamp had them both staring at it, a small flame flickering through smoky glass.

"You hate them, don't you?" said the boy.

The man only smiled. He might have been thinking of something else.

"What is your name?" he asked the boy after a while.

"Stamos."[4]

"And you are—eighteen?"

"Nineteen."

"I don't suppose you've actually been in the fighting."

"Not *in* the fighting . . . but I hang around. I've lived with them in the mountains, up north. I help Apergis with his papers, I look after his clothes, his boots. Sometimes I help the cook. I carry messages. Apergis lets me carry a gun. My father was a friend of his. He is good to me."

"But you don't stay in the mountains all the time? You go down to the cities?"

"Yes, sometimes. I can go and come, I'm only a boy, so they don't think I'm dangerous," sighed the boy. "Though it's getting more difficult now."

"The cities must be almost back to normal, now that the fighting is far away."

"Yes. In Salonica,[5] you still feel a kind of tension, like in wartime. But in Athens you can hardly tell there's anything going on. The wireless of course, bragging and mouthing big words, all that silly propaganda; but who listens to the wireless. You hear about arrests; houses are raided; there are a lot of uniforms in the streets. But it's as if it were all the State's private affair. Most people are beginning to have a good time again, to think of their own affairs. Much they care what we go through."

"Tell me more about Athens."

The tone of his voice made Stamos look up sharply; and he had time to capture on the lined face an extraordinary expression of avidity. He asked suspiciously: "You miss Athens then?"

Rigas shrugged. Finally he said: "Perhaps I fear it more than I miss it. Tell me more about Athens all the same. To pass the time."

Stamos told him about Athens. Most of the theatres were playing reviews, musicals, political satires, but the censorship was still strict. The cinemas had begun bringing American and English films. There were a lot of Americans about. For some time now there had been a big organization in Athens, with many offices, it was called UNRRA[6]; some of his friends had found jobs there as lorry-drivers, messenger-boys even. They paid well. You could get American cigarettes quite cheaply. The autumn had been long and warm. A month ago there had still been cane chairs outside the cafés

---

4. *Stamos* (sta′ məs). 5. *Salonica* (sə lon′ ə kə), a port of Greece. 6. *UNRRA* (un′ rə), United Nations Relief and Rehabilitation Administration.

in Constitution Square. At the Old Palace, the men who guarded the Unknown Soldier were no longer evzones but members of the armed forces. They took turns; one week it was sailors, then airmen, then soldiers. The evenings were still clear, the sunsets very bright, but now you could see grey clouds racing behind the Acropolis, over the sea. The shops had turned on their luminous signs again; Omónoia Square[7] looked wonderful at night; and so crowded. . . . The whole of Athens was crowded; thousands of people streaming in from the provinces, the destroyed villages.

Rigas listened, his face quite hermetic.[8] The boy slowly came to a stop. After a long silence, he asked: "I suppose it must be lonely up here. Why don't you go and live down in the village? You're allowed to, aren't you?"

"Yes. But I don't want to. I can't have the sergeant watching me all the time. And people are a nuisance. They ask questions, they take sides, they argue, they quarrel. You get mixed up without wanting to."

"And you're fed up with all that. . . ," said the boy reverently. He walked to the open door and looked out. "It takes guts to live out here," he said.

"It's all right," said Rigas neutrally.

"Will you show me around tomorrow? You must know the place inside out. It is your kingdom," he said shyly.

"There is not much to see. But I'll take you around."

"Do you ever sleep out of doors? When the weather's good, I love doing that."

"No, never." His voice had gone very cold. "Shut the door. We will make a bed for you."

He passed a hand across his face. "Your coming has done strange things to me," he said. "You must forgive me if I seem moody."

In one bed there was Stamos, who slept off the fatigue and the novelties of yesterday, who slept with all his body, thickly, wholly. In the other bed, Rigas, who slept badly. He groaned and tossed; the boy's presence was like a clock ticking in the room; he couldn't shut it out, it dragged him back to the slow, parceled minutes of consciousness. Rigas could not cross over the border into freedom; the freedom of sleep, where there is no time; the blank freedom of the days before the boy's arrival. He was caught in the ticking minutes; this was time, this was the night going by, trickling away in minutes towards a dawn, a day—a day in which Stamos would awake and talk and question, in which there would be changes and shiftings, actual happenings that had repercussions, that would affect his companion, then himself, then others beyond, in ever-widening circles, in a concatenation unbroken like the ticking minutes of this time-bound night. His thoughts exhausted him; each minute a new thought, each minute fashioning its own thought; a continuous refraction in the passing stream, a dazzling, maddening light distributed into a thousand watery fragments.

Twice he lifted his head from his pillow to look at Stamos' dark form at the other end of the room. He could not get used to this being in the room, this obstacle against which all his silent words broke and came flickering back to him, instead of being lost forever, like the innumerable words he had lost before Stamos came; words lost, gone, swallowed by the watery waste which had served him as time until now.

He nearly got up from his bed to go and look at Stamos, stoop over him—curious, passionate, fearful Psyche stooping over Eros, and in his limbs the same strange

---

7. *Constitution Square . . . evzones* (ev′ zōz) . . . *Acropolis . . . Omónoia* (ō mon′ yə) *Square.* Constitution, or Syntagma, Square is located in the center of downtown Athens. The evzones are members of a special corps of infantrymen in the Greek army known for their great valor and picturesque uniform. The Acropolis is a high fortified part of Athens upon which was built the famous Parthenon. Omonoia Square is located in an older, more congested section of Athens. 8. *hermetic* (hėr met′ ik), closed tightly so that air cannot get in; airtight.

weakening that shook the hand that held the fatal taper.[9] And Stamos, not quite oblivious, sensed something of these strange movements and sounds from the other bed. Round his thick sleep they circled, infinitely repeated, elongated in the peculiar perspective of sleep, like a cry stretched out in a tunnel, so that he had the impression the whole night was one single groan; not his groan. As if he lived the other man's nightmare indirectly, ran parallel to it without ever being touched by it; so that he woke with a borrowed, alien anxiety nagging at his brain, an anxiety incongruous in this body of his which lay quite intact, the same familiar body he found in his bed every morning.

Rigas had already left his bed, the house was empty. With disappointment, but without surprise, Stamos discovered he was alone. He had expected this, known that he and Rigas could not wake together, start the day together. Rigas was the man you could not catch up with, the man whose direction could never be towards you. In his very few memories of Rigas, the memories of one evening, it was always a profile that appeared, a half-face only; a face in the process of turning away.

Stamos wanted to leave the house at once, find him. Rigas was up in the dark hills, breaking through what trees, climbing over what rocks, listening to what voices? Rigas was already conversing with this blank new day, he held the shape of it. And Stamos was alone in a house where Rigas was not. He was of no use to himself, his single existence suddenly of no value at all.

There was no sign of Rigas outside. Stamos looked round the back of the house, then down the path that led to the house. The evening before, arriving from the village, he had looked for him in the same way. All during the long march from the village to the hut his eyes had been on the lookout for him. "I am hunting down a free man," he thought, and felt sordid. But he went on searching, and even formulated a separate thought: "I must bring the conversation back to Apergis. I must make him decide."

Rigas was not very far away. He was drawing water from a well, hardly a well, a hole in the ground, down in a small ravine on the left of the hut.

Rigas and Stamos did not speak much at first; as if the long, long night with its own happenings had left them with nothing to say, had enacted all the important conversations. Stamos, in his youth, was the first to shake off the predestination and set his face determinedly towards the day ahead. "Let's go," he pleaded.

"You'll have to wait," Rigas said gruffly. He went into the house, and after some time reappeared with a saw and axe, and a piece of bread. He was also carrying his gun. "We are going to cut down some wood in the hills," he said. "I hate purposeless wanderings. You take the axe, I'll carry the rest."

"Do you always carry your gun?" the boy asked, slightly abashed, but happy all the same, happy they were setting out, he and Rigas.

"Always. You never know."

They started to climb the slope behind Rigas' hut. Stamos halted a minute to look up and take in the whole sky, the hills, the wilderness. Rigas, in front of him, advanced slowly, sturdily, his eyes fixed on the path, like a laborer tilling a field.

All through that day Stamos tried to see with Rigas' eyes, hear with his ears. And he thought he sensed things he had never sensed before. This landscape was not the green, sylvan nature of mythology and fairy-stories; nor was it the blue and white nature of postcard Greece. This landscape was almost northern in its ruggedness. He tried to remember the mountains up north with Apergis and the guerillas; there had been many more trees, taller and fuller ones. But that had not been nature; it had

---

9. *Psyche . . . taper.* In legend Eros, god of love, warned his bride Psyche not to look upon him. Curious, she held a lamp over his sleeping form. A drop of oil fell on his shoulder; he awoke and fled.

been "headquarters," "center of operations," "our side of the slope," "a good vantage point."

The ground had never been so hard, harsh, grainy under his feet. His ankles knocked against stones like wood against wood, the low thyme-shrubs scraped against the rock like metal instruments. Even the few gaunt trees seemed to scrape the sky. The muted tints, clear grey rock, green-black foliage, patchy brown earth, dry purple thyme and heather, were as violent in their clearness as the most fiery of colors. The smells, frozen and concentrated by the winter, were as strong as ether. And the whole air was occupied by a vast unexpressed booming, which was the voice of silence, but not of solitude; not even solitude, it was too inhuman for that; solitude is a man separated from his surroundings; this place would allow no separation, it was all there was.

Stamos looked at Rigas as if he had been the revelation itself, not simply the revelator; as if the great absent booming had issued from his frame. Yet Rigas had pointed out nothing, made no comments. He had limited himself strictly to practical information, technical details. He showed the boy where the wild rabbits had their burrows. He examined the weather. He chose passages through the rocks. He picked a few herbs. When they began to cut down the wood, he knew at a touch whether a tree was sound or rotten inside. Rigas' knowledge impressed Stamos more than the unveiling of loftier mysteries. These were the certain signs of the initiate, they indicated a sure, casual mastery, a communication with nature that was made not of words and emotions, but of acts.

"Are you cold?" Rigas asked Stamos, noticing that the boy was blowing on his fingers. "The winter is hard here."

"Can you see the village from up here?" the boy asked.

"No, the village is hidden away, from wherever you stand."

"One might even forget it's there," said the boy, bemused.

"Yes."

"Is this the part of the forest you set on fire?"

"So they told you about that too!" He was amused; or only contemptuously amused. "They must have told you a whole lot of nonsense about it. I can imagine."

"They did talk about it quite a lot," the boy nodded; "it's become a kind of legend in the village."

Rigas' face turned ferocious. "It was an accident," he said. Towards noon he took Stamos to a small, shallow cave in the rock; before entering it, he knocked and prodded at the creviced walls with the muzzle of his gun. "You never know," he said mechanically. "We may not be the only ones who thought this would make a good shelter." They sat down and ate bread and rested.

Rigas looked from his boots to his gun to his piece of bread. Stamos looked outward; the narrow aperture from which he looked made the landscape open out away from him in an even wider sweep. The rocky slope falling away below him had the power of one continuous, suspended avalanche.

"I've never seen a place like this," said the boy in a low voice. "A place fit for eagles."

"I haven't seen any eagles around here," Rigas said smiling. "Only crows. They make an ugly sound, I don't like them. Perhaps I'm afraid of them. If I get killed up here—a fall, an accident, it's easy— they're the ones who'll get me, and no one will know."

"You've forgotten," said the boy, "you're supposed to be coming back with me. So the crows will never get you. Or perhaps you haven't forgotten. Perhaps you've decided to stay. Is that what I must tell Apergis?"

"Apergis, ah, yes," sighed Rigas. He lifted his head and looked outward for the first time, like the boy.

Stamos didn't wait for anything more; he trod on Rigas' vagueness with perfect assurance. "From the moment I met you I knew there wasn't much hope of your coming," said Stamos. "Even before I met you perhaps, I knew."

"What was the use of coming here then?"

"Apergis sent me. He should have known better. I could never have persuaded you. Because if I'd been you, I'd have done the same. I'd have stayed. At least, I hope so. I don't know—I'm younger than you, weaker. Perhaps I'd have been tempted a bit at first."

Stamos glanced at Rigas sideways. Rigas was silent, he was chewing bread, listening or not listening, but certainly not judging. The cave, and the stony landscape outside, the mountain, were as silent; enormous, powerful, yet not overwhelming. Stamos felt a great freedom.

"There is something about those cities," Stamos said. "Athens, Piraeus,[10] Salonica. Athens . . . I know Athens better. I like the noise. Up in the mountains I couldn't sleep the first nights because there was no noise. I like the smell of petrol from the cars on the thoroughfares. I can't see why, it's a dirty smell. The pollution of the cities! But I like it, every time I come back from the mountains I like it better. And the people. That's the big problem. One gets tied to them—not just the ones you love. One can't do without them, I can't do without them. . . . Even in the house, I like having my mother, my sisters around, and the dressmaker perhaps, and neighbors calling—I don't talk to them much, they bore me, but I like them being around. And then I go out! It's an adventure every time. I'm on the lookout. . . . People, people. I think it's because . . . " he blushed, he was confessing, he was saying everything; "it's because I like showing off. You have to have people to show off to. I like talking, that's showing off. Even listening is showing off sometimes. Walking, moving your hand, turning your head, smiling, when you come to think of it almost everything you do is showing off. Doing well, making a success; even making a success of small things, like jumping off the bus neatly, fixing a plug, all that is showing off; all that you do for the others. You can't do it just for yourself. It wouldn't make sense. But for the others it does. You're showing them something; who you are, what you are. And once they know, you know too; you understand yourself, you see yourself, you are there. It is a wonderful feeling. I don't know why it is so wonderful. Whenever I feel happy I know that's what's behind it, I can tell at once, there's nothing as good, as warm. And so there's always something to look forward to, because there's always someone new to show off to; or a new way of showing off to the same person. Something is always happening. You are carried on, life is on the move."

Rigas had finished his bread. He was listening now, very still, concentrated. He wasn't even looking at the rapturous boy, only listening. But Stamos faltered. He remembered where he was. He looked at Rigas and sighed.

"That's all very well," he continued in a small voice. "But would you call that a life? It's wrong, it's stupid. You show off—it means you feed on others. Like those crows. You're a parasite." He cried: "What sort of a man are you if you need others to tell you you're a man? Some things you've got to know for yourself. And that's not all, you've got to know it all the time, when you're alone on the top of a mountain or walking down University Street with a crowd. You've got to know it even when somebody new comes into the room, even when you hear new things being said and you want to say them too. Once I said something like this to some friends of mine, and they laughed. They said: 'You ought to be a monk.' "

He gave a little tentative laugh, but cut it short very quickly, not hoping for a

---

10. *Piraeus* (pī rē′ əs), a seaport city for Athens.

moment that he could draw Rigas, so somber, so still, into any kind of complicity.

"That's stupid," he went on, "it's not only monks who like to be alone; besides it's easy for those who believe in God, they're not really alone. I'm thinking of the others, the philosophers, the poets, the kings. They found out things by thinking hard. By looking inside, not by listening to other people. I've never looked inside me," he cried in distress. "I don't even know what's there. I've never been alone, just me and nothing else. All right, I've been alone in my room at night, waiting for the morning, for someone to come in—getting ready for that. I've been alone on the mountain, in the tent, waiting for the boys to come back, preparing all sorts of questions. But I mean alone, as alone as can be. Without waiting for the next move. How alone can one be? What happens? You cut off everything, the luxuries, the growths, the unnecessary things, the borrowed things; you cut it all off, and what is left? That's what I want to know. That's what I want to lay my hands on. The thing that is left. It must be a great and precious thing; a tiny great precious thing, like a tiny stone. It must be the truth. If that isn't the truth . . ."

Rigas had closed his eyes.

"So perhaps I wouldn't be tempted after all," Stamos said softly. He clasped his hands: "Can you imagine—can it be possible, not to be tempted by anything? Not to envy anything, not to fear anything?"

He looked around at the empty landscape, he breathed deeply. "No interference. To move your hand like this, to say this or the other thing, because you want it, mean it, no other reason. To do only what is necessary. To look at the next day and ask nothing. To sit still, without this waiting, this looking forward. I'm tired of waiting for something more, something better. I want to be where there is nothing more. I want to get there. What are we doing, playing hide-and-seek? Comparing, postponing, changing our mind. I say something and then I think: 'No, that wasn't quite right.' I buy something and I say: 'It could have been better.' I meet a man and I think: 'Now I want to meet his friend.' I earn some money and I think: 'What would it be like if I had the money double?' I love a girl and I think: 'What would it be like if she were another?' and I have no rest and I am always hungry and always waiting."

He looked at Rigas and added gently: "You don't want to go back to all that. You'll get torn to bits again. All broken up, here and there, little bits of you in every house, every street. One bit of you living today, another tomorrow. You've forgotten all that, haven't you? You've forgotten what it's like."

"I haven't forgotten," said Rigas.

The boy was taken aback. Rigas was quite close, the nearness of his voice startled him, their boots were touching.

"I've been talking for myself," said Stamos. "Take no notice. You know best. You know it all."

But he couldn't leave Rigas alone. He still wanted to question, probe, explore. He turned in circles, uncertain yet ruthless. He had to make everything clear. Rigas was his dream, he must possess his dream.

"How did you feel when they took you away?"

"What did you expect me to feel? I felt terrible."

"Yes, but did you want to go away?"

"Oh, I was fed up," said Rigas.

"Yes," said Stamos, "of course. You must have been pretty disgusted at them all. I suppose disgust is not a bad thing. It protects you. You needn't be afraid even of remembering. Disgust takes care of that; it keeps all the memories far away, unimportant."

"And yet," he dreamed, "I would have thought one did forget. Completely. Just yourself and this place, nothing else. All the rest faded out. No interference."

Rigas smiled. "Don't worry. Sometimes

one can't remember even if one tries." But his eyes were very serious, in spite of the smile.

"You'll see, you'll see," Stamos said, his excitement returning, "soon you won't remember at all; it will all go, and leave you alone, free. It's too early still, only two years."

"Only two years," said Rigas.

"You'll see, perhaps if I come back here in another two years, you won't even be able to speak to me. You'll have forgotten the language, you'll have another language."

"I'll have turned into a wild beast," said Rigas, and Stamos laughed.

"Even now you don't say much. It's me that does all the talking. But don't worry. You don't have to listen to me. Take no notice. I know you're not really taking any notice." He piled up the distance between them recklessly, lavishly. There was all the space in the world, the space of the sky, in which to look up, in which to fling up his admiration, a stone in the vastness of the sky.

"You must only listen to one thing," said Stamos. "You must listen when I say that I understand. I will explain to Apergis. I know what to say, I understand."

Rigas lowered his eyes. He hesitated: "You haven't thought that it's perhaps necessary I should go back to them. Since they need me. Perhaps that's more necessary than the rest."

Stamos didn't answer. Even his silence was not an answer, Rigas' words had simply slipped over him. He still looked outwards, smiling. Rigas glanced at him curiously: "You're eighteen, you've lived in the mountains with brave men, you've helped them, yet you have no loyalty. You're not interested in their fighting. Don't you care what happens over there? Don't you think they're doing something worthwhile?"

Stamos was untouched by the accusation. "Yes," he said easily, "yes, I like the boys, I admire Apergis. What they are doing is brave. But this," he said almost slyly, "this is better. This is the thing." He went on impatiently: "All right, they may be fighting for something worthwhile, but who thinks of that, who remembers! In the meantime they get mixed up in all kinds of messes. Look at what they did to you! It's like I told you; when you are with people, you change all the time, you live by the day and by the moment, changing, wanting something else, something more. You can't stick to one thing. Look at Apergis. He was the Chief's friend, your friend. Then he betrayed you. Then he became chief; he became gentle, sensible, a different man. When you come, if you come, he will be your friend once more. Then perhaps you'll want to be chief. Or he will think so. He will make you think so, and then hate you for it. Can you see any sense in it all? And what about you? You will hate him. The men around you will shift from you to Apergis, from Apergis to you, helping you or lying to you. And with each man you will be a different person. You will be afraid, you will defend yourself, you will try to win over the men. Or you will be sorry, and you will be betrayed again. And so it goes on. A racket, a big mess. If you think one has time to think of the fighting and what will happen after the fighting. One can't see clearly, it's too far, and all this changing, changing in between."

"If they need me," insisted Rigas with a great intensity.

"I don't know," muttered Stamos leaning back. "Perhaps you'd be safe anywhere. Even with them. After having lived here."

"I wouldn't want to show off," said Rigas, smiling as he used the boy's words. Then turning austere, impersonal: "That's not what I want."

Stamos cried: "So you still want something?" Innocent and inquisitorial, he was like a child-priest, a child-king, whom one can obey more blindly than a grown, knowing man.

"Perhaps I only want to serve," said Rigas.

The boy shook his head contemptuously. "You've gone beyond all that."

Rigas recoiled a little at the contempt, although it was not directed at him. Then he remembered whom Stamos was talking to. He looked out of the cave again, far out, the tautness went from his face. He seemed to let go of something. He shrugged: "To hell," he said, "what business have I over there. What business have I with Apergis. You've made me dizzy with all your talking. I'm not used to it, I'd rather cut wood all day. We're going back now, it will be dark soon. And I'm tired."

Yet he got up with a strange alacrity. For a second he looked down at Stamos searchingly, as if to confirm something. Having found what he wanted, he picked up two bundles of wood and swung them onto his shoulder; then glanced at the great slope spreading away, and the dark trees gathered below; and he raced towards them as if to meet something found again, or something newly discovered. He didn't wait for Stamos, didn't look back once, knowing that he was followed, and watched.

It turned dark very quickly. Rigas broke into a song, his voice raucous and mocking. It was a soldier's song, the words were coarse and gay. The race down the slope seemed to have intoxicated him. The owls began hooting, and Rigas answered them, with great bursts of laughter. Once or twice he disappeared into the trees; when he emerged he did not explain what he had been up to. Stamos didn't ask him. Now he was completely safe in his admiration. The change in Rigas did not surprise him. Perhaps he did not even notice it, for this was the image of Rigas he had been carrying in his thoughts all along, he had seen no other. The idol was becoming itself, making itself visible.

Stamos stayed another day. He admitted it was not necessary; the decision had been made, he had his message ready for Apergis. The matter had been settled yesterday, on the hilltop. He sensed there had been conflict, though he had been

almost the only one to speak and there had been no argument. Then Rigas had freed himself, had left it all behind him as he raced down the slope, declaring himself at last, taking open possession of his territory. And Stamos could not speak any more, after having spoken so much. He had nothing to say; he was empty and happy. His dream was completed, his dream had grown real; he felt wonderfully unnecessary.

Only Rigas existed, who after having been so tentative, so veiled, seemed guided now by an extraordinary assurance. "He has come to himself," Stamos thought, "he's recovered from my intrusion, he is himself again."

Rigas came and went, leapt to his feet, lay down on the ground, with clean-cut suddenness, obeying himself without question. His hidden power, released, branched out in all directions, a constant assertion. He neglected Stamos, left him alone, often ignored him completely. All day long he sang the coarse mocking soldier's song. From the hut, Stamos heard snatches of it echoing through the trees, and felt the whole mountain was inhabited and that he was listening to forbidden music. Towards evening he couldn't hear Rigas' song any more, only the rippling shots from his gun. Several times the rocks clapped back their ghostly applause. Then a long time passed during which he heard neither song nor gunshots. He waited, perfectly patient.

Rigas came back at night, carrying a hare and two turtledoves. He threw them on the table, and sat down with his legs stretched out. He appeared glad to see Stamos. "We'll eat these tomorrow," he said. "Sometimes when I'm alone I can't be bothered. I forget about them, and they rot."

Stamos said: "I must leave tomorrow. I must leave early, the ship sails at four."

Rigas was silent. Stamos wondered if he had heard.

Then Rigas waved Stamos away with a heavy hand and fell headlong on his bed like a stone. He went to sleep almost at once.

On his last morning, Stamos hoped to be the first up for a change. To see Rigas asleep, the mountain asleep, to get some hold, some knowledge of the place before he left. Even the most sordid of eavesdroppers is better than a spectator, he sees what is forbidden, not what is offered. During these last hours something like ambition stirred in him, rising above his usual humility, though impregnated with it; for it was only a humble ambition after all, quickly gone. He knew he must go without leaving a mark.

Rigas' bed was empty as usual. There was a great glittering day outside, immense because of the clarity of the air, which revealed everything, in a complete, crushing statement. The sun had the perfection of winter sunshine; hard, frozen, still, flawless, as if protected by an enormous sheet of glass. The ink-black shadows made the rocks look sharper, more cruel. In the distance, the sea, no longer misty, barred the horizon with a definite, violent blue.

Stamos edged his way out into the glass-encased landscape and went, resigned, towards the ravine in search of Rigas. He was washing his feet at the well, stripped to the waist. His body was white; so white and clean-cut as it stood out against the dark bushes of the ravine that it had nothing fleshly about it; it belonged to a cold, hard, mineral world. He cleaned his feet meticulously; ugly feet deformed by heavy boots, ugly, useful feet. He said to Stamos:

"Get ready quickly. We should be on our way already." He jerked his head upwards to the sun, which already seemed vertical in its brightness. "He wants me out of the way," thought Stamos. He was sad, but not bitter. He obeyed, he hurried. From the first moment the hut on the mountain had been unattainable; he had never tried to be Rigas, the distance had never lessened.

"I'll go and heat some milk," said Rigas.

"Something hot in the stomach for the long walk."

"Yes," said Stamos.

But Rigas changed his mind. "All right, I might as well wait for you," he said.

"What a day," said Stamos. "The place looks even more beautiful like this."

"You'll have a good trip," said Rigas. He looked at the sea.

Stamos thought of the ship, the people on the ship, the people on the quay at Piraeus. He felt he'd been away a long time. "Back again soon," he thought. And he didn't really mind, his heart even leapt a little, forward to the sea, the arrival. Immediately afterwards he felt vaguely guilty, the same feeling he had when he left his mother sitting vacantly by the window watching the evening while he went out into the lighted city. He resented his own involuntary comparison. "It doesn't apply in the least," he thought. "This time I'm leaving what is best. Yet I don't mind. All I really think of is having a good time." He followed Rigas with bent head. "I'm no good, I'll never be any good," he said. He felt cheap and comfortable, underneath his sadness.

Until the moment they left, Rigas did not go off on his own as on the day before. He stayed with Stamos the whole time, watchful and silent. He had the brooding face of their first evening together, except that now there was a hard line in his jaw.

"Let's go," said Rigas. "I'll walk down the path with you a bit."

He led the way as usual. The sun was full in their faces, small white stones rolled beneath their feet.

"What a day," repeated Stamos. "Will you go out shooting?"

"Perhaps," said Rigas. He shot forward, letting his body go, carried by the downhill path, by a sudden exuberance, an impatience; nothing could possibly check his flight. And where was he fleeing like this? Stamos hurried behind him. But Rigas did stop; he leapt onto a rock on the edge of the path, pulling up with a jerk. He turned round slowly and faced the mountain, his back to the sea, his shoulders squared.

"Yes, it is a good day for shooting," he said. He had quickly mastered the interrupted movement, the flight, the unknown urge; he was ready, he was making an end. "I will leave you here," he said to Stamos, who was not ready. "You know the way. Follow the path."

He stooped to Stamos from his rock, his hand outstretched. "Give my regards to Apergis," he said with his strange grimacing smile, his irony.

Stamos, in a turmoil, a last brief storm of confused feelings before becoming an ordinary person going down to meet a ship, said very quickly: "I will. Thank you for everything. Forgive me for staying so long."

"No, not at all. I would have liked you to stay much longer."

Stamos turned away and raced down the path, wanting to cry in a sudden rage: "I don't believe you." Yet when he reached the first bend in the path his rage dropped away and he couldn't help looking back. Rigas hadn't moved from the rock. His face was no longer clear. He was a figure of stone, a faceless statue merged to the rock.

Rigas stood on the rock for a long time. He did not dare move. The outspread landscape in its glass sheath, the man in his mold of stone, they were timeless, and yet a cloud passed, a wild rabbit scurried through a bush, and it was enough to break it up.

Rigas cracked from top to toe. He stared down the path wildly, not knowing if the boy had been there an hour or a minute ago. He screamed: "Come back, damn you!"

His crazed voice kept shooting upward into the light, empty air; it got lost at once, it spread everywhere and reached nothing. He flung himself face down on the rock and sobbed. "Take me with you, for heaven's sake take me with you."

He clung shuddering to the rock until he heard the ship's siren. Then he scrambled back to the hut, a blind crumpled animal, and shut himself in.

Stamos did not leave at four o'clock. The ship had brought Apergis from the mainland. Stamos was numb as he greeted him, he was indifferent, as if his story were over; this had the taste of an epilogue. Of course he had to ask Apergis why he had come; his curiosity was logical and detached.

Apergis cut him short with a question of his own: "Well, where is Rigas?"

"He won't come," said Stamos quickly, lightly, very near to insolence, as if it were his own refusal.

"I thought so," said Apergis. "That's why I've come. When you didn't return at once, I imagined something must have gone wrong. I thought you needed some reinforcement."

"Nothing's gone wrong. He won't come, that's all. He's not interested." Stamos was not interested. There were no problems, no necessities. Apergis was slightly ridiculous; his strong active body, ready to start, his tired excited traveler's face, his thick traveler's clothes put on like a disguise, a uniform. His eyes were quick, full of thoughts and plans. He came from the crowded ship, he came from the tents on the mountain, from the city, where he had made contacts; the touch of human hands was all over him. He smelt like a dormitory.

"Many people were sick on the boat, it was a bad crossing," said Apergis, laughing away his disgust. "Now then," he said when they were clear of the passenger crowd, "how far off does our friend live? Can we get there before dark? I don't want to be seen by too many people. It's a bit risky, my coming here."

"It's four hours to the hut. I've only just come down from there, I'm tired," said Stamos. The idea of going back to the hut revolted him.

"Come now! A boy of your age."

"Anyway there's no fear about your being seen. They're very curious here, but not suspicious. The police sergeant isn't around, he must be having his siesta. Besides you're not that famous."

"All right. Let's have some coffee first."

Apergis enjoyed his coffee, and the cigarette he smoked with it. He looked round at the people in the café with a tireless appetite in his eyes. Stamos' news had not disturbed him in the least.

"Well, what else does our friend say?" he asked Stamos.

"He's nobody's friend. That's what you don't understand."

"Oh, Rigas and I will always be friends, even though he doesn't know it."

He dropped the jaunty tone and looked Stamos in the eyes: "Let me tell you something: Rigas can't do without friends."

Stamos cried proudly: "You don't know him."

"I know him better than you. We've spent the best years of our lives together. Rigas," he mused with a silent laugh, "I know him like the inside of my pocket."

Suddenly Stamos wanted to get up and go back to the hut, with Apergis, at once. His reluctance was gone. He no longer wanted to keep his dream to himself. He must show it, prove it, communicate it, the whole world must know. The time for transactions was back; Apergis' claim must be answered, and bettered.

Apergis was examining the boy shrewdly. "I wonder what he told you," he said. "He must have done a lot of talking, to get all these ideas into your head."

Stamos jumped eagerly at this triumph, which trapped him. "That's where you're wrong," he said. "Rigas hardly spoke at all."

"Then how do you know? How do you know so much about him?"

Stamos had to make a detour, offer some other merchandise. "Besides," he threw in carelessly, "these papers you're so keen on, the Chief's memoirs; he's destroyed them."

Apergis' eyes grew steely, the mouth lost its manly charm; all that humane curiosity, that interest in the world abroad was put aside. Now was business.

"All right, let's go," he said putting down his cup with a sharp click.

"Why don't you leave him alone?" cried Stamos. "Why don't you leave us alone?"

"You needn't come if you don't want to," Apergis said. He was calling the waiter, to ask for the bill, to ask for information. He knew his way around.

A panic of despair came over Stamos. The drama was about to start now, up on those hills, without him. The drama was to come; it had not been beautifully completed, as he had thought. Nothing had happened. The curtain had not even risen. He had suffered, raved, applauded, and the curtain hadn't even risen yet.

"I'm coming," he whispered, and followed Apergis.

The hut was in darkness, the door and windows sealed.

"He must be out," said Stamos.

"At this time of the night? For God's sake, doing what?"

"He often goes out like that, at any time of the day or night. He is free to come and go, after all." Obstinately he answered in whispers, ignoring Apergis' loud voice.

"Yes, but doing what? He can't go shooting in the dark or gathering wood—what then?"

"I don't know," said Stamos, glorying in his ignorance, unfolding it like a treasure.

"Well, I'll go and find out," Apergis said simply. As he moved away he added: "He was never much of an outdoor man. But a man can change in two years. You stay here in case he comes back from another path."

Stamos cried after him: "It's dark, you'll get lost. This place is big and wild, you have to know it well."

He added: "Only Rigas knows all the by-paths," more as reassurance to himself than warning to Apergis. Rigas must not be found. He must arrive around midnight, down from the mountain top and the trees, and find them sitting on his doorstep, cold and sleepy, hungry and patient, seeking audience.

He saw Apergis was using a flashlight.

Apergis was always well-equipped, he had the necessary things for every occasion. Stamos watched the wavering light, anxiously, contemptuously. "Worse than a policeman," he thought. To cover his anxiety, which was the stronger, he gloried again: "Rigas doesn't need a flashlight. Never uses one."

The night was as still as the day had been. The stillness built up an enormous, smooth high sky, steep as a cliff. There were very few owls this time. Over the skyline the gathered trees emerged like a herd of wild dark beasts, bisons, elephants in waiting. The hut did not interrupt the wilderness; it was simply another rock, on the side of the night, not on men's side. Yet Stamos moved closer to it. He felt fear, which he quickly turned into awe. He climbed the doorstep, and gently tried the door. It gave.

By the light of a match he saw Rigas lying on his bed, his eyes wide open. His face showed no surprise. He did not even look at Stamos.

"You've come back. You've come back for me," he said, like a very sick man.

Stamos lit the storm lamp. He sat on the edge of the bed, cautiously. Rigas got hold of his hand and gripped it hard. The boy couldn't utter a word. And Rigas only smiled, shamelessly, beatifically.

Stamos burst out desperately: "I must go and call him, he's out there looking for you, I won't be long. . . ."

"Don't leave me," said Rigas.

But Apergis was already on the doorstep. He had seen the light of the storm lamp through the door which Stamos had left open.

"So here he is," said Apergis.

Stamos said very quickly, as if Rigas had not spoken, had not gripped his hand, as if this were a clean start, this, now: "Rigas, Apergis has come to take you away by force."

Ignoring him, Apergis came and stood over the bed. "Well, Rigas." He smiled broadly, he touched Rigas' knee. "Well, well, old friend."

Rigas stared back at him.

"You're not ill, are you?"

Rigas came back to the narrowing world, to the hut, to this room in the hut. There was Stamos by the table, in an attitude of suspense, hanging on his lips. And there was Apergis, facing him. He did not know whom to satisfy. He did not know whom to fear most.

"I fell asleep," he said slowly. "Once the sun's gone, I haven't much notion of the time."

"I have," said Apergis. "My stomach has. I'm hungry. Can you feed us?"

"There isn't much in the house," said Rigas, and he got up from his bed with an effort.

"The birds," said Stamos. "The turtledoves. What about those?"

"That's right," decided Apergis. "Stamos, you will prepare us a good meal. Rigas and I have things to talk over."

They sat at the table, the lamp between them. Apergis began giving Rigas a detailed description of the situation on the mainland; information about the men, accounts of their activities. He gave Rigas the news in a good-hearted manner, doing him a favor, a service, taking his interest for granted. And so in spite of Rigas' total silence, the two men seated at the table with the lamp between them composed a picture of intimacy. Such relations, such moments in a relationship are exclusive, and Stamos felt excluded. He clung to Rigas' silence, watched it, guarded it, insisted on it so as to neutralize the illusion of that intimacy. But the impression remained. Two old friends reunited, brothers at arms, talking about the past and already sharing a future.

Stamos opened the door and looked out into the night, restless, trying to say something. He was opening the door of Rigas' cage, he was showing Rigas his own true royal way, out there, in the night. But Rigas had his back turned to the door, and Apergis said carelessly: "Close that door, there's a draft."

When the food was ready, Stamos

brought the dishes to the table and inserted himself between them with great deliberation, like a sword, like a silent judge. Apergis did not mind the intrusion; he drew Stamos into their circle easily and without second thought. He did not feel menaced; his generosity was a mark of his assurance.

Rigas had still not uttered a word. He sat hunched and stolid, like a man in somebody else's house; not opposing Apergis' invasion, but detaching himself from it. Only when he raised his glass of wine, ceremoniously, in Apergis' direction, did he make a mechanical attempt to play host. It was only a gesture, he still said nothing. Apergis took over. Raising his own glass, he said: "What shall we drink to?" He looked at Rigas steadily. "Shall we drink to your return?" he asked, very clearly, without a trace of persuasion in his voice; a straightforward question.

Rigas could not move, or speak.

Stamos watched, fascinated. Apergis could shift from courtesy, cordiality, to utter ruthlessness; from bantering to dead seriousness, and with such mastery that he managed never to give the impression of wile, diplomacy. His maneuvers never appeared sordid. They were not maneuvers, they were perfect, clear-cut, well-balanced moves. Even when he had betrayed Rigas, his face must have been stamped with this same unquestionable honesty. He was infallible. How was one to face him? With what was one to face him? What greater, darker faith could stand up to his daylight? Stamos, powerless, disarmed, looked towards Rigas, who was still all shadow, all mystery. He quickly drowned his own small, anticipated defeat in the shadow that was Rigas, in the mystery that could hold all possibilities. He waited.

Apergis also waited; not for very long. He put down his glass and asked, simply: "No?"

Rigas fixed his eyes not on Apergis, but on Stamos. "No," he replied to Apergis. But he seemed to speak in a dream.

Apergis tapped his fingers on the table thoughtfully. There was no anger or disappointment on his face; but the smiling courtesy had gone completely, so that there was a frightening bareness in his attitude. He was naked purpose.

He turned to Rigas: "Well, since it's like that, at least you must let me have the Chief's papers."

As Rigas didn't answer, he asked patiently: "Stamos says you have destroyed them. Have you?"

There was another pause.

"If you have destroyed them, you'd better tell me, we needn't sit here wasting our time."

"Wasting *your* time, you mean," said Rigas, roused at last.

"Yes, mine, since you have no notion of it."

He meant what he said. He was already calculating, planning, thinking whether it would be safe to go back to the village at this time of the night, catch the early ship. . . .

Rigas cried, too quickly: "I haven't destroyed the papers." Then fiercely: "But I won't part with them."

"I see," said Apergis. "Then you'll just have to come along with the papers."

"You can't make me come," sneered Rigas. Pride was an effort to him, something slow and tortuous and unnatural. But he kept it up, stubbornly. "You can beg as much as you like," he went on. "I don't need you any longer. Things have changed. You may need me, I thank you greatly for your interest, but I don't need you any longer."

Apergis' face lit up with a cool gaiety. "Rigas, let's get things clear. It's not you we need, it's the papers. We don't need you, yourself as such, any more now than we used to need you when you had the Chief's ear. Then as now, you were an intermediary, a carrier. Nothing else."

"Yet I was the one he chose," cried Rigas.

"Because you listened so well. You had the gift of devotion, which was more than

I could give him," said Apergis, laughing softly to himself. He straightened his face almost at once; he was never private for long. He turned back to Rigas with the same smiling interest: "Rigas, have you got it clear now?"

Rigas gripped the table; pride no longer had anything to do with the naked desperate claim that choked him. "What you say is not true," he said, holding back his breath, holding back his panic, his ruin; "he chose me because he could trust me; because I was loyal; because I lent myself to none of your conspiracies."

"You were afraid to," said Apergis, almost with compassion. "How could you venture out, with us, after such a glorious shelter?"

Rigas closed his eyes. Apergis went on, casually but very softly: "You saw it yourself. When the Chief was killed, when the shelter was gone, you became a thing once more, an object. That's why it was so easy to betray you. Among all of us, you were the easiest, the least costly to betray, because you didn't count. My poor Rigas, even the police must have thought the same. They did not bother to shoot you. They sent you here, like the silly little dissenting members of parliament of the old days."

At the other end of the table, Stamos sat petrified. He had eyes for Rigas only. He kept postponing, with a frightful intensity within himself, the catastrophe that had already happened. He was caught in an absurd race for time. The revelation of the hero would come before the catastrophe, the revelation would come at the eleventh hour. At the point of extreme tension the truth would be irresistibly ejected. Until then he must believe nothing.

And indeed, tracked, trapped, strangulated, Rigas seemed about to give out his great justifying cry. But all he did was hurl himself in a byway.

"The fact remains," he panted, "the fact remains that I have the papers and you can't have the papers without me."

Apergis, from the depths of his perfect wholeness, gazed at him in mild wonder. "I can understand your accepting to hide in the shadow of a man like the Chief. But to hide behind a bundle of papers!"

Rigas bowed his head. "They are all I have, you said so yourself," he whispered. His struggle was over.

Stamos saw the body slackening, the voice dying out, and he surged forward to pick up the tension, the passion, like a fallen flag. He called urgently: "Rigas, Rigas, wake up, Rigas, answer him. You don't know what you're saying. You haven't heard properly. You must tell him. You mustn't say lies, he will believe them. What do you care about the papers? You've got this place, it belongs to you, you're its master; you go out at night in the mountain, you're among the trees, on the rocks, everywhere. The sky holds you up, you speak without words. You know what none of us knows, Rigas. Tell him, tell him that when you stand on a rock you are no longer a man; I saw you, I saw you myself, standing on that rock. Good God, nothing dared move while you were there! Rigas, throw away the papers, give him the papers and tell him to go!"

He was drunk. He didn't need to look at Rigas any longer. He wasn't even appealing to Rigas, though his words were appealing. He was simply obeying his deepest preference; he was telling a truth he had dreamed of; selfish and childish, he made himself a Rigas of his own to fit his need. In the small wooden room, at the side of the two older men already acquainted with destruction, he was very much alone and absurd. Apergis looked on this absurdity quite tenderly, only just seriously enough. But on Rigas the effect was violent. Listening with face averted in weary exasperation, following step by step the operation Stamos was performing upon him, his eyes slowly turned round to the boy and fixed themselves there in a terrible hardening of hatred. The boy raved on, he felt nothing. Then Rigas pounced and gripped him brutally by the shoulder. He opened the door, pushed

Stamos towards it. "There's your night," he shouted, "your big wonderful night. There's your mountain, your trees, your rocks. All yours! Go out in it then, go out and tell me what you've seen, what you've heard! Go out then! You had me once, with your big words. You filled me with words till I was dizzy. Then you left, carefree as a bird, off to your ship, like a damned inspector after his round; you left and there was nothing, nothing, the words were all gone, as good as the wind. That is what was left. That is what is always left. You wanted to know, didn't you? Then go out and find out! Go!"

He shook him, held him half-bent over the threshold, as over a window with the void below. Then he let him go abruptly. Stamos remained where he was, a flung thing against the open door. He didn't move or speak.

"Why don't you go?" raged Rigas. "Go on, it's all there! It's waiting for you! There!" He pointed at the dark frenziedly.

Stamos closed his eyes tightly and whispered: "There's no place for me out there."

"No place? There's plenty of place! All the place in the world!" Rigas checked himself, moved swiftly forward and gripping Stamos by the hand dragged him outside.

"I'll take you out," he said in a low hurried voice. "I'll show you. I'll show you the works! Everything. I am doing the honors!"

When they had gone a small distance from the house and the darkness settled in a circle around them, he let go of Stamos' hand, and the boy, lost, was aware of nothing but a ferocious laughter bobbing madly around him, up and down, now close by, now farther away.

"Rigas," he called, "don't go, I don't know where I am."

Behind him he could just see the hut, the narrow light coming through the open door, and the black figure of Apergis, leaning idly against the doorpost. The lineaments were quite clear, yet the dis-

tance seemed infinite, because Apergis, the hut, could not be reached; the way onlookers on a quay, no matter how close, seem minute and lost forever to the person on the deck of a ship that is sailing away.

Stamos cried out again: "I can't move, come back."

"I'm here," said Rigas, quite near. "Don't be afraid. I was afraid too, the first months. Not like you, much worse. Because I am the kind of man who is always afraid. Apergis told you so and you must believe him."

"I am only afraid of the dark, really," Stamos said unsteadily.

"I was afraid of the dark, I was afraid of the daylight, I was afraid of the sun at its brightest. I was alone. I had never been alone before. There had always been the Chief—Apergis told you—or someone like the Chief. I was soft and naked as a worm flung out of his dark hole."

His voice moved away. A tree seemed to stand between them, or his back was turned to Stamos, because the sound came a bit muffled. Then it was clear again, echoing slightly, as if he were flinging it at the mountain.

"It was all evil" said Rigas, facing the mountain, "every bit of it, alive and evil. I walked in the woods, and it was like crossing a minefield The birds were looking for me with their beaks. The trees stretched out their fingers to me. Secret animals waited for me in the cracks of every rock I sat on. Even the owls, they exchanged signals to locate my whereabouts, they had me trapped. There was a rustle in the shrubs—it turned out to be a hare—but that was not the real cause. All of me was vulnerable, I was afraid, afraid in my flesh, and my flesh tingled through and through as if it had been flayed. The first night you came you asked me if I slept out of doors! Even in my hut, door and windows locked, I cringed through sweaty nights and I couldn't make myself small enough, there was always a piece of flesh left to tingle and die of terror. And every morning I began again, I was whole again, I was a fresh, new prey. The sky forced me to exist, it made me visible, it offered me up, threw me into the awful arena. Why didn't I leave the hut and go to stay in the village? I thought of it. It wasn't safe enough. It wasn't a refuge. The mountain would still get me; the nights would be the same; big dark awful nights as up here; in the silence, houses and people would be abolished by the same devouring darkness. No one could protect me. Every time I came down to the village for tobacco or food, it was as if my enemies up here were simply lending me for a while to the people of the village, and after that I must go back. I told myself that I was afraid of going to live in the village because the authorities might change their minds about me and decide to have me shot after all. They could come and fetch me any day, so I'd better keep to the mountain where I could hide. But it wasn't really that. It was a greater fear that bound me to the mountain."

Stamos crouched on the ground now, and the whispered confession whistled all around him like a discordant wind out of the dark. There were moments when he thought he could see Rigas; he glimpsed a hand waving, two arms raised, a darting body. But the fragments never coalesced, only the voice remained in the end, out of the dark.

"But you mastered your fear," Stamos said in a small voice, still clinging to a credible Rigas. "I heard you out there, shooting and singing. I saw you standing on the rock; there was no fear, you mastered it."

"Out of sheer exhaustion," sighed the voice. "Fear is exhausting, it is a hemorrhage of the spirit. Out of exhaustion one day I stayed up in the mountain, I lived it through. I went beyond panic. It is only a small step. I don't know how long I stayed, as a woman doesn't know how long it took her to have her child. When I opened my eyes again, I was on the other side of fear. There was silence. For the

first time there was silence. Nothing moved. There was nothing suspect in this stillness. It couldn't be otherwise; since there was nobody there, since there was nothing. Nothing! I thought I'd go mad with joy. I breathed, I stretched. I couldn't believe it. I lay on the ground. I rubbed my face in the grass, which had once seemed infested with a secret life. I touched the trees, I clung to them. Their trunks were dry and rough, they smelt very clean. I broke off a branch and inside I recognized the dead, passive wood of tables and chairs and beds. I prodded with a stick into the cracks of the rocks; they were all empty. I trampled on the rustling shrubs, and they gave way under my foot, their twigs broke like small fragile bones. And then, I shot down a bird, a black crow, with my gun. It died slowly at my feet, an ordinary death, without much blood."

The voice was quieter. It was punctuated now by Rigas' footsteps, regular footsteps trudging back and forth on the hard ground. The sound was mechanical. Stamos was caught in its rhythm, so that the other rhythm, that of time, habits, acts performed in the ordinary world, was blotted out. And the hut with the lighted door that framed Apergis was like what one sees with second sight, in another country.

The footsteps and the voice were saying: "After that I killed many things. I excavated, I investigated in all sorts of ways. But always the answers I got were ordinary; very poor. After a time, I got no answers at all. For everything was as it should be. The wind made noises, the lack of wind made silence. The dark was the absence of sun. The birds croaked because they were hungry. The sky was vast because it was nothingness. It was very sensible. But I didn't know what to do with it. There was nothing to do with it. I didn't mind too much. I had cleaned up the place of fear, and now it was empty, except for myself. Myself. I thought, now that I am free and the place is empty,

I can be myself. I can let the prisoner out of the cage! Bring out the buried treasure!"

There was a pause, then Stamos felt two hands on his shoulders; gently the two hands cupped themselves round his face, directing his gaze straight ahead of him, facing the blinding darkness. "You see?" Rigas said. "It is a mirror. We mirrored each other endlessly. In vain. This place possessed nothing apart from what my fear put into it. I possessed nothing apart from the fear with which this place had filled me. Now there was nothing. I threw out all there was, when I threw out fear, the imagination of fear. My mind was still busy; but busy like a factory worker at the conveyor belt. There were thoughts in my head. But they only turned round and round, fell back on themselves and undid themselves, without conclusion. I had a few memories. But they soon became fixed, as if pinned to a piece of paper; I had to drag them out, and they were always the same, with their stupid, fixed air. Nothing new came out of the darkness; nothing came of its own accord. You have to be reminded in order to remember. A memory is not itself, it is echo, and there has to be another voice to make the echo. I had feelings, emotions, of course. They are always there, they never stop. They came and went, rose and fell, they changed color and shape without reason. One day I was in a hating mood. The next day I was full of despair. Or of joy. Or cruelty. Or humility. What did they mean? What did they do? They had no consequences. They undid each other, like waves; in the end it all came to the same. Nothing happened. I couldn't make anything happen to me. There was a big hole in me, and everything fell through it. Perhaps all that fear at the beginning—it had just been a presentiment of this final void, a shield against it. No wonder I had clung to it, as one clings to life itself."

Stamos felt the two hands on his temples turn to steel; they slid down to his shoulders, turned him round and shook him. Now he could feel Rigas' breath, and Rigas' head was both a little darker and a little paler than the night.

"When I speak to you," Rigas said, "you answer me; or you close your eyes, or you turn your head away; and then I know I have spoken, I even know what I have spoken. If I hit you, I know something has changed; it is a definite change; you are there to show it to me. You stand before me, extraordinary foreign surface, against which my act collides and is captured, instead of reverberating endlessly in space till it dies away. You hit me back, or you reason with me, ask me a question, and my act is cut loose from me, it is active, it starts living, it makes other things happen. Here I am, stifling in the endless tangle of acts and thoughts that will not leave me—that will not leave me."

The hands dropped from Stamos' shoulders. The pale face, the dark hair shifted, were blurred, melted away. The voice drifted off wearily.

"One turns to God, of course. They say you can find Him in the silence, in the darkness. But I had emptied the dark, I had emptied it all. The trees, the rocks had once been symbols of fear; I made them shrink to their own limited shape; they could never serve as symbols again, for anything else. So, without symbols, without signs—no, I knew I could not create Him. He was only another thought, as arbitrary as the others. He was only my need in disguise. He tasted of me; when I was looking for something that had nothing to do with me. I knew that wasn't the way. The priests say that God is in you, He is part of you. It isn't true. He is the perfect stranger, He is the other voice. I should not utter His voice for Him. I had to be silence, so that there would be a voice that was not mine. I was silence. For days I walked about, absent from myself. It became easy. Silence grew and spread around me. Silence answered silence. My nothingness was offered up and received in full, engulfed into the wider nothingness that surrounded me. They merged like water with water. So perfectly merged that I forgot what I had asked, just as the trees forgot why they were there; we lived on, condemned to eternal absent-mindedness. We forgot why we were nothing. And so He did not come. Nothing happened, nothing changed. Whatever there was in me was as stupid, as useless as the wind, the falling leaves, the night, the hooting owls, the clouds. There were only natural laws. The winter came. The summer came. I grew older. I was hungry, I slept. What was done was undone, and done again endlessly. Hunger, sleep, they were like the seasons; being ill was a kind of storm; cutting my finger, a tree struck by lightning, those were the only signs that we existed, this place and me. That was all the knowledge I could get from nature. It could not confirm sorrow or joy; it could not prove a truth. So sorrow and joy did not exist, and truth could be anything."

Now Stamos could see nothing at all. The light from the hut had gone out. The footsteps had ceased. The voice seemed to come from above, monotonous like snow.

"The mirrors were perfectly faithful to each other. They exchanged their nothingness. They were one. The marriage of man and nature was accomplished."

The voice was silent, but Stamos still felt the dark snow falling, falling; it thickened till it muffled the whole world and there was nothing left but to die.

"Rigas," he screamed, "Rigas."

Nothing moved. Rigas was no more a name, it was a word and he couldn't remember what it meant, so he couldn't call it again. After a long time he remembered his hand, his left one; it took form in the dark, because it was being touched. Rigas was at his side, touching his hand.

"So you've seen it," he said to Stamos.

Stamos sighed: "Yes. It was like dying."

They sat on the ground, quite close, like shipwrecks on a raft. Stamos became human again, without strict limits, his body only; at least his body; it was there in the dark, but weighed down by terrible sadness.

"Why didn't you say anything the first time," he complained. "Why did you pretend, coming down from the mountain?"

Rigas' voice was down to neutral now, narrow and neutral. "You offered me a role. I took it. How I took it! I jumped at it. It didn't last long. But nothing so good had come my way for a long time. You gave me something to do. You gave me something to be. What did you expect?"

Stamos shuddered a little; half pride, half horror. He had given birth, unknowingly; it was the first time; and the child was a monster.

Rigas said: "Apergis is offering me a role too. Not like yours! A ridiculous one. He will be at my side constantly, reminding me without pity that I mustn't ask for more. I won't. I am no Philoctetes, I have no god Hercules to tell me why I must serve, or to promise glory after the suffering.[11] I only know I'll take the role. Unconditionally."

After a time, a point of light appeared in the direction of the hut. It began to move in zigzags.

"It must be Apergis, with his torch," said Stamos. "He is looking for us."

They didn't move. The light was coming closer. Apergis found the two men and led them away.

THE END

---

11. *I am no Philoctetes* (fil′ ok tē′ tez) . . . *suffering.* Sophocles' play *Philoctetes,* upon which "The Exile" is based, concerns a man who has been punished by the gods for an unknown offense. His fate is to suffer from a wounded foot which never heals. Because of his festering wound so repulsive to sight and smell, Philoctetes is banished by his fellow Greeks to the lonely island of Lemnos. His sole strength lies in his prized bow. Because the bow is needed to overcome the Trojans, Odysseus turns to *Neoptolemus* (nē op tol′ ə məs), the son of Achilles, for help in claiming the weapon. After deceiving Philoctetes and receiving the bow, the boy experiences a "terrible compassion" for Philoctetes and reveals the treachery of Odysseus to the wounded man. Philoctetes refuses to return with Neoptolemus until Heracles suddenly appears before the two and convinces Philoctetes that in returning to Troy he will be cured of his sickness.

Development

INTERPRETATION

1. The young boy Stamos eagerly anticipates his meeting with Rigas, for in his mind he has already fashioned his own image of the man. *(a)* What is the image which Stamos forces upon Rigas? *(b)* What in the boy's character causes him to create this image? *(c)* Why does Rigas accept the role Stamos offers him? *(d)* Does he at any time believe the boy?

2. What does nature symbolize to Stamos? to Rigas? Cite passages which reveal their attitudes toward nature.

3. At one point Stamos cries out, "I've never looked inside me. . . . I don't even know what's there" (page 399, column 1, paragraph 1). In the course of the story Stamos looks inside himself. What does he find?

4. What part does Apergis play in the story?

5. Study the following quotations carefully and discuss their meaning:

> Even the most sordid of eavesdroppers is better than a spectator, he sees what is forbidden, not what is offered (Stamos: page 402, column 1, paragraph 1).

> Fear is exhausting, it is a hemorrhage of the spirit. Out of exhaustion one day I stayed up in the mountain, I lived it through. I went beyond panic. It is only a small step (Rigas: page 409, column 1, paragraph 3).

6. *(a)* Why does Rigas choose to return with Apergis? *(b)* What limitations does Rigas accept in making this decision? *(c)* Do you consider Rigas a free man as he descends the mountain with Apergis and Stamos? Explain.

7. Who changes in the story? How does he change?

8. *(a)* Which character in "The Exile" is based on Philoctetes? *(b)* Do you consider this character a hero? Explain.

9. Do the words of Philoctetes, "It is not the sting of wrongs past, but what I must look for in wrongs to come," apply to Rigas? Explain.

TECHNIQUE

1. *(a)* What point of view has Kay Cicellis adopted in "The Exile"? *(b)* What advantages are there in this point of view?

2. Discuss the relationship between theme and setting, considering particularly how setting serves to enhance theme.

3. Knowledge of a character may come from his reactions more than from his actual words. Rigas speaks little at first yet we learn much about the man. *(a)* Cite details from the story which reveal the real Rigas. *(b)* Do you see Rigas as a simple, one-dimensional character or as a complex man? Explain. *(c)* Basing your comments on the author's characterization of Rigas, discuss the possibility of Rigas' acting other than as he does.

EXTENSIONS

1. Contrast Rigas' attitude toward nature with the attitudes of characters in other works you have read which also reveal man's attitude toward nature.

2. *(a)* Does a man freely choose bondage of any type in his life? Explain. *(b)* If so, what might prompt him to do so?

Comparison

1. A man bound by limitations would seem to have one of three choices: he may remain within his constrictions and learn to live with them; he may exchange one form of bondage for another; or he may grow out of his bonds and achieve freedom. *(a)* Which of the above possibilities becomes a reality for the bound man in the Aichinger story? for Professor Gori? for Rigas? for Xuma? *(b)* Compare the type and difficulty of struggle experienced by the bound man, Gori, Rigas, and Xuma in reacting to their limitations.

2. The proprietor's wife ("The Bound Man") and Stamos ("The Exile") play quite similar roles. *(a)* Describe the function of each and explain their reasons for acting as they do. *(b)* What effect do the actions of each have on the bound man and on Rigas? *(c)* As "The Bound Man" ends, has the proprietor's wife, like Stamos, given birth to a "monster"? Explain.

3. The settings of the five selections in this unit vary greatly. Select two of the settings and discuss how each affects *(a)* the unfolding of the action, *(b)* the representation of character, and *(c)* the emotional quality of the work.

4. In "To B. Akhmadulina" Voznesensky says, "What if the maps ahead are enigmatical?" (page 389, line 36). *(a)* What advice is the poet suggesting in this line? *(b)* In what ways are the bound man, Gori, and Xuma all confronted with enigmatical maps? *(c)* Which character seems the most capable of acting upon Voznesensky's implied advice? Why? *(d)* There is little element of the enigmatical in Rigas' future. What in the man's character will not allow him to lead the sort of life Voznesensky proposes?

5. Discuss the following quotations and their implications for the selections in this group:

Is freedom anything but the right to live as we wish? Nothing else? (Epictetus)

Man is free at the moment he wishes to be. (Voltaire)

6. From your reading of the selections in this unit, would you agree that freedom and happiness are synonymous? Why or why not?

7. H. L. Mencken, a critic of American society, once said:

Not one of us is a free agent. Not one of us actually thinks for himself, or in any orderly and scientific manner. The pressure of environments, of mass ideas, of the socialized intelligence, improperly so called, is too enormous to be withstood.

(a) Do you agree or disagree with Mencken's statement? Why? *(b)* What effect does society have on the bound man, Gori, Rigas, Bela, and Xuma?

8. Defend or criticize the following: Of the four men examined in this unit, Gori is the only one who can be called a hero. He acts without a human prod while the bound man, Rigas, and Xuma are dependent upon the stimulation of others.

9. Study carefully the characters of the bound man, Gori, and Rigas. Compare and contrast the pattern of growth and change evident in these individuals.

10. Consider "The Bound Man," "Episode in Malay Camp," and "The Exile" as three views on the problem of natural freedom in conflict with social bondage. *(a)* As Rigas' story ends, what possible threat to his self-realization does society pose? *(b)* How is this threat similar to that encountered by the bound man in the circus? To that which Xuma faces in the society in which he lives? *(c)* Is it possible for a man to be in any way free while at the same time bound by situation or circumstances? Why or why not?

DEDICATION TO OSKAR PINAZZA by George Grosz. Courtesy of the Staatsgalerie, Stuttgart.

The Group

COMMUNITY WELFARE SERVICE / MARIA KONOPNICKA / POLAND

THE CHILDREN'S CAMPAIGN / PÄR LAGERKVIST / SWEDEN

MAN OF MY TIME / SALVATORE QUASIMODO / ITALY

A WORLD ENDS / WOLFGANG HILDESHEIMER / GERMANY

CEMETERY OF WHALES / YEVGENY YEVTUSHENKO / RUSSIA

Community Welfare Service

MARIA KONOPNICKA[1] / Poland

(1842–1910)

translated from the Polish by Ilona Ralf Sues

On the clock of the Community Building it is almost nine. The azure sky shimmering through the light morning mist promises fine clear weather.

In front of the building groups of people are awaiting the arrival of Councillor Storch, whose grey felt hat and cane with the silver knob one can see in front of Gehr's Café, by the table of the justice of the peace, who is reading his morning paper and sipping an insipid coffee.

The councillor is due at any moment now, at least in the opinion of the caretaker, who stands at the entrance in a semi-official attitude and acknowledges the greetings of passers-by by touching his navy-blue, white-rimmed cap with two fingers.

One can hear the lively voices of the two gentlemen talking at Gehr's. The councillor stopped there just for a moment, he did not even sit down, but the conversation with the justice of the peace is evidently amusing him, for every now and then he bursts into gay, candid laughter, which is echoed by the short barks of a splendid brown setter that lies by the table like a sphinx.

Meanwhile people gather in front of the building, greet one another and stand around chatting. Some go straight inside, others sit down on the stone posts whose loosely hanging chains fence off the street from the pebble-strewn square; still others stand with their heads raised and look at the building. It is new, erected on a square where old trees used to grow. Two of them have been left standing—large plane trees with delicate scaly bark; the autumn sun is already beginning to gild their lush green foliage.

The building itself is simple, grey, almost square; there is a low iron railing with golden knobs on its flat roof, and four pillars and a memorial tablet with an inscription on its façade. The inscription, with its gaily gilt letters, attracts attention. Practically every newcomer raises his head and reads it, his expression serious. Has he not a perfect right to do so? Hasn't everyone made his little contribution towards building it? The building is the common property and the common accomplishment of the community. No less attractive is the clock placed at the very apex of the triangle which rests on the flat capitals of the pillars; but somehow its hands seem to move more slowly than usual round the polished face. Such, at least, is the opinion of the owner of the nearby brewery, who keeps pulling his huge round silver watch out of his pocket to compare the time with that on the community clock. Good God, why—after all—should a man hurry? Time flies anyway.

It is only a few minutes to nine now,

"Community Welfare Service" by Maria Konopnicka, translated by Ilona Ralf Sues from POLISH SHORT STORIES, compiled by Zbigniew Zabicki, edited by Jadwiga Lewicka. Published 1960 by Polonia Publishing House.
1. *Konopnicka* (kô nôp′ nits kä).

and the groups begin to gather at the entrance, laughing and talking loudly. There is nothing particularly festive about this meeting: people have come in their working clothes. Simply on business.

Men in grey workday *joppen*[2]; Wallauer, the butcher, wearing his pink kaftan[3]; Jan Blanc, the saddler from Höschli, his green denim apron fastened with a brass hook and chain; many are only in shirt-sleeves, in spite of the chilly morning; Mrs. Knaus,[4] the widow, has come straight from the market with her basket full of vegetables and a new broom tucked under her arm. Why not? They are among themselves, aren't they?

At last the square tower of the New Münster starts chiming the quarters and simultaneously comes the gay barking of the setter following the councillors. It runs ahead, returns, runs ahead again, comes back in a few leaps, and in high spirits they enter the open door of the office building. The groups of waiting people follow them into the building.

They enter the hall and split into two groups: the curious ones and those who have come on business. The latter push in a solid mass toward the yellow baluster railing that divides the official part from that reserved for the public; the curious ones advance more slowly and occupy the benches along the walls.

Yet this division is not final. Every now and then people have things to tell to someone in the other groups; sometimes one of the curious suddenly decides that he too has a more pressing interest, and tries to find a place at the barrier. Anyone has a right to make up his mind even at the last minute.

The immediately interested group is the smaller; theirs is the more important role in this hall. There is Sprüngli the rope-maker, who recently married a widow and wants to enlarge his shop; there is Kägi Tobiasz, the owner of the Green Rose brewery; there is Lorche the baker; the innkeeper from Mainau; Dödöli, the owner of some vineyards; Wetlinger Urban, the malt manufacturer; Tödi Mayer, the locksmith; Kissling the boiler-maker; Dörfli, the gardener; Leu Peter, the joiner—and a number of others.

Each of them needs some help—either at the workshop or at home or on the land. And each prefers to get it more cheaply than by hiring a helper. They lean against the barrier and talk in low voices. Widow Knaus is also among them. Since her son got married she could not push anyone to work for the glory of the Lord. She has a charitable heart and would be quite ready to take in any poor creature, provided she could get some real help out of it. And provided, of course, the subsidy isn't too mean. One can't very well take in a ne'er-do-well for nothing, can one? And the commune has a fund to pay for the upkeep of poor people who can no longer work.

They can't go begging, for that's forbidden. She wonders if there will be any choice? Round autumn, they get as weak as flies. She'd rather get an old woman. Well, she'll take an old man, of course, if they have no woman. Just in order to get around, to get around. And isn't there a lot of that rabble in the community? Hardly a week goes by without some pauper or other calling at the office convinced that he can no longer manage to work. Nonsense. If you know how to make a fellow like that work, he'll soon enough do as well as a young one. And whatever the commune may pay is welcome. It happens time and again that an old timer like that kicks the bucket before he's eaten up his feed money. The Hoppingers had thirty francs left over when old Regula popped off; they had it from the office in Spring. And what about Egli? Egli made Alois sweat more than a farmhand, and he hadn't spent half the allowance when the old man turned up his toes. The Lord is merciful and wants no one to come to harm.

---

2. *joppen.* A joppe is a lightweight jacket worn for work or sport. [*German*] 3. *kaftan,* a long garment tied at the waist. 4. *Knaus* (kä′ nauz).

At that point, the widow sighed and the black camlet kaftan over her big breasts rustled.

But one after another the people keep looking at the door: Why hasn't Probst shown up? He was expected to be the first to take part in the auction, and he hasn't come yet?

At last the room quiets down and the councillor raises his head from his desk, where he has been standing reading a paper.

He is still young, a handsome, imposing figure, with light brown hair; that small bald spot doesn't seem to make him look any worse. He has a round, fleshy face, a reddish moustache, and a frank, pleasant way of looking. He is dressed with a certain elegance, which is not usually the case with Swiss officials. Particularly remarkable is the snow-white shirt front with its tiny golden buttons. Having raised his head, the councillor screws up his eyes behind the gold-rimmed glasses and looks at the people. Now the caretaker shuts the door. No one else will come, it seems.

"Well, gentlemen," the councillor begins, and passes his fat white finger between his slightly too tight collar and his slightly bulging throat. "Well, gentlemen, as you all know, we have met here."

"That's right. Sure." A few voices agree.

"Well then, gentlemen," continues the councillor, pushing his finger along between his collar and his neck with its overlapping pleat of fat skin, "well then, let us begin."

"Certainly. Quite right." Some voices are again raised in agreement. But the councillor, an official just recently elected, does not like to miss any opportunity of making one of those brief speeches that might enhance his popularity. He therefore clears his throat, places his hands firmly on the top of his desk, leans forward and begins:

"Gentlemen, you all know the generous welfare laws of our commune. You all know that our commune does not let any of its members suffer from want. It dries their tears, it clothes the naked, it feeds the hungry, it provides a roof for the homeless, it offers support to the weak."

Proud of this very successful opening, he makes a brief, but significant pause. Then he looks round the audience and continues:

"The laws of this commune are the laws of Christian charity; they are more than merely an achievement of our civilization—they are our pride. You know that youth does not last, that human strength declines, illness and want break a person. Such is the universal law that governs the world. But our commune has taken up the fight against that law. How? Very simply: it takes care of those whom life has hurt, it takes care of the poor and the disinherited, it takes care of the cripples and the weak and aged."

The councillor himself is astonished at how well it is going; he makes another pause. A pity there's only that handful of people listening. A speech like this, made before any large gathering, would boost his reputation enormously. He looks down condescendingly upon his audience and concludes:

"That's how it is, gentlemen. The commune takes care of them. Using its common sense and its kind heart, it concludes: this old man, this pauper, this cripple can no longer work for a living. He cannot work any longer. He has no family to feed him, or else his family is poor and their work hardly gives enough to keep body and soul together. Are we to let him roam the streets as a disreputable beggar? Never."

He shakes his head energetically and raises his voice:

"Bailiff, bring in the candidate."

The caretaker crosses the hall in long strides and disappears behind a door leading to a small storeroom used occasionally as a prison cell. A murmur spreads among the assembled people, while the councillor still stands with his head raised high, holding his attitude with care. A short pause. Then a head appears in the side door, trembling on a long, thin neck; then enter a pair of badly bending knees, then a pair of feet stuck in what used to be shoes, then two shaking, withered hands grasping the knobs on both sides of the door, to help the legs to cross the threshold, and finally a pitifully bent back. It is Kuntz Wunderli,[5] an old porter whom everyone knows.

The murmur in the hall grows louder.

"Do you call that a candidate? For pity's sake, what sort of a candidate? Who would ever agree to take in a corpse like that? What help could he possibly be? What use? Well, well! What's the community ready to pay for taking in that dead wood? A bagful of bones is about all there is."

Indignation is rampant. Some reach for their caps and withdraw from the barrier.

But the councillor pays no attention to the murmuring, and as soon as Kuntz Wunderli appears in the doorway he winds up his speech:

"That's how it is, gentlemen. Our admirable laws have done away with begging in our land and have brought in charity instead. No man is forsaken. The commune is his mother, the commune feeds him. Now here is an old man incapable of working any longer. Which one of you, gentlemen, will take him into your household? He can still render some service. The commune does not ask its members to do it for nothing. The commune is ready to contribute to the upkeep of this old man, in accordance with its laws. Approach, candidate. Gentlemen, look at the candidate."

The councillor bows his head and mops his forehead with a handkerchief. He perspires easily, and it is beginning to get hot in the hall.

Meanwhile Kuntz Wunderli, pushed a little from behind by the caretaker to help him get over the threshold, succeeds in passing through the door and then stops. The bright light coming through the window that opens on a large meadow falls on his stooping, emaciated figure. He stands still for a while fingering his old felt hat, and his bony knees tremble more and more. He is very nervous. Suddenly he straightens his back, raises his head and looks with a smile at those present. An inviting smile, almost merry. Kuntz Wunderli does not know who will become his master. So he smiles at all of them and twinkles vigorously. His eyes are cold, baffled and worried, but old Kuntz tries to make them twinkle lightheartedly and almost roguishly. When one of them gets tired and turns dead and motionless in its deep hole, he blinks with the other, as if he wanted to say: "I'm still strong, you don't know how strong! You won't have to feed me for nothing. I'll work, I can manage any kind of job. I'll carry water, chop wood, peel your potatoes, and sweep the floors. I've still got a lot of strength, a lot of it. . . "

And as he looks round with such an effort, his old head shakes more and more, his eyes become immobile and fill with big tears, and his hands grope for support. Only his thin-lipped, sunken mouth keeps smiling, smiling while two cold heavy tears roll slowly down the wrinkled cheeks. Here and there somebody starts looking him over, attentively. The old man still looks fairly sound. He shaved this morning, the caretaker lent him his razor. It is in the commune's interest that a candidate should make the best possible impression; otherwise no one will want him. So besides the razor the caretaker lent him an old coat and a blue scarf that he will take back after the auction. Old Kuntz appreciates that. He knows the commune's motives for helping him so graciously, and he is glad to show off the details of his attire. But the sleeves are too long and the coat itself is too large, doesn't fit, just hangs on him, and the showy blue cotton kerchief contrasts oddly with his scrawny neck with its million wrinkles that Kuntz cranes and

---

5. *Kuntz Wunderli* (kunz vun′ der lē).

pulls in again, for he isn't quite sure how best to display that kerchief. To be quite frank, his position is rather difficult.

He has to arouse their pity, and yet he mustn't seem to be too infirm. He knows that he stands there as an old man who can work no longer, but he is also aware that everyone of them is looking at his hands and figuring whether they are fit to do any work. The community is charitable, certainly, but it won't pay much for his keep. He knows quite well that he can't ask for much. Embarrassed, anxious, he watches the eyes of the people and wonders what each one is thinking; he also casts a glance every now and then at the caretaker, as if to reassure him that the razor, the coat and the kerchief won't prove useless.

The people look at the old man and discuss the matter loudly. No one cares to seem too eager. They might have kept that up till noon, leaning against the barrier and sniffing their tobacco, but the councillor is not fond of protracted meetings.

"Well, gentlemen," he asks loudly, "have you looked the candidate over?"

"What is there to look over?" asks Kissling after a moment of silence. "Don't we see him every day? The old fellow's wheezy, he can't pull anything, or lift anything. What do you think, brother-in-law," he turns to Faustin Tröndi, "I reckon he must be eighty or over?"

The old man clears his throat; he is over eighty-two. Eighty-two! But he just smiles and keeps quiet.

"How old are you, old man?" asks Tödi Mayer.

Kuntz winks at the caretaker and says:

"Seventy-four, my dear, seventy-four."

"Show your teeth, old fellow," says the innkeeper from Mainau.

Kuntz casts another glance at the caretaker and opens his dry lips, showing two rows of quite good teeth.

The public begins to laugh.

"Well, well," someone says. "Good enough to bite through a bone."

"He won't shrink from bread," adds another.

Leu Peter, the joiner, leans over towards him:

"Swing your fist, old man, come on!"

Wunderli takes a step forward, raises his head a little, straightens his back and swings his arm a few times; the fist is lost somewhere in the long sleeve of the borrowed jacket. Every time his arm falls down again like the broken limb of a tree. His joints crack mercilessly.

"Well, doesn't he swing 'em all right?" asks someone from a bench.

"Phew," says another one, well aware that no remarks from the gallery are ever lost on the people interested.

"What about his legs?"—again it's Tödi Mayer who asks: he is evidently interested in getting Kuntz. "Let's see you march, old man."

But the old man is evidently perplexed. His legs are his weakest point. Oh, if it weren't for those legs! And it isn't so much the legs as the knees. At the mere thought of stretching them, he feels a shooting pain.

But Kuntz Wunderli will not let the community down. With the greatest effort he lifts one foot from the ground and puts it down immediately in the same spot. No, no, he must have made a mistake. It isn't this one; this is the sorer one! So he lifts the other foot, but lets it down even more quickly, with a loud hiss. What the devil . . . is it the other, after all, that hurts less?

The clients frown and don't say a word. The gallery have left their benches and approached the barrier. They are laughing loudly.

"Go ahead, come on, march, march, old fellow."

The councillor looks severely at the laughing gallery, then he turns to the old man, rather annoyed:

"Why do you keep standing there? Get out of that corner."

Kuntz Wunderli smiles, timidly, painfully. All right. All right. Sure. Why does he keep standing there? He'll move away at once.

And abruptly, pulling himself together, he raises his head, his faded eyes bulge, he cranes his neck, straightens his back, presses his knees down with his hands and he marches towards the door.

That sight is so funny that the whole audience bursts into loud laughter. Those closer to the benches flop down on them, holding their sides. The councillor covers his mouth discreetly with a document, and the caretaker turns away puffing with laughter.

"Fine, splendid," they call from the benches.

"Go ahead, march on!" call some others.

The old man walks on. His stiff legs don't bend at all; he lifts them like sticks in a tremendous effort—and lets them down again, pressing his hands desperately against the sore, swollen knees. And, as if to spite him, the hall becomes longer and bigger, the door seems to withdraw, the walls assume a terrifying depth; old Kuntz thinks that he will never be able to reach the door. But he feels all those people looking at him, the entire community looking at him! He sets his teeth and again raises a stiff, heavy leg.

Suddenly he stops and opens his eyes wide. At the door, among the crowd, he sees the head of his son. That he had not expected. No, no, not that!

Deep red colour rushes into his face, the rest of his heart's blood. No longer does he hear the laughter, not even the voice of the councillor ordering him back to his place. His son is all he sees.

He looks at him spellbound and begins to tremble as if there were a terrible frost; all his old bones shake. His frightened face pales, becomes white, very white, deathly white. There is a hard, severe frown on his forehead; his eyes light up and become dull again. Desperate eyes, dead, staring with fear and amazement at his son. No, no! He does not want his son to bid for him at the community auction. That he will not have!

He shrinks, lets go of his knees and spreads out his hands to ward it off. No, no! He is afraid! He does not want that!

But the caretaker approaches and takes him by the arm.

"What the devil's the matter? Why are you standing here like a fool? Can't you see the boss is waiting? Go ahead!"

But old Wunderli is too weak at that moment—weak as a child. He simply cannot move. His legs fail him, his teeth chatter, his head wags to right and left like a leaf in autumn. The caretaker pushes him along, holding him up a bit. If he didn't hold him up, the old man might fall down. But to his mind there is very little hope of the community's getting rid of the old man. He realizes now that neither his razor, the kerchief nor the jacket were of any help. None whatever.

"Hurry up," the councillor calls impatiently.

Kuntz Wunderli pulls himself together somehow and is back at his former place. It is well chosen. Golden light falls through the wide open window on the miserable man. In that light his deathly face looks a livelier colour. His bald skull reflects the serene fair weather. His dull eyes gaze up somewhere far away into the blue sky.

Who knows? Maybe it wouldn't be so bad after all if the son's bid were accepted? Who can tell? True, his daughter-in-law is bad-tempered and stingy. But he could at least die in the midst of his own folk. And then the children . . . he would be able to see his grandchildren every day!

His eyes grow moist, they become soft and kind; an unspoken word trembles on his lips; the hard, harsh frown smoothes out and disappears.

Now he certainly does not look more than seventy-four. The interest of the clients is reawakened.

"Not very firm on his feet," says baker Lorche, shaking his head.

"What d'you mean, not very firm?" retorts somebody from a bench.

"He'll outjump all of us yet," adds someone else.

"Gallant old fellow!" calls yet another.

"What do you think, brother-in-law?" asks Tödi Mayer of his neighbour in a low voice.

"If you ask me, I'd take him. He's weak in the knees but he'll do at the workshop."

"I wouldn't even think of looking at that weakling," says Dödöli, "if they had anyone else."

"So what? Round the house even that can be useful," argues Kissling.

The councillor eyes the audience keenly. The moment seems propitious to start the auction. The whole thing has lasted too long already. Too many spectators.

He pulls out his watch, holds it up close to his eyes, compares the time with that of the clock on the wall, beckons to the caretaker and says in a businesslike tone:

"Gentlemen, let's make an end of this. The candidate presented to you by the community is most worthy of your attention. He is in good health, not too old, quite strong and will be useful at any easier work. Which one of you is ready to consider the matter? And at what price?"

A moment of silence follows. Some are considering whether they need help and if they can afford it.

Sprüngli starts fidgeting and shifts his weight from foot to foot. The councillor notices it and says politely, bowing to the rope-maker:

"Gentlemen, Mr. Sprüngli will start us off."

"Mr. Sprüngli, what subsidy would you consider to take the candidate into your home?"

"Two hundred francs," replies the rope-maker and stops, not quite sure if he has not asked too little.

"What? Two hundred francs?" repeats the councillor, feigning astonishment. Then he makes a short pause. "Gentle-

men, I should be only too happy if the finances of the community permitted the social welfare section to incur such formidable expenses. But as this is not the case, we have to suggest more reasonable figures. Think it over, Mr. Sprüngli. Well, gentlemen? You've seen the candidate's teeth? He is still quite strong."

"Who cares about his teeth?" says the innkeeper from Mainau. "So much the worse if they are sound. If the old one eats a lot, I won't be able to fill him up, and he won't work."

"Oh, don't you worry, we'll make him work all right," says Kägi, winking with his squinting eye.

"Come, come," Kägi continues, "you know how to squeeze a farmhand."

"What you talking about? I'm not Probst, am I?"

They both laugh.

"Who can tell if it was Probst's fault?" says Kissling. "Maybe the old man was a drunk?"

"Believe me, I never saw him drunk," counters Lorche. "It wasn't Probst's doing, anyway; it was his wife's. She's a hag. . ."—says a voice from the bench.

"A hellcat she is," someone else adds.

"Never mind who's to blame," says Sprüngli. "The fact is that old Hänzli hanged himself in his house."

"He must have had a sweet life there!"

"What's that?" cries Wettinger the butcher. "So I'm expected to feed him, clothe him and take him under my roof for the few miserable coppers I get from the community—and I won't even be allowed to make him work?"

"Sure you can, but—on the other hand . . ."

"Gentlemen," interrupts the councillor, "we must make an end of this. There's a time limit for official business. Mr. Sprüngli had bid 200 francs. Which of you is going to lower that?"

Silence.

"Which one of you gentlemen is ready to bid?" asks the councillor again. "Will you reconsider, Mr. Sprüngli?"

"I've already reconsidered," says Sprüngli. "I can't take less than 200 francs."

The councillor turns away from him.

"Do I hear another bid? Your bids, gentlemen!"

"I'll take 185," says Lorche in a slow, deliberate voice. "But he's got to wear his own clothes, this winter at least. It's warm in my place."

Old Wunderli looks down at his clothes and then round at the others and begins to shiver. He has the impression that his very bones are freezing. Wear his own suit? What suit has he got? Has he been earning enough to afford a suit? All he earned was his daily bread, and even that by hard work. He has a cotton blouse, badly patched. How can he wear that through the winter? One can't even call it a piece of clothing.

"180, on the same condition," says Dödöli, who owns a vineyard, in a booming voice.

"On the same condition," thinks old Kuntz, and his miserable legs tremble more violently. "Dear God. Why do they insist on that condition. And me standing here before them like poor Lazarus.[6] What a condition."

Silence again after Dödöli's bid. The councillor is on tenterhooks.

For a while he plays with a coral trinket on his watch chain, then he says as politely as he can manage:

"Let's go on, gentlemen. Let us proceed: will you give me another bid?"

"175," says Tödi Mayer in a clear voice. He is terribly pressed for help. Work is piling up at his place.

"160," someone calls from the corner.

They look round, disbelieving their ears. It is customary to go down five francs at a time, seven at the most; there has never been a precedent for anyone bidding 15 francs lower!

The councillor himself looks in surprise towards the corner. Old Kuntz also raises his head and looks.

At the side near the door, behind the backs of the bidders, his son is leaning against the barrier, a short pipe between his teeth. He is holding his youngest son by the hand.

The old man opens his mouth and watches, half afraid, half hopeful.

The son comes up to the barrier, takes the pipe out of his mouth and stands in the first row, holding his head high. No one blames him.

He has a bunch of children, works hard himself. One more mouth to feed is quite a problem where the people themselves haven't enough to eat. He couldn't possibly keep his father for nothing. God knows he couldn't. But he will try with whatever the community will chip in. He doesn't want much. He has bid three times less than any stranger would. He doesn't want to make money out of the community or out of the old man. He just wants to get back his own.

Everybody understands that perfectly well; everyone would do exactly the same. A person grows worn out just like everything else, and worn out he becomes a burden. Those that can afford it can keep even a grandfather, to say nothing of a father; but people who haven't enough can't go out and steal to do it. That's as clear as daylight.

But though it is as clear as daylight, it throws an ominous shadow upon all the faces. The people look away as if they do not want, as if they dare not look one another in the eye. The silence lasts longer than usual. And in that silence one hears old Kuntz's deep sigh, that sounds almost like a moan.

The councillor watches the people with his eagle eye. Obviously the son's bid will stand.

"Well then, gentlemen," he begins, after a pause.

"Well then, the last bid stands: 160 francs. I am pleased, I am very pleased."

6. *poor Lazarus,* referring to the story of Lazarus and the rich man in the New Testament. Lazarus lay with dogs at the gate of the rich man, waiting in vain for scraps from his table.

He stops abruptly. He really doesn't know why he should be pleased. Perhaps at the fact that they will all leave at last. He can't tell them that to their faces, can he? Anyway his speech appears to have been premature.

"155," bids Tödi Mayer, wiping his broad forehead with a red cotton kerchief.

The son withdraws quietly from the barrier and blows into the bowl of his pipe to keep it alight. But the child he is holding by the hand suddenly spots the old man.

"Grandpa, grandpa," he calls in a thin, squeaky voice.

The old man cannot see his grandson, he can only hear him. A tender smile appears on his faded lips. He shakes his head cheerfully and makes a gesture as if he were taking a sniff of tobacco. Things seem to be turning out all right, thank God. Everything may still end up well!

"One hundred and fifty," bids the son.

But Tödi Mayer has no intention giving way. He is stubborn—one of those who take a firm grip and hold on. What does a son matter?

The son could have taken him in for nothing. So long as the community pays everybody has a right to bid.

"145," he calls, raising his voice.

The son tilts his head, half closes his eyes and looks down at Tödi Mayer.

He thinks it over for a while, then he shrugs indifferently. He can't risk more than that. He's done his duty, but he can't afford any more. His head with the straight hair and the square wooden face withdraws from the line of bidders and the tall, bony, slightly-stooping figure moves through the crowd towards the door.

The old man's eyes follow him. He is anxious; he opens his mouth and cranes his neck; his left eyelid begins to twitch nervously. He looks old now, very old. Tödi Mayer suddenly realizes that the deal is not a particularly advantageous one; he talks in a whisper with his brother-in-law.

Meanwhile the councillor taps on the desk.

"Well, then," he says in his clear, refined voice. "The bid is 145 francs. For the first time, for . . ."

"Just a moment," Tödi Mayer interrupts him suddenly. "I want to ask if the *joppe* really belongs to the old man?"

A frown appears on the councillor's fine, smooth forehead.

"That is not a question to be discussed by the community office," he replies in a dignified tone, while the caretaker turns towards the corner and coughs loudly.

"Why isn't it?" Spengler steps in for his neighbour. "The community's got to know what it's giving away, and the one that takes it has got to know what he's taking. That's only fair."

"Is the *joppe* yours?" Tödi Mayer turns directly to old Kuntz.

But old Kuntz does not hear him.

His left eyelid twitches more and more violently, as his eyes turn glassy. He sees his son disappearing behind the door. A moment later he sees him again through the open window and hears the child's prattling. They walk along. . . They are gone.

The old man bows his head and shakes it quietly. Then he shuts his eyes tightly, as tightly as he can. Something is stinging his eyes, something salty, bitter. . . It stings and burns. . .

"Can you hear me, old man," Tödi Mayer repeats in a louder voice, "did anyone lend you that *joppe* or is it your own?"

He hears the question at last, looks down at himself, his reddened eyes blink quickly, then they cast a stealthy glance at the caretaker in the corner.

Tödi Mayer bangs his fist on the barrier.

"That's plain cheating!" he shouts angrily.

"It certainly is. He's right," several voices agree.

The noise increases; everyone is indignant.

"Look here, a fellow wants to be charitable," cries Tödi Mayer, throwing up his huge red hands, "he's ready to take on such a burden like that for a miserable sum of money, but he has a right to be treated on the level. I'm sorry, but that's how it is!"

"That's fair, that's right." More voices join in the chorus. Spengler's voice dominates all the others. The councillor flushes with anger.

"Off with your coat!" he yells at the old man, and Kuntz Wunderli starts to unbutton it hastily.

That is not so easy. His hands are trembling; the stiff, crooked fingers do not find the buttonholes right away; the caretaker helps the old man, furiously pulling off the sleeves. As an official of the chancery, he feels almost as offended as the councillor.

"You fool! You idiot," he whispers furiously, pulling alternately at each sleeve of the ill-fated coat. Once the coat is off, the whole appalling misery of the candidate becomes apparent, his sunken chest, his protruding ribs, barely hidden by a sorely patched-up shirt and the ragged remnants of a summer waistcoat. Old man Wunderli trembles frightfully, partly from the cold, partly with fear. It's come out. What will happen now? Everything's come out!

Horribly embarrassed, he tries to undo the kerchief round his neck which the caretaker had knotted with such care.

"The kerchief isn't yours either?" yells Tödi Mayer, at the end of his tether.

"Not. . . mine. . ." replies Kuntz Wunderli in a hardly audible whisper.

The caretaker jerks it out of his hands.

"Numbskull, blockhead, stupid ass," mutters the caretaker, his teeth set.

The case of the kerchief makes him even more furious than the coat. The idea of the coat was not his own; it came to him when the councillor had casually remarked that the candidate was too poorly dressed to appear in the administrative part of the office.

But the kerchief? The kerchief was his own idea. He had tied the bow himself, with an artist's taste; he had put his soul into that bow. And besides, it wasn't at all necessary to remove that kerchief! No one had any suspicion, no question had been asked. So furious is the caretaker that he crumples the blue piece of cotton between his hands and throws it down on the floor under the coat-hanger at the door. For the moment he cannot find any more drastic means of giving vent to his anger and his boundless disdain.

And meanwhile Kuntz Wunderli stands before the public, shamefaced, depressed, robbed of his glamour. Only now can one see his knees bent forward so sharply that he seems to be squatting; now one can see his twisted, heavy feet and his white elbows. But the neck is the funniest part of him. It is so thin you could whip it off. It makes the old man look like a plucked bird, especially since the head which is no longer supported by the stiff bow looks disproportionately big and heavy on top of that thin neck. It wags to right and left, almost touching the scrawny shoulders.

There is a burst of merriment in the room: some laugh good-naturedly, others maliciously, with a glance at Tödi Mayer. The most charitable souls just nod and smile faintly.

"Ecce homo,"[7] says Kissling, the boilermaker, ostentatiously. His brother serves as janitor at the canton library and he can read all the books free of charge.

Thunderous laughter greets that comparison. The majority presume that he is referring to the peak just behind the Big and Small Mythen, called Mount Ecce Homo as a counterpart to the rugged Mount Pilatus; some of the audience have seen that mountain at close quarters.

The old man has of course no resem-

---

7. *Ecce homo* (ek′e hō′mō), the Latin phrase meaning "Behold the man!" spoken by Pontius Pilate as he delivered Jesus Christ, scourged and wearing a crown of thorns, to be crucified.

blance whatever to any mountain peak, but that makes the joke even funnier.

Tödi Mayer is the only one who takes no part in the general gaiety. His round, protruding eyes run over the figure of the old pauper as if they were making every one of those dried-up, trembling bones responsible for his great disappointment. He looks at him piercingly, as one might look at a counterfeit coin; he examines him like an old rag, dissects him to the last vein, to the last bit of breath in his chest.

"I withdraw my bid," he calls out finally. "I can't do it for so small an a. . .!"

"No bid can be withdrawn," says the councillor gravely.

"What do you mean? The bailiff hasn't knocked him down to the bidder yet."

"He hasn't knocked him down! He hasn't!" confirm some people from the benches. Then there is a silence.

Everybody is waiting to see how things will turn out. The councillor is rather dissatisfied. He looks askance at the audience, wrinkles his handsome forehead and pulls at his moustache.

"I won't take the old fellow wearing rags like that, not even if they give me 180 francs," Tödi Mayer asserts with determination, feeling himself backed up by the whole room.

"I wouldn't take him even for 200," seconds Spengler.

"What? 200? Even 210 wouldn't be too much!" chips in the innkeeper from Mainau.

Old Wunderli listens to all this with fear in his heart. What will happen? What is going to become of him? Maybe no one will want to take him in? And why on earth do they want so much money? Why that much?

His wretched old face shows his great anxiety and amazement. He raises his grey eyebrows higher and higher, looking down at the ground; his head keeps wagging faster and faster, dropping now on one shoulder, now on the other.

"Now then, Mr. Tödi Mayer," says the councillor in a conciliatory tone, "stop joking and let's make an end of this, gentlemen."

"All right," cries the locksmith energetically, "I'll take him at 200."

"Oh, come on, come on!"—the councillor is losing patience. "How can you expect the community to pay out such an amount? Do you gentlemen think the community is sitting on a gold mine? The community has to be careful with every penny it spends. The community has expenses, considerable expenses! It holds charity sacred, but there is a limit even to charity!"

The councillor has hardly finished his last sentence when the door opens wide and in comes Probst. A stout man with a thick neck and a broad red face. His brown unbuttoned coat exposes a formidable chest, upon which is a dangling silver chain. He has small piercing eyes and a narrow oily forehead, with curly red hair growing low down on his temples. Probst advances, self-assured, swinging his huge arms and fists; but he has no need to make room for himself, for everyone steps aside with something like respect. A strong, powerful fellow with a sullen aggressive look—a fellow you'd rather not pick a fight with. Probst approaches the barrier, bows to the councillor, nods to some acquaintances.

Would the councillor please excuse him. . . He has come late, but it was no fault of his. That damned worker he took on after old Hänzli's death got sick, just as if to spite him. So he had to deliver the milk himself, and it's a devil of a long way down one hill and up another.

The councillor listens and nods sympathetically; those whom Probst has greeted smile sympathetically, shaking their heads.

"He had to do the delivery himself? Oh, my! Such a long route, too!"

Outside the window they hear the barking of the dog whom everyone knows: three times a day it arrives pulling the car stacked full with tall milk cans.

Probst has a fine herd of cows. A fine cowshed.

And presently they all feel great respect for his powerful fists and his fat neck. Spengler turns away from Tödi Mayer and looks at Probst; the locksmith feels already half beaten by the mere arrival of the milkman. He looks from one to another pretending indifference, in reality he is sorry not to have clinched the deal. Well, he will see what happens.

Probst wastes no time. He places one fist on the barrier, stretches his thick neck, pulls at the hairy yellow chin, screws up his grey eyes and sights them on the old man like a gun.

Kissling and Dödöli nudge each other with their elbows.

"Look at him staring. That beast knows how to look. Heaven knows everybody's got a pair of eyes, but nobody can look through a man like he does. He's an expert all right, don't you worry."

The whole atmosphere in the room has changed. They all feel that a connoisseur has arrived. Faces become livelier. The people who were sitting on the benches get up and draw closer. Now things promise to become really interesting. Only Kuntz Wunderli is fidgeting anxiously, nervously, at the sight of Probst. He knows that Hänzli, whom Probst got also from the community, hanged himself in the attic three months later. He recalls Mrs. Probst selling his boots. He also remembers the sores the harness had made on Hänzli's shoulders, his sunken eyes, and his face that had become sallow and haggard. The old man shrinks visibly, he pulls his head in between his shoulders, presses his bony elbows to his sides, makes himself small, very small, so small they must barely be able to see him. If only he could hide underground. He is afraid to breathe, to stir, and so tense that even his knees have stopped trembling.

But Probst knows all these tricks. He has been getting these rascals at the community auctions for the past six or seven years. He knows full well that such an old fellow is like a cracked pot: wired together carefully, it will outlast a new one. And anyway, it's the cheapest labour to be found. You can always squeeze enough work out of him—by treating him either roughly or kindly—to pay for his food, and whatever subsidy the community pays is like money found. People grumble that he ruins the prices. A lot he cares! So long as it suits him, everyone can look after himself, and that's that.

Now Probst tilts his big flat head to the right then to the left, takes a quick look at the official's face and declares in a clear, booming voice:

"One hundred and twenty-five."

His words make a big impression. Even the most indifferent among the crowd wag their heads admiringly. Fancy, not even asking what had been going on and throwing down his trump like a bombshell!

There is complete silence in the room, broken only by the furious barking of the dog outside at the milk-wagon. Old Wunderli looks round to right and left, as if he were trying to find an alley of escape. But he does not run away; he stands there as if turned to stone or riveted to the floor. Only his jaw is drooping lower and lower and his eyes are opening wider and wider.

"One hundred and twenty-five," Probst calls out again.

The councillor is beaming. For a while he looks about keenly at the audience, waiting to see if anyone will outbid the milkman. Then he taps the papers before him with his white hand and motions to the caretaker.

"One hundred and twenty-five, for the first time," calls the caretaker bailiff, knocking the floor with his stick. And waits.

"For the second time," he repeats still louder, and old Kuntz Wunderli screws up his eyes and squirms painfully, as if the stick that knocks to confirm this act of charity were going to hit him next.

"And for the thi-r-d t-i-me," calls the bailiff, and the councillor joins in triumphantly.

A moment later Kuntz Wunderli is standing in the shafts of the milk-wagon, his poor old grey head trembles as his shaking hands try to put the harness strap over his shoulders. On the other side of the shaft, hitched in a similar harness, the husky, shaggy dog jumps up and down, barking loudly.

THE END

Development

INTERPRETATION

1. (a) What is your emotional reaction to the conclusion of "Community Welfare Service"? (b) What would you surmise was Maria Konopnicka's purpose in writing this story? (c) In what ways does her characterization of Kuntz Wunderli reflect what you feel to be her intentions?

2. (a) What are the ideals of the Community Welfare Service? (b) What practical advantages does it offer the community? (c) What first leads you to doubt their realization of these ideals?

3. (a) What is ironic about Kuntz Wunderli's attitude toward the Community Welfare Service? (b) Why do you think Kuntz is upset at the appearance of his son?

4. (a) Why do you think the people of the community "dare not look one another in the eye" after Kuntz has been bid for by his son? (b) What might motivate Tödi Mayer's stubbornness in underbidding Kuntz' son?

5. Why is it appropriate that the interjection of "Ecce homo" follows directly the incident of Kuntz' being stripped?

6. (a) What is Probst's philosophy? (b) In what way does he serve the interests of the councillor and the caretaker?

(c) Why is this situation ironic for an institution promoted as a welfare service? (d) Of what might Kuntz' final labor be symbolic?

TECHNIQUE

1. Reread the meditation of Widow Knaus page 417, column 2, paragraphs 1 and 2. (a) By what means has Konopnicka been able to uncover all of the Widow's underlying prejudice and hypocrisy without, directly, criticizing her in any way? (b) Why is it appropriate that the Widow's meditation should be followed almost immediately by the first mention of Probst?

2. Study the final confrontation between Kuntz Wunderli and Probst. (a) What effect is created by the physical description of both men? (b) In what way does this amplify the theme of the story?

EXTENSIONS

1. (a) Do you think the failure of the Community Welfare Service results from a poorly structured system, improper administration, or some other reason? Explain. (b) If you had the power to change the system, how would you improve it?

2. The Christian idea of charity is defined in section 13 of the Apostle Paul's first letter to the Corinthians. In essence, charity is said to be an honest compassion without which all attempted good acts are hollow and meaningless. Do you feel that "Community Welfare Service" provides us with sufficient testimony to conclude that the ideal of charity is incompatible with human nature? Explain your view.

3. Kuntz Wunderli tries to appear as something other than what he is in order to increase, very literally, his value. Do you think a man can avoid conforming completely to his society's standard of values if he is dependent upon a system as arbitrary as the Community Welfare Service? Discuss.

The Children's Campaign

PÄR LAGERKVIST[1] / Sweden

(1891 – 1974)
translated from the Swedish

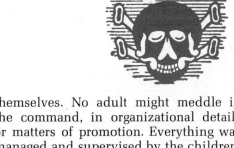

Even the children at that time received military training, were assembled in army units and exercised just as though on active service, had their own headquarters and annual maneuvers when everything was conducted as in a real state of war. The grown-ups had nothing directly to do with this training; the children actually exercised themselves and all command was entrusted to them. The only use made of adult experience was to arrange officers' training courses for specially suitable boys, who were chosen with the greatest care and who were then put in charge of the military education of their comrades in the ranks.

These schools were of high standing and there was hardly a boy throughout the land who did not dream of going to them. But the entrance tests were particularly hard; not only a perfect physique was required but also a highly developed intelligence and character. The age of admission was six to seven years and the small cadets then received an excellent training, both purely military and in all other respects, chiefly the further molding of character. It was also greatly to one's credit in after life to have passed through one of these schools. It was really on the splendid foundation laid here that the quality, organization and efficiency of the child army rested.

Thereafter, as already mentioned, the grown-ups in no way interfered but everything was entrusted to the children themselves. No adult might meddle in the command, in organizational details or matters of promotion. Everything was managed and supervised by the children; all decisions, even the most vital, being reached by their own little general staff. No one over fourteen was allowed. The boys then passed automatically into the first age group of the regular troops with no mean military training already behind them.

The large child army, which was the object of the whole nation's love and admiration, amounted to three army corps of four divisions: infantry, light field artillery, medical and service corps. All physically fit boys were enrolled in it and a large number of girls belonged to it as nurses, all volunteers.

Now it so happened that a smaller, quite insignificant nation behaved in a high-handed and unseemly way toward its powerful neighbor, and the insult was all the greater since this nation was by no means an equal. Indignation was great and general and, since people's feelings were running high, it was necessary to rebuke the malapert and at the same time take the chance to subjugate the country in question. In this situation the child army came forward and through its high command asked to be charged with the

"The Children's Campaign" by Pär Lagerkvist from I DEN TIDEN by Pär Lagerkvist. © Albert Bonniers Förlag 1935.
1. *Pär Lagerkvist* (par lä′ gər kvist′).

crushing and subduing of the foe. The news of this caused a sensation and a wave of fervor throughout the country. The proposal was given serious consideration in supreme quarters and as a result the commission was given, with some hesitation, to the children. It was in fact a task well suited to this army, and the people's obvious wishes in the matter had also to be met, if possible.

The Foreign Office therefore sent the defiant country an unacceptable ultimatum and, pending the reply, the child army was mobilized within twenty-four hours. The reply was found to be unsatisfactory and war was declared immediately.

Unparalleled enthusiasm marked the departure for the front. The intrepid little youngsters had green sprigs in the barrels of their rifles and were pelted with flowers. As is so often the case, the campaign was begun in the spring, and this time the general opinion was that there was something symbolic in it. In the capital the little commander in chief and chief of general staff, in the presence of huge crowds, made a passionate speech to the troops in which he expressed the gravity of the hour and his conviction of their unswerving valor and willingness to offer their lives for their country.

The speech, made in a strong voice, aroused the greatest ecstasy. The boy— who had a brilliant career behind him and had reached his exalted position at the age of only twelve and a half—was acclaimed with wild rejoicing and from this moment was the avowed hero of the entire nation. There was not a dry eye and those of the many mothers especially shone with pride and happiness. For them it was the greatest day in their lives. The troops marched past below fluttering banners, each regiment with its music corps at the head. It was an unforgettable spectacle.

There were also many touching incidents, evincing a proud patriotism, as when a little four-year-old, who had

been lifted up on his mother's arm so that he could see, howled with despair and shouted, "I want to go, too. I want to go, too!" while his mother tried to hush him, explaining that he was too small. "Small am I, eh?" he exclaimed, punching her face so that her nose bled. The evening papers were full of such episodes showing the mood of the people and of the troops who were so sure of victory. The big march past was broadcast and the c in c's speech, which had been recorded, was broadcast every evening during the days that followed, at 7:15 P.M.

Military operations had already begun, however, and reports of victory began to come in at once from the front. The children had quickly taken the offensive and on one sector of the front had inflicted a heavy defeat on the enemy, seven hundred dead and wounded and over twelve hundred prisoners, while their own losses amounted to only a hundred or so fallen. The victory was celebrated at home with indescribable rejoicing and with thanksgiving services in the churches. The newspapers were filled with accounts of individual instances of valor and pictures several columns wide of the high command, of which the leading personalities, later so well-known, began to appear now for the first time. In their joy, mothers and aunts sent so much chocolate and other sweets to the army that headquarters had to issue a strict order that all such parcels were, for the time being at any rate, forbidden, since they had made whole regiments unfit for battle and these in their turn had nearly been surrounded by the enemy.

For the child army was already far inside enemy territory and still managed to keep the initiative. The advance sector did retreat slightly in order to establish contact with its wings but only improved its positions by so doing. A stalemate ensued in the theater of war for some time after this.

During July, however, troops were concentrated for a big attack along the whole line and huge reserves—the child army's, in comparison with those of its opponent, were almost inexhaustible—were mustered to the front. The new offensive, which lasted for several weeks, resulted, too, in an almost decisive victory for the whole army, even though casualties were high. The children defeated the enemy all along the line but did not manage to pursue him and thereby exploit their success to the full, because he was greatly favored by the fact that his legs were so much longer, an advantage of which he made good use. By dint of forced marches, however, the children finally succeeded in cutting the enemy's right flank to pieces. They were now in the very heart of the country and their outposts were only a few days' march from the capital.

It was a pitched battle on a big scale and the newspapers had enormous headlines every day which depicted the dramatic course of events. At set hours the radio broadcast the gunfire and a résumé of the position. The war correspondents described in rapturous words and vivid colors the state of affairs at the front— the children's incredible feats, their indomitable courage and self-sacrifice, the whole morale of the army. It was no exaggeration. The youngsters showed the greatest bravery; they really behaved like heroes. One only had to see their discipline and contempt of death during an attack, as though they had been grown-up men at least.

It was an unforgettable sight to see them storm ahead under murderous machine gun fire and the small medical orderlies dart nimbly forward and pick them up as they fell. Or the wounded and dying who were moved behind the front, those who had had a leg shot away or their bellies ripped open by a bayonet so that their entrails hung out—but without one sound of complaint crossing their small lips. The hand-to-hand fighting had been very fierce and a great number of children fell in this, while they were superior in the actual firing. Losses were estimated at 4,000 on the enemy side and 7,000 among the children, according to the secret reports. The victory had been hard won but all the more complete.

This battle became very famous and was also of far greater importance than any previously. It was now clear beyond all doubt that the children were incomparably superior in tactics, discipline and individual courage. At the same time, however, it was admitted by experts that the enemy's headlong retreat was very skillfully carried out, that his strength was evidently in defense and that he should not be underrated too much. Toward the end, also, he had unexpectedly made a stubborn resistance which had prevented any further penetration.

This observation was not without truth. In actual fact the enemy was anything but a warlike nation, and indeed his forces found it very difficult to hold their own. Nevertheless, they improved with practice during the fighting and became more efficient as time went on. This meant that they caused the children a good deal of trouble in each succeeding battle. They also had certain advantages on their side. As their opponents were so small, for instance, it was possible after a little practice to spit several of them on the bayonet at once, and often a kick was enough to fell them to the ground.

But against this, the children were so much more numerous and also braver. They were everywhere. They swarmed over one and in between one's legs and the unwarlike people were nearly demented by all these small monsters who fought like fiends. Little fiends was also what they were generally called—not without reason—and this name was even adopted in the children's homeland, but there it was a mark of honor and a pet name. The enemy troops had all their work cut out merely defending themselves. At last, however, they were able to check the others' advance and even venture on one or two counterattacks.

Everything then came to a standstill for a while and there was a breathing space.

The children were now in possession of a large part of the country. But this was not always so easy. The population did not particularly like them and proved not to be very fond of children. It was alleged that snipers fired on the boys from houses and that they were ambushed when they moved in small detachments. Children had even been found impaled on stakes or with their eyes gouged out, so it was said. And in many cases these stories were no doubt true. The population had quite lost their heads, were obviously goaded into a frenzy, and as they were of little use as a warlike nation and their cruelty could therefore find no natural outlet, they tried to avenge themselves by atrocities. They felt overrun by all the foreign children as by troublesome vermin and, being at their wits' end, they simply killed whenever they had the chance. In order to put an end to these outrages the children burned one village after the other and shot hundreds of people daily, but this did not improve matters. The despicable deeds of these craven guerrillas caused them endless trouble.

At home, the accounts of all this naturally aroused the most bitter resentment. People's blood boiled to think that their small soldiers were treated in this way by those who had nothing to do with the war, by barbarous civilians who had no notion of established and judicial forms. Even greater indignation was caused, however, by an incident that occurred inside the occupied area some time after the big summer battle just mentioned.

A lieutenant who was out walking in the countryside came to a stream where a large, fat woman knelt washing clothes. He asked her the way to a village close by. The woman, who probably suspected him of evil intent, retorted, "What are you doing here? You ought to be at home with your mother." Whereupon the lieutenant drew his saber to kill her, but the woman grabbed hold of him and, putting him over her knee, thwacked him black and blue with her washboard so that he was unable to sit down for several days afterward. He was so taken aback that he did nothing, armed though he was to the teeth. Luckily no one saw the incident, but there were orders that all outrages on the part of the population were to be reported to headquarters. The lieutenant therefore duly reported what had happened to him. True, it gave him little satisfaction, but as he had to obey orders he had no choice. And so it all came out.

The incident aroused a storm of rage, particularly among those at home. The infamous deed was a humiliation for the country, an insult which nothing could wipe out. It implied a deliberate violation by this militarily ignorant people of the simplest rules of warfare. Everywhere, in the press, in propaganda speeches, in ordinary conversation, the deepest contempt and disgust for the deed was expressed. The lieutenant who had so flagrantly shamed the army had his officer's epaulettes ripped off in front of the assembled troops and was declared unworthy to serve any longer in the field. He was instantly sent home to his parents, who belonged to one of the most noted families but who now had to retire into obscurity in a remote part of the country.

The woman, on the other hand, became a heroic figure among her people and the object of their rapturous admiration. During the whole of the war she and her deed were a rallying national symbol which people looked up to and which spurred them on to further effort. She subsequently became a favorite motif in the profuse literature about their desperate struggle for freedom; a vastly popular figure, brought to life again and again as time passed, now in a rugged, everyday way which appealed to the man in the street, now in heroic female form on a grandiose scale, to become gradually more and more legendary, wreathed in saga and myth. In some versions she was shot by the enemy; in others she lived to a ripe old age, loved and revered by her people.

This incident, more than anything else, helped to increase the bad feelings between the two countries and to make them wage the war with ever greater ruthlessness. In the late summer, before the autumn rains began, both armies, ignorant of each other's plans, simultaneously launched a violent offensive, which devastated both sides. On large sectors of the front the troops completely annihilated each other so that there was not a single survivor left. Any peaceful inhabitants thereabouts who were still alive and ventured out of their cellars thought that the war was over, because all were slain.

But soon new detachments came up and began fighting again. Great confusion arose in other quarters from the fact that in the heat of attack men ran past each other and had to turn around in order to go on fighting; and that some parts of the line rushed ahead while others came behind, so that the troops were both in front of and behind where they should have been and time and again attacked each other in the rear. The battle raged in this way with extreme violence and shots were fired from all directions at once.

When at last the fighting ceased and stock was taken of the situation, it appeared that no one had won. On both sides there was an equal number of fallen, 12,924, and after all attacks and retreats the position of the armies was exactly the same as at the start of the battle. It was agreed that both should claim the victory. Thereafter the rain set in and the armies went to earth in trenches and put up barbed wire entanglements.

The children were the first to finish their trenches, since they had had more to do with that kind of thing, and settled down in them as best they could. They soon felt at home. Filthy and lousy, they lived there in the darkness as though they had never done anything else. With the adaptability of children they quickly got into the way of it. The enemy found this more difficult; he felt miserable and homesick for the life above ground to which he was accustomed. Not so the children. When one saw them in their small gray uniforms, which were caked thick with mud, and their small gas masks, one could easily think they had been born to this existence. They crept in and out of the holes down into the earth and scampered about the passages like mice. When their burrows were attacked they were instantly up on the parapet and snapped back in blind fury. As the months passed, this hopeless, harrowing life put endurance to an increasingly severe test. But they never lost courage or the will to fight.

For the enemy the strain was often too much; the glaring pointlessness of it all made many completely apathetic. But the little ones did not react like this. Children are really more fitted for war and take more pleasure in it, while grown-ups tire of it after a while and think it is boring. The boys continued to find the whole thing exciting and they wanted to go on living as they were now. They also had a more natural herd instinct; their unity and camaraderie helped them a great deal, made it easier to hold out.

But, of course, even they suffered great hardship. Especially when winter set in with its incessant rain, a cold sleet which made everything sodden and filled the trenches with mud. It was enough to unman anyone. But it would never have entered their heads to complain. However bad things were, nothing could have made them admit it. At home everyone was very proud of them. All the cinemas showed parades behind the front and the little c in c and his generals pinning medals for bravery on their soldiers' breasts. People thought of them a great deal out there, of their little fiends, realizing that they must be having a hard time.

At Christmas, in particular, thoughts went out to them, to the lighted Christmas trees and all the sparkling childish eyes out in the trenches; in every home people sat wondering how they were faring. But the children did not think of home. They were soldiers out and out, absorbed by their duty and their new life. They attacked in several places on the morning of Christmas Eve, inflicting fairly big losses on the enemy in killed and wounded, and did not stop until it was time to open their parcels. They had the real fighting spirit which might have been a lesson even to adults.

There was nothing sentimental about them. The war had hardened and developed them, made them men. It did happen that one poor little chap burst into tears when the Christmas tree was lighted, but he was made the laughing-stock of them all. "Are you homesick for your mummy, you bastard?" they said, and kept on jeering at him all evening. He was the object of their scorn all through Christmas; he behaved suspiciously and tried to keep to himself. Once he walked a hundred yards away from the post and, because he might well have been thinking of flight, he was seized and court-martialed. He could give no reason for having absented himself and since he had obviously intended to desert he was shot.

If those at home had been fully aware of the morale out there, they need not have worried. As it was, they wondered if the children could really hold their ground and half-regretted having entrusted them with the campaign, now that it was dragging on so long because of this nerve-racking stationary warfare. After the New Year help was even offered in secret, but it was rejected with proud indignation.

The morale of the enemy, on the other hand, was not so high. They did intend to fight to the last man, but the certainty of a complete victory was not so general as it should have been. They could not help thinking, either, how hopeless their fight really was; that in the long run they could not hold their own against these people who were armed to the very milk teeth, and this often dampened their courage.

Hardly had nature begun to come to life and seethe with the newly awakened forces of spring before the children started with incredible intensity to prepare for the decisive battle. Heavy mechanized artillery was brought up and placed in strong positions; huge troop movements went on night and day; all available fighting forces were concentrated in the very front lines. After murderous gunfire which lasted for six days, an attack was launched with great force and extreme skill. Individual bravery was, if possible, more dazzling than ever. The whole army was also a year older, and that means much at that age. But their opponents, too, were determined to do their utmost. They had assembled all their reserves, and their spirits, now that the rain had stopped and the weather was fine, were full of hope.

It was a terrible battle. The hospital trains immediately started going back from both sides packed with wounded and dying. Machine guns, tanks and gas played fearful havoc. For several days the outcome was impossible to foresee, since both armies appeared equally strong and the tide of battle constantly changed. The position gradually cleared, however. The enemy had expected the main attack in the center, but the child army turned out to be the weakest there. Use was made of this, especially because they themselves were best prepared at this very point, and this part of the children's front was soon made to waver and was forced farther and farther back by repeated attack. Advantage was also taken of an ideal evening breeze from just the right quarter to gas the children in thousands. Encouraged by their victory, the troops pursued the offensive with all their might and with equal success.

The child army's retreat, however, turned out to be a stratagem, brilliantly conceived and carried out. Its center gave way more and more and the enemy, giving all his attention to this, forgot that at the same time he himself was wavering on both wings. In this way he ran his head into a noose. When the children considered that they had retreated far enough they halted, while the troops on the outermost wings, already far ahead, advanced swiftly until they met behind the enemy's back. The latter's entire army was thereby surrounded and in the grip of an iron hand. All the children's army had to do now was to draw the noose tighter. At last the gallant defenders had to surrender and let themselves be taken prisoner, which in fact they already were. It was the most disastrous defeat in history; not a single one escaped other than by death.

This victory became much more famous than any of the others and was eagerly studied at all military academies on account of its brilliantly executed, doubly effective encircling movement. The great general Sludelsnorp borrowed its tactics outright seventy years later at his victory over the Slivokvarks in the year 2048.

The war could not go on any longer now, because there was nothing left to fight, and the children marched to the capital with the imprisoned army between them to dictate the peace terms. These were handed over by the little commander in chief in the hall of mirrors in the stately old palace at a historic scene which was to be immortalized time and again in art and even now was reproduced everywhere in the weekly press. The film cameras whirred, the flashlights hissed and the radio broadcast the great moment to the world. The commander in chief, with austere and haughty mien and one foot slightly in front of the other, delivered the historic document with his right hand. The first and most important condition was the complete cession of the country, besides which the expenses of its capture were to be borne by the enemy, who thus had to pay the cost of the war on both sides, the last clause on account of the fact that he had been the challenging party and, according to his own admission, the cause of the war. The document was signed in dead silence, the only sound was the scratching of the fountain pen, which, according to the commentator's whisper, was solid gold and undoubtedly a future museum piece.

With this, everything was settled and the children's army returned to its own country, where it was received with indescribable rapture. Everywhere along the roads the troops were greeted with wild rejoicing; their homecoming was one long victory parade. The march into the capital and the dismissal there of the troops, which took place before vast crowds, were especially impressive. People waved and shouted in the streets as they passed, were beside themselves with enthusiasm, bands played, eyes were filled with tears of joy. Some of the loudest cheering was for the small invalids at the rear of the procession, blind and with limbs amputated, who had sacrificed themselves for their country. Many of them had already got small artificial arms and legs so that they looked just the same as before. The victory salute thundered, bayonets flashed in the sun. It was an unforgettable spectacle.

A strange, new leaf was written in the great book of history which would be read with admiration in time to come. The nation had seen many illustrious deeds performed, but never anything as proud as this. What these children had done in their devotion and fervent patriotism could never be forgotten.

Nor was it. Each spring, on the day of victory, school children marched out with flags in their hands to the cemeteries with all the small graves where the heroes rested under their small white crosses. The mounds were strewn with flowers and passionate speeches were made, reminding everyone of the glorious past, their imperishable honor and youthful, heroic spirit of self-sacrifice. The flags floated in the sun and the voices rang out clear as they sang their rousing songs, radiant childish eyes looking ahead to new deeds of glory.

THE END

Development

INTERPRETATION

The interpretation of satire is largely a matter of understanding and appreciating the satirist's evaluation of mankind. The following statements refer to events described in "The Children's Campaign." In each instance identify what you feel is the object, institution, or human tendency which Lagerkvist is satirizing.

1. The military schools will accept only boys of superior intelligence and perfect physique.

2. The war was caused by the intolerable insolence of the smaller, enemy nation.

3. The Children's Army adorned their rifles with green sprigs and were pelted with flowers as they left for the front.

4. A four-year-old spectator was moved by a wave of patriotism to bloody his mother's nose.

5. In battle the children displayed a heroic contempt for death worthy of grown-up men.

6. Back home, the children were fondly referred to as "little fiends."

7. The proliferation of enemy atrocities could be attributed to the fact that,

not being a warlike people, they had no natural outlet for their cruelty.

8. One lieutenant suffered an unspeakable indignity at the hands of a peasant woman, who was ignorant of the most elementary rules of warfare.

9. The children's morale was sustained by the exciting camaraderie of trench warfare, while the enemy despaired.

10. The children made several attacks on the morning of Christmas Eve and did not let up until it was time to open their presents.

11. The boy found crying was deemed subversive and he was shot.

12. The enemy, being the cause of the war, had to pay the expense of both sides.

13. Each spring, the school children decorated with flowers the graves of their fallen compatriots and looked forward to new deeds of glory.

TECHNIQUE

1. (a) What is the attitude of the narrator toward the events in "The Children's Campaign"? (b) In what way does this attitude contribute to the shock value of the story?

EXTENSIONS

1. Lagerkvist has given us a starkly unsentimental view of childhood. Do you think that children are liable to act the way Lagerkvist describes, given his conditions of indoctrination? Explain your opinion.

2. "The Children's Campaign" throws into question the worth of heroism in battle. Do you think that the type of motivation that Lagerkvist assigns to the child warriors is common among adult soldiers? Explain.

3. "The Children's Campaign" is set in the year 1978, a time far in the future when Lagerkvist published the story in 1935. Do you feel that, since 1935, the world has moved closer to a condition that might witness the formation and employment of a Children's Army? Explain your view.

Man of My Time

SALVATORE QUASIMODO[1] / ITALY / 1901–1968

translated from the Italian by Allen Mandelbaum

You are still the one with the stone and the sling,
man of my time. You were in the cockpit,
with the malign wings, the sundials of death,
—I have seen you—in the chariot of fire, at the gallows,
5 at the wheels of torture. I have seen you: it was you
with your exact science persuaded to extermination,
without love, without Christ. Again, as always, you
have killed, as did your fathers kill, as did
the animals that saw you for the first time, kill.
10 And this blood smells as on the day
one brother told the other brother: "Let us
go into the fields." And that echo, chill, tenacious,
has reached down to you, within your day.
Forget, o sons, the clouds of blood
15 risen from the earth, forget the fathers:
their tombs sink down in ashes,
black birds, the wind, cover their heart.

Development

1. *(a)* What accusation has Quasimodo made in "Man of My Time"? *(b)* Do you feel he has directed it at you personally? Why or why not? *(c)* Do you think that there is any truth to his claim? Explain your view.

2. There is a great diversity of historical references in "Man of My Time." *(a)* Choose three of these references from the poem and elaborate on the associations of time, place, or events that they bring to your mind. *(b)* Do you feel that Quasimodo would have done better to stick with a specific example of destructiveness? Why or why not?

3. In accepting the Nobel Prize for Literature, Quasimodo said: "The politician wants men to be able to die with courage; the poet wants man to live with courage." Do you think that courage is needed to forget "the clouds of blood" and "the fathers," as Quasimodo urges in "Man of My Time"? Explain your view.

4. Would you want to read more of Quasimodo's poetry? Why or why not?

1. *Salvatore Quasimodo* (säl′vä tô′re kwä′sə mō′dō).

A World Ends

WOLFGANG HILDESHEIMER / Germany

(1916–   )

translated from the German by Christopher Holme

The Marchesa Montetristo's[1] last evening party has impressed itself indelibly on my memory. This is partly due, of course, to its extraordinary conclusion but in other ways as well the evening was unforgettable.

My acquaintance with the Marchesa—a Waterman by birth, of Little Gidding, Ohio—came about by a coincidence. I had sold her, through the intermediary of my friend, Herr von Perlhuhn (I mean of course the Abraham-a-Santa Clara expert,[2] not the neo-mystic), the bathtub in which Marat was murdered.[3] It is perhaps not generally known that it had been until then in my possession. Gambling debts obliged me to offer it for sale. So it was that I came to the Marchesa who had long wanted this appliance for her collection of eighteenth century washing utensils. This was the occasion of my getting to know her. From the bathtub our conversation soon passed to more general esthetic topics. I noticed that the possession of this collector's piece had given me a certain prestige in her eyes. And I was not surprised when one day I was invited to one of her famous parties in her palazzo on the artificial island of San Amerigo. The Marchesa had had the island thrown up a few miles southeast of Murano[4] on a sudden whim, for she detested the mainland—she said it was hurtful to her spiritual equilibrium, and she could find nothing to suit her in the existing stock of islands. So here she resided, devoting her life to the cult of the antique and forgotten, or, as she liked to put it, of the "true and eternal."

The invitation card gave the time of the party as eight o'clock, which meant that the guests were expected at ten. So custom ordered it. Further it ordered that the guests should come in gondolas. In this fashion, it is true, the crossing lasted nearly two hours and was moreover uncomfortable when the sea was rough, but these were unwritten rules of behavior at which no one but a barbarian would cavil—and barbarians were not invited. Besides, many of the younger guests, not yet fully sensible of the dignity of the occasion, would hire a *vaporetto*[5] to take them within a hundred yards

1. *Marchesa Montetristo* (mär kä′zä môn′te trēs′tô). 2. *Abraham-a-Santa Clara expert,* one of a number of obscure references, many of them probably bogus, mixed in with actual events and places to increase the satiric effect. 3. *Marat . . . . murdered.* Jean Paul Marat, a radical leader of the French Revolution and an executor of the Reign of Terror, was finally murdered in his own bathtub. 4. *Murano,* an island town a mile north of Venice, Italy. 5. *vaporetto,* a small steam launch used on the canals of Venice. [*Italian*]

of the island whence they were ferried over one by one in a gondola which had been brought in tow.

The splendor of the building needs no description from me. For outside it was an exact replica of the Palazzo Vendramin, and inside every period, from the Gothic onward, was represented. But of course they were not intermingled. Each one had its own room. The Marchesa could really not be accused of breaches of style. Nor need the opulence of the catering be referred to here. Anyone who has ever attended a state banquet in a monarchy—and it is to such that I principally address myself—knows what it was like. Moreover it would hardly be true to the spirit of the Marchesa and her circle to mention the pleasures of the table, especially here, where I have to describe the last hours on earth of some of the most eminent figures of the age, which I as sole survivor had the privilege to witness.

After exchanging a few civilities with my hostess and stroking the long-haired Pekinese which never stirred from her side, I was introduced to the Dombrowska, a woman doubly famous, first for her contributions to the rhythmic-expressionist dance, a vanishing art form, and secondly as the author of the book *Back to Youth,* which, as the title indicates, argued in favor of a return to youthfulness of style and which, I need hardly remind the reader, has won adherents far and wide. While we were chatting together, an elderly gentleman of upright bearing came up to us. It was Golch. The Golch. (Unnecessary to give further particulars of a man whose share in the enrichment of our intellectual life is so widely known.) The Dombrowska introduced me: "Herr Sebald, the late owner of Marat's bathtub." My fame had spread.

"Aha," said Golch. I inferred, from the inflection he gave to these syllables, that he was weighing my potentialities as a candidate for the cultural élite. I asked him how he had liked the exhibition of

contemporary painting in Luxemburg. For one might, indeed one must, assume that those here assembled had seen, read, and heard everything of any real importance. That was why they were here. Golch raised his eyes as if looking for a word in space and said, "Passé." (He used the English accentuation of the word which was then in fashion. The words "cliché" and "pastiche" too were pronounced *à l'anglaise.*[6] I don't know what the current usage is. I am now too much taken up with everyday affairs to concern myself with such matters.) I noticed in any case that I had blundered in thus mentioning the contemporary. I had gone down a step, but I had learnt my lesson.

A move was made to the buffet. Here I encountered Signora Sgambati, the astrologer, who had recently made a considerable stir by her theory that not only the fate of individuals but whole trends in the history of ideas could be read in the stars. She was no ordinary phenomenon, this Sgambati, as was at once clear from her appearance. Yet I find it incomprehensible in the circumstances that she did not see in the constellation of the heavens the imminent engulfment of so many substantial members of the intellectual world. She was deep in conversation with Professor Kuntz-Sartori, the politician and royalist, who had been trying for decades to introduce a monarchy in Switzerland. Another notable figure.

After taking some refreshment the company moved to the Silver Room for what was to be the climax of the evening's entertainment, a performance of a special kind—the world première of two flute sonatas by Antonio Giambattista Bloch, a contemporary and friend of Rameau,[7] who had been discovered by the musicologist Weltli. He too of course was there. They were played by the flautist Beranger

---

6. *a l'anglaise,* in the English manner. [*French*]
7. *Rameau,* the renowned eighteenth-century French composer, Jean Philippe Rameau.

(yes, a descendant) and accompanied by the Marchesa herself, on the self-same harpsichord on which Celestine Rameau had initiated her son into the fundamental principles of counterpoint, and which had been sent for from Paris. The flute too had a history, but I have forgotten it. The two performers had put on rococo costume for the occasion, and the little ensemble looked—they had purposely so arranged themselves—like a picture by Watteau.[8] The performance of course took place by the dimmest of candle-light. There was not a person there who would have found electric light for such an occasion anything but intolerable. By a further sensitive whim of the Marchesa the guests were required after the first sonata (D major) to move over from the Silver Room (Baroque) to the Golden Room (early Rococo), there to enjoy the second sonata. For the Silver Room had a major resonance, the Golden, it could not be disputed, a minor.

At this point I must remark that the tedious elegance which clings to the flute sonatas of second-rank, and more particularly of the newly discovered masters of this period, was in the present case to be explained by the fact that no such person as Giambattista Bloch had ever lived. The works here performed had in reality been composed by the musicologist Weltli. Although this circumstance did not become known till later, I cannot, in retrospect, help feeling it a humiliation for the Marchesa that she should have employed her last moments in the interpretation, however masterly, of a forgery.

During the second movement of the F minor sonata I saw a rat creeping along the wall. I was astonished. At first I thought it might have been lured from its hole by the sound of the flute—such things do happen, they say—but it was creeping in the opposite direction. It was followed by another rat. I looked at the guests. They had not noticed anything, and indeed most of them were keeping their eyes closed in order to be able to abandon themselves to the harmonies of Weltli's forgery. I now heard a dull reverberation, like very distant thunder. The floor began to vibrate. Again I looked at the guests. If they had heard anything—and something they must be hearing—it was at any rate not discernible from their hunched-up postures. I, however, was made uneasy by these strange symptoms.

A manservant entered. This is barely the place to remark that in the unusual costume worn by the Marchesa's domestic staff he looked like a character out of *Tosca*.[9] He went up to the performers and whispered something in the Marchesa's ear. I saw her turn pale. How well it suited her in the dim candlelight! But she controlled herself and without interruption played the *andante*[10] calmly to the end. Then she nodded to the flautist, stood up, and addressed the company.

"Ladies and gentlemen," she said, "I have just learnt that the foundations of the island and those of the palace with them are breaking up. The Office of Submarine Works has been informed. The right thing, I think we shall all agree, is to go on with the music."

She sat down again, gave the sign to Monsieur Beranger, and they played the *allegro con brio*,[11] the last movement, which did seem to me at the time, though I had yet no inkling that it was a forgery, little suited to the uniqueness of the situation.

On the polished floor small puddles were forming. The reverberation had grown louder and sounded nearer. Most of the guests were now sitting upright, their faces ashen in the candlelight, and looking as if they were long dead already. I stood up and said, "I'm going," not so

---

8. *Watteau,* an eighteenth-century French painter who excelled in stylized depictions of courtly life. 9. *Tosca,* an opera by Puccini, set in late eighteenth-century Rome. 10. *andante,* a movement of moderately slow tempo. [*Italian*] 11. *allegro con brio,* a movement played in a lively tempo. [*Italian*]

loud as to give offense to the musicians, but loud enough to intimate to the other guests that I had the courage to admit my fear. The floor was now almost evenly covered with water. Although I walked on tiptoe, I could not help splashing an evening dress or two as I passed. But, in view of what was soon to come, the damage I did must be reckoned inconsiderable. Few of the guests thought me worthy of a glance, but I did not care. As I opened the door to the passage a wave of water poured into the room and caused Lady Fitzjones (the preserver of Celtic customs) to draw her fur wrap more closely about her—no doubt a reflex movement, for it could not be of any use. Before shutting the door behind me I saw Herr von Perlhuln (the neo-mystic, not the Abraham-a-Santa Clara expert) casting a half-contemptuous, half-melancholy glance in my direction. He too was now sitting in water almost to his knees. So was the Marchesa, who could no longer use the pedals. I do not as a matter of fact know how essential they are on the harpsichord. I remember thinking that if the piece had been a cello sonata, they would perforce have had to break it off here since the instrument would not sound in water. Strange what irrelevant thoughts occur to one in such moments.

In the entrance hall it was suddenly as quiet as in a grotto; only in the distance a sound of rushing water was to be heard. I divested myself of my tail coat and was soon swimming through the sinking palace toward the portals. My splashes echoed mysteriously from the walls and columns. Not a soul was to be seen. Evidently the servants had all fled. And why should they not? They had no obligation to the true and eternal culture, and those assembled here had no further need of their services.

Outside the moon shone as if nothing were amiss, and yet a world, no less, was here sinking beneath the ocean. As if at a great distance I could still hear the high notes of Monsieur Beranger's flute.

He had a wonderful *embouchure*,[12] that one must allow him.

I unhitched the last gondola which the escaping servants had left behind and pushed out to sea. Through the windows past which I paddled the water was now flooding into the palace. I saw that the guests had risen from their seats. The sonata must be at an end, for they were clapping, their hands held high over their heads, since the water was now up to their chins. With dignity the Marchesa and Monsieur Beranger were acknowledging the applause, though in the circumstances they could not bow.

The water had now reached the candles. Slowly they were extinguished, and as the darkness grew, it became quiet; the applause was silenced. Suddenly I heard the crash and roar of a building in collapse. The Palazzo was falling. I steered the gondola seaward so as not to be hit by plaster fragments.

After paddling some hundreds of yards across the lagoon in the direction of the island of San Giorgio,[13] I turned round once more. The sea lay dead calm in the moonlight as if no island had ever stood there. A pity about the bathtub, I thought, for that was a loss which could never be made good. The thought was perhaps rather heartless but experience teaches us that we need a certain distance from such events in order to appreciate their full scope.

THE END

---

12. *embouchure* (äm′bü shür′), the configuration of the lips required to play a woodwind or brass instrument. [*French*] 13. *San Giorgio* (sän jôr′ jô), an island forming the southern quarter of Venice.

Development

1. *(a)* What qualifies one to be a friend of the Marchesa Montetristo? *(b)* Why has the Marchesa built an island for herself? *(c)* Why do you think the Marchesa's friends put up with her idiosyncrasies, such as the necessity of arriving at the island by gondola?

2. Discuss the character of Hildesheimer's narrator, Herr Sebald, as revealed by: *(a)* his interests; *(b)* his attitudes; *(c)* his style of writing; *(d)* the references he makes to his personal life; and *(e)* the assumptions he makes about you as a reader.

3. *(a)* What is the difference in tone and connotation between the phrases "the true and eternal" and "the antique and forgotten"? *(b)* What is ironic about the two flute sonatas by Antonio Giambattista Bloch? *(c)* Do you agree with the narrator that they are inappropriate for the occasion? Why or why not?

4. What might be satirized or symbolized by: *(a)* the Marchesa's decision to continue with the music; *(b)* the immobility of the guests; *(c)* the exit of the narrator; *(d)* the flight of the servants; and *(e)* the final dissolution of the palace.

5. *(a)* Do you feel that Hildesheimer is sympathetic to the passing of the Marchesa's world? Upon what evidence have you based your opinion? *(b)* If you feel the same way as Hildesheimer, what are your reasons? If not, what prompts you to view the situation differently?

TECHNIQUE

1. *(a)* In what ways has Hildesheimer anticipated the conclusion of "A World Ends"? *(b)* Do you feel that this antici-pation has lessened the impact of the conclusion? Why or why not?

2. Has Hildesheimer, in your opinion, been consistent in his portrayal of the Marchesa and her world? Give references to support your answer.

3. Look again at the narrator's observations on the Marchesa's paleness (page 440, column 2, paragraph 1), on Monsieur Beranger's *embouchure* (page 441, column 1, paragraph 2), and on the Marchesa's difficulty in acknowledging her applause (page 441, column 2, paragraph 1). *(a)* How do you react to the inclusion of these details? *(b)* Do you feel that this approach is appropriate to the theme of "A World Ends"? Why or why not?

EXTENSIONS

1. Assume you have a friend who might enjoy reading "A World Ends." What would you tell him to excite his interest in the story, without giving away the ending?

2. Hildesheimer's story makes an amusing comment on the wisdom of worshiping antiquity. Can you think of any attitudes or institutions in your society that have an addiction to the past which might prove as foolhardy as the Marchesa's? Explain.

3. The ending of Hildesheimer's story recalls such high points in American literature as the conclusions of Edgar Allan Poe's "The Fall of the House of Usher" and of Herman Melville's *Moby Dick*. Why do you think this is a popular kind of ending for stories involving a form of obsession? Discuss.

Cemetery of Whales

YEVGENY YEVTUSHENKO[1] / RUSSIA / 1933 –

translated from the Russian by John Updike and Albert C. Todd

A cemetery of whales:
    in a snowy graveyard
instead of crosses
    their own bones stand.
5 They couldn't be gnawed by teeth;
    teeth are too soft.
They couldn't be used for soup;
    pots are too shallow.
The straining wind bends them,
10   but they keep their position,
rooted in ice,
    arching like black rainbows.
Thirsty for a snort,
    an Eskimo hunchback,
15 shaped like a question mark,
    huddles in them as in parentheses.
Who playfully clicked a camera?
    Restrain your photophilia.
Let's leave the whales in peace,
20   if only after death.
They lived, these whales,
    without offense to people,
in infantile simplicity,
    reveling in their own fountains,
25 while the crimson ball of the sun
    danced in a torrent of rays . . .
Thar she blows!
    Come on, lads, let's get 'em!
Where can we hide?

But you're broader than space! 30
The world doesn't hold enough water
    for you to dive under.
You think you're God?
    A risky bit of impudence.
One harpoon, smack in the flank, 35
    rewards enormity.
Enormity commands everyone
    to hunt for it.
Whoever is big is stupid.
    Who's smaller is wiser. 40
Sardines, like vermicelli,[2]
    are an impossible target,
lost in the generic—
    but greatness is helpless.
On board, binoculars tremble 45
    as the crew takes aim;
streaming harpoon in his side,
    huge Tolstoy[3] runs from the Kodak.
A baby whale, not full-fledged,
    though evaluated as a whale, 50
Esenin[4] flutters and kicks,
    hoisted high on a harpoon shaft.
The title of Whale is a bloody dignity.
    Greatness kills greatness.
Mayakovsky[5] himself 55
    pounds in the lance.
The shallows are also a menace:
    dashed on the shoals by the chase,

"Cemetery of Whales" by Yevgeny Yevtushenko, translated by Updike and Todd, from HOLIDAY Magazine (November 1968). Reprinted by permission of the translators.
1. *Yevgeny Yevtushenko* (yef gān′ē yef′tü shen′kō). **2.** *vermicelli* (ver′mə sel′ē), a pasta, like spaghetti, characterized by noodles that are very thin. **3.** *Tolstoy,* Count Leo Tolstoy (1828-1910), Russian novelist, author of *War and Peace.* (See biographical appendix.) **4.** *Esenin* (ye se′ nin). Sergei Esenin (1895-1925), a tumultuous Russian poet, was denounced by the authorities and committed suicide at the age of thirty. **5.** *Mayakovsky* (mä yä kôf′ ski). Vladimir Mayakovsky (1893-1930), who was at one time considered the unofficial Communist poet laureate, became disillusioned with the revolution in Russia and also committed suicide.

Gorky[6] hawks and disgorges
60   fragments of steel and hickory.
Without even moaning,
        gliding along the path of blood,
Pasternak[7] with a snatch of lime
        sinks into Lethe.[8]
65 Hemingway is silent;
        but from his grave a threatening
                shaft
shoots out of the grass,
        growing up from the coffin.
And hidden behind the mob,
70   murder in his eye,
the Dallas whaler
        with a telescopic sight.
A big drive is on;
        we cherish their names
                posthumously.
75 Your law is more honest,
        cruel Alaska.
In the cemetery of whales
        by the hummocks of ice
there are no sanctimonious flowers:
80   the Eskimos have tact.

Hey, Eskimo hunchback,
        white men have a funny custom:
after planting the harpoon,
        they weep over the corpse.
Murderers mourn like maidens,   85
        and tearfully suck tranquilizers,
and parade in crêpe,
        and stand honor guard.
The professional hunters,
        who would look out of place,   90
send wreaths to the whales
        from the State Bureau of
                Harpoonery.
But the flowers are twisted together
        with steel cables and barbs.
Enough of such goodness!   95
        Let me live among Eskimos!

6. *Gorky* (gôr′ kē). Maxim Gorky (1868-1936), the champion of the Russian proletariat in his writing, died mysteriously while under medical treatment. **7.** *Pasternak.* Boris Pasternak (1890-1960), one of Russia's greatest lyrical poets, was forced by public opinion to refuse the Nobel Prize for Literature in 1958. **8.** *Lethe* (lē′ thē), the mythological river of forgetfulness. [*Latin*]

Development

---

1. *(a)* Why have the whales' skeletons remained intact? *(b)* How would you describe the attitude toward the dead symbolized by the hunchback? *(c)* What conflicting attitude is dramatized by lines 17-18? *(d)* Do you feel that Yevtushenko has tried to make a hero out of the hunchback? Explain your view.

2. *(a)* What qualities might you associate with the whales from Yevtushenko's description of them in lines 21-26? *(b)* What common traits link the real whales with the metaphoric whales of lines 47-72?

3. Would you have the same reaction to this poem if the lines about the "Dallas whaler" were cut out? Discuss.

4. *(a)* What form of hypocrisy does Yevtushenko lash out at? *(b)* To whom do you think he is referring by his classification of "professional hunters"? *(c)* Is Yevtushenko's attack justified? Why or why not?

5. Do you think it plausible that the heroic individual, by raising himself too far above the common level, endangers the stability of the whole social structure? Why or why not?

6. Is there a realistic way to combat the hypocrisy Yevtushenko talks about, or must one quit trying and, literally or symbolically, live among Eskimos? If so, how? If not, why?

Comparison

1. Konopnicka, Lagerkvist, and Hildesheimer have each outlined a very distinct type of society. If you were forced to live in one of these environments, which would be your first and last choices? Explain.

2. Suppose that in some future society you, as Commissar of Literature, had the job of censoring all writings that did not promote the ideal of unflagging allegiance to the state. The selections in this group have just been submitted to you for judgment. (a) Which ones would you pass for publication and which would you suppress? Give your reasons. (b) If the selections you suppressed had already been published in other countries, in what way would you attack and degrade them in your monthly column for *The International Review of Literature*?

3. Satire is the art of using wit to diminish a subject by making it appear ridiculous or contemptible. Traditionally, satire has been classified as either *Juvenalian* or *Horatian.* The first type, named after the Roman poet Juvenal, is bitterly angry in its denunciation of human corruption. The second, patterned after Horace, who succeeded Juvenal in Rome, scoffs more gently at the follies of mankind. (a) Which selection in this group best represents each type of satire? (b) Do you feel that each of the two authors has chosen the form of satire most appropriate to his subject? Why or why not? (c) Choose a subject relating to group behavior which, you feel, deserves satiric treatment. Now decide which of the two satiric approaches is more appropriate to your subject. Explain your reasoning.

4. If you read literature for pleasure, you will inevitably develop a liking for certain authors whom you know only through their writing. The way an author projects himself, the way he puts the imprint of his personality onto words, is generally termed his style. (a) Rank the five authors in this group, beginning with the one you liked most and ending with your least favorite, on the grounds of the image of themselves they project through their styles. (b) Start at the bottom of your list and proceed to the top, explaining for each successive author the qualities of his style which prompted you to rank him as you did.

5. In "Man of My Time" Quasimodo has made a plea for the cessation of violence as a way of life. If his poem were submitted to the soldiers of Lagerkvist's Children's Army and to the "professional hunters" of Yevtushenko's "State Bureau of Harpoonery," what might be their respective responses? Be specific.

6. The figure of Councillor Storch in "Community Welfare Service" suggests George Bernard Shaw's epigram: "When a stupid man is doing something he's ashamed of, he always declares that it is his duty." In like manner, the character of the Marchesa Montetristo recalls Oscar Wilde's epigrammatic definition: "Duty is what one expects of others." Choose from the selections in this group one character or one group of characters who seem senselessly duty-bound, and think up an epigram that fits that situation.

7. Lagerkvist and Yevtushenko have both used physical smallness as symbolic of a particular way of thinking and acting. What common themes can you find either by comparing Yevtushenko's poem with the account of the Lilliputians in Jonathan Swift's *Gulliver's Travels* or by comparing Lagerkvist's short story with William Golding's novel *Lord of the Flies*?

CHURCH OF THE BAREFOOT FRIARS by Lyonel Feininger. Courtesy of The Staatsgalerie, Stuttgart.

The Performers

THE MAN WITH THE KNIVES / HEINRICH BÖLL / GERMANY

THE TIGER / KUME MASAO / JAPAN

THE INFANT PRODIGY / THOMAS MANN / GERMANY

The Man with the Knives

HEINRICH BÖLL[1] / Germany

(1917–   )

translated from the German by Leila Vennewitz

Jupp[2] held the knife by the tip of the blade, letting it joggle idly up and down; it was a long, tapering bread knife, obviously razor-sharp. With a sudden flick of the wrist he tossed the knife into the air: up it went, whirring like a propeller; the shining blade glittered like a golden fish in a sheaf of lingering sunbeams, struck the ceiling, lost its spin, and plunged down straight at Jupp's head. In a flash Jupp had placed a wooden block on his head; the knife scored into the wood and remained embedded there, gently swaying. Jupp removed the block from his head, withdrew the knife, and flung it with a gesture of annoyance at the door, where it stuck, quivering, in the frame until it gradually stopped vibrating and fell to the floor. . . .

"It makes me sick," said Jupp quietly. "I've been working on the logical assumption that people who've paid for their tickets really want to see turns where life and limb are at stake—like at the Roman circuses—they want to be convinced of at least the *possibility* of bloodshed, know what I mean?"

He picked up the knife and tossed it neatly against the top crossbar of the window, with such force that the panes rattled and threatened to fall out of the crumbling putty. This throw—confident and unerring—took me back to those hours of semidarkness in the past when he had thrown his pocketknife against the dugout post, from bottom to top and down again.

"I'll do anything," he went on, "to give the customers a thrill. I'll even cut off my ears, only it's hard to find anyone to stick them back on again. Here, I want to show you something."

He opened the door for me, and we went out into the hallway. A few shreds of wallpaper still clung to the walls where the glue was too stubborn for them to be ripped off and used for lighting the stove. After passing through a moldering bathroom we emerged onto a kind of terrace, its concrete floor cracked and moss-covered.

Jupp pointed upward.

"The higher the knife goes, of course, the greater the effect. But I need some resistance up there for the thing to strike against and lose momentum so that it can come hurtling down straight at my useless skull. Look!" He pointed up to where the iron girders of a ruined balcony stuck out into the air.

"This is where I used to practice. For a whole year. Watch!" He sent the knife soaring upward: it rose with marvelous symmetry and evenness, seeming to climb as smoothly and effortlessly as a bird; then it struck one of the girders, shot down with breathtaking speed, and crashed into the wooden block. The impact itself must have been terrific. Jupp didn't bat an eyelid. The knife had buried itself a couple of inches in the wood.

1. *Böll* (Boel). 2. *Jupp* (yüp).

"But that's fantastic!" I cried. "It's absolutely sensational, they'll have to like it—what an act!"

Jupp nonchalantly withdrew the knife from the wood, grasped it by the handle and made a thrust in the air.

"Oh they like it all right, they pay me twelve marks[3] a night, and between the main acts they let me play around a bit with the knife. But the act's not elaborate enough. A man, a knife, a block of wood, don't you see? I ought to have a half-naked girl so I can send the knife spinning a hair's breadth past her nose. That'd make the crowd go wild. But try and find that kind of a girl!"

He went ahead as we returned to his room. He placed the knife carefully on the table, the wooden block beside it, and rubbed his hands. We sat down on the crate beside the stove and were silent. Taking some bread out of my pocket I said: "Be my guest."

"Thanks, I will, but let me make some coffee. Then you can come along and watch my performance."

He put some more wood in the stove and set the pot over the opening. "It's infuriating," he said. "Maybe I look too serious, a bit like a sergeant still, eh?"

"Nonsense, you never were a sergeant. D'you smile when they clap?"

"Of course—and bow too."

"I couldn't. I couldn't smile in a cemetery."

"That's a great mistake: a cemetery's the very place to smile."

"I don't get it."

"Because they aren't dead. They're none of them dead, see?"

"I see all right, but I don't believe it."

"There's still a bit of the lieutenant about you after all. Well, in that case it just takes longer, of course. The point is, I'm only too glad if they enjoy it. They're burned out inside, I give them a bit of a thrill and get paid for it. Perhaps one of them, just one, will go home and not forget me. 'That man with the knife, for Christ's sake, he wasn't scared, and I'm scared all the time, for Christ's sake,' maybe that's what he'll say because they're all scared, all the time. They trail their fear behind them like a heavy shadow, and it makes me happy if they can forget about it and laugh a little. Isn't that reason enough to smile?"

I said nothing, my eyes on the water, waiting for it to boil. Jupp poured the boiling water onto the coffee in the brown enamel pot, and we took turns drinking from the brown enamel pot and shared my bread. Outside the mild dusk began to fall, flowing into the room like soft gray milk.

"What are *you* doing these days, by the way?" asked Jupp.

"Nothing . . . just getting by."

"A hard way to make a living."

"Right—for this loaf of bread I had to collect a hundred bricks and clean them. Casual labor."

"Hm. . . . Want to see another of my tricks?"

In response to my nod he stood up, switched on the light, and went over to the wall, where he pushed aside a kind of rug, disclosing the rough outline of a man drawn in charcoal on the reddish color-wash: a strange lump protruded from what was supposed to be the head, probably signifying a hat. On closer inspection I saw that the man had been drawn on a skillfully camouflaged door. I watched expectantly as Jupp proceeded to pull out a handsome little brown leather suitcase from under the miserable affair that served as his bed and put it on the table. Before opening it he came over and placed four cigarette butts in front of me. "Roll those into two thin ones," he said.

I moved my seat so that I could watch him as well as get a bit more of the gentle warmth from the stove. While I was carefully pulling the butts apart on the bread paper spread over my knees, Jupp had snapped open the lock of the suit-

3. *twelve marks.* A mark is a German monetary unit worth about twenty-five cents.

case and pulled out an odd-looking object: one of those flannel bags consisting of a series of pockets in which our mothers used to keep their table silver. He deftly untied the ribbon and let the bundle unroll across the table to reveal a dozen wood-handled knives, the kind that, in the days when our mothers danced the waltz, were known as "hunting cutlery."

I divided the tobacco shreds scrupulously in half onto the two cigarette papers and rolled them. "Here," I said.

"Here," Jupp said too, and: "Thanks," bringing over the flannel bag for me to look at.

"This is all I managed to salvage from my parents' belongings. Almost everything was burned or lost in the rubble, and the rest stolen. When I got back from P.O.W. camp I was really on my beam ends, didn't own a thing in the world—until one day a dignified old lady, a friend of my mother's, tracked me down and brought along this nice suitcase. A few days before my mother was killed in an air raid she had left it with the old lady to be looked after, and it had survived. Funny, isn't it? But of course we know that when people are in a panic they try to save the strangest things. Never the essential ones. So then at least I was the owner of the contents of this suitcase: the brown enamel pot, twelve forks, twelve knives, and twelve spoons, and the long bread knife. I sold the spoons and forks, living off the proceeds for a year, and practiced with the knives, thirteen of them. Watch. . . ."

I passed him the spill I had used to light my cigarette. Jupp stuck his cigarette to his lower lip, fastened the ribbon of the flannel bag to a button on the shoulder of his jacket, and let the flannel unroll along his arm like some exotic panoply of war. Then with incredible speed he whisked the knives out of their pockets, and before I could follow his movements he had thrown all twelve like lightning against the dim human outline, which

reminded me of those sinister, shambling figures that came lurching at us toward the end of the war from every billboard, every corner, harbingers of defeat and destruction. Two knives were sticking out of the man's hat, two over each shoulder, and the others, three a side, along the dangling arms. . . .

"Fantastic!" I cried. "Fantastic! But you've got your act right there, with a bit of dramatizing."

"All I need is a man, better still a girl. But I know I'll never find anyone," he said with a sigh, plucking the knives out of the door and slipping them carefully back into their pockets. "The girls are too scared and the men want too much money. Can't blame them, of course, it's a risky business."

Once again he flung the knives back again at the door in such a way as to split the entire black figure accurately down the middle with dazzling symmetry. The thirteenth knife, the big one, stuck like a deadly arrow just where the man's heart should have been.

Jupp took a final puff of the thin, tobacco-filled roll of paper and threw the scant remains behind the stove.

"Let's go," he said, "it's time we were off." He stuck his head out of the window, muttered something about "damned rain," and added: "It's a few minutes to eight, I'm on at eight-thirty."

While he was packing the knives away in the suitcase I stood with my face by the open window. Decaying villas seemed to be whimpering softly in the rain, and from behind a wall of swaying poplars came the screech of the streetcar. But nowhere could I see a clock.

"How d'you know what time it is?"

"Instinct—that's part of my training."

I gaped at him. First he helped me on with my coat and then put on his windbreaker. My shoulder is slightly paralyzed and I can't move my arms beyond a certain radius, just far enough to clean bricks. We put on our caps and went out into the dingy corridor, and I was glad to hear at least some voices in the house, laughter, and a subdued murmuring.

"It's like this," said Jupp as we went down the stairs. "What I've tried to do is trace certain cosmic laws. Like this." He put the suitcase down on a stair and spread his arms, an Icarus[4] poised for flight in the way the ancient Greeks used to show him. His matter-of-fact expression assumed a strangely cool and dreamlike quality, something between obsession and detachment, something magical, that I found quite spine-chilling. "Like this," he said softly, "I simply reach out into the atmosphere, I feel my hands getting longer and longer, reaching out into a dimension governed by different laws, they push through a ceiling, and beyond are strange, spell-binding tensions—I just take hold of them, that's all . . . and then I seize their laws, snatch them away, part-thief, part-lover, and carry them off." He clenched his fists, drawing them close to his body. "Let's go," he said, and his expression was its usual matter-of-fact self. I followed him in a daze. . . .

Outside a chill rain was falling softly and steadily. We turned up our collars and withdrew shivering into ourselves. The mist of twilight was surging through the streets, already tinged with the bluish darkness of night. In several basements among the bombed-out villas a meager light was burning under the towering black weight of a great ruin. The street gradually became a muddy path where to left and right, in the opaque twilight, shacks loomed up in the scrawny gardens like junks afloat in a shallow backwater. We crossed the streetcar tracks, plunged into the maze of narrow streets on the city's outskirts, where among piles of rubble and garbage a few houses still stand intact in the dirt, until we emerged suddenly into a busy street. The tide of the crowds carried us along for a bit, until we turned a corner into a dark side street where a garish illuminated sign saying "The Seven Mills" was reflected in the glistening asphalt.

The foyer of the vaudeville theater was empty. The performance had already begun, and the buzzing of the audience penetrated the shabby red drapes.

With a laugh Jupp pointed to a photograph in a display case where he was shown in cowboy costume between two coyly smiling dancers whose breasts were hung with sparkling tinsel. Beneath was the caption: "The Man with the Knives."

"Come on," said Jupp, and before I grasped what was happening I found myself being dragged through a half-hidden door. We climbed a poorly lit staircase, narrow and winding, the smell of sweat and greasepaint indicating the nearness of the stage. Jupp was ahead— suddenly he halted in a turn of the stairs, put down the suitcase and, gripping me by the shoulders, asked in a hushed voice:

"Are you game?"

I had been expecting this question for so long that when it came its suddenness startled me. I must have looked nonplussed, for after a pause he said: "Well?"

I still hesitated, and suddenly we heard a great roar of laughter that seemed to come pouring out of the narrow passage and engulf us like a tidal wave; it was so overwhelming that I jumped and involuntarily shuddered.

"I'm scared," I whispered.

"So am I. Don't you trust me?"

"Sure I do . . . but . . . let's go," I said hoarsely, pushing past him and adding, with the courage born of despair: "I've nothing to lose."

We emerged onto a narrow corridor with a number of rough plywood cubicles right and left. A few colorful figures were scurrying about, and through an opening in the flimsy wings I could see a clown on the stage, his enormous mouth wide open; once again the roar of the

---

4. *Icarus*, in Greek mythology, the son of Daedalus, who, with a pair of wax wings, flew so close to the sun that the wings melted and he drowned in the Aegean Sea.

crowd's laughter engulfed us, but Jupp pulled me through a door and shut it behind us. I looked round. The cubicle was tiny, practically bare. On the wall was a mirror, Jupp's cowboy costume hung on the single nail, and on a rickety chair lay an old deck of cards. Jupp moved with nervous haste; he took my wet coat from me, flung the cowboy suit onto the chair, hung up my coat, then his windbreaker. Over the top of the partition I could see an electric clock on a fake red Doric column, showing twenty-five after eight.

"Five minutes," muttered Jupp, slipping into his costume.

"Shall we rehearse it?"

Just then someone knocked on the cubicle door and called: "You're on!"

Jupp buttoned up his shirt and stuck a ten-gallon hat on his head. With a forced laugh I cried: "D'you expect a condemned man to rehearse his own hanging?"

Jupp snatched up the suitcase and dragged me through the door. Outside stood a bald-headed man watching the clown going through his final motions on the stage. Jupp whispered something to the man that I didn't catch, the man glanced up with a start, looked at me, looked at Jupp, and shook his head vehemently. And again Jupp whispered something to him.

I couldn't have cared less. Let them impale me alive. I had a crippled shoulder, I had just finished a thin cigarette, tomorrow I would get three-quarters of a loaf for seventy-five bricks. But tomorrow. . . . The applause almost blew down the wings. The clown, his face tired and contorted, staggered toward us through the opening in the wings, stood there for a few seconds looking morose, and then went back onto the stage, where he smiled graciously and bowed. The orchestra played a fanfare. Jupp was still whispering to the bald-headed man. Three times the clown came back into the wings and three times he went out onto the stage and bowed, smiling.

Then the orchestra struck up a march and, suitcase in hand, Jupp strode smartly out onto the stage. His appearance was greeted with subdued clapping. Weary-eyed I watched Jupp fasten the playing cards onto nails that were already in place and then impale each card with a knife, one by one, precisely in the center. The applause became more animated, but not enthusiastic. Then, to a muffled roll of drums, he performed his trick with the bread knife and the block of wood, and underneath all my indifference I was aware that the act really was a bit thin. Across from me, on the other side of the stage, a few scantily dressed girls stood watching. . . . And suddenly the bald-headed man seized me by the shoulder, dragged me onto the stage, greeted Jupp with a grandiose sweep of the arm and, in the spurious voice of a policeman, said: "Good evening, Mr. Borgalevsky."

"Good evening, Mr. Erdmenger," replied Jupp, likewise in ceremonious tones.

"I've brought you a horse-thief, a proper scoundrel, Mr. Borgalevsky, for you to tickle a bit with your shiny knives before we hang him . . . a real scoundrel. . . ." I found his voice totally ridiculous, pathetically artificial, like paper flowers or the cheapest kind of greasepaint. I glanced at the audience, and from that moment on, faced by that glimmering, slavering, hydra-headed[5] monster crouching there in the dark ready to spring, I simply switched off.

I didn't give a damn, I was dazzled by the glare of the spotlight, and in my threadbare suit and shabby shoes I probably made a pretty convincing horse-thief.

"Oh leave him here with me, Mr. Erdmenger, I know how to deal with him."

"Splendid, let him have it, and don't spare the knives."

---

5. *hydra-headed.* In Greek mythology, the Hydra was a many-headed monster slain by Hercules.

Jupp took hold of me by the collar while the grinning Erdmenger ambled wide-legged off the stage. Someone threw a rope onto the stage, and Jupp proceeded to tie me by the feet to a cardboard column that had a fake door, painted blue, propped up behind it. I was aware of something like an ecstasy of insensibility. To my right I heard the eerie stirring of the tense audience, and I realized Jupp had been right in speaking of its bloodlust. Its thirst quivered on the sickly, stale air, and the orchestra, with its facile drum-roll, its muffled lasciviousness, heightened the effect of grisly tragicomedy in which real blood would flow, stage-blood that had been paid for. . . . I stared straight ahead, letting my body sag, the rope being so firmly tied that it held me upright. The drum-roll became softer and softer as Jupp calmly pulled his knives out of the playing cards and slipped them back into their pockets, from time to time casting melodramatic glances my way as if to size me up. Then, having packed away all his knives, he turned to the audience and in the same odiously stagy voice announced: "Ladies and gentlemen, I am now about to outline this young man with knives, but I wish to demonstrate to you that I do not throw blunt knives. . . ." He produced a piece of string, and with perfect sang-froid removed one knife after another from its pocket, touched the string with each, cutting it into twelve pieces, and then replaced the knives one by one in their pockets.

While all this was going on I looked far beyond him, far beyond the wings, far beyond the half-naked girls, into another life, it seemed. . . .

The tension in the audience was electrifying. Jupp came over to me, pretended to adjust the rope, and said softly into my ear: "Don't move a muscle, and trust me. . . ."

This added delay nearly broke the tension, it was threatening to peter out,

but he suddenly stretched out his arms, letting his hands flutter like hovering birds, and his face assumed that look of magical concentration that I had marveled at on the stairs. He appeared to be casting a spell over the audience too with this sorcerer's pose. I seemed to hear a strange, unearthly groan and realized that this was a warning signal for me.

Withdrawing my gaze from limitless horizons, I looked at Jupp, now standing opposite me so that our eyes were on a level; he raised his hand, moving it slowly toward a pocket, and again I realized that this was a signal for me. I stood completely still and closed my eyes. . . .

It was a glorious feeling, lasting maybe two seconds, I'm not sure. Listening to the swish of the knives and the short sharp hiss of air as they plunged into the fake blue door, I felt as if I were walking along a very narrow plank over a bottomless abyss. I walked with perfect confidence, yet felt all the thrill of danger. . . . I was afraid, yet absolutely certain that I would not fall; I was not counting, yet I opened my eyes at the very moment when the last knife pierced the door beside my right hand. . . .

A storm of applause jerked me bolt upright. I opened my eyes properly to find myself looking into Jupp's white face: he had rushed over to me and was untying the rope with trembling hands. Then he pulled me into the center of the stage, right up to the very edge. He bowed, and I bowed; as the applause swelled he pointed to me and I to him; then he smiled at me, I smiled at him, and we both bowed smiling to the audience.

Back in the cubicle not a word was said. Jupp threw the perforated playing cards onto the chair, took my coat off the nail and helped me on with it. Then he hung his cowboy costume back on the nail, pulled on his windbreaker, and we put on our caps. As I opened the door the little bald-headed man rushed up to us shouting: "I'm raising you to forty marks!" He handed Jupp some cash. I realized then that Jupp was my boss, and I smiled; he looked at me too and smiled.

Jupp took my arm, and side by side we walked down the narrow, poorly lit stairs that smelled of stale greasepaint. When we reached the foyer Jupp said with a laugh: "Now let's go and buy some cigarettes and bread. . . ."

But it was not till an hour later that I realized I now had a proper profession, a profession where all I needed to do was stand still and dream a little. For twelve or twenty seconds. I was the man who has knives thrown at him. . . .

Development

INTERPRETATION

1. (a) How does Jupp see himself: as a superman, a mystic, a possessor of occult powers, a magician, or something else? (b) How do you see him?

2. What circumstances in the lives of Jupp and the narrator may have influenced their actions?

3. (a) What notable differences are there between Jupp's character and the narrator's? (b) Do they have any traits in common? (c) Does the narrator appear to record his impressions honestly, or does he glamorize and exaggerate in his descriptions? Cite passages to support your answer.

4. (a) Jupp tells the narrator: ". . . a cemetery's the very place to smile . . . Because they aren't dead. They're none of them dead, see?" (page 449, column 1, paragraphs 10-12). What does he mean? (b) Compare this to his comment on his audience: "They're burned out inside" (page 449, column 1, paragraph 14). What do these comments reveal about Jupp's opinion of his fellow creatures? (c) Do you think Jupp's claim that his act helps his audience to overcome fear is an honest belief or a mere rationalization?

5. (a) Why do you think Jupp's mother chose to save the brown enamel pot and the cutlery? (b) In the light of Jupp's present life, comment on the irony that lies in his statement: "Funny, isn't it? But of course we know that when people are in a panic they try to save the strangest things. Never the essential ones."

6. Early in the story, the narrator tells Jupp of his inability to smile, yet we find him smiling repeatedly at the conclusion of the act. What significant change has taken place in his attitude?

TECHNIQUE

1. (a) Describe the characters' feelings toward the audience. (b) Assuming the author is using the audience to symbolize society in general, what is he implying about the state of society?

2. (a) Has Böll succeeded in making his two young characters seem lifelike? (b) Do you find the characters' attitudes consistent with their conditions? (c) What further information, if any, do you think is required from the author on the characters' background? (d) In your opinion, does the lack of information about the characters' background weaken the author's theme?

EXTENSIONS

1. (a) The narrator says: "I walked with perfect confidence, yet felt all the thrill of danger" (page 453, column 2, paragraph 2). What is so attractive about danger that makes people deliberately seek it? (b) When is exposing oneself to danger justifiable?

2. The two protagonists' lives have been disrupted by war. Martin Luther once said: "War is the greatest plague that can afflict humanity; it destroys religion, it destroys states, it destroys families. Any scourge is preferable." Do you agree or disagree with the above quotation?

The Tiger
KUME MASAO[1] / Japan
(1891 – 1952)
translated from the Japanese by Robert H. Brower

As was his custom, Fukai Yasuke,[2] the Shimpa[3] actor, did not awaken until it was nearly noon. With a rather theatrical blink of his sleep-laden eyes, he looked out at the blue sky of a cloudless autumn day, and surrendered himself to a huge, deliberate stretch. But, with a sudden realization that this performance was somewhat overdone, even for him, he darted a furtive glance about the room and smiled sheepishly at the thought of how much a part of him the grandiose gestures of the stage had become. He was, even for an actor, a born exaggerator: the very essence of his acting style lay in his ability to create farcical effects through the overuse of the bombastic and the grandiloquent. He was the best known comic actor of the Shimpa.

Fukai had started life as the dashing young man of a fish market down by the river; but when he heard that Kawakami,[4] the founder of the Shimpa Theatre, was rounding up a collection of bit-players, Fukai had gone at once to apply for a job, ignoring the caustic comments of his friends. When it at last came Fukai's turn to undergo his stage test, Kawakami had taken one hard look at the young fishmonger with his close-cropped head, and said in tones of undisguised contempt, "You'll never make an actor, I can see."

Fukai had poured forth in his defense every argument he could muster, but Kawakami only smiled and paid him no

"The Tiger" by Kume Masao, translated by Robert H. Brower from MODERN JAPANESE LITERATURE, ed. by Donald Keene. Reprinted by permission of the translator.

1. *Kume Masao* (kü me′ ma sa ô′). In Japanese, Kume, the author's surname, precedes Masao. 2. *Fukai Yasuke* (fü ki′ ya′ sü ke). Fukai is a surname; Yasuke is a first name. 3. *Shimpa,* the "New School" of Japanese drama which was devised in 1890, and was an extension of Kabuki, the traditional popular drama. 4. *Kawakami* (ka wa ka′ mē).

further attention. Even this experience did not chasten Fukai. The next time he shaved every last hair from his head, and went in disguise to take another test. It so happened that one theatre needed a large number of players, and Fukai, by mingling in with the other applicants evaded Kawakami's watchful eye long enough to get himself hired. Once he entered the company, however, Kawakami noticed him immediately.

"So! You've finally wormed your way in!" Kawakami said in considerable surprise.

"That's right. I'm a thickheaded fellow," Fukai replied, knocking on his shaven pate.

Kawakami laughed. "It can't be helped, I suppose. Now that you're in, let's see you buckle down and work hard." It had occurred to him that such a man might possibly have his uses, and there was no reason not to let him into the company gracefully.

Such was Fukai's initiation into the theatre. Since then he had become an outstanding player of comic parts, and having weathered the various vicissitudes of Shimpa, he had eventually succeeded in making himself indispensable. His salary was quite a handsome one; he would every now and then, in true actor's fashion, take up with some woman; there was no doubt but that he had made quite a success of himself.

That did not mean, however, that he was satisfied with his present lot. He was already over thirty-five. Had he followed one of the more usual vocations, at this time of life he would have been at the height of his powers and his capacity to work, but as things stood with him now, his sole function was to play the clown on the stage. He had never had a single straight part. He served merely to give the audience a good laugh, or to liven them to the proper pitch for some other actor. It was obvious even to Fukai that this was no better than being the comic assistant in some juggler's act.

Obvious, but there was nothing he could do about it. At the prime of life, he was still continuing in the same old way.

Fukai had a son nearly eight years old. Last year the boy had made his debut on the stage, and like his father—or rather, with much more confidence than his father—could look forward to a future as a Shimpa actor. Fukai had no intention of letting his son play comic parts. No, he was determined to see to it that, unlike himself, the boy was given the chance to play serious roles.

At the moment Fukai still lay indolently in bed, thinking about the part he had been assigned the day before. Yesterday at the Kabuki Theatre there had been a reading of the script of the forthcoming production *The Foster Child,* and he had been assigned the part of "the tiger." This was not the name of a character: it was the beast itself, and *that* was his whole part.

Play a tiger! He was disgusted at the thought, but it had struck him as so amusing that he could not bring himself to complain. He had played a cat once. He had also pranced around in front of the curtain in the role of a dog. People had dubbed him "the animal actor." What, then, was so strange in his being cast as a tiger? On the contrary, it would have been really hard to understand if the part had *not* devolved upon him.

Still it saddened him a little to think that there was nothing unusual about his playing a tiger. Long years of experience had accustomed him to this disappointment: he knew it was the way he earned his living, and he was, after all, a comedian. And yet it seemed as if the "humanity" in him were being affronted. He even felt a moment of anger.

At the reading of the script the day before, all eyes had automatically turned his way when the author paused and said, with a glance that took in the whole company, "I thought I'd change the old plot here a bit, and bring out Tamae's extravagance by having him keep a tiger on his front porch. The tiger's a savage brute from Malaya, and at the end of the scene he goes wild and turns on Tamae. How does that strike you?"

"Sounds all right to me," the head of the company had answered. "That gives us a chance to fit in a part for Fukai here. I take it he won't turn it down?"

Once more everyone had looked his way, and this time Fukai could sense in their expressions a kind of mocking contempt. Nevertheless, when Kawahara, the leading actor of female roles, remarked, "It's a sure hit! The act will be devoured by Fukai's tiger!", he too had joined in the laughter. He had even felt a glow of pride.

"Well, anyhow," he thought, still lying in bed, "I've got to play the part of the tiger, and play it well. It's nothing to be ashamed of. . . . Just so long as you do a part well, whether it's a beast or a bird, you're a good actor. Besides, when all's said and done, I'm the only actor in the whole of Japan that can play a tiger. I'll do a tiger for them that'll make the audience stand up and shout. And I'll give the other actors a good kicking around. If I'm to go on making my living, that's the only thing I *can* do."

He jumped out of bed, called to his wife downstairs, and got dressed. This accomplished, he went down with a cheerful countenance. His late morning meal was waiting for him on a tray covered with a yellow cloth. After a cursory brushing of his teeth, he applied himself eagerly to the food.

His son Wataru[5] was lying on the veranda, idly leafing through the pages of an old issue of *Theatre Arts Illustrated,* no doubt an issue—one of the very rare ones—with a tiny photograph of Fukai on the first page, printed out of pity for him. He felt—it was nothing new—an embarrassment before his son. What kind of image of him as an actor was reflected in his son's eyes? And to what extent did this conflict with the boy's impression of him as a father?—These

were some of the vague thoughts that ran through his head as he mechanically ate his meal.

Wataru called to him, "Father! Haven't you a rehearsal today?"

"No—at least I don't have to go to the theatre."

As he said this, his chagrin at being cast as a tiger, without a single word of dialogue to memorize, returned to him in full force. This time there was no necessity even for working out his cues with the other actors. All he had to do was decide in his own mind the most tiger-like manner in which to jump around the stage.

But come to think of it, just how *did* a tiger spring upon its victim? He had seen paintings of tigers, of course, and knew how tigers were represented in old-fashioned plays. But he had only the haziest notion what real tigers were like. When it actually came to playing the part of one, even Fukai, "animal actor" that he was, was ignorant of their special qualities. One thing was sure—they belonged to the cat family. He probably could not go too far wrong if he thought of them as huge, powerful cats. Still, if he failed to do any better than behave like a cat in one of those cat fights of the old plays, some malicious critic might say that Fukai had literally come on a tiger and exited a cat, which would be very irritating indeed.

"Do you have to go see anybody about anything?" Wataru, unaware of his father's troubled thoughts, persisted with his interrogation, his voice taking on that wheedling tone that children affect when they want to get something out of their parents.

"Let's see. No, I suppose not. But what are you asking me for, anyway?"

"I thought if you hadn't anything to do, maybe you'd take me to Ueno[6] today. It's such a nice day. Please take me."

"Why do you want to go to Ueno?

5. *Wataru* (wa ta′ rü). 6. *Ueno* (ü′ e′ nō), a park in Tokyo with zoological gardens.

There's nothing to interest you. A kid your age wouldn't get anything out of the art museum. . . ."

"But I want to go to the zoo! I haven't been there once since last year!"

"The zoo?" Fukai repeated the word mechanically. Various ideas fluttered through his mind. Ought he to regard his child's words as a kind of divine revelation and be duly thankful? Or should he take them as an irony of fate, to which the proper response was a bitter smile? It was hard to know how to react. But even assuming that the gods were manifesting their contempt for him through the child, his long professional experience told him that his first concern should be to make good use of this opportunity for finding out how a tiger really behaves.

"They've got a hippopotamus at the zoo now, Father! Come on, take me, please."

He turned to his wife and said, as if in self-explanation, "Shall Wataru and I go to see the hippopotamus and the tiger?"

"Why don't you, if you haven't anything else to attend to? You never can tell—it might prove more of a distraction than going somewhere else," agreed his wife, showing by the special emphasis she placed on the words "somewhere else" that her mind was on quite a different subject than the tiger.

He was by no means impervious to the irony of her remark, but knew how to parry the thrust by taking it lightly. His laugh was intentionally loud.

"Let's get started, Father, shall we?"

"All right! All right!"

Unashamedly he had leapt at this Heaven-sent opportunity, but somewhere deep inside him there still lurked an uneasiness which made him feel embarrassed before the child. However, he told himself, it was, after all, his job; cheered by this thought, he light-heartedly abandoned all compunctions. He had become once more the true son of Tokyo, who consoles himself by laughing at his own expense.

Less than half an hour later, he and Wataru boarded a streetcar headed for Ueno. Like most actors, he hoped when on a streetcar or in some other public place, to enjoy by turns the pleasure of elaborate efforts to remain unrecognized, and the agreeable sensation of being noticed and pointed out, despite his precautions. Decked out in a kimono of a pattern garish enough to attract anyone's attention, and with Wataru dressed in one of those kimonos with extra-long sleeves that are the mark of a child actor, Fukai sat down in a corner of the car, his elbows close to his sides, as if to appear as inconspicuous as possible. True, he did not especially wish to have any of his acquaintances catch sight of him on the way to the zoo; still, it would be amusing to meet someone unexpectedly and tell him with a straight face about his strange errand, making the whole business into a good joke.

At Suda-chō a man got on who filled the bill to perfection: the drama critic from the J newspaper, with whom Fukai had a casual acquaintance. Fukai recognized him instantly from under the felt hat pulled low over his brow, and sat with bated breath, waiting for it to dawn on the other man who he was. The critic presently discovered him and came over. With a conspiratorial, friendly air, he tapped Fukai silently on the shoulder.

Fukai looked up eagerly. "Is that you, sir? What an unexpected place to run into you!"

"I seem to be sharing the same car with a strange fellow! That's what makes riding these spark-wagons such an adventure."

"Where are you heading for? Are you on the way to her house or on your way back?"

"Which answer should I choose, I wonder? You might say I was on my way there, and then again you might say I was on my way back."

"That's because you've reached the

point where you don't remember any-more where your real home is, I suppose."

"I'm not so much of a man about town as all that! But what about you? Where are you off to?"

"Me? Oh, a really fashionable place! —Look for yourself! I'm with my little millstone." He pointed with his chin at the child, whom the critic had not noticed up to this point.

"Is that you, Wataru? So you're keeping your father company today, are you? Or is your father keeping *you* company?"

"That's it, that's what makes me so stylish today—I'm being dragged off to Ueno by the kid!"

"What? To the exhibition at the art museum? Sounds pretty impressive!"

"Oh no, we wouldn't go to such an unrefined place. It's the zoo for us," he said, adding hastily, "to see the hippopotamus."

"The zoo?" The drama critic raised his eyebrows. Then his face lighted into a broad smile, and he slapped his knee. "I get it! But I'll bet it's not the hippopotamus you're going to see! You're off to see the tiger. I've heard all about the plot of the new play. They say the big boss himself thought up that idea. He's a smart man."

"Is that right? It's news to me. Here I've been furious at the leading man all along, thinking it was one of his tricks. I see I had better take the part more seriously. I've got to keep on the good side of the boss, you know."

"Now you've confessed it! But if you want to see a tiger, you needn't go to all the trouble of making a trip to the zoo."

"You mean a couple of quarts will make anybody a tiger?"[7]

"How about it? What do you say we have a look at one of those tigers?"

"No, can't do it. After all, I can't just ditch this fellow here," said Fukai, glancing once more at the child.

"You're getting old, aren't you?" the critic said casually, looking fixedly at Wataru.

At these words, like cold water dashed in his face, Fukai became serious again. He felt moreover profoundly ashamed that he had carried on this tiresome prattle without the least regard for his son's feelings. But his whole training had been much too frivolous for him to let the conversation drop, even at this juncture.

"I may be getting along in years, but they still treat me like a child as far as my parts are concerned. A tiger is more than even I can put up with."

"The other parts are just as bad. Who knows? The tiger may in the long run bring you more credit. It could easily turn out to be the hit of the show."

"That's what I keep telling myself, and that's why I have every intention of doing my best."

"Of course you will! We're all looking forward to your tiger."

"You overwhelm me!" Fukai smiled ironically, but secretly derived considerable solace from the critic's words.

The streetcar by this time had arrived at Ueno, and prodded impatiently by his son, Fukai hurriedly got off, taking an unceremonious leave of the critic.

The trees in Ueno Park had turned their bright autumn colors, and streams of people were moving along the broad gravel walks, with here and there a parasol floating in their midst. For Fukai, who was used to being indoors all the time, to be out under the blue sky at once raised his spirits. They made straight for the zoo.

Once inside the wicket, Wataru started to skip off happily. Fukai restrained him. "I'll be looking at the tiger, and after you've seen everything, come back and meet me there."

Wataru was in too much of a hurry to ask why his father was so interested in the tiger. Rejoicing in this release from parental authority, he bounded off gaily, and was soon lost in the crowd of children before the monkeys' cage.

---

7. *tiger,* Japanese slang for a rowdy drunkard.

Fukai for his part was also glad to be free of the child. Relying on his vague memories of the layout of the zoo from a previous visit years ago, he slowly walked in search of the cages where they kept the dangerous animals. He found the tiger almost immediately.

He had a queer feeling as he stopped in front of the cage. Inside the steel bars crouched the tiger that he sought, its forelegs stretched out indolently. When Fukai first noticed its dirty coat and lackluster eyes, glimmering like two leaden suns, he felt a certain disappointment—it was too unlike the fierce power of the beast he had hitherto imagined. But as he intently observed the tiger, a feeling of sympathy gradually came over him. He felt pity for the tiger, but that was not all—a strange affection welled up. Shut up in a dank cage on this brilliant autumn day, robbed of all its savage powers, forced to crouch there dully, not so much as twitching under the curious stares of people: Fukai felt the wild beast's circumstances much resembled his own. But just wherein the resemblance lay was not clear, even to himself.

Deeply moved by these emotions, which remained nevertheless vague and unformulated, he stood in rapt contemplation before the cage, forgetting that he was to play the part of this tiger, forgetting to note the tiger's posture or the position of the legs.

The tiger and Fukai were both absolutely motionless. For a long time the man and the beast stared at each other. In the end, Fukai felt as if he were experiencing the same feelings as the tiger, as if he were thinking the tiger's thoughts.

Suddenly the tiger contorted its face strangely. At the same instant, it opened its jaws ringed with bright silver whiskers, and gave vent to an enormous yawn. The inside of its gaping mouth was a brilliant scarlet, rather like a peony, or rather, a rose in full bloom. This action took less than a minute, after which the tiger lapsed back into its silent apathy.

Startled out of his trance, Fukai summoned back to mind the nearly forgotten purpose on which he had come. The tiger, after demonstrating only that single yawn, remained immovable as a tree in some primeval forest, but Fukai was content. It seemed to him that, having penetrated this far into the tiger's feelings, he would be able to improvise the pouncing and roaring and all the rest.

"Yes, I'll really do the tiger! I can understand a tiger's feelings a whole lot better than those of a philandering man about town," he cried to himself.

Presently his son rejoined him, and taking the boy's hand, Fukai walked out the gate of the zoo, with a lighter step than when he had come.

The following day he happened to glance at the gossip column called "A Night at the Theatre" in the J newspaper. There, in unadorned terms, appeared the following paragraph:

Fukai Yasuke, well known as a popular actor of animal roles, has recently severed the last of his few tenuous connections with the human species. He devours his lunch in seclusion, emitting weird meows and grunts. He is still intent enough on getting his salary to stand up on his hind legs and beg for it, but now that he finally seems to have won a part in the forthcoming production at the Kabuki Theatre, he is so pleased with his role as a tiger that he spends his days going back and forth to the zoo to study.

This was the drama critic he had met the day before, giving free rein to his pen. A feeling of resentment rose up in Fukai when he read the article. However, that quickly vanished, and an embarrassed smile took its place, to be followed in turn by an expression of contentment. "After all, that's what my popularity depends on."

Viewed in that light, it seemed more important than ever that he should make a success with the role of the tiger. Now, whether smoking a cigarette or eating his lunch or lying in bed, his thoughts were completely absorbed with the actions of tigers.

Opening day arrived at last. The play developed through its various scenes, and soon it was time for the third act, in which he was to appear as the tiger. There was no trace of a smile on his features as he put on the tiger costume. He stretched out on the balcony of Tamae's villa, just as the wooden clappers announced the beginning of the act.

The curtains parted. No one else was on stage. The tiger raised itself slightly, as if it had finally awakened from its long midday slumber, and uttered a few low growls. At that moment five or six voices called out "Fukai! Fukai!" from up in the top gallery. Fukai felt considerable gratification.

The principal actor and Kawahara, the female impersonator, come on stage. But the shouts of recognition from the gallery when they made their entrances were certainly no more enthusiastic than those that had greeted him. "Look at that!" he thought, feeling more and more pleased with himself.

The play advanced. As he listened to the dialogue, he was waiting only for the instant when he would spring into action. The play reached its climax. The moment for him to act was here at last.

He stretched himself once, with a movement that might have been that of a cat just as well as a tiger. He growled lazily once or twice. Then, as Tamae began to tease him, he made a sudden savage lunge straight at Tamae's chest. The chain by which he was fastened sprang taut with a snap as he bounded fiercely about.

The audience was in an uproar. "Fukai! Fukai!" voices shouted all over the theatre. Fukai was almost beside himself as he pounced and leapt. He had no complaints now. Nor any resentment. His depression and shame had vanished. All that remained in his ecstatic heart was an indescribable joy.

The curtains closed just as he was executing the most daring and savage leap of all. The applause of the audience echoed through the theatre. He was utterly content. Still dressed in his costume, he withdrew triumphantly. In the dark shadows of the wings someone unexpectedly caught his hand. He turned his head, somewhat startled, and looked through the peepholes of his mask. There stood his son, Wataru. "Father!" he said.

With sickening suddenness, Fukai plunged from the heights of pride to the depths of shame. He blushed as he stood before his son. But when he looked down once more into the boy's eyes, there was no hint of reproach in them for the role his father had played. Their expression was tearful, as if he could have wept in sympathy with his father.

"Wataru!" exclaimed Fukai, clasping the boy tightly in his arms. The tears fell in big drops and trickled along the stripes in the tiger costume. . . .

Thus the tiger and the human child stood for a while, weeping together in the shadows of the dark scenery.

THE END

Development

INTERPRETATION

INTERPRETATION

1. *(a)* As Fukai awakens at the beginning of the story, what element in his personality becomes apparent? *(b)* What indication is the reader given of Fukai's self-awareness?

2. In spite of his success, why isn't Fukai fully satisfied with his career?

3. *(a)* Why does Fukai find the role of a tiger so unappealing? *(b)* When he reflects, "Just so long as you do a part well, whether it's a beast or a bird, you're a good actor" (page 457, column 1, paragraph 3), does he reveal himself as a rationalizer, a genuine actor, or an incurable optimist? Discuss.

4. *(a)* Fukai is troubled by his relationship with his son. Is he concerned with how his son views him as a father, an actor, or both? Explain. *(b)* Point out the contrast between the behavior of Fukai the actor and the feelings of Fukai the father.

5. *(a)* Describe Fukai's mood when he boards the streetcar with Wataru. *(b)* What is the tone of Fukai's conversation with the critic? *(c)* Why does he disregard his son's feelings with such remarks as "my little millstone" and "I can't just ditch this fellow here"?

6. *(a)* Fukai feels that the tiger's circumstances much resemble his own. In your opinion, does any similarity exist? *(b)* What is one basic difference between Fukai's lot and the tiger's? *(c)* Why is Fukai, who came to study the tiger's movements, not disappointed by its immobility?

7. *(a)* What does Fukai learn about his son's feelings when he looks into his eyes? *(b)* What genuine emotion do father and son feel for each other as they stand weeping together?

8. Which of the following statements best defines the author's theme? *(a)* Actors continue acting off the stage to the point where they are unable to distinguish between reality and illusion. *(b)* Human beings and wild animals share very much the same emotions. *(c)* A father needs neither celebrity nor success to earn his son's love. *(d)* Human nature is ambivalent: a man often takes pride in the skillful performance of a task while he is at the same time ashamed of its absurdity.

TECHNIQUE

1. Kume Masao has created in Fukai a composite character who is outwardly brazen and impudent yet inwardly self-conscious and sensitive. In what way has the author created an inverse parallelism between Fukai and the tiger at the zoo? Explain.

2. Has the author written a social, historical, lyrical, psychological, or political story? Explain your answer.

3. There is total absence of misfortune, violence, ugliness, meanness, or any other form of evil in this story. In your opinion, does this make the story too saccharine to be convincing? Discuss.

EXTENSIONS

1. An actor sometimes identifies himself so thoroughly with a part he plays that he becomes indistinguishable from it. Does Fukai become dehumanized by his role? Explain.

2. *(a)* In order for a father-son relationship to succeed, what do you think a son should expect from his father? *(b)* What may a father hope for from a son? *(c)* What, in your opinion, are the main reasons for failure in this delicate area of human relations? Discuss.

The Infant Prodigy

THOMAS MANN / Germany

(1875 – 1955)

translated from the German by H. T. Lowe-Porter

The infant prodigy entered. The hall became quiet.

It became quiet and then the audience began to clap, because somewhere at the side a leader of mobs, a born organizer, clapped first. The audience had heard nothing yet, but they applauded; for a mighty publicity organization had heralded the prodigy and people were already hypnotized, whether they knew it or not.

The prodigy came from behind a splendid screen embroidered with Empire garlands and great conventionalized flowers, and climbed nimbly up the steps to the platform, diving into the applause as into a bath; a little chilly and shivering, but yet as though into a friendly element. He advanced to the edge of the platform and smiled as though he were about to be photographed; he made a shy, charming gesture of greeting, like a little girl.

He was dressed entirely in white silk, which the audience found enchanting. The little white jacket was fancifully cut, with a sash underneath it, and even his shoes were made of white silk. But against the white socks his bare little legs stood out quite brown; for he was a Greek boy.

He was called Bibi Saccellaphylaccas. And such indeed was his name. No one knew what Bibi was the pet name for, nobody but the impresario, and he regarded it as a trade secret. Bibi had smooth black hair reaching to his shoulders; it was parted on the side and fastened back from the narrow domed forehead by a little silk bow. His was the most harmless childish countenance in the world, with an unfinished nose and guileless mouth. The area beneath his pitch-black mouselike eyes was already a little tired and visibly lined. He looked as though he were nine years old but was really eight and given out for seven. It was hard to tell whether to believe this or not. Probably everybody knew better and still believed it, as happens about so many things. The average man thinks that a little falseness goes with beauty. Where should we get any excitement out of our daily life if we were not willing to pretend a bit? And the average man is quite right, in his average brains!

The prodigy kept on bowing until the applause died down, then he went up to the grand piano, and the audience cast a last look at its programmes. First came a *Marche solennelle,* then a *Rêverie,* and then *Le Hibou et les moineaux*[1]—all by Bibi Saccellaphylaccas. The whole programme was by him, they were all his compositions. He could not score them, of course, but he had them all in his extraordinary little head and they possessed

1. *Le Hibou et les moineaux,* "The Owl and the Sparrows." [*French*]

real artistic significance, or so it said, seriously and objectively, in the programme. The programme sounded as though the impresario had wrested these concessions from his critical nature after a hard struggle.

The prodigy sat down upon the revolving stool and felt with his feet for the pedals, which were raised by means of a clever device so that Bibi could reach them. It was Bibi's own piano, he took it everywhere with him. It rested upon wooden trestles and its polish was somewhat marred by the constant transportation—but all that only made things more interesting.

Bibi put his silk-shod feet on the pedals; then he made an artful little face, looked straight ahead of him, and lifted his right hand. It was a brown, childish little hand; but the wrist was strong and unlike a child's, with well-developed bones.

Bibi made his face for the audience because he was aware that he had to entertain them a little. But he had his own private enjoyment in the thing too, an enjoyment which he could never convey to anybody. It was that prickling delight, that secret shudder of bliss, which ran through him every time he sat at an open piano—it would always be with him. And here was the keyboard again, these seven black and white octaves, among which he had so often lost himself in abysmal and thrilling adventures—and yet it always looked as clean and untouched as a newly washed blackboard. This was the realm of music that lay before him. It lay spread out like an inviting ocean, where he might plunge in and blissfully swim, where he might let himself be borne and carried away, where he might go under in night and storm, yet keep the mastery: control, ordain—he held his right hand poised in the air.

A breathless stillness reigned in the room—the tense moment before the first note came. . . . How would it begin? It began so. And Bibi, with his index finger,

fetched the first note out of the piano, a quite unexpectedly powerful first note in the middle register, like a trumpet blast. Others followed, an introduction developed—the audience relaxed.

The concert was held in the palatial hall of a fashionable first-class hotel. The walls were covered with mirrors framed in gilded arabesques, between frescoes of the rosy and fleshly school. Ornamental columns supported a ceiling that displayed a whole universe of electric bulbs, in clusters darting a brilliance far brighter than day and filling the whole space with thin, vibrating golden light. Not a seat was unoccupied, people were standing in the side aisles and at the back. The front seats cost twelve marks[2]; for the impresario believed that anything worth having was worth paying for. And they were occupied by the best society, for it was in the upper classes, of course, that the greatest enthusiasm was felt. There were even some children, with their legs hanging down demurely from their chairs and their shining eyes staring at their gifted little white-clad contemporary.

Down in front on the left side sat the prodigy's mother, an extremely obese woman with a powdered double chin and a feather on her head. Beside her was the impresario, a man of oriental appearance with large gold buttons on his conspicuous cuffs. The princess was in the middle of the front row—a wrinkled, shrivelled little old princess but still a patron of the arts, especially everything full of sensibility. She sat in a deep, velvet-upholstered arm chair, and a Persian carpet was spread before her feet. She held her hands folded over her grey striped-silk breast, put her head on one side, and presented a picture of elegant composure as she sat looking up at the performing prodigy. Next to her sat her lady-in-waiting, in a green striped-silk

2. *twelve marks.* A mark is a German monetary unit which was worth about twenty-five cents when this story was written.

gown. Being only a lady-in-waiting she had to sit up very straight in her chair.

Bibi ended in a grand climax. With what power this wee manikin belaboured the keyboard! The audience could scarcely trust its ears. The march theme, an infectious, swinging tune, broke out once more, fully harmonized, bold and showy; with every note Bibi flung himself back from the waist as though he were marching in a triumphal procession. He ended *fortissimo*,[3] bent over, slipped sideways off the stool, and stood with a smile awaiting the applause.

And the applause burst forth, unanimously, enthusiastically; the child made his demure little maidenly curtsy and people in the front seats thought: "Look what slim little hips he has! Clap, clap! Hurrah, bravo, little chap, Saccophylax or whatever your name is! Wait, let me take off my gloves—what a little devil of a chap he is!"

Bibi had to come out three times from behind the screen before they would stop. Some latecomers entered the hall and moved about looking for seats. Then the concert continued. Bibi's *Rêverie* murmured its numbers, consisting almost entirely of *arpeggios*,[4] above which a bar of melody rose now and then, weak-winged. Then came *Le Hibou et les moineaux*. This piece was brilliantly successful, it made a strong impression; it was an effective childhood fantasy, remarkably well envisaged. The bass represented the owl, sitting morosely rolling his filmy eyes; while in the treble the impudent, half-frightened sparrows chirped. Bibi received an ovation when he finished, he was called out four times. A hotel page with shiny buttons carried up three great laurel wreaths onto the stage and proffered them from one side while Bibi nodded and expressed his thanks. Even the princess shared in the applause, daintily and noiselessly pressing her palms together.

Ah, the knowing little creature understood how to make people clap! He stopped behind the screen, they had to wait for him; lingered a little on the steps of the platform, admired the long streamers on the wreaths—although actually such things bored him stiff by now. He bowed with the utmost charm, he gave the audience plenty of time to rave itself out, because applause is valuable and must not be cut short. "*Le Hibou* is my drawing card," he thought—this expression he had learned from the impresario. "Now I will play the fantasy, it is a lot better than *Le Hibou*, of course, especially the C-sharp passage. But you idiots dote on the *Hibou*, though it is the first and the silliest thing I wrote." He continued to bow and smile.

Next came a *Méditation* and then an *Étude*—the programme was quite comprehensive. The *Méditation* was very like the *Rêverie*—which was nothing against it—and the *Étude* displayed all of Bibi's virtuosity, which naturally fell a little short of his inventiveness. And then the *Fantaisie*. This was his favourite; he varied it a little each time, giving himself free rein and sometimes surprising even himself, on good evenings, by his own inventiveness.

He sat and played, so little, so white and shining, against the great black grand piano, elect and alone, above that confused sea of faces, above the heavy, insensitive mass soul, upon which he was labouring to work with his individual, differentiated soul. His lock of soft black hair with the white silk bow had fallen over his forehead, his trained and bony little wrists pounded away, the muscles stood out visibly on his brown childish cheeks.

Sitting there he sometimes had moments of oblivion and solitude, when the gaze of his strange little mouselike eyes with the big rings beneath them would lose itself and stare through the painted stage into space that was peopled with

---

3. *fortissimo*, very loud (a musical direction).
4. *arpeggio*, in music, the sounding of the notes of a chord in rapid succession instead of together.

strange vague life. Then out of the corner of his eye he would give a quick look back into the hall and be once more with his audience.

"Joy and pain, the heights and the depths—that is my *Fantaisie*," he thought lovingly. "Listen, here is the C-sharp passage." He lingered over the approach, wondering if they would notice anything. But no, of course not, how should they? And he cast his eyes up prettily at the ceiling so that at least they might have something to look at.

All these people sat there in their regular rows, looking at the prodigy and thinking all sorts of things in their regular brains. An old gentleman with a white beard, a seal ring on his finger and a bulbous swelling on his bald spot, a growth if you like, was thinking to himself: "Really, one ought to be ashamed." He had never got any further than "Ah, thou dearest Augustin" on the piano, and here he sat now, a grey old man, looking on while this little hop-o'-my-thumb performed miracles. Yes, yes, it is a gift of God, we must remember that. God grants His gifts, or He withholds them, and there is no shame in being an ordinary man. Like with the Christ Child. —Before a child one may kneel without feeling ashamed. Strange that thoughts like these should be so satisfying—he would even say so sweet, if it was not too silly for a tough old man like him to use the word. That was how he felt, anyhow.

Art ... the business man with the parrot-nose was thinking. "Yes, it adds something cheerful to life, a little good white silk and a little tumty-ti-ti-tum. Really he does not play so badly. Fully fifty seats, twelve marks apiece, that makes six hundred marks—and everything else besides. Take off the rent of the hall, the lighting and the programmes, you must have fully a thousand marks profit. That is worth while."

That was Chopin he was just playing, thought the piano teacher, a lady with a pointed nose; she was of an age when the understanding sharpens as the hopes decay. "But not very original—I will say that afterwards, it sounds well. And his hand position is entirely amateur. One must be able to lay a coin on the back of the hand—I would use a ruler on him."

Then there was a young girl, at that self-conscious and chlorotic[5] time of life when the most ineffable ideas come into the mind. She was thinking to herself: "What is it he is playing? It is expressive of passion, yet he is a child. If he kissed me it would be as though my little brother kissed me—no kiss at all. Is there such a thing as passion all by itself, without any earthly object, a sort of child's play of passion? What nonsense! If I were to say such things aloud they would just be at me with some more cod-liver oil. Such is life."

An officer was leaning against a column. He looked on at Bibi's success and thought: "Yes, you are something and I am something, each in his own way." So he clapped his heels together and paid to the prodigy the respect which he felt to be due to all the powers that be.

Then there was a critic, an elderly man in a shiny black coat and turned-up trousers splashed with mud. He sat in his free seat and thought: "Look at him, this young beggar of a Bibi. As an individual he has still to develop, but as a type he is already quite complete, the artist *par excellence*. He has in himself all the artist's exaltation and his utter worthlessness, his charlatanry and his sacred fire, his burning contempt and his secret raptures. Of course I can't write all that, it is too good. Of course, I should have been an artist myself if I had not seen through the whole business so clearly."

Then the prodigy stopped playing and a perfect storm arose in the hall. He had to come out again and again from behind his screen. The man with the shiny but-

5. *chlorotic*, pertaining to a type of anemia in an adolescent girl.

tons carried up more wreaths: four laurel wreaths, a lyre made of violets, a bouquet of roses. He had not arms enough to convey all these tributes, the impresario himself mounted the stage to help him. He hung a laurel wreath round Bibi's neck, he tenderly stroked the black hair—and suddenly as though overcome he bent down and gave the prodigy a kiss, a resounding kiss, square on the mouth. And then the storm became a hurricane. That kiss ran through the room like an electric shock, it went direct to peoples' marrow and made them shiver down their backs. They were carried away by a helpless compulsion of sheer noise. Loud shouts mingled with the hysterical clapping of hands. Some of Bibi's commonplace little friends down there waved their handkerchiefs. But the critic thought: "Of course that kiss had to come—it's a good old gag. Yes, good Lord, if only one did not see through everything quite so clearly—"

And so the concert drew to a close. It began at half past seven and finished at half past eight. The platform was laden with wreaths and two little pots of flowers stood on the lamp stands of the piano. Bibi played as his last number his *Rhapsodie grecque,* which turned into the Greek national hymn at the end. His fellow-countrymen in the audience would gladly have sung it with him if the company had not been so august. They made up for it with a powerful noise and hullabaloo, a hot-blooded national demonstration. And the aging critic was thinking: "'Yes, the hymn had to come too. They have to exploit every vein—publicity cannot afford to neglect any means to its end. I think I'll criticize that as inartistic. But perhaps I am wrong, perhaps that is the most artistic thing of all. What is the artist? A jack-in-the-box. Criticism is on a higher plane. But I can't say that." And away he went in his muddy trousers.

After being called out nine or ten times the prodigy did not come any more from behind the screen but went to his mother and the impresario down in the hall. The audience stood about among the chairs and applauded and pressed forward to see Bibi close at hand. Some of them wanted to see the princess too. Two dense circles formed, one round the prodigy, the other round the princess, and you could actually not tell which of them was receiving more homage. But the court lady was commanded to go over to Bibi; she smoothed down his silk jacket a bit to make it look suitable for a court function, led him by the arm to the princess, and solemnly indicated to him that he was to kiss the royal hand. "How do you do it, child?" asked the princess. "Does it come into your head of itself when you sit down?" *"Oui, madame,"* answered Bibi. To himself he thought: "Oh, what a stupid old princess!" Then he turned round shyly and uncourtierlike and went back to his family.

Outside in the cloak room there was a crowd. People held up their numbers and received with open arms furs, shawls, and galoshes. Somewhere among her acquaintances the piano teacher stood making her critique. "He is not very original," she said audibly and looked about her.

In front of one of the great mirrors an elegant young lady was being arrayed in her evening cloak and fur shoes by her brothers, two lieutenants. She was exquisitely beautiful, with her steel-blue eyes and her clean-cut, well-bred face. A really noble dame. When she was ready she stood waiting for her brothers. "Don't stand so long in front of the glass, Adolf," she said softly to one of them, who could not tear himself away from the sight of his simple, good-looking young features. But Lieutenant Adolf thinks: What cheek! He would button his overcoat in front of the glass, just the same. Then they went out on the street where the arc lights gleamed cloudily through the white mist. Lieutenant Adolf struck up a little dance on the frozen snow to keep warm, with his hands in his slanting overcoat pockets and his collar turned up.

A girl with untidy hair and swinging arms, accompanied by a gloomy-faced youth, came out just behind them. A child! she thought. A charming child. But in there he was an awe-inspiring . . . and aloud in a toneless voice she said: "We are all infant prodigies, we artists."

"Well, bless my soul!" thought the old gentleman who had never got further than Augustin on the piano, and whose boil was now concealed by a top hat. "What does all that mean? She sounds very oracular." But the gloomy youth understood. He nodded his head slowly.

Then they were silent and the untidy-haired girl gazed after the brothers and sister. She rather despised them, but she looked after them until they had turned the corner.

Development

INTERPRETATION

1. (a) What is the prodigy's attitude toward his audience? (b) What continuous conflict takes place inside him throughout the performance?

2. (a) Consider the thoughts of the old man, the business man, the piano teacher, the young girl, and the officer during the performance. Are their thoughts on the performance objective or subjective? (b) What common thread runs through their musings? (c) What point, if any, is the author trying to make about audiences in general?

3. What does the critic mean when he says: ". . . I should have been an artist myself if I had not seen through the whole business so clearly" (page 466, column 2, paragraph 3)?

4. (a) After the performance, why does the audience pay homage to the prodigy and the princess? (b) What might be the author's purpose in depicting the audience's homage to both characters?

5. When the untidy-haired girl says,

"We are all infant prodigies, we artists," is she referring to the exploitation of the artist, or the genuine artist's continual struggle to improve on and develop his art, or something else? Discuss.

6. Can you find a parallel between the untidy-haired girl's feelings toward the brother and sister and the prodigy's feelings toward his audience? Between her feelings and the reader's reaction to the story? Discuss.

7. Mann has created an artist who feels he can only impress his audience by a display of showmanship which is incompatible with pure art. Is the author saying that art is always corrupted by a materialistic society, or that only pure art can resist corruption and remain unblemished? Explain.

TECHNIQUE

1. Thomas Mann has used what many critics describe as "delicate irony" in writing about a subject close to his heart: the role of the artist in society. Do you find his irony consistently delicate, or can you pick out passages that are heavy-handed?

2. (a) As a talented artist paints a portrait with a few bold strokes of his brush, a skillful author portrays a character with a few descriptive details. What similarity do you find in the author's descriptions of the prodigy's mother, the impresario, and the princess (page 464, column 2, paragraph 2)? (b) What significant differences are there between the aforementioned descriptions and those relating to the critic, and the boy and girl who appear at the end of the story? (c) With which group do the author's sympathies lie? Why do you think he prefers this group to the other?

EXTENSIONS

1. (a) The impresario believed "that anything worth having was worth paying for," which is similar to the current dictum, "you get what you pay for." Should

these assertions apply to the arts? Why or why not? *(b)* Specify areas of life where these assertions are valid and invalid.

2. In the second paragraph the author writes, ". . . the audience began to clap, because somewhere at the side a leader of mobs, a born organizer, clapped first." Considering that the story was written in Germany at the beginning of the century, does this comment have a prophetic ring? Explain.

Comparison

1. The three selections in this group are placed in disparate settings: Mann's story in a highly artificial one; Böll's in one of ugliness and extreme poverty; Kume's in an unobtrusive one. *(a)* Do Mann's and Böll's stories gain plausibility from their settings? Discuss. *(b)* Why do you think Kume places less emphasis on the setting of his story?

2. Four performers—a musician, a knife-thrower, his partner, and a comic actor—strive for and win the applause of their audiences. In the event of failure, which one of them do you think is best equipped to sustain it? Explain your answer.

3. *(a)* Comment on the following statement: The public's applause can be a two-edged sword: sometimes it spurs a performer to greater accomplishment; at other times it tends to stagnate his artistic development. *(b)* In your opinion, has the audience had a beneficial or harmful effect on the four performers? Explain your answer. *(c)* Do you think any of them would have agreed with the Spanish author Vicente Blasco Ibáñez when he said that the only beast at the bull fight is the crowd? Discuss.

4. Much literature has no heroes, only characters who are caught up in a maelstrom of uncontrollable events. *(a)* Which characters in these stories are, to the greatest extent, victims of circumstances beyond their control? *(b)* Which seems to exercise the greatest measure of control over his destiny? Explain.

5. The performers take leave of their public with bows and smiles. Behind the smiles, each one has wrestled with a personal conflict which is mirrored in a quotation from W. M. Thackeray: "And when he's laughed and said his say,/ He shows, as he removes the mask,/ A face that's anything but gay." *(a)* Do any of them finally resolve their conflicts? *(b)* Which performer, or performers, will carry the conflict into the next performance?

6. Support or refute the following charges: *(a)* Heinrich Böll in "The Man with the Knives" has created a setting that is much more convincing than his two characters. *(b)* Thomas Mann in "The Infant Prodigy" describes the audience with an irony that is colored by a snobbish sense of artistic superiority. *(c)* In portraying a meeting on a streetcar between Fukai, Wataru, and the critic, Kume Masao has introduced a scene that is both meaningless and irrelevant to the theme of "The Tiger."

7. It has been said that the stage is a microcosm of the world of mankind. If this is true, then the performers should have helped you to a better understanding of your fellow-men. Which story or stories added something to your knowledge of human nature, or confirmed something you were already aware of? Explain.

8. "A Hunger Artist" and "The Bound Man" touch on some of the problems common to performers. *(a)* In what ways does the attitude of the audience in "The Man with the Knives" resemble the response of the spectators in "The Bound Man" and "A Hunger Artist"? *(b)* Does the protagonist of "A Hunger Artist" have more in common as a performer with the infant prodigy or with the narrator of "The Man with the Knives"? Discuss.

DOC by Romulo Maccio. Owned by artist, Buenos Aires.

The Absurd Man

PICNIC ON THE BATTLEFIELD / FERNANDO ARRABAL / SPAIN

THE THIRD BANK OF THE RIVER / GUIMARÃES ROSA / BRAZIL

THE PHOTOGRAPH OF THE COLONEL / IONESCO / FRANCE

Picnic on the Battlefield

FERNANDO ARRABAL / Spain

(1932 –   )
translated from the French by James Hewitt

CHARACTERS

ZAPO, A SOLDIER
MONSIEUR TÉPAN, THE SOLDIER'S FATHER
MADAME TÉPAN, THE SOLDIER'S MOTHER
ZÉPO, AN ENEMY SOLDIER
FIRST CORPSMAN
SECOND CORPSMAN

SCENE: *A battlefield. Barbed wire stretches from one end of the stage to the other, with sandbags piled against it.*

Battle is in full swing. We hear bombs bursting, rifle shots and machine-gun fire.

Alone on stage, hidden flat on his belly among the sandbags, ZAPO is very frightened.

The fighting stops. Silence.

From a knitting bag, ZAPO takes out a ball of wool, knitting needles, and starts knitting a sweater that is already quite well along. The field telephone beside him suddenly rings.

ZAPO. Hello . . . hello . . . yes, sir, Captain. . . . Yes, this is the sentry in Section 47. . . . Nothing new, Captain. . . . Excuse me, Captain, when are we going to start fighting again? . . . And what am I supposed to do with the grenades? Should I send them on up front or to the rear? . . . Don't get annoyed, I didn't say that to upset you. . . . And, Captain, I'm really feeling pretty lonesome. Couldn't you send me a companion out here? . . . Even the goat. (*Evidently the* CAPTAIN *gives him a good dressing down.*)

Yes sir, Captain, yes sir! (ZAPO *hangs up. We hear him grumbling to himself.*) (*Silence.*)

(*Enter* MONSIEUR *and* MADAME TÉPAN, *carrying baskets as though they are off on a picnic. Their son, who is sitting with his back turned, does not see them arriving.*)

M. TÉPAN (*ceremoniously*). My boy, get up and kiss your mother on the forehead. (*Taken by surprise,* ZAPO *gets up and, with a great deal of respect, gives his mother a kiss on the forehead. He is about to speak, but his father beats him to it.*)
Now give me a kiss.

ZAPO. My dear sweet parents, how did you ever dare come all the way out to a dangerous spot like this? You must leave here right away.

M. TÉPAN. Are you trying to tell your father what war and danger are all about? For me, all this is only a game. How many times do you think I've jumped off the subway while it was still moving?

MME. TÉPAN. We thought you were probably bored, so we came to pay you a little visit. After all, this war business must get pretty tiresome.

ZAPO. It all depends.

M. TÉPAN. I know perfectly well what goes on. In the beginning, it's all new and exciting. You enjoy the killing and throwing grenades and wearing a helmet; it's quite the thing, but you end up bored as hell. In my day, you'd have really seen something. Wars were a lot livelier, much more colorful. And then best of all, there were horses, lots of horses. It was a real pleasure: if the captain said "Attack!" before you could shake a stick we were all assembled on horseback in our red uniforms. That was something to see. And then we'd go galloping forward, sword in hand, and suddenly find ourselves hard against the enemy. And they'd be at their finest too, with their horses—there were always loads and loads of beautiful round-bottomed horses and their polished boots, and their green uniforms.

MME. TÉPAN. No, the enemy uniform wasn't green. It was blue. I remember perfectly well it was blue.

M. TÉPAN. And I say it was green.

MME. TÉPAN. When I was little I went out on the balcony any number of times to watch the battle, and I'd say to the little boy next door, "I'll bet you a gumdrop the Blues win." And the Blues were our enemies.

M. TÉPAN. All right, so you win.

MME. TÉPAN. I always loved battles. When I was little, I always said that when I grew up I wanted to be a Colonel in the Dragoons. But Mama didn't want me to. You know what a stickler she is.

M. TÉPAN. Your mother's a real nincompoop.

ZAPO. Forgive me, but you've got to leave. You just can't go walking into a war when you're not a soldier.

M. TÉPAN. I don't give a damn. We're here to have a picnic with you in the country and spend a nice Sunday.

MME. TÉPAN. I even made a lovely meal. Sausage, hard-boiled eggs, I know how much you like them! Ham sandwiches, red wine, some salad and some little cakes.

ZAPO. O.K., we'll do whatever you say. But if the Captain comes along he'll throw a fit. Plus the fact that he doesn't much go for the idea of visiting the battle-front.[1] He keeps telling us: "War calls for discipline and grenades, but no visits."

M. TÉPAN. Don't you worry about it, I'll have a few words with your Captain.

ZAPO. And what if we have to start fighting again?

M. TÉPAN. You think that scares me, I've seen worse. Now if it was only cavalry battles! Times have changed, that's something you don't understand. (A pause.) We came on motorcycle. Nobody said anything.

ZAPO. They probably thought you were arbitrators.

M. TÉPAN. We did have some trouble getting through, though. With all those jeeps and tanks.

MME. TÉPAN. And the very minute we arrived, you remember that bottleneck because of the cannon?

M. TÉPAN. During wartime, you've got to be prepared for anything. Everybody knows that.

MME. TÉPAN. Well now, we're ready to start eating.

M. TÉPAN. Right you are, I could eat a horse. It's the smell of gunpowder that does it.

MME. TÉPAN. We'll eat sitting down on the blanket.

ZAPO. All right to eat with my rifle?

MME. TÉPAN. Let your rifle alone. It's bad manners to bring your rifle to the table. (A pause.) Why, child, you're filthy as a little pig. How did you manage to get in such a mess? Let's see your hands.

ZAPO (ashamed, he shows them). I had to crawl along the ground during maneuvers.

MME. TÉPAN. How about your ears?

ZAPO. I washed them this morning.

MME. TÉPAN. That should do then. Now how about your teeth? (He shows them.) Very good. Now who's going to give his little boy a great big kiss for brushing his teeth so nicely? (To her

1. *idea of visiting the battlefront.* The practice of visiting soldiers on the battlefront was formerly an accepted one.

husband:) Well, give your son a kiss for brushing his teeth so nicely. *(*M. TÉPAN *gives his son a kiss.)* Because, you know, one thing I just won't allow is not washing, and blaming it on the war.

ZAPO. Yes, Mama. *(They eat.)*

M. TÉPAN. Well, my boy, have you been keeping up a good shooting score?

ZAPO. When?

M. TÉPAN. Why, the last few days.

ZAPO. Where?

M. TÉPAN. Right here and now. After all, you *are* fighting a war.

ZAPO. No, no great shakes. I haven't kept up a very good score. Practically no bull's-eyes.

M. TÉPAN. Well, what have you been scoring best with in your shooting, enemy horses or soldiers?

ZAPO. No, no horses. There aren't any horses anymore.

M. TÉPAN. Well, soldiers then?

ZAPO. Could be.

M. TÉPAN. Could be? Aren't you sure?

ZAPO. It's just that I. . . . I fire without taking aim *(a pause)* and when I fire I say an *Our Father* for the guy I shot.

M. TÉPAN. You've got to show more courage. Like your father.

MME. TÉPAN. I'm going to put a record on the phonograph. *(She puts on a record: a Spanish pasodoble.[2] Sitting on the ground, they all three listen.)*

M. TÉPAN. Now that's real music. Yes, ma'am, I tell you. Olé!

(As the music continues, an enemy soldier, ZÉPO, *enters. He is dressed like* ZAPO. *Only the color of his uniform is different.* ZÉPO *wears green;* ZAPO *wears gray.*

(Standing unseen behind the family, his mouth agape, ZÉPO *listens to the music. The record comes to an end.* ZAPO, *getting up, spots* ZÉPO. *Both raise their hands in the air, while* M. *and* MME. TÉPAN *look at them, startled.)*

M. TÉPAN. What's going on?

*(*ZAPO *seems about to act, but hesitates. Then, very decisively, he points his rifle at* ZÉPO.*)*

ZAPO. Hands up!

*(*ZÉPO, *more terrified than ever, raises his hands still higher.* ZAPO *doesn't know what to do. All of a sudden, he hurriedly runs toward* ZÉPO *and taps him gently on the shoulder, saying:)* You're it. *(Pleased as punch, to his father.)* There you are! A prisoner!

M. TÉPAN. That's fine. Now what are you going to do with him?

ZAPO. I don't know. But could be they'll make me a corporal.

M. TÉPAN. In the meantime, tie him up.

ZAPO. Tie him up? What for?

M. TÉPAN. That's what you do with prisoners, you tie 'em up!

ZAPO. How?

M. TÉPAN. By his hands.

MME. TÉPAN. Oh yes, you've definitely got to tie his hands. That's the way I've always seen it done.

ZAPO. All right. *(To the prisoner.)* Please put your hands together.

ZÉPO. Don't do it too hard.

ZAPO. Oh, no.

ZÉPO. Ouch! You're hurting me.

M. TÉPAN. Come on now, don't mistreat your prisoner.

MME. TÉPAN. Is that the way I brought you up? Haven't I told you over and over again that you've got to be considerate of your fellow-man?

ZAPO. I didn't do it on purpose. *(To* ZÉPO.*)* Does it hurt the way it is now?

ZÉPO. No, like this it doesn't hurt.

M. TÉPAN. Speak right up and tell him if it does. Just pretend we're not here.

ZÉPO. This way it's O.K.

M. TÉPAN. Now his feet.

ZAPO. His feet too? How long does this go on?

M. TÉPAN. Didn't they teach you the rules?

ZAPO. Sure.

M. TÉPAN. Well?

ZAPO *(to* ZÉPO, *very politely).* Would you kindly be good enough to please sit down on the ground?

2. *pasodoble,* a light march often played at bullfights.

zépo. All right, but don't hurt me.

mme. tépan. See! Now he's taking a dislike to you.

zapo. No. No he's not. I'm not hurting you, am I?

zépo. No, this is fine.

zapo (out of nowhere). Papa, suppose you took a snapshot with the prisoner down there on the ground and me standing with my foot on his stomach?

m. tépan. Say, yes! That'll look classy.

zépo. Oh, no you don't. Not that.

mme. tépan. Let him. Don't be so stubborn.

zépo. No. I said no and I mean no.

mme. tépan. Just a little old snip of a snapshot. What difference could that possibly make to you? Then we could put it in the dining room right next to the Lifesaving Certificate my husband got thirteen years ago.

zépo. No, you'll never talk me into it.

zapo. But why should you refuse?

zépo. I've got a fiancée. And if she ever sees the snapshot, she'll say I don't know how to fight a war.

zapo. No, all you have to do is tell her it isn't you at all, it's a panther.

mme. tépan. C'mon, say yes.

zépo. All right, but I'm only doing it to please you.

zapo. Stretch all the way out.

(zepo stretches all the way out. zapo puts one foot on his stomach and grabs his rifle with a military air.)

mme. tépan. Throw your chest out more.

zapo. Like this?

mme. tépan. Yes, that's it. Don't breathe.

m. tépan. Make like a hero.

zapo. How do you mean a hero, like this?

m. tépan. It's a cinch. Make like the butcher when he was telling us what a lady-killer he is.

zapo. Like so?

m. tépan. Yes, that's it.

mme. tépan. Just be sure your chest is puffed way out, and don't breathe.

zépo. Are you about finished?

m. tépan. Have a little patience. One . . . two . . . three.

zapo. I hope I'll come out all right.

mme. tépan. Oh yes, you looked very military.

m. tépan. You were fine.

mme. tépan. That makes me want to have my picture taken, too.

m. tépan. Now there's a good idea.

zapo. All right. I'll take it if you want me to.

mme. tépan. Give me your helmet so I'll look like a soldier.

zépo. I don't want any more pictures. Even one was too much.

zapo. Don't feel that way. Come right down to it, what difference could it make?

zépo. That's my final say.

m. tépan (to his wife). Don't push him. Prisoners are always very touchy. If we keep it up, he'll get mad and spoil all our fun.

zapo. Well now, what are we going to do with him?

mme. tépan. We could ask him to eat with us. What do you think?

m. tépan. I don't see any reason why not.

zapo (to zépo). All right then, how'd you like to eat with us?

zépo. Uh . . .

m. tépan. We brought along a nice bottle of wine.

zépo. Well, in that case O.K.

mme. tépan. Make yourself right at home. Don't be afraid to ask for things.

zépo. Fine.

m. tépan. Well now, how about you, have you been keeping up a good shooting score?

zépo. When?

m. tépan. Why, the last few days.

zépo. Where?

m. tépan. Right here and now. After all, you *are* fighting a war.

zépo. No, no great shakes. I haven't kept up a very good score. Practically no bull's-eyes.

m. tépan. Well, what have you been

scoring best with in your shooting, enemy horses or soldiers?

ZÉPO. No, no horses. There aren't any horses any more.

M. TÉPAN. Well, soldiers then?

ZÉPO. Could be.

M. TÉPAN. Could be? Aren't you sure?

ZÉPO. It's just that I. . . . I fire without taking aim *(a pause)* and when I fire I say a *Hail Mary* for the guy I shot.

ZAPO. A *Hail Mary?* I'd have thought you'd say an *Our Father.*

ZÉPO. No. Always a *Hail Mary.* *(A pause.)* It's shorter.

M. TÉPAN. Come, my boy, you have to be courageous.

MME. TÉPAN *(to zÉPO).* If you like, we can untie you.

ZÉPO. No, leave me this way. It doesn't matter.

M. TÉPAN. You're not going to start putting on airs with us? If you want us to untie you, just say the word.

MME. TÉPAN. Please feel free.

ZÉPO. Well, if you really mean it, untie my feet. But it's just to please you people.

M. TÉPAN. Zapo, untie him. *(zAPO unties him.)*

MME. TÉPAN. Well now, feel better?

ZÉPO. Sure do. But listen, maybe I'm causing you too much trouble.

M. TÉPAN. Not at all. Make yourself right at home. And if you want us to undo your hands, just say so.

ZÉPO. No, not my hands, too. I don't want to overdo it.

M. TÉPAN. Not at all, my boy, not at all. I tell you, you don't disturb us one bit.

ZÉPO. All right, go ahead and untie my hands then. But just while we eat, huh? I don't want you to think when you give me an inch I'm going to take a mile.

M. TÉPAN. Untie his hands, sonny.

MME. TÉPAN. Well, since our honorable prisoner is so nice, we're going to have a lovely day out here in the country.

ZÉPO. Don't call me "honorable" prisoner. Just say "prisoner" plain and simple.

MME. TÉPAN. You're sure that won't make you feel bad?

ZÉPO. No, not at all.

M. TÉPAN. Well, you're certainly unpretentious, anyway.

(Sound of airplanes.)

ZAPO. Airplanes. They're going to bomb us for sure.

(zAPO and zÉPO dive for the sandbags and hide.)

ZAPO *(to his parents).* Run for cover! The bombs are going to land right on you.

(The sound of the planes drowns out everything. Immediately bombs start falling. Shells explode nearby. Deafening racket. zAPO and zÉPO are crouching among the sandbags. M. TÉPAN goes on calmly talking to his wife, who answers him with equal calm. Because of the bombardment we cannot hear their conversation.

(MME. TÉPAN heads for one of the picnic baskets, from which she takes an umbrella. She opens it. The TÉPANS take shelter under the umbrella, as though it were raining. Standing there, they shift from one foot to the other, in rhythm, all the while discussing personal matters. The bombardment continues.

(At last, the airplanes take off. Silence. M. TÉPAN stretches one arm out from under the umbrella to make certain there is no longer anything coming down from the sky.)

M. TÉPAN. You can close your umbrella now.

(MME. TÉPAN closes it. Together they go over to their son and prod him on the behind a couple of times with the umbrella.)

M. TÉPAN. All right, come on out. The bombing's over.

(zAPO and zÉPO come out of their hiding place.)

ZAPO. They didn't get you?

M. TÉPAN. You don't expect anything to happen to your father, do you? *(Proudly.)* Little bombs like that? Don't make me laugh.

(From the left, a pair of Red Cross corpsmen enter, carrying a stretcher.)

1ST CORPSMAN. Any bodies?

ZAPO. No, none here.

1ST CORPSMAN. You're sure you took a good look?

ZAPO. Absolutely.

1ST CORPSMAN. And there's not one single body?

ZAPO. Didn't I just say so?

1ST CORPSMAN. Not even someone wounded?

ZAPO. Not even.

2ND CORPSMAN. Well, we're really up the creek! *(To* ZAPO, *persuasively.)* Take a good look all around here, see if you don't turn up a stiff someplace.

1ST CORPSMAN. Don't press the issue. They told you once and for all there aren't any.

2ND CORPSMAN. What a lousy deal!

ZAPO. I'm really very sorry. I swear I didn't plan it that way.

2ND CORPSMAN. That's what they all say. That there aren't any corpses, and that they didn't plan it that way.

1ST CORPSMAN. So let the man alone!

M. TEPAN *(obligingly)*. If we can help you at all, we'd be delighted to. At your service.

2ND CORPSMAN. Well, I don't know. If we keep on like this, I really don't know what the Captain's going to say to us.

M. TÉPAN. What seems to be the trouble?

2ND CORPSMAN. Just that the others are all getting sore wrists carrying out the dead and wounded, while we still haven't come up with anything. And it's not because we haven't been looking.

M. TÉPAN. I see. That really is a bore. *(To* ZAPO.*)* You're quite sure that there are no corpses?

ZAPO. Obviously, Papa.

M. TÉPAN. You looked under the sandbags?

ZAPO. Yes, Papa.

M. TÉPAN *(angry)*. Why don't you come right out and say you don't want to have any part in helping these good gentlemen?

1ST CORPSMAN. Don't jump on him like that. Leave him alone. We'll just hope we have better luck in some other trench where maybe everybody'll be dead.

M. TÉPAN. I'd be delighted for you.

MME. TÉPAN. So would I. Nothing pleases me more than to see people who take their work seriously.

M. TÉPAN *(indignantly, to anyone within hearing)*. Well, isn't anyone going to do anything for these gentlemen?

ZAPO. If it was up to me, it'd be good as done.

ZÉPO. Same here.

M. TÉPAN. Look here now, isn't one of you at least wounded?

ZAPO *(ashamed)*. No, not me.

M. TÉPAN *(to* ZÉPO*)*. What about you?

ZÉPO *(ashamed)*. Me either. I never was lucky.

MME. TÉPAN *(delighted)*. I just remembered! This morning, while I was peeling onions, I cut my finger. How's that?

M. TÉPAN. Why of course! *(Really in the swing of things.)* They'll put you on the stretcher and carry you right off!

1ST CORPSMAN. Sorry, it's no good. Women don't count.

M. TÉPAN. Well, that didn't get us anywhere.

1ST CORPSMAN. It doesn't matter.

2ND CORPSMAN. Maybe we can get our fill in the other trenches. *(They start to go off.)*

M. TÉPAN. Don't you worry, if we find a corpse, we'll hang onto it for you. There's not a chance we'd give it to anybody but you.

2ND CORPSMAN. Thank you very much, sir.

M. TÉPAN. It's nothing, my boy. It's the very least I could do.

(The corpsmen make their goodbyes. All four of the others reply in kind. The corpsmen exit.)

MME. TÉPAN. That's what's so pleasant about spending Sunday out in the battlefield. You always run into such nice folks. *(A pause.)* Come to think of it, why is it you're enemies?

ZÉPO. I don't know. I'm not too well educated.

MME. TÉPAN. I mean is it from birth, or did you become enemies after?

ZÉPO. I don't know. I don't know a thing about it.

M. TÉPAN. Well then, how did you come to go to war?

ZÉPO. One day I was home fixing my mother's iron and a man came by and said to me: "Are you Zépo?" . . . "Yes." . . . "Good, you've got to go to war." So I asked him, "What war?" And he said to me: "Don't you read the newspapers? You *are* a hick!" So I told him yes I did, but not all that war stuff . . .

ZAPO. That's just what happened to me; exactly what happened to me.

M. TÉPAN. Sure, they came after you, too.

MME. TÉPAN. No, it's not the same. You weren't fixing the iron that day, you were repairing the car.

M. TÉPAN. I was talking about the rest of it. *(To* ZÉPO.*)* Go on. Then what happened?

ZÉPO. Well then I told him I had a fiancée, and if I didn't take her to the movies on Sunday, she wouldn't know what to do with herself. He said that that didn't matter.

ZAPO. Same as me. Exactly the same as me.

ZÉPO. Well, then my father came down and he said I couldn't go to war because I didn't have a horse.

ZAPO. Like my father said.

ZÉPO. The man said they didn't use horses any more, and I asked him if I could take along my fiancée. He said no. Then I asked him could I take along my aunt to make me custard every Thursday. I like custard.

MME. TÉPAN *(realizing that she has forgotten something).* Oh! The custard!

ZÉPO. Again he said no.

ZAPO. The way he did to me.

ZÉPO. And ever since then, here I am, nearly always alone in the trench here.

MME. TÉPAN. As long as you're so much alike, and both so bored, I think you and your honorable prisoner might play together this afternoon.

ZAPO. Oh no, Mama! I'm too scared. He's an enemy.

M. TÉPAN. Oh come on now, don't be scared.

ZAPO. If you knew what the general told us about the enemy.

MME. TÉPAN. What did he tell you?

ZAPO. He said the enemy soldiers are very mean. When they take prisoners, they put pebbles in their socks so it hurts when they walk.

MME. TÉPAN. Horrible! What savages!

M. TÉPAN *(indignantly, to* ZÉPO*).* Aren't you ashamed to be part of an army of criminals?

ZÉPO. I didn't do anything. I'm not mad at anybody.

MME. TÉPAN. He's trying to put one over on us, acting like a little saint.

M. TÉPAN. We should never have untied him. Probably all we have to do is have our backs turned for him to go putting pebbles in our socks.

ZÉPO. Don't be so mean to me.

M. TÉPAN. How do you expect us to be? I'm shocked. I know just what I'm going to do. I'm going to find the Captain and ask him to let me go into battle.

ZAPO. He won't let you. You're too old.

M. TÉPAN. Well then I'll go buy a horse and a saber and I'll go to war on my own.

ZÉPO. Please, madame, don't treat me like this. Besides, I was just going to tell you, *our* general said the same thing about you people.

MME. TÉPAN. How could he dare tell such a lie?

ZAPO. The very same thing, honest?

ZÉPO. Yes, the very same thing.

M. TÉPAN. Maybe it's the same one who talked to both of you.

MME. TÉPAN. Well, if it is the same general, the least he could do is use a different speech. Imagine telling everybody the same thing.

M. TÉPAN *(to* ZÉPO, *changing his tone).* Can I fill your glass again?

MME. TÉPAN. I hope you enjoyed our little lunch.

M. TÉPAN. It was better than last Sunday, anyway.

ZÉPO. What happened then?

M. TÉPAN. Well, we went out to the country and laid all our chow out on the blanket. While we had our backs turned, a cow came along and ate the whole lunch, including the napkins.

ZÉPO. What a glutton, that cow!

M. TÉPAN. Yes, but then to get even, we ate the cow. *(They laugh.)*

ZAPO *(to* ZÉPO*)*. I bet they weren't hungry after that.

M. TÉPAN. To your health! *(They all drink.)*

MME. TÉPAN *(to* ZÉPO*)*. Tell me something, what do you do for amusement in the trenches?

ZÉPO. Just to pass the time and keep myself amused, I take odds and ends of rags and make little flowers out of them. See, I get bored a lot.

MME. TÉPAN. And what do you do with these rag flowers?

ZÉPO. At first I used to send them to my fiancée, but one day she told me that the cellar and the greenhouse were already filled with them, that she didn't know what to do with them any more, and would I mind sending her something else for a change?

MME. TÉPAN. And what did you do?

ZÉPO. I tried learning something else, but I couldn't do it. So, to pass the time, I just go on making my rag flowers.

MME. TÉPAN. And then do you throw them away?

ZÉPO. No, now I've found a way to make use of them: I furnish one flower for each of my buddies who dies. That way, I know that even if I make a whole lot, there'll never be enough.

M. TÉPAN. You found a good way out.

ZÉPO *(timidly)*. Yes.

ZAPO. Well, you know what I do so's not to get bored is knit.

MME. TÉPAN. But tell me, do all the soldiers get bored the way you two do?

ZÉPO. That depends on what they do for relaxation.

ZAPO. Same thing over on our side.

M. TÉPAN. Well then, let's stop the war.

ZÉPO. But how?

M. TÉPAN. Very easy. You tell your buddies that the enemy doesn't want to fight, and you tell the same thing to your comrades. And everybody goes home.

ZAPO. Terrific!

MME. TÉPAN. That way you can finish fixing the iron.

ZAPO. How come nobody ever thought of that before?

MME. TÉPAN. It takes your father to come up with ideas like that. Don't forget he's a Normal School[3] graduate, and a philatelist,[4] too.

ZÉPO. But what will all the field marshals and the corporals do?

M. TÉPAN. We'll give 'em guitars and castanets to keep 'em quiet.

ZÉPO. Excellent idea.

M. TÉPAN. See how easy it is? It's all settled.

ZÉPO. We'll wow 'em!

ZAPO. Boy, will my buddies be glad!

MME. TÉPAN. What do you say we celebrate and put on that pasodoble we were listening to before?

ZÉPO. Wonderful!

ZAPO. Yes, put on the record, Mama.

*(*MME. TÉPAN *puts on the record. She winds the phonograph and waits. Not a sound is heard.)*

M. TÉPAN. You can't hear anything.

MME. TÉPAN *(going to the phonograph)*. Oh!...I made a boo-boo! Instead of putting on a record, I put on a beret.

(She puts the record on. A lively pasodoble is heard. ZAPO *dances with* ZÉPO; MME. TÉPAN *with her husband. (The field telephone rings. None of the group hears it. They go on dancing in a lively manner. (The phone rings again. The dancing continues. Battle breaks out once*

---

3. *Normal School,* a school for training teachers.
4. *philatelist,* a stamp collector.

more with a great din of bombs, rifle fire and the crackle of machine guns. Having noticed nothing, the two couples keep on dancing gaily.

(A sudden machine-gun blast mows them all down. They fall to the ground, stone dead. One bullet seems to have nicked the phonograph: the music keeps repeating the same strain over and over, like a record with a scratch in it. We hear this repeated strain for the remainder of the play.

(From the left, the two corpsmen enter, carrying the empty stretcher.)

FAST CURTAIN

Development

INTERPRETATION

1. *(a)* Compare and contrast Zapo's attitude toward the war he is in with the attitude of M. Tépan toward the war in which he fought. *(b)* How would you account for the differences? *(c)* Does the father's attitude seem more admirable than his son's? Why or why not?

2. When the bombs begin to fall, M. Tépan uses an umbrella to protect himself. *(a)* What is the significance of this comic detail to the characterization of M. Tépan? *(b)* What does this gesture suggest about his generation?

3. What point about war and propaganda has Arrabal made by stressing the similarity between Zapo and Zépo?

4. Which of the following best expresses the meaning and feeling of the play's conclusion?
(a) War is hell.
(b) Man is a pawn of society.
(c) Existence is in vain.
(d) Seize the day, for tomorrow we die.

5. Discuss the appropriateness of the pasodoble [see note 2] to the play, and compare its effect with that of some other possible choices, for example, a Strauss waltz or a nationalistic march.

TECHNIQUE

1. *(a)* A critic has said, "Arrabal's elegant little satire is totally ruined by the abrupt change in tone at the end." Discuss. *(b)* Is the ending a complete surprise, or are you prepared for it in some ways? Discuss.

2. Explain the ironic tone operating in each of the following. Consider the context where it is relevant.
(a) The title of the play, "Picnic on the Battlefield."
(b) ". . . you've got to be considerate of your fellow-man." (Mme. Tépan, page 474, column 2, lines 31-32)
(c) ". . . have you been keeping up a good shooting score?" (M. Tépan, page 474, column 1, lines 7-8 *and* page 475, column 2, lines 40-41)
(d) "He's an enemy." (Zapo, page 478, column 2, line 5)
(e) "Well, then, let's stop the war." (M. Tépan, page 479, column 2, line 4)

EXTENSIONS

1. How are the characters in "Picnic" similar to the one described in the following passage from George Orwell's "Politics and the English Language"?

When one watches some tired hack on the platform mechanically repeating the familiar phrases—*bestial atrocities, iron heel, bloodstained tyranny, free peoples of the world, stand shoulder to shoulder*—one often has a curious feeling that one is not watching a live human being but some kind of dummy. . . . And this is not altogether fanciful. A speaker who uses that kind of phraseology has gone some distance towards turning himself into a machine. The appropriate noises are coming out of his larynx, but his brain is not involved as it would be if he were choosing his words for himself.[1]

---

1. "Politics and the English Language" from SHOOTING AN ELEPHANT AND OTHER ESSAYS by George Orwell. Copyright 1945, 1946, 1949, 1950 by Sonia Brownell Orwell. Reprinted by permission of Harcourt Brace Jovanovich, Inc., Martin Secker & Warburg, Ltd., and the author's executrix.

The Third Bank of the River

JOÃO GUIMARÃES ROSA[1] / Brazil

(1908 – 1967)

translated from the Portuguese by Barbara Shelby

Father was a reliable, law-abiding, practical man, and had been ever since he was a boy, as various people of good sense testified when I asked them about him. I don't remember that he seemed any crazier or even any moodier than anyone else we knew. He just didn't talk much. It was our mother who gave the orders and scolded us every day—my sister, my brother, and me. Then one day my father ordered a canoe for himself.

He took the matter very seriously. He had the canoe made to his specifications of fine *vinhático*[2] wood; a small one, with a narrow board in the stern as though to leave only enough room for the oarsman. Every bit of it was hand-hewn of special strong wood carefully shaped, fit to last in the water for twenty or thirty years. Mother railed at the idea. How could a man who had never fiddled away his time on such tricks propose to go fishing and hunting now, at his time of life? Father said nothing. Our house was closer to the river then than it is now, less than a quarter of a league[3] away: there rolled the river, great, deep, and silent, always silent. It was so wide that you could hardly see the bank on the other side. I can never forget the day the canoe was ready.

Neither happy nor excited nor downcast, Father pulled his hat well down on his head and said one firm goodbye. He spoke not another word, took neither food nor other supplies, gave no parting advice. We thought Mother would have a fit, but she only blanched white, bit her lip, and said bitterly: "Go or stay; but if you go, don't you ever come back!" Father left his answer in suspense. He gave me a mild look and motioned me to go aside with him a few steps. I was afraid of Mother's anger, but I obeyed anyway, that time. The turn things had taken gave me the courage to ask: "Father, will you take me with you in that canoe?" But he just gave me a long look in return: gave me his blessing and motioned me to go back. I pretended to go, but instead turned off into a deep woodsy hollow to watch. Father stepped into the canoe, untied it, and began to paddle off. The canoe slipped away, a straight, even shadow like an alligator, slithery, long.

Our father never came back. He hadn't gone anywhere. He stuck to that stretch of the river, staying halfway across, always in the canoe, never to spring out of it, ever again. The strangeness of that truth was enough to dismay us all. What had never been before, was. Our relatives, the neighbors, and all our acquaintances met and took counsel together.

Mother, though, behaved very reasonably, with the result that everybody believed what no one wanted to put into words about our father: that he was mad. Only a few of them thought he might be keeping a vow, or—who could tell— maybe he was sick with some hideous disease like leprosy, and that was what had made him desert us to live out another life, close to his family and yet far enough away. The news spread by word

1. *João Guimarães Rosa* (jō ou′ gē mä′ resh rō′ zä).
2. *vinhático* (vē nyä′ tē kō). 3. *quarter of a league*, slightly less than a mile.

of mouth, carried by people like travelers and those who lived along the banks of the river, who said of Father that he never landed at spit or cove, by day or by night, but always stuck to the river, lonely and outside human society. Finally, Mother and our relatives realized that the provisions he had hidden in the canoe must be getting low and thought that he would have to either land somewhere and go away from us for good—that seemed the most likely—or repent once and for all and come back home.

But they were wrong. I had made myself responsible for stealing a bit of food for him every day, an idea that had come to me the very first night, when the family had lighted bonfires on the riverbank and in their glare prayed and called out to Father. Every day from then on I went back to the river with a lump of hard brown sugar, some corn bread, or a bunch of bananas. Once, at the end of an hour of waiting that had dragged on and on, I caught sight of Father; he was way off, sitting in the bottom of the canoe as if suspended in the mirror smoothness of the river. He saw me, but he did not paddle over or make any sign. I held up the things to eat and then laid them in a hollowed-out rock in the river bluff, safe from any animals who might nose around and where they would be kept dry in rain or dew. Time after time, day after day, I did the same thing. Much later I had a surprise: Mother knew about my mission but, saying nothing and pretending she didn't, made it easier for me by putting out leftovers where I was sure to find them. Mother almost never showed what she was thinking.

Finally she sent for an uncle of ours, her brother, to help with the farm and with money matters, and she got a tutor for us children. She also arranged for the priest to come in his vestments to the river edge to exorcise[4] Father and call upon him to desist from his sad obsession. Another time, she tried to scare Father by getting two soldiers to come. But none

of it was any use. Father passed by at a distance, discernible only dimly through the river haze, going by in the canoe without ever letting anyone go close enough to touch him or even talk to him. The reporters who went out in a launch and tried to take his picture not long ago failed just like everybody else; Father crossed over to the other bank and steered the canoe into the thick swamp that goes on for miles, part reeds and part brush. Only he knew every hand's breadth of its blackness.

We just had to try to get used to it. But it was hard, and we never really managed. I'm judging by myself, of course. Whether I wanted to or not, my thoughts kept circling back and I found myself thinking of Father. The hard nub of it was that I couldn't begin to understand how he could hold out. Day and night, in bright sunshine or in rainstorms, in muggy heat or in the terrible cold spells in the middle of the year, without shelter or any protection but the old hat on his head, all through the weeks, and months, and years—he marked in no way the passing of his life. Father never landed, never put in at either shore or stopped at any of the river islands or sandbars; and he never again stepped onto grass or solid earth. It was true that in order to catch a little sleep he may have tied up the canoe at some concealed islet-spit. But he never lighted a fire on shore, had no lamp or candle, never struck a match again. He did no more than taste food; even the morsels he took from what we left for him along the roots of the fig tree or in the hollow stone at the foot of the cliff could not have been enough to keep him alive. Wasn't he ever sick? And what constant strength he must have had in his arms to maintain himself and the canoe ready for the piling up of the floodwaters where danger rolls on the great current, sweeping the bodies of dead animals and tree trunks downstream—

---

4. *exorcise*, to free from an evil spirit.

frightening, threatening, crashing into him. And he never spoke another word to a living soul. We never talked about him, either. We only thought of him. Father could never be forgotten; and if, for short periods of time, we pretended to ourselves that we had forgotten, it was only to find ourselves roused suddenly by his memory, startled by it again and again.

My sister married; but Mother would have no festivities. He came into our minds whenever we ate something especially tasty, and when we were wrapped up snugly at night we thought of those bare unsheltered nights of cold, heavy rain, and Father with only his hand and maybe a calabash to bail the storm water out of the canoe. Every so often someone who knew us would remark that I was getting to look more and more like my father. But I knew that now he must be bushy-haired and bearded, his nails long, his body cadaverous and gaunt, burnt black by the sun, hairy as a beast and almost as naked, even with the pieces of clothing we left for him at intervals.

He never felt the need to know anything about us; had he no family affection? But out of love, love and respect, whenever I was praised for something good I had done, I would say: "It was Father who taught me how to do it that way." It wasn't true, exactly, but it was a truthful kind of lie. If he didn't remember us any more and didn't want to know how we were, why didn't he go farther up the river or down it, away to landing places where he would never be found? Only he knew. When my sister had a baby boy, she got it into her head that she must show Father his grandson. All of us went and stood on the bluff. The day was fine and my sister was wearing the white dress she had worn at her wedding. She lifted the baby up in her arms and her husband held a parasol over the two of them. We called and we waited. Our father didn't come. My sister wept; we all cried and hugged one another as we stood there.

After that my sister moved far away with her husband, and my brother decided to go live in the city. Times changed, with the slow swiftness of time. Mother went away too in the end, to live with my sister because she was growing old. I stayed on here, the only one of the family who was left. I could never think of marriage. I stayed where I was, burdened down with all life's cumbrous baggage. I knew Father needed me, as he wandered up and down on the river in the wilderness, even though he never gave a reason for what he had done. When at last I made up my mind that I had to know and finally made a firm attempt to find out, people told me rumor had it that Father might have given some explanation to the man who made the canoe for him. But now the builder was dead; and no one really knew or could recollect any more except that there had been some silly talk in the beginning, when the river was first swollen by such endless torrents of rain that everyone was afraid the world was coming to an end; then they said that Father might have received a warning, like Noah, and so prepared the canoe ahead of time. I could half-recall the story. I could not even blame my father. And a few first white hairs began to appear on my head.

I was a man whose words were all sorrowful. Why did I feel so guilty, so guilty? Was it because of my father, who made his absence felt always, and because of the river-river-river, the river— flowing forever? I was suffering the onset of old age—this life of mine only postponed the inevitable. I had bed spells, pains in the belly, dizziness, twinges of rheumatism. And he? Why, oh why must he do what he did? He must suffer terribly. Old as he was, was he not bound to weaken in vigor sooner or later and let the canoe overturn or, when the river rose, let it drift unguided for hours downstream, until it finally went over the brink of the loud rushing fall of the cataract, with its wild boiling and death? My heart shrank. He was out there, with none of my easy security. I was guilty of I knew not what, filled with boundless sorrow in the deepest part of me. If I only knew— if only things were otherwise. And then, little by little, the idea came to me.

I could not even wait until next day. Was I crazy? No. In our house, the word *crazy* was not spoken, had never been spoken again in all those years; no one was condemned as crazy. Either no one is crazy, or everyone is. I just went, taking along a sheet to wave with. I was very much in my right mind. I waited. After a long time he appeared; his indistinct bulk took form. He was there, sitting in the stern. He was there, a shout away. I called out several times. And I said the words which were making me say them, the sworn promise, the declaration. I had to force my voice to say: "Father, you're getting old, you've done your part. . . . You can come back now, you don't have to stay any longer. . . . You come back, and I'll do it, right now or whenever you want me to; it's what we both want. I'll take your place in the canoe!" And as I said it my heart beat to the rhythm of what was truest and best in me.

He heard me. He got to his feet. He dipped the paddle in the water, the bow pointed toward me; he had agreed. And suddenly I shuddered deeply, because he had lifted his arm and gestured a greeting—the first, after so many years. And I could not. . . . Panic-stricken, my hair standing on end, I ran, I fled, I left the place behind me in a mad headlong rush. For he seemed to be coming from the hereafter. And I am pleading, pleading, pleading for forgiveness.

I was struck by the solemn ice of fear, and I fell ill. I knew that no one ever heard of him again. Can I be a man, after having thus failed him? I am what never was—the unspeakable. I know it is too late for salvation now, but I am afraid to cut life short in the shallows of the world.

At least, when death comes to the body, let them take me and put me in a wretched little canoe, and on the water that flows forever past its unending banks, let me go —down the river, away from the river, into the river—the river.

THE END

Development

1. The mother finds it hard to believe that the father would go out in the canoe "at his time of life." What is "his time of life," and why does his action appear incredible at this particular time?

2. What thematic conflict is suggested by the contrast between the mother's and neighbors' attitudes on the one hand, and father's and son's on the other?

3. *(a)* Recount the action of the story. *(b)* This action is open to various interpretations. Following are three possibilities. Defend the one which seems most valid to you.

(1) The father's action indicates that he is mad. His madness, in turn, almost causes madness in his son. Luckily, however, the son escapes this fate.

(2) The father's action is heroic. He alone, among all the villagers, has the courage to live according to his convictions. Unfortunately, his son is not so courageous: he submits to the bonds of conformity in the end.

(3) The father's action is one of giving up. Unable to face the responsibilities of a social being, he prefers to retreat to an elemental kind of existence and to let his son support him. He is a coward, and his son is a dupe.

4. Discuss the meaning of the story's title: Who or what do you think is the third bank of the river?

5. Would this have been a more or less interesting story if the son *had* taken his father's place in the end? Discuss.

The Photograph of the Colonel

EUGENE IONESCO / France

(1912 –   )

translated from the French by Stanley Read

One afternoon the municipal architect and I went to see the wealthy residential district: a suburb of white houses surrounded by gardens full of flowers and wide streets lined with trees. Shiny new cars stood before the entrances, the paths, and the gardens. Bright sunlight flooded down from a blue sky. I took off my topcoat and carried it over my arm.

"In this part of town," my companion said to me, "the weather is always fine. The land commands a high price, and the villas are constructed of the best materials; only well-to-do people, the cheerful, the healthy, the likable, live here."

"So I see. Here," I pointed out, "the trees are already in leaf and the light is filtered, but not so much as to shade the façades of the houses, while in all the rest of the city the sky is as gray as an old woman's hair, frozen snow still clings to the edges of the sidewalks, and the wind blows cold. This morning it was freezing when I got up. How curious it is to find ourselves in the midst of spring here, as though we had suddenly been transported a thousand miles to the south. When you take a plane, you often have the feeling that you are witnessing the transfiguration of the world. And yet you'd have to go to the airfield and fly for at least two hours in order to see the landscape metamorphose itself into the Riviera,[1] for instance. But here, we've done no more than take a short streetcar ride, and the trip, if you can even call it a trip, took place in the same places, if you'll permit me this little play on words, which, moreover, is unintentional,

I assure you," I said with a smile which was both witty and constrained. "How do you account for it? Is this district more sheltered? But I don't see any hills around to protect it from bad weather? In any case, as everyone knows, hills don't turn away the clouds, nor do they protect us from the rain. Are there bright, warm currents of air coming from below or above? But if that were the case, surely we'd have heard of it. There's no wind, although the air smells fresh. It's very curious."

"It's an island, quite simply," the municipal architect replied, "an oasis, just as sometimes in the desert you see astonishing cities rise up in the midst of arid sand, covered with fresh roses and surrounded with fountains and rivers."

"Ah, yes, that's right. You mean the kind of cities we call 'mirages'!" I said, to show that I was not completely ignorant.

At that time we were strolling alongside a park which I noticed had a pool in its center. We walked for almost a mile and a half through the villas, private residences, gardens and flowers. The calm weather was perfect; relaxing—too much so, perhaps. It began to be disturbing.

"Why don't we see anyone in the

"The Photograph of the Colonel" by Eugene Ionesco, translated by Stanley Read, from EVERGREEN REVIEW, Vol. 1, No. 3. Reprinted by permission of Grove Press, Inc. and Faber and Faber Limited. Copyright © 1957 by Grove Press, Inc.
1. *Riviera,* a coastal region in southeastern France, frequented as a resort area.

streets?" I asked. "We're the only strollers out. No doubt it's the hour for lunch and all the people are at home. But why don't we hear laughter and the clinking of glasses? There's not a sound. All the windows seem to be closed!"

We had stopped before two buildings that appeared to have been abandoned before they were finished. There they stood half erected, white in the midst of the greenery, waiting for the builders.

"It is so pleasant here!" I said. "If I were rich—alas, I earn but little—I'd buy one of these lots. In a few days the house would be built and I'd no longer have to live among the unhappy, in that dirty suburb, on those factory streets darkened by winter, dust, or mud. Here, the air smells so good," I said, inhaling the soft yet potent air which intoxicated my lungs.

My companion knit his brows: "The police have suspended all construction in this area. It was a pointless regulation, for no one is buying these lots today, anyway. The residents of the district even want to move out. But they have no other place to live. If it weren't for that, they'd have all packed their bags by now. Perhaps with them it's also a point of honor not to flee. They prefer to remain hidden in their beautiful homes. They don't go out except in case of extreme necessity, and then in groups of ten or fifteen. Even so, there is still danger."

"You're joking! Why are you putting on this serious air? You're darkening the day; do you want to discourage me?"

"I'm not joking, I assure you."

I felt a sudden pain in my heart. Everything clouded over for me. The resplendent landscape, in which I had taken root, which had, all at once, become part of me or of which I had become part, detached itself, became completely exterior to me, was no longer anything but a landscape in a frame, an inanimate object. I felt myself alone, outside of everything, lost in a dead clarity.

"Explain yourself!" I implored. I who had looked forward to a pleasant outing! "I was so happy a few moments ago!"

We were retracing our steps, as it happened, toward the pool.

"This is the place," the municipal architect said. "Right here is where they find two or three drowned, every day."

"Drowned?"

"Come and see for yourself that I'm not exaggerating."

I followed him. From the edge of the pool, I could see that there was, in fact, the swollen corpse of an officer in the engineering corps, floating in the water, as well as that of a little boy of five or six years, rolled up inside his hoop, and still holding his rod in his clenched hand.

"There are three today," my guide murmured. "There's another," he pointed with his finger.

A red head, that I had taken, for a moment, to be aquatic vegetation, emerged from the depths, but remained caught beneath the marble rim of the pool.

"How horrible! It's a woman, I believe."

"Apparently," he said, shrugging his shoulders. "The other is a man, and there's a child. That's all we know."

"Maybe she's the mother of the little one. . . . How sad! Who did this?"

"The murderer. It's always the same person. They can't catch him."

"But our life is in danger. Let's get out of here," I cried.

"As long as you're with me you're not in danger. I am the municipal architect, a city functionary; and he doesn't attack the administration. When I retire, it will be a different matter, of course, but, for the present . . ."

"Let's get away from here, anyway," I said.

We walked away at a fast clip. I was in a hurry to leave the wealthy residential district. The rich are not always happy, I thought, experiencing an indescribable distress. I suddenly felt dead tired, sick at heart, that existence was in vain. "What good is anything," I said to myself, "if this is what we end up with?"

"You surely expect that he'll be apprehended before your retirement begins?" I asked.

"That's not so easy! . . . You must know that we are doing everything we can . . ." he replied with a mournful air. Then he added: "Not that way, we'll lose our direction, we'll keep going around and around in circles . . ."

"Show me the way. . . . Ah! the day began so well. But now, I will always see those drowned people, that image will never leave my memory!"

"I should not have let you see them . . ."

"It can't be helped; it is better to know everything, better to know everything."

In a few moments we had reached a way out of the district, at the end of a drive on the edge of the outer boulevard and across from the streetcar stop. Some people were standing there, waiting. The sky was somber. I was cold, frozen. I put on my topcoat and wrapped my scarf around my neck. Thin rain was falling, water mixed with snow, and the pavement was wet.

"You don't have to go home right away, do you?" the commissioner asked me (that is how I learned that he was also a commissioner). "Surely you have time for a drink with me . . ."

The commissioner seemed to have regained his cheerfulness. Not I.

"There's a bar over there, near the streetcar stop, just a step from the cemetery; they sell wreaths there too."

"I don't feel very thirsty now, you know . . ."

"Don't worry about it. If one dwells on all the misfortunes of humanity, one cannot go on living. Every day children are massacred, old people starve, the widows, the orphans, the dying."

"Yes, Mr. Commissioner, but having seen this close up, seen it with my own eyes. . . . I cannot remain unconcerned."

"You are too impressionable," my companion replied, giving me a hearty slap on the shoulder.

We entered the bar.

"We're going to try to cheer you up! . . . Two beers!" he ordered.

We sat down near the window. The stout proprietor, wearing a vest and with his rolled-up shirt sleeves exposing his enormous hairy arms, came to serve us:

"For you, I have real beer!"

I started to pay him.

"No, no," said the commissioner, "it's on me!"

I was still heavy-hearted.

"If only you had his description!" I said.

"But we do have it. At least the one under which he operates. His portrait is posted all over the city."

"How did you get it?"

"From the drowned. Some of his victims, in their final agony, have regained consciousness for a moment and have been able to give us additional details. We also know how he goes about his game. As a matter of fact everybody in the district knows."

"But then why aren't they more prudent? All they have to do is to be on their guard."

"It's not so simple as all that. I tell you, every evening there are always two or three who fall into his trap. But he, he never lets himself get caught."

"I still can't understand."

I was astonished to perceive that this appeared to amuse the architect.

"Look," he said, "over there at the streetcar stop is where he makes his attack. When the passengers get off, on their way home, he goes up to them, disguised as a beggar. He whines, begs for money, tries to work on their pity. That's his usual dodge. He'll say that he's just been discharged from the hospital, has no job but is looking for one, has nowhere to spend the night. But that's only the opening. He singles out a kindly soul. He engages her in conversation, hooks onto her, doesn't let go for a moment. He offers to sell her various small objects that he takes out of his basket: artificial flowers, scissors, obscene pictures, all kinds of things. Generally, his offers are refused, the good soul is in a hurry, she hasn't got time. Spieling all the while, he moves along with her until they're near the pool that you saw. Then, all of a sudden, he pulls his master stroke; he offers to show her the photograph of the colonel. It's irresistible. Since there's no longer much light, the good soul bends over in order to see it better. At that moment she is lost. Seizing his chance while she is looking at the photograph, he pushes her and she falls into the pool. She drowns. The deed is done. All he has to do is to look for a new victim."

"What's so amazing is that they recognize him and yet they let him surprise them."

"It's a trap, that's what it is. He's crafty. He's never been caught in the act."

Mechanically, I looked through the window at the people descending from the streetcar, which had just arrived. I didn't see any beggar.

"You won't see him," the commissioner said, divining my thought. "He won't show himself, for he knows that we are here."

"Perhaps you ought to post a plain-clothes man on permanent duty at this place."

"That's not possible. Our inspectors are snowed under with work, they have other duties to perform. Moreover, they too would want to see the photograph of the colonel. Five of them have already been drowned in just that way. Ah! if we only had some evidence, we wouldn't have any trouble finding him!"

I parted company with my companion, not without having thanked him for being kind enough to take me to see the wealthy residential district, and also for so amiably permitting himself to be interviewed on the subject of all these unpardonable crimes. Alas, his instructive revelations will never appear in any newspaper: I am not a journalist, nor have I ever claimed to be one. The information of the architect-commissioner had been given to me entirely gratuitously. And it had filled me with anguish, gratuitously. Overcome with an indefinable malaise, I regained my house.

Edouard was waiting for me in the low-ceilinged, gloomy, autumnal sitting room (the electricity doesn't work during the day). There he was, seated on the chest near the window, dressed in black, very thin, his face pale and sad, his eyes burning. Presumably he still had a touch of fever. He noticed that I was distraught and asked me the reason. When I began to tell him of my experiences, he stopped me at the first words; he knew the whole story, he said, in a trembling, almost childish voice, and he was even surprised that I myself had not heard of it long before this. The whole city knew about it. That was why he had never spoken of it to me. It was something that everyone had talked about for a long time and now that it was old news it had been assimilated. But regrettable, certainly.

"Very regrettable!" I said.

In my turn, I did not conceal my surprise that he was not more disturbed. But perhaps I was unjust, perhaps his thoughts were on the disease that was consuming him, for he was tubercular. One can never hope to know the heart of another.

"Would you like to go for a little stroll?" he asked. "I've been waiting for you for a whole hour, and I'm freezing here in your house. Surely it must be warmer outside."

Although I was depressed and exhausted (I'd much rather have gone to bed), I agreed to go with him.

He got up and put on his felt hat with its black ribbon, and his dark-gray topcoat; then he lifted up his heavy, bulging brief case, but let it fall before he had taken a step. It fell open as it hit the floor. We both bent down, at the same time. From one of the pockets of the brief case some photographs had slipped out; they showed a colonel in full-dress uniform, mustachioed—an ordinary colonel with a good, even rather striking head. We placed the brief case on the table to look through it more easily; we took out several hundred more photographs, all of the same subject.

"What does this mean?" I demanded. "This is the photograph, the famous photograph of the colonel! You had it here and you never told me a word about it!"

"I don't keep looking in my brief case all the time," he replied.

"Still, it's your brief case, and you always carry it with you!"

"That's not a reason."

"Anyway, let's make use of the opportunity while we can, let's look further."

He plunged his white, sick man's hand, with its crooked fingers, into the other pockets of the enormous black brief case. Then he drew out (how was it able to contain so much?) incredible quantities of artificial flowers, of obscene pictures, of candies, of toy banks, of children's watches, of brooches, fountain pens, cardboard boxes, of I don't know what all—a hundred objects and some cigarettes. ("Those belong to me," he said.) The table was filled to overflowing.

"These are the things the monster uses!" I cried. "And you had them there!"

"I was unaware of it."

"Empty it all out," I encouraged him. "Go ahead!"

He went on taking out more things. There were calling cards with the name and the address of the criminal, his card of identity complete with photograph, and then, in a little case, some slips of paper on which were written the names of all the victims, and an intimate diary that we leafed through, with all its revealing details, his projects, his plan of action minutely described, his declaration of faith, his doctrine.

"You've got all the evidence right here. We can have him arrested."

"I didn't know," he mumbled, "I didn't know . . ."

"You could have saved so many lives," I reproached him.

"I feel embarrassed. I didn't know. I never know what I have, I'm not in the habit of looking in my brief case."

"It's a condemnable negligence!" I said.

"I apologize. I'm very sorry."

"And really, Edouard, these things couldn't have got into your brief case all by themselves. Either you've found them or you've received them!"

I felt pity for him. He had flushed red, he was truly ashamed.

He made an attempt to remember.

"Ah, yes!" he cried after several seconds. "I recall it now. The criminal sent me his private diary, his notes, his lists, a long time ago, begging me to publish them in a literary review—that was long before he carried out the murders and I had completely forgotten all about it. At the time it never occurred to me that he would perpetrate them; it was only later that he must have decided to carry out his plans; as for me, I regarded all this as so much daydreaming, without any relation to reality, a sort of science fiction. Now, of course, I regret that I did not carefully consider the matter, that I did not associate his papers with subsequent events.

"In any case the relationship is between intention and realization, neither more nor less; it's as clear as the light of day."

From the brief case he also took out a large envelope that we opened; it contained a map, a very detailed map carefully marked to show all the places where the assassin had been encountered and it gave his exact schedule, minute by minute.

"It's simple," I said. "We'll notify the police, and all they have to do is nab him. Let's hurry, the office of the prefecture closes before nightfall. If we're late, there'll be no one there. And by tomorrow he may have changed his schedule.

Let's go to the architect and show him the evidence."

"All right," said Edouard, rather indifferently.

We left on the run. In the hallway, we bumped into the concierge, who cried, "What do you mean by . . ." The rest of her sentence was lost in the wind.

By the time we had reached the main avenue we were winded and had to slow down. To the right, plowed fields extended as far as the eye could see. To the left were the first buildings of the city. And straight ahead of us, the setting sun was purpling the sky. Some bare trees straggled along both sides of the avenue. Only a few people were out.

We followed along the rails of the streetcar tracks (had it already stopped running?) which extended far into the distance.

Three or four large military trucks (I don't know where they came from) suddenly blocked our way. They were parked along the sidewalk, which, at this point, lay beneath the level of the roadway, which seemed, because of this difference of level, to be raised.

It was fortunate that Edouard and I had to pause to catch our breath, for I suddenly noticed that my friend did not have his brief case with him.

"What have you done with it? Here I assumed that you were carrying it with you," I said. The scatterbrain! In our hurry he had left it in the house. "There's no point in going to see the commissioner without our evidence! What were you thinking of! You're incomprehensible. Go back quickly and look for it. I'll run on so that I can at least warn the commissioner in time and get him to wait. Hurry back to the house and try to rejoin me as soon as possible. The prefecture is at the end of the street. I don't like being alone on an errand like this: it's unnerving, you understand."

Edouard disappeared. I began to experience a sensation of fear. Here the sidewalk descended even lower, so much

so that some steps should have been built, four to be exact, so that pedestrians might have access to the roadway. By now I was very close to one of the big trucks in the center of the line (the others were ahead and behind). This was an open truck, with rows of benches on which were sitting, pressed tightly together, forty young soldiers in dark-colored uniforms. One of them held a big bouquet of red carnations in his hand. He was using it as a fan.

Several policemen came up to direct the traffic, loudly blowing their whistles. I was grateful for their help: the traffic jam was holding me up. These policemen were unusually tall. One of them, who was standing near a tree, looked taller than the tree itself when he raised his night stick.

Then I saw a small, modestly dressed gentleman with white hair, hat in hand, standing before the policeman whose great height made him appear even smaller; he was asking him very politely, perhaps too politely, but with real humility for some small item of information. Without interrupting his signaling, the policeman, in a rough voice, replied abruptly to the retiring gentleman (who might perfectly well have been his father, given the difference in age, but excluding the difference in stature, which did not favor the old man). The policeman sent him on his way with a rude word, turning back to continue his work and blowing his whistle.

The policeman's attitude shocked me. In any case it was his *duty* to be polite to the public—surely that was incorporated in the regulations. "When I see his chief, the architect, I will try to remember to speak to him about this!" I said to myself. As for us, we are all too polite, too timid with the police; we've encouraged them in their bad habits and it's basically our fault.

A second policeman, as huge as the first, came over and stood near me on the sidewalk. He was visibly annoyed by the traffic jam, about which, it must be admitted, he had every right to be annoyed. Having no need of steps to mount up from the sidewalk to the road-way, he approached very near the truck full of soldiers. Although his feet were on a level with mine, his head was some-what higher than their heads. Accusing them of tying up the traffic, he harshly reprimanded the soldiers, who were scarcely to blame, least of all the young man with the bouquet of red carnations.

"You've nothing to do but amuse your-self with this?" he asked him.

"I'm not doing anything wrong, Mr. Policeman," replied the soldier very gen-tly, in a timid voice. "This isn't holding up the truck."

"Insolence, it's jamming the motor!" cried the policeman, slapping the soldier, who didn't say a word. Then the police-man grabbed the flowers and threw them away; they disappeared.

I was personally outraged by this be-havior. I firmly believe that there is no hope for a country where the police have the upper hand over the army.

"Why are you meddling in this? Is it any of your business?" he said, turning toward me.

In no wise had I expressed my thoughts aloud. They must have been easy to di-vine.

"In the first place, what are you doing here?"

I seized upon his question as an excuse to explain my case, possibly to ask his advice, even his assistance.

"I have all the evidence," I said, "and now the murderer can be arrested. I must hurry on to the prefecture. It's not very far from here. Can you go there with me? I'm a friend of the commissioner, of the architect."

"That's not my branch. I'm in traffic control."

"Yes, but . . ."

"That's not part of my job, don't you understand! Your story doesn't interest me. Since you're connected with the chief, go on and see him and get the hell out of here. You know the way, get going, nothing's stopping you."

"All right, Mr. Policeman," I said, as politely as the soldier but in spite of my-self: "Very well, Mr. Policeman!"

The policeman turned to his colleague who was standing beside the tree and said with harsh irony: "Let the gentle-man pass!"

This man, whose face I could see through the branches, gave me the signal to advance. As I passed near him, he screamed at me in a rage, "I hate you!" Though surely it was I who had more of a right to say that than he.

I found myself alone in the center of the road, the trucks already far behind me. Onward I hurried, straight toward the prefecture. Night was fast approach-ing, the north wind was freezing, and I was worried. Would Edouard be able to rejoin me in time? And I was furious with the police: these people are good for nothing but to annoy us, to teach us good manners, but when we have a real need for them, when it is a question of defending us—then it's a case of "tell it to the Marines"—they let us down every time!

On my left there were no more houses. Only gray fields on both sides of the road. There seemed to be no end to this route, or this avenue, with its streetcar rails. I walked and walked: "If only he's not too late, if only he's not too late!" I thought to myself.

Abruptly, he surged up in front of me. There could be no doubt of it: it was the murderer; and all about us there was only the darkened plain. The wind was wrapping an old sheet of newspaper around the trunk of a gaunt tree. Behind the man, at a distance of several hundred yards, I could see in profile, against the setting sun, the prefecture office build-ings, not far from the stop where the streetcar had just arrived; I could see some people descending—they seemed very small at that distance. No help was possible, they were much too far away, they would not be able to hear me.

I stopped short, frozen in my tracks. "These lousy cops," I thought, "they've left me alone with him on purpose. They want people to think that it was only a private quarrel!"

We were face to face, but two steps from each other. I looked at him in silence, on my guard. He stared at me and he was almost laughing.

He was a man of middle age, skinny, stunted, very short of stature, and ill-shaven; he appeared to be weaker than I. He was wearing a dirty, worn gabardine coat, torn at the pockets, and some of his toes were sticking out of the gaps in his broken-down shoes. He had a dilapidated, almost shapeless hat on his head; he kept one hand in his pocket, while with the other he clenched a knife with a large blade that reflected a livid gleam. He fixed me with his single cold eye, made of the same material and glittering with the same light which was reflected from his weapon.

Never had I seen an expression so cruel, of such hardness—and why?—of such ferocity. An implacable eye, that of a snake, perhaps, or of a tiger, a heedless murderer's. No word, friendly or authoritative, no reasoning would be able to persuade him; no promise of happiness, not all the love in the world would be able to touch him; nor could beauty cause him to give way, nor irony shame him, nor all the sages of the world succeed in making him comprehend the vanity of crime, which is as vain as charity.

The tears of the saints might fall on this lidless eye, on this steely look, without softening it in the least; battalions of Christs could have followed one another to their Calvaries for him in vain.

Slowly I drew from my pockets my two pistols, and in silence, for two seconds, held them aimed at him. He did not flinch. I lowered them, let my arms fall. I felt myself disarmed, desperate: what could bullets—any more than my feeble strength—do against the cold hate and obstinacy, against the infinite energy of this absolute cruelty, without reason and without mercy?

THE END

Development

INTERPRETATION

1. (a) When are you first aware that the world of this story is somewhat fantastic? (b) Cite some of the fantastic elements in the story. (c) How do these elements affect your reaction to the persons and events in the story? (d) What concepts might the following represent: the fancy suburb, the narrator, the killer, Edouard, the architect?

2. (a) What is the narrator's attitude toward his life when the story opens? (b) How has this attitude changed by the end of the story?

3. After the disappearance of Edouard, the story takes on the increasingly strange character of a dream, which concludes with a nightmare. What mental or emotional states might the following events in this "dream" suggest? (a) The narrator runs into a traffic jam. (b) The narrator sees abnormally large policemen beating innocent soldiers. (c) A man screams, "I hate you!" at the narrator. (d) The narrator finds himself facing the killer alone, at night, on a deserted road.

TECHNIQUE

1. Reread the paragraph wherein Edouard apologizes for not reporting the killer when he receives the briefcase from him (page 489, column 2, paragraph 9). (a) Is Edouard's apology worded as you would expect, given the situation? Explain. (b) Characterize the tone of the paragraph. (c) What comment does Edouard's apology imply about man's abuse of language?

2. In the play version of this story (called "The Killer") Ionesco states that the killer need not actually appear at the end of the play, i.e., the narrator may speak to an "invisible" killer. *(a)* Why, in the stage version, might Ionesco consider the representation of the killer by an actor to be unnecessary? *(b)* Would the appearance of the actor make the ending more or less effective? Discuss. *(c)* Why is it impossible for Ionesco to suggest an invisible killer in the short story?

3. Some readers might object to "The Photograph of the Colonel" because of its ridiculous events and incredible characters. Discuss how you would defend Ionesco's technique against these objections. Consider the following quotation of Ionesco's in your discussion: "We need to be virtually bludgeoned into detachment from our daily lives, our habits and mental laziness, which conceal from us the strangeness of the world."[1]

Comparison

1. The idea of the absurd is considered to be a modern concept, particularly relevant to the problems and the thinking of today. Discuss these three stories in terms of their modernity, considering the following points. *(a)* How do the protagonists in the stories differ from the usual hero figures? *(b)* What modern disillusionments are suggested in the action of each story? *(c)* Which of the three selections is the most relevant to the modern situation? Discuss.

2. The writers in this group tend to be concerned with the limitations and abuses of language. Compare and contrast the significance of the silent killer at the end of "The Photograph of the Colonel" with that of the silent father in "The Third Bank of the River." Consider the following points in your discussion. *(a)* What do the other characters wish them to talk about? *(b)* Why is each silent? *(c)* How do their "listeners" react?

3. Compare the narrators of "The Third Bank of the River" and "The Photograph of the Colonel" in terms of: *(a)* what their goals appear to be at the beginning of the story; *(b)* how they have altered these goals by the end of the story; *(c)* what each has learned from the experience.

4. An absurd world is one which deals unjustly with the people in it. *(a)* What elements of injustice do you find in "Picnic on the Battlefield" and in "The Photograph of the Colonel"? *(b)* Could either or both of these stories be considered "protest" literature? Discuss.

5. "Picnic on the Battlefield" and "The Photograph of the Colonel" both have tragic endings; however, much of the tone of both stories is comical. Explain the reason for and the effect of this odd combination of tragic and comic elements. Consider the following quotation in your discussion:

> . . . the comic is the intuition of the absurdity of a universe in which man has neither dignity nor absolutes, and therefore a more starkly depressing universe than that of tragedy which confers upon man a certain nobility and meaning in the midst of his defeat.[2]

6. *(a)* Although these stories end tragically, what positive traits do the characters exhibit? *(b)* What values do these stories affirm?

7. *(a)* Someone might object to the characters in these stories as cardboard figures devoid of humanity. Do you agree? Discuss. *(b)* To what extent are they accurate reflections of the human condition?

8. Formulate a concise definition of "absurd man" as you have come to understand the term from reading these three stories.

1. From NOTES AND COUNTER NOTES by Eugene Ionesco, translated by Donald Watson. Copyright © 1962, by Editions Gallimard, and 1964 by Grove Press. **2.** Paragraph by Leonard C. Pronko from EUGENE IONESCO. Reprinted by permission of Columbia University Press.

MASKS CONFRONTING DEATH by James Ensor. Courtesy of Musée des Beaux-Arts, Liège.

The Intruder

THE END OF IACOB ONISIA / GEO BOGZA / RUMANIA

THE INTRUDER / MAURICE MAETERLINCK / BELGIUM

LAMENT FOR IGNACIO SANCHEZ MEJIAS / GARCÍA LORCA / SPAIN

The End of Iacob Onisia[1]

GEO BOGZA / Rumania

(1908–   )

translated from the Rumanian

Christmas had come throughout Jiu Valley.[2]

This great, dismal holiday had set in from Lonea as far as Lupeni, though many did not know what to do with it. The mining villages were wrapped in a deep, almost oppressive stillness. Not a single wheel was seen turning anywhere; everything stood stock-still, buried in silence. The last train had left the station at midnight, and no whistle had been heard since then. The siren had not sounded at ten o'clock at night nor at four in the morning.

At dawn the light fog soon lifted; by nine in the morning, a cold, clear sunshine flooded the whole valley, and everything looked like a mass of ice that no one dared break. Through its transparency everything looked as if it had fallen deep into water which had then frozen around, bringing all things to an absolute standstill. Christmas, with the perfect stillness it had brought, had pushed the valley farther north overnight, turning it into a polar region.

All around, things seemed to be congealed everlastingly. Who would have dared shatter the giant mass of ice covering the world? It was Christmas day in Jiu Valley.

Then, in this immutable vastness a human body tumbled down into the void from a height of over six hundred feet, and all around and a long way off, the air was rent by a fearful scream. Doors were opened, heads peered out of windows; that was how Jiu Valley finally began stirring. A little later the telephones began to buzz like mad at the managing office of the pits and at the mining inspector's offices in Petrosani.

"A man has fallen off the funicular railway at Dilja, sir! He's dead, sir!"

That was how the first telephone call began on that Christmas morning. It must have been quite unusual and unbelievable, for the chief of the inspectors' offices was staring with eyes wide open and kept speaking into the receiver: "It can't be! It is impossible!"

Impossible in this valley where so many misfortunes and so many disasters had occurred? The engineer said the man could not have fallen off the funicular railway that morning, because it had stopped running the evening before.

"He's just fallen, sir, this very minute!" the hoarse voice that announced the misfortune insisted at the other end of the wire. Then they rang up the funicular station of Aninoasa, then that of Petrila, the Cermini, and the police station. In Jiu Valley the telephone bells started ringing everywhere, and for a long time. The people, who had expected a day of rest and quiet, heard the long buzzing of the telephone bells and they all felt that they were ringing in an unusual way that boded no good. They reached out their hands, picked up the receivers, listened in astonishment, and spoke several times into them: "It can't be! It's impossible!"

"The End of Iacob Onisia" by Geo Bogza from INTRODUCTION TO RUMANIAN LITERATURE, edited by Jacob Steinberg. Reprinted by permission of Twayne Publishers, Inc.

1. *Iacob Onisia* (yä′kob ô nē′sē ä). 2. *Jiu* (zhē′u) *Valley,* in southwest Rumania near the Jiu River. All the towns mentioned in the story are in this general vicinity.

The chief engineer of Aninoasa, who controlled the funicular, was away at Vulcan; they made the electric echo of the telephone bell ring after him, wherever it could be heard, and finally it found him. When he had listened to what was being said to him, he answered as the others had before him, but with even greater assurance: "It's impossible! The funicular stopped running last night!"

"The man is lying dead in the valley at Dilja. He fell and died this morning. . . . All the snow is splashed with blood."

Then, all of them visualized this picture and accepted it as something real and not subject to doubt. However, a question occurred to all of them, and some spoke it out, pushing it along the telephone wires, between the mountains, towards the station of Dilja: "How? How did it happen?"

At first no one could answer. The telephone bell rang everywhere. In the offices, in the engineers' homes, at the termini, at the gates—everywhere—those who had been called, called others in turn and questioned each other. It was Christmas day and a vast silence had pervaded the valley, but now the telephones were breaking it, in the air as in people's hearts.

Everyone was called two or three times from two or three different places and in his turn called others just as many times, as in a wood where a hundred people hail each other, awakening all possible echoes at once. They were sitting in well-heated rooms which they could not bring themselves to leave, while away among the snowcapped mountains a mangled man was lying, about whom they were trying to learn, from afar, why he had died and how, on that clear, motionless Christmas morning.

"Get some men to carry him away on a stretcher. He can't be left here overnight; the wolves would eat him up . . ." the same hoarse voice at the other end of the wire was saying once again, the same voice that had roused them all and that now could hardly utter the words. The telephone started buzzing again, calling the life-saving team from Petrila.

It was a quarter to ten when the schoolmaster of Aninoasa reached the market place in Petrosani, where several people had already gathered. As he came up to the first group, he said suddenly, gesticulating with both arms: "Listen, friends, a great misfortune has happened at Dilja. A terrible thing! I saw it with my own eyes."

He need not have added the last word. His eyes were still wide with fright and white, and his face, although frozen, was as pale as a dead man's. "I've never before seen a man so pale on such a frosty day," those who met him that day said later. "He had death in his eyes, frozen and white like a ghost."

The schoolmaster of Aninoasa had witnessed the terrible misfortune that had occurred that morning.

And that was how it all became known —what the people had vainly tried to find out by asking one another on the telephone: how the misfortune had happened.

Then, on all sides, the telephone bell started ringing anew. At the mining inspectors' offices it was ringing for the twelfth time.

"Yes, I'm listening. He was in the car and came out of it? But, good God, what was he doing there?"

"Wanted to follow the wire cable with his hands? He fell into the precipice; yes, I see."

And that is how, on that Christmas morning, the chief of the mining inspectors at Petrosani started investigating the strangest and most distressing misfortune that had ever happened in Jiu Valley.

That morning two sledges started from the managing offices of the pits, loaded with men wearing black coats, among which the policeman's khaki overcoat was discernible. At the same time, the men of Petrila had left, carrying a stretcher, taking a short cut over the hills. The schoolmaster of Aninoasa was returning in one of the sledges to the place where he had experienced his great terror. The mining villages were smoking quietly through hundreds of chimneys.

At first the sun shone right in front of them, and they found it almost pleasant. Mount Paring rose along the skyline like one single dazzling mass. The sunlight came straight down on its snowcapped crests, while its three large peaks soared up into the sky like so many gorgeous pyramids of light. Only the mountains to the south, standing in the shade, had darker outlines, wrapped, as it were, in a thin, bluish mist. In contrast, everything in the west shone. They went on in this way for a good while. The bells of the sledge kept tinkling with a metallic sound almost sweet to the ear. They listened to them in silence, feeling the sound enter their brains, soothing them after the jarring buzzing of the telephones. Over and above the buzzing that still filled the people's heads, the melodious rhythm of the sledge bells fell like a layer of snow, quieting and covering everything.

Then they felt the cold. The sledges had taken another turn and started along a valley towards the north. The ridge of a hill had hidden the sun, and in the shade the cold became so bitter that they had to wrap themselves up well in their coats, shivering.

"It was twenty degrees last night," said a voice from one of the sledges. And the men felt even colder. Still, to the north, towards which they were going, the mountains, all bathed in light, shone more brilliantly than anywhere else. As they faced the south, the sunshine did not fall straight on the crests only, but on their entire height; they shone in one single mass, from one end to the other, on all sides, like a vast, white realm exposed to the sun. But the sledges were gliding along the foot of the hills in the shade and the cold, and the people in them seldom raised their heads from the upturned collars of their coats to gaze

sadly and mistrustfully at the dazzling white light in front of them.

They had almost reached the heights above the place from which they had started, right against Petrosani, on the other side of the mountain, and they went on, still further uphill. Then, one of them happened to look up suddenly and see in the air, against the white background of the mountains, a black dot hanging above the chasm. It looked like an eagle, motionless in the air, watching for its prey. It was one of the carriages of the funicular railway. Soon another one became visible, hanging above the precipice. For a time this one too looked like an eagle, as the sledge advanced, the two birds of prey moved against the spotless background of the mountains, gliding along constantly until they stood out against the calm, blue vastness of the sky. There was not one single cloud.

Now the sledges were beneath them. On either side of the valley, on either crest of the mountain, stood, higher still, two iron supports, the tops of which were connected by four cables spanning the chasm at a height that shut them out beyond the boundaries of the world. There, as under a circus top where trapezes swing, was the realm of daring and madness. The men gazed at the two black dots, remembered why they were there, and shuddered.

They started climbing the western slope on foot, along a narrow path. They had to reach the other side where there was no road for the sledge. They walked briskly. There was no buzzing of telephones, no jingling of sledge bells—only the dry, harsh cracking of the snow. Sometimes it crunched under their boots like a piece of linen being torn. The iron support in front grew bigger and bigger, and gradually the numerous iron girders of which it was made became distinct. The ascent was becoming wearisome. The men were hot and panting. Then one of them said: "On these slopes, no matter how bitter the cold, you are sure to sweat."

Then something quivered painfully like an indescribable foreboding in the heart of one of the six men climbing the mountain. It was as though two black birds which had long been looking for each other had met in the air, and the fluttering of their wings had come to his ears, troubling him.

If, at that moment, the chief engineer had slipped down in the snow and had been able to doze off and dream, he might have seen in his dream a man coming towards him with arms and legs broken, his face smeared with coal and blood and wet with snow, whispering again into his ear: "Yes, on these slopes, no matter how bitter the cold, you are sure to sweat." Then the two black birds would have been recognizable and known by name. Unaware, one of these men had uttered the sentence that cleared up the strange event they were witnessing; it was another who felt his heart flutter with premonition.

Twenty-four hours before, the same words had been spoken in this same place by the man who now lay crushed on the other side of the mountain.

On these slopes, no matter how bitter the cold, you are sure to sweat! And indeed the sweat was running in drops down Onisia's chest and back. And he had gone only half of the way over the hills. He had another mile and a half to go along the river Jiu, to reach Petrila.

From Aninoasa to Petrosani there were three deep valleys and the ridges of three tall hills to cross, at the edge of the mountains. The footpath led across them, dipping low into the valleys, then up the crests, and down again. There could not be a more severe ordeal. Each time he reached the summit of a hill with great difficulty and saw that he had to go down the other side at once and then to climb the opposite slope again, a dull rage seized him. "A real punishment!" he muttered. And he would remember he was really being punished.

He was not ashamed of being punished.

The chief engineer had laid his hand on his shoulder and said: "Onisia, you've got to understand!" And, he had understood indeed. Two months would soon be over! He had not been sorry at the time. It was autumn, the plum brandy was being made, and he had come to the second shift walking rather unsteadily. As a matter of fact, he had walked quite unsteadily. They would not let him go down into the pit. So he had struggled and entered the cage by force. Those on the ground had tried in vain to shout at him. Did anything happen? No. They all admitted nothing wrong had happened. He had gone to the workings, had not quarreled with anyone, had worked quietly, and had loaded an extra truck of coal. But they punished him all the same.

Neither the overseer, nor the foreman, nor the engineer wanted to punish him. They knew Iacob Onisia too well to want to punish him. They knew Iacob Onisia well; indeed they did. But the chief engineer was easily alarmed: he said he'd have to report to the general board in Bucharest. "Why do we need to report to Bucharest?" the head of the sector had asked. "You're young," the engineer had answered. "You haven't seen much of life yet. Suppose some day others did the same and there'd be trouble and we'd want to punish them. Then they'd complain to Bucharest that we did not punish Onisia. And suppose the bigwigs asked why we had not punished Onisia. So we had better write and be on the safe side."

And they wrote to Bucharest all that had happened, that Onisia had been a decent collier for seventeen years at Aninoasa and that he did not deserve to be punished. A fortnight later the answer came from Bucharest: he had to be punished! He must be transferred to Petrila for two months. They were all sorry; they laid their hands on his shoulder and said: "Onisia, you've got to understand!"

And he had begun his punishment on November 1. From Aninoasa to Petrila there were three kilometers in a beeline along the wire cable of the funicular railway. It took three quarters of an hour. But, on foot, over the hills, it took him nearly three hours. When he was in the first shift, he left home at three in the morning. His wife and children were asleep. At half past four, when the sirens whistled to wake up the men for the shift, he was climbing the second hill. By six he had hardly got to Petrila.

It had been going on like that for five weeks. Twice he had been in the third shift, from ten at night till morning, and twice in the first. Now he went down at two in the afternoon and came up at ten at night. A few days more and his trials would be over. And a good thing, too, for he was quite worn out. The way was hard. He had already worn out a pair of boots. It seemed as if all his life, as far back as he could remember, he had done nothing but go up and down hills. Above his head, the cars of the funicular railway kept coming and going like big, black birds. And he kept walking, sometimes on the ridge of the hill, sometimes low down in the valley.

At first it had still been autumn. Along the way there were straggling birches, their leaves turning yellow. Had it been only a walk, it would have been a lovely one indeed. Mount Paring was always before his eyes, dark about the middle of its height, but snowcapped. Nevertheless, here on the sun-scorched hills, the people of Dilja grazed their cattle among the peaceful birches.

About a week later, rain set in, and the footpath filled with mud. The way had become very hard. He struggled with the hills and thought wrathfully of the big men in Bucharest. "To be transferred to Petrila for two months! What did they know about the distance between Aninoasa and Petrila? They ought to come here and get into the mud if only once, at three in the morning, like ghosts, long before the cocks have crowed." Then things became worse. The rain became chillier and changed into sleet. If, at least, they'd

allowed him to take the funicular! But no one was allowed to take it. Only the surveyor of the line passed once a day from one end to the other and then back, standing in the car like a huge bat, its wings spread.

A week before St. Nicholas' day—he was in the second shift then—the blizzard began, and for three days after there was nothing but snow everywhere. Sometimes it would snow for a whole night, but the following day the people of Dilja would make a footpath again. They needed money for Christmas and started for Aninoasa or Petrosani, carrying to market a sack of apples or a young pig.

When Onisia reached Petrila, a few old women dressed in black—they were widows—were standing in front of the entrance to the pit, selling *sorcovas*[3] to the men of the first shift, just coming out. He entered the courtyard and then remembered his children at home; he went back and bought a *sorcova*. At night, when he'd leave work there would be no one at the gate. The siren blew long to announce the two o'clock shift. He hurried toward the mine. A large iron stove filled with coals was blazing in the yard, and a young girl in trousers was warming her hands. He went by smiling and called to her without stopping: "Good luck!"

Seeing him come with the *sorcova* the men at the gate teased him: "Say, Onisia, if you take it down to the mine, it'll be a pretty sight when you come out!" and "Come along, Iacob, and wish the ponies a Happy New Year."

He left it at the surface, however, with one of the truckers. In the mine, he had found a good helper in a man from Cimpa, with whom he got on very well. Together they filled fourteen trucks.

That day all in the pit spoke only of wine, sausages, and roast pork.

Onisia had killed his pig three days before. And he would buy wine the next

---

3. *sorcovas*, sticks adorned with ribbons and artificial flowers which Rumanian children hold while they wish adults a Happy New Year.

day, at Aninoasa. In front of them, all the while, they had a hard black wall of coal, but in their mind's eye they saw large joints of red meat, such as they had seen at home in their troughs, and then they swung their picks with increased mettle, almost with fury. Large lumps of coal fell to their feet. Only the ponies, well fed every day, fat and calm, pulled the trucks without sharing the eagerness that was exciting the miners and the joy that filled their thoughts. Not even the oldest of the ponies, who knew a lot of the secrets of the pit and had a sixth sense, suspected that the following day was Christmas and that they were to be blessed with two days' rest in the stables.

However, in order to see to it that nothing amiss could happen in the following two days, about five o'clock the miners lay down their picks and, taking hold of their hatchets, started the propping. By the end of the shift the workings were lined with new white boards, well supported on all sides. The seam of coal was hardly visible, and there was a smell of fresh pine wood. Now the pit could be left alone for two days to spend Christmas in quiet.

In the courtyard lighted by electric bulbs snow sifted down in small flashes. The colliers walked to the gate, their shoulders slightly bent, like living shadows. Each of them carried his round log of wood under his arm or on his back. They parted, wishing each other good luck; then Onisia was left alone, and he quickened his pace. He crossed the Jiu over the railway bridge and started climbing towards the mining village of Bucovina. In the dark he could hear the cars of the funicular railway pass. Tonight it was to be the fifth time. Only it was colder than ever and high up there he could freeze to death. But rather than cut across those hills, he'd . . .

Four times already Onisia had returned to Aninoasa by the ropeway, stealthily,

in the dark, and he was going to do it again this time too.

No one suspected anything, and he passed over the three deep valleys, in a beeline, like a bird, without going up their slopes and then down into their depths. He crossed above and looked down at them with hatred and joy as on mortal enemies now become quite harmless. Down below, the valleys writhed like vile dragons, and they would still have liked to torture him, but could not get at him. He passed overhead in the funicular, and each time he felt as though he were thrusting a spear into their throats, like Saint George when he rode over the dragon.

Iacob Onisia walked through the village of Bucovina, between the two rows of lighted houses where people were making their Christmas preparations. In front of every house there was a black stain in the snow where the women had thrown out the basinfuls of lye with which they had scrubbed the floors of their homes. In his house, too, the floors had been scrubbed and there was a holiday smell about.

The cages kept clattering in the air, passing above the houses in the village. Somewhere on the hill, children were singing Christmas carols, going from house to house.

Onisia climbed the wooden scaffolding at the terminus as stealthily as a cat. He reached the platform, and then the cars passed by him slowly, one after the other, like the carriages of a train in a station when the train is starting; all you've got to do is to jump into one. He looked a couple of times towards the surveyor's lighted cabin, let two cars pass, and, when the third came up, threw his hatchet and the *sorcova* into it, and, taking firm hold of it with both hands, leaped into it over its iron railing. He felt the walls with his boots, found a log, and quickly sat down on it. Below, near the surveyor's cabin, a dog had begun to bark, so he buried his head between his shoulders, squatting on the floor of the car. Who could have seen him now? The car was gliding smoothly above the ground, towards Aninoasa. In an hour he would be home.

People who have pictured heaven to themselves and then related what it is like, have had little imagination. This thought dawned upon Iacob Onisia repeatedly in the first moments when he felt so happy to be carried through the air in the carriage. To be in heaven was to travel by the funicular over hills and deep valleys, without the slightest fatigue.

Far behind, Petrila was vanishing in the distance, looking like the Pleiades when they are setting. A short while after, however, when he was above Petrosani, the world burst into a fairy-like vision which no one could have credited. Holding the *sorcova* in his hand, Onisia sat on and gazed.

As far as eye could reach, the earth was like a sea of burning embers glittering all the time. Hundreds upon hundreds of lights, a myriad of will-o'-the-wisps, were shining in the night, far away, to the edge of the mountains. So many were crowded in the middle of the town that one could scarcely distinguish them from one another. It was like a jumble of lamps of all kinds—like people on a market day. One, a very tall one, rose high above the others, like a lonely man who does not mix with the crowd. On the outside came those in rows along the streets of the mining village, one behind the other, in straight lines. Then, they became sparser but kept stretching one by one farther and farther away into the depths of night.

In the middle of this sea of light, cleaving it in two, ran a river of darkness. Yet, against its pitch-black background there still could be seen here and there a few glimmers, red or green like so many sickly glowworms about to die. It was the railway station with its twenty lines, and between them the snow had been covered with coal dust and cinder so that everything was blacker than the very darkness of the night.

From the town there rose a sort of din, wave after wave, like a hum of an apiary in which the bees, coming across some sweet flower, want to carry all its nectar home. Above this sea of lights the car carried Onisia slowly towards Aninoasa. The lights gradually started sinking, but very, very slowly, like a world sinking into the depths. Lightly, almost imperceptibly, the cable was dragging the carriage towards the crest of the first hill.

To the north the snowcapped mountains loomed out of the dark and drew nearer, ever nearer, as though eager to be touched by him. When he was quite high up, at the side of the first mountain, Petrosani was still discernible far behind, as at the bottom of an ocean, with its lights merging and forming a huge diadem. One of the termini was drawing near, and Onisia lay low in the carriage lest he should be seen. Then he realized he was chilled with the cold, and he crouched close to the wooden partition to ward off the stinging cold a little. Above the frozen deserted plateau, the car was gliding between the iron supports like a ghost.

Then came the first of the three valleys. The cables of the funicular railway spanned the precipice from one end to the other, without any support, curving only slightly, and the car followed them, floating above the chasm in the dark. The cables then rose up the opposite slope, reached the strong support on which they rested for an instant as though to gather new strength, and immediately started across the second valley, which was also the lowest. At its bottom one could scarcely make out a few vague lights—the cottages in the hamlet of Dilja. The cage seemed to be on the same level with them as it passed in its aerial progress, moved forward slowly for a while, then stopped. The grinding of the wheels gliding along the cables stopped too. Suddenly there was a deep silence.

It could not be more than half past ten. Onisia huddled at the end of the carriage and waited. He thrust his fists into his pockets as far as he could, but between their edge and his coat sleeves, which were too short, there still remained a strip of bare flesh, and he felt the cold there as biting as though he had been wearing handcuffs. From there the pain ran up under his coat to his elbows, where it became very sharp. He tried to soothe it by pressing them against his ribs as hard as he could. Maybe it would have been better if he had gone on foot, seeing it was so bitterly cold. But he would have got home past midnight. A good thing there was no wind. The car would soon start. He rolled a cigarette and lit it with great difficulty.

The cigarette was almost smoked and still the car did not move. Then, at the moment when he was taking the last puff at it, the greatest misfortune in his life happened. As if kindled by a spark, everything was destroyed in an instant.

That is how things happen in the pit when gas takes fire. The rails of the trucks are wrenched from the ground and twisted in the air. Along the shafts men lie dead, their hair and clothes burnt. And some pony blocks the way— a mass of charred flesh.

Since evening, when he had left by the funicular, a gas had made its way into his head, accumulated within him, and now it exploded. And he was as completely destroyed as if he had been in a pit where gas had taken fire. Nothing might have happened. But a spark had kindled it at the very moment when the shafts were full. Now, within him, everything turned into smoking ruins. When had a man ever done so much harm to himself with one single thought? Suddenly it had occurred to him, "Tomorrow would be Christmas! The funicular would not start. It would be stopped for two days." And these last two thoughts, which were so closely linked with the first that he scarcely had had time to

think them, flashed through him, sparking the catastrophe.

In one single instant everything was ruined: a real explosion had taken place within his heart and mind when he realized in a flash that he was the prisoner of the chasm, of night and frost. He suffered terribly. With eyes frozen by dread he viewed the world differently. It seemed to him a terrible, treacherous enemy; everything that had happened, beginning with the day in autumn when he had got drunk, seemed now a fearful trap into which he had stumbled.

All the men were at home now, enjoying the warmth of the hearth, and would stay there for two days. The pits and the installations above ground were deserted. For two days and two nights nothing would stir while he, suspended in the car above the precipice, would perish with hunger and cold. He felt like howling. Instead, it was a wolf that howled, away in the valley, at Dilja, on the skirts of the forest.

How would the hours pass for him from now on? And what would become of him? Like colliers who, having been saved from the bottom of the shafts, come out staggering, their lamps out, their clothes torn, his thoughts shaped out, torturing him, and prolonging the catastrophe. But this violent anguish of mind began to wane when, instead, two precise sensations arose and took possession of his whole being, like two implacable demons thrusting long, sharp spears into his flesh. He felt hungry. He felt cold. More and more, without any way of escape, he became a prey to this excruciating suffering. He was unable to endure it any longer.

And then, above Mount Paring, the moon rose.

Has any man ever had so fairy-like a sight before his eyes while suffering the pangs of death? A few tears gushed out of Iacob Onisia's eyes, trickled down his rugged cheeks and froze there. "O Lord, do not desert me!" his lips muttered while, mortified, he was gazing at the grand sight unfolding before his eyes.

The long shadows of the mountains had begun to move, gliding above the earth with a stately slowness that seemed to send a shiver over the world. Bulky masses of darkness hovered over the snow, turning round and round and trying to catch up with each other, like beasts of bygone times, roused to life in the dead of the night. Meanwhile, high upon the crests, the mountains shone as though ablaze. Glittering flames, some white, some blue, just as cold and unreal, danced above the peaks, as if all the treasures of the earth lay within them. Cold, silent and white, the moon flitted about the frozen glass surface of the sky.

To the north, the mountains nearly rose into the air like gigantic temples of white marble.

"O Lord, do not desert me!" the thoughts and lips of the man hanging above the precipice kept murmuring in a sort of mechanical prayer. Then this cold, polar landscape in which the big shadows of the mountains were the only moving things, suddenly became alive, and hope kindled in Iacob Onisia's heart. Yet this hope, like the lights that danced above the mountaintops, was unreal, unrelated to the heavy fate which from the beginning had pressed down upon the breast, on the life, on the heart of the poor collier from Aninoasa.

As in almost every year, as though it were a tradition, wolves entered the hamlet of Dilja on this Christmas Eve too. There were a few sheepfolds there. At first some muffled noises came up from the peasants' yards; then the dogs broke into a medley of frightful, desperate barking. The next minute all the doors were flung open, and inside, while the women turned up the light of the oil lamps, the men dashed out roaring at the top of their voices, like wild beasts.

Seizing pitchforks or clubs, they rushed towards the sheep pens, running barefooted in the snow.

The fight seemed to be taking place at one end of the hamlet. There, men were roaring louder than anywhere else, urging one another while the dogs rushed forward, concentrating their barking on this place. Black patches were gliding over the snow. Most likely the wolves had stolen a sheep and were falling back with it towards the forest. Small, reddish flames blazed up several times, and the reports of a gun rang out from valley to valley.

Hanging above the chasm, Iacob Onisia looked down at what was going on, at first hopefully, then as though at a performance from another world. How could all this be of any help to him? The men's feet down below were stamping the ground, and they could fight the wolves. Lucky for them! His mind was sending them desperate messages: "Please don't leave me to die here; don't, please!" But his throat, stiff and dry, could not utter a single word. Who could have heard him?

Down below, the uproar of the dogs died down, and frightened bleating was heard. Towards him, too, big wolves were coming from the void, about to tear him to pieces; and he would not be able even to feel the warmth of his own blood flowing out his veins. He was frozen to the marrow of his bones. His fur cap, the worse for wear but still good enough, which had always kept his head warm, now seemed as thin as cigarette paper. Still, when he took it off, to stick his closed fists into it and warm them a little, he felt his forehead bound all around in a narrow circle of ice which burned like vitriol; so he put on his cap again at once. His feet were as stiff and cold as stumps. And he was hungry, a deep, black hunger that drained all his strength. In the depth of his belly was a torturing, painful emptiness, more distressing than the chasm gaping below him. There in the thick of the forest, the wolves were eating the sheep and having their fill. They too were lucky. And so were all those whose feet touched the ground. He alone hung between sky and earth, surrounded by the cold air, by the waves of cold that tore at him mercilessly.

His agony was to last long and to be accompanied by delusion. Several times he strained his ears; his heart was flooded by a sudden warmth when it seemed to him that the cage was starting. . . . Maybe the ropeway had only been out of order; maybe it would still run all night, until dawn. Those thoughts cast a warm, friendly light upon the world. He would soon be home, in the cozy, warm room, on the floor well scrubbed with lye. But, alas, the funicular was still motionless, still as a stone, in the black mass of the frosty night.

Had they known he was here, they might have started it and hauled him to the village. But what would the chief engineer have said? Another punishment—no doubt about it. Thousands of thoughts and familiar faces crossed his mind; his mate at Petrila, his own wife, his children, the chief engineer, the publican at Aninoasa, the shepherds of Dilja—all in turn came to him in the cage, spoke to him, scolding or advising him what to do, then faded away in the dark.

He felt the handle of his hatchet, the log at the bottom of the carriage, and an idea, a grand one, occurred to him, making its way with difficulty through his frozen mind. He sat the log upright and started chipping it. The hatchet rang against the frozen wood. Then he dealt a sure blow at it and split it in two. Plying his hatchet in the moonlight, he looked like a man busy at his work—weirdly at that late hour of the night and so high up, cut off from the rest of the world.

His hands numb with cold, he struck a first match under the heap of chips, but it went out before it could kindle them. He struck another, impatiently,

held it underneath until the whole match burned and the flame licked his fingers, but still the chips would not kindle. Then he took the *sorcova* and set fire to it with a third match. The paper flowers caught fire at once, one after the other; their petals writhed, and he stuck them under the heap of chips which finally started crackling.

It may have been one o'clock in the morning, or later. The moon had sailed past the white crests of Mount Paring and was now above the dark forests of the Surduc pass. The huge shadows of the mountains kept moving, flitting over the whiteness of the snow. Now there were other shadows too, small, quivering, fleeting shadows that attended the unfolding of the drama being played in the silent realm of the night and the snows.

The shadow of Onisia's figure stood out up to the waist against the partition of the carriage, while his shoulders and head emerged from it; they were lost in the dark, their outline dim and much enlarged, like that of a giant. Maybe his shadow reached the white columns of the mountains to the north, beyond which lay, not a long way off, the site of the ancient Sarmizegethusa. Iacob Onisia was the last Dacian[4] in those ancestral parts to spend the night in the open air, by the light of a pine-wood fire. But of the millions of men who in the course of two thousand grim years had spent the night in loneliness with nothing but a fire to keep them company, had there ever been a more tortured, unfortunate soul than his?

There was an old shepherd at Dilja, made rather simple because of a beating at the hands of the police back in the

---

4. *Sarmizegethusa* (sär mē zā gä tü′ zä) . . . *Dacian* (dā′ shŭn). Dacia was the old name for a European region corresponding approximately to modern Rumania. It was inhabited before the Christian era by people called Getae by the Greeks and Daci by the Romans. Sarmizegethusa is the Rumanian town believed to be the site of the ancient capital of Dacia.

time of the Empire.[5] The next morning, after hearing what had happened, he related the following: after the incident with the wolves, when the cocks crowed for the third time, he went out again and found himself standing stock-still with fright. In the black sky, very high up, his eyes saw quite distinctly a part of Hell. There, in the murky night, was a cauldron with pitch like those in which sinners burn in Hell, such as are seen painted in church. Red flames and sparks rose from within it, and in the middle a man was writhing his body about. Alarmed at this apparition of Hell, especially because of its appearance during the holy night of Christmas, he went in, crossing himself. A little later, looking through the window, he saw the flames going out, and shortly after the cauldron of pitch vanished in the dark.

The schoolmaster from Aninoasa, whose wife had died in childbirth that autumn, had been asked to spend Christmas day with the priest of the Orthodox Church at Petrosani. Since he wished to attend Mass, he had left home early in the morning. There was a hard, dull bitterness of frost. He had climbed the first hill, then the second, and when coming down the valley to Dilja, the footpath he had taken suddenly showed the traces left by the fight waged that night. The snow had been swept away, and in the place where the dogs had fought the wolves, were strewn big tufts of hair. Soon, bloodstains could be seen, which made him sick. The memory of the hospital, as white as the snow, with stains of blood here and there, was still vivid in his mind and painful.

To avoid this sight, he looked up and in the very first moment saw the unusual thing that was about to happen.

High up, on the wire cable of the funicular, a man sat astride the side of the cage, looking down as though to sound the depth of the precipice. Whatever was he doing up there? The schoolmaster

had been walking for one hour, and all the while he had seen the cars lined out along the route, motionless, at their great height. How had that man got into the cage above the precipice? It was not one of the red cages in which people down below were used to seeing the line surveyors pass. But he had not too long to wonder.

Dumfounded, he saw the man in the carriage, after a brief hesitation, take hold of the cable with both hands, letting his feet hang in the void. Then, after wavering one more moment, he advanced along the cable holding on with his hands.

Catching his breath, his blood frozen with fear, the schoolmaster realized what was going on. That man moving hand over hand along the cable above the precipice was trying to reach the iron support at the top of the hill. He might have some forty-five yards to go. And the cold up there. . . .

Against the blue background of the sky, the car and the man were two distinct blotches. The car stood still, while the long, thin shadow of the man moved slowly to the left. Hanging above the void, he was advancing. When he released one hand to place it farther on, his body lost its balance and threatened to break away from the wire that supported it. Then the man quickly brought his other hand up, resting like that for a few moments, while he hung on with both hands and his body got back its balance as he seemed to gather new strength. Then he rapidly jerked one hand farther along, as though to catch a bird, and brought his other hand ever more rapidly into line with the first, avoiding the danger of hanging on by only one hand. And his legs kept beating the air as though they were trying to help him along.

However, like a tired swimmer who sees the shore is still far away, his arms found it harder and harder to move. He

---

5. *Empire*, the Austrian Empire.

had managed to move perhaps ten yards from the car. The time he spent clinging with both hands to recover strength was getting longer and longer. Once he lifted his hand to move on, but brought it back in no time. Shaking all over, his teeth chattering, the schoolmaster stood and gazed.

The man on high no longer had the strength to move on. Once more he tried to lift his hand and set it a bit farther on, but he pulled it back even more quickly.

Clinging to the cable with both his hands, he hung quite still while his legs beat the air slower and slower, as in the throes of death. The schoolmaster felt his heart throbbing violently in his chest, sending hot waves of blood to his temples and his throat. And the ghastly climactic moment was not long in coming.

A bird flew past the line of the rope-way; perhaps the man up there had time to see it with his eyes wide with fear, thinking his last thought: "Oh, if only I had wings!" Then one hand detached itself from the cable, without moving as it had hitherto. The body hung for one moment by one hand; then his other hand detached itself too, and he began falling. He came down in the air, wheeling 'round and 'round, his arms and legs moving frantically as in an epileptic fit; at the same time the schoolmaster felt him falling through his own body, cleaving it like a knife from top to toe. When he had almost reached the ground, the schoolmaster thought he saw the doomed man's face under his disheveled hair, his eyes looking at him with awe and hatred; and at the very same moment the valley was roused by a heart-rending scream.

It was Christmas day.

Down in the village, at Dilja, there was a wide expanse of snow. When the men who had started from Petrosani reached the top of the second hill, they perceived far down on the white expanse of snow a somber group of men moving slowly hither and thither, changing places in turn. Those who had left from Petrila with the stretcher were waiting there.

The place where the man had fallen from the car bore tracks of the night fight where the wolves had crossed on their way to the forest: tufts of hair and stains of blood. The impact of the man's fall had scattered the snow about as a big stone would have, and bespattered it with his blood. He was completely crushed —a hodgepodge of flesh, bones, clothes and snow mixed with blood and coal dust, all frozen into a single mass of different colors, painful to behold. His big hands, which had held his whole life in them and had not been able to keep it, were swollen and blue. His face, intact, was turned upward to the sky. His eyes, wide open and frozen, gazed at the heights from which he had tumbled. His struggle was over now. The valleys that had tortured him all through the autumn and which he had then crossed over in the funicular railway, like dragons transfixed by his spear, had taken a most terrible revenge on him. He had fallen into the lowest of them all as into the mouth of the most wicked and ruthless of all those dragons. High up, the car out of which he had fallen stood black and immobile, like an airbound coffin.

On either side the iron supports rose on the mountain ridges, rising to dazzling heights.

With shovels in their hands, the men from Petrila were drawing nearer, to clear away the snow.

The funeral passed through Aninoasa about noon, watched from all windows by sad, gloomy faces. Everyone knew Iacob Onisia, and this sudden violent death on Christmas day had filled them with deep sorrow.

In the dead man's kitchen, which they had to cross in order to carry the body into the room, the pig killed a few days before was still in the trough—large pieces of red bleeding meat. On the stretcher the four men were carrying other large pieces of crushed bleeding meat. While the dead man's wife sobbed and beat her head with her fists, all those present crossed themselves when the procession entered; and it was a dismal, somewhat threatening feeling of mournful silent protest rather than pious awe that could be read on their faces.

Yet another one of them had met a sudden, unfair death.

Two days later, when the funicular railway started running again and all the cages were searched, at the bottom of the one in which Iacob Onisia had traveled was found the hatchet, the heap of ashes from the fir-wood fire he had made, and in a corner the *sorcova* only half-burnt, its remaining flowers crumpled and covered by coal dust.

Development

INTERPRETATION

1. *(a)* Recount the series of events which lead Iacob Onisia to take the funicular railway on the night before he dies. *(b)* What in these events might explain the reaction of his friends to his death: ". . . it was a dismal, somewhat threatening feeling of mournful silent protest rather than pious awe that could be read on their faces" (page 508, column 1, lines 8-11)?

2. At the beginning of the story, the narrator refers to the cars of the funicular railway as black birds (note: *black birds*, not *blackbirds*). *(a)* Explain the appropriateness of this metaphor. *(b)* Reread paragraph 2 on page 499, column 1. What is the meaning of the sentence, "Then the two black birds would have been recognizable and known by name"?

3. Reread the section in which the nature of Iacob's catastrophe is described (page 503, column 1, paragraphs 1-4). *(a)* Explain the meaning of the sentence, "Since evening, when he had left by the funicular, a gas had made its way into his head, accumulated within him, and now it exploded." *(b)* What is the nature of the spark which kindles this explosion? *(c)* According to the passage, who or what is the cause of Iacob's death?

4. *(a)* How do the following details affect the significance and impact of Iacob's tragedy: *(1)* the incident of the wolves, *(2)* the metaphor of the valleys as dragons, *(3)* the Christmas Eve setting? *(b)* How is the Christmas Eve setting also relevant to the plot of the story?

TECHNIQUE

1. Bogza is noted in his native Rumania primarily as a writer of nonfiction. In what ways does "The End of Iacob Onisia" suggest the style of a nonfiction writer?

2. Reread the first four paragraphs. *(a)* Describe their tone. *(b)* What do they forebode?

3. This story begins at a point in time after the main action has been completed (*in medias res*). Since we know of Iacob's death early in the story, what sustains the reader's interest during the section in which he is alive?

EXTENSIONS

1. In his essay "Self-Reliance," Ralph Waldo Emerson maintains that "society everywhere is in conspiracy against the manhood of every one of its members." Is "The End of Iacob Onisia" an illustration of this idea? Discuss.

2. Hamlet mused that fear ". . . makes us rather bear those ills we have/Than fly to others that we know not of." Iacob's action in climbing out of the funicular car seems to contradict this theory. Which, in your opinion, seems truer to human nature, Hamlet's thought or Iacob's act? Discuss.

The Intruder

MAURICE MAETERLINCK[1] / Belgium

(1862 – 1949)

translated from the French by Haskell M. Block

CHARACTERS

THE GRANDFATHER (He is blind.)
THE FATHER (Paul)
THE UNCLE (Oliver)
THE THREE DAUGHTERS (Ursula, Genevieve, and Gertrude)
THE SISTER OF MERCY
THE MAID

A dimly lit room in an old country-house. A door on the right, a door on the left, and a small concealed door in a corner. At the back, stained-glass windows in which the color green predominates, and a glass door opening on to a terrace. A tall Dutch clock in one corner. A lighted lamp.

THE THREE DAUGHTERS. Come here, grandfather. Sit down under the lamp.

THE GRANDFATHER. It does not seem to be very light here.

THE FATHER. Shall we go on to the terrace, or stay in this room?

THE UNCLE. Would it not be better to stay here? It has rained the whole week, and the nights are damp and cold.

THE ELDEST DAUGHTER. Still, the stars are shining.

THE UNCLE. Oh, the stars—that's nothing.

THE GRANDFATHER. We had better stay here. You never know what may happen.

THE FATHER. We don't have to worry any more. The danger is past, and she is saved. . . .

THE GRANDFATHER. I believe she is not doing well. . . .

THE FATHER. Why do you say that?

THE GRANDFATHER. I have heard her voice.

THE FATHER. But since the doctors assure us that we need not worry . . .

THE UNCLE. You know quite well that your father-in-law likes to worry us needlessly.

THE GRANDFATHER. I don't see these things as you do.

THE UNCLE. Then you ought to rely on those who see. She looked very well this afternoon. She is sleeping quietly now, and we are not going to spoil the first pleasant evening that luck has given us. . . . It seems to me we have a right to relax and even to laugh a little this evening, without being afraid.

THE FATHER. That's right; this is the first time I have felt at home with my family since this terrible childbirth.

THE UNCLE. Once illness has come into a house, it is as though there were a stranger in the family.

THE FATHER. And then, you see too, that apart from the family, you cannot count on anyone.

THE UNCLE. You are absolutely right.

THE GRANDFATHER. Why could I not see my poor daughter today?

THE UNCLE. You know quite well that the doctor has forbidden it.

THE GRANDFATHER. I do not know what to think. . . .

THE UNCLE. There is no point worrying.

THE GRANDFATHER (*pointing to the door on the left*). She cannot hear us?

From MASTERS OF MODERN DRAMA, edited by Haskell M. Block and Robert G. Shedd. © Copyright 1962 by Random House, Inc. Reprinted by permission.

1. *Maeterlinck* (mãt′ ər lingk).

THE FATHER. We won't talk too loud; besides, the door is very thick, and the Sister of Mercy is with her and would warn us if we made too much noise.

THE GRANDFATHER (pointing to the door on the right). He cannot hear us?

THE FATHER. No, no.

THE GRANDFATHER. He is asleep?

THE FATHER. I suppose so.

THE GRANDFATHER. Someone should go and see.

THE UNCLE. I would worry more about the little one than about your wife. It is now several weeks since he was born, and he has hardly moved. He has not cried once all the time. He is like a wax doll.

THE GRANDFATHER. I think he will be deaf—dumb too, perhaps. The usual result of marriage between cousins. . . . (A reproving silence.)

THE FATHER. I am almost angry with him for the suffering he has caused his mother.

THE UNCLE. We must be reasonable; it is not the poor little one's fault. He is all alone in the room?

THE FATHER. Yes. The doctor does not want him to stay in his mother's room any longer.

THE UNCLE. But the nurse is with him?

THE FATHER. No. She has gone to rest a little; she has earned it these past few days. Ursula, just go and see if he is sleeping well.

THE ELDEST DAUGHTER. Yes, father. (THE THREE DAUGHTERS get up, and go into the room on the right, hand in hand.)

THE FATHER. When is our sister coming?

THE UNCLE. I think she will come about nine.

THE FATHER. It is after nine. I hope she will come this evening. My wife is anxious to see her.

THE UNCLE. She is sure to come. This will be the first time she has been here?

THE FATHER. She has never been in the house.

THE UNCLE. It is very difficult for her to leave her convent.

THE FATHER. She will be alone?

THE UNCLE. I think one of the nuns will come with her. They cannot go out alone.

THE FATHER. But she is the Superior.

THE UNCLE. The rule is the same for all.

THE GRANDFATHER. You are no longer anxious?

THE UNCLE. Why should we feel anxious? What's the good of harping on that? There is nothing more to fear.

THE GRANDFATHER. Your sister is older than you?

THE UNCLE. She is the eldest of us all.

THE GRANDFATHER. I do not know what is wrong with me; I feel uneasy. I wish your sister were here.

THE UNCLE. She will come; she promised to.

THE GRANDFATHER. I wish this evening were over!

(THE THREE DAUGHTERS come in again.)

THE FATHER. He is asleep?

THE ELDEST DAUGHTER. Yes, father, very soundly.

THE UNCLE. What shall we do while waiting?

THE GRANDFATHER. Waiting for what?

THE UNCLE. Waiting for our sister.

THE FATHER. You see nothing coming, Ursula?

THE ELDEST DAUGHTER (at the window). No, father.

THE FATHER. Not in the avenue? Can you see the avenue?

THE DAUGHTER. Yes, father; there is moonlight, and I can see the avenue as far as the cypress woods.

THE GRANDFATHER. And you do not see anyone?

THE DAUGHTER. No one, grandfather.

THE UNCLE. How is it outside?

THE DAUGHTER. Beautiful. Do you hear the nightingales?

THE UNCLE. Yes, yes.

THE DAUGHTER. A little wind is rising in the avenue.

THE GRANDFATHER. A little wind in the avenue?

THE DAUGHTER. Yes; the trees are trembling a little.

THE UNCLE. I am surprised that my sister is not here yet.

THE GRANDFATHER. I do not hear the nightingales any more.

THE DAUGHTER. I think someone has come into the garden, grandfather.

THE GRANDFATHER. Who is it?

THE DAUGHTER. I do not know; I can't see anyone.

THE UNCLE. Because there is no one there.

THE DAUGHTER. There must be someone in the garden; the nightingales have suddenly stopped singing.

THE GRANDFATHER. But I do not hear anyone walking.

THE DAUGHTER. Someone must be passing by the pond, because the swans are frightened.

ANOTHER DAUGHTER. All the fishes in the pond are diving suddenly.

THE FATHER. You cannot see anyone?

THE DAUGHTER. No one, father.

THE FATHER. But yet the pond is in the moonlight . . .

THE DAUGHTER. Yes; I can see that the swans are frightened.

THE UNCLE. I am sure it is my sister who frightens them. She must have come in by the little gate.

THE FATHER. I cannot understand why the dogs do not bark.

THE DAUGHTER. I can see the watch-dog at the very back of his kennel. The swans are crossing to the other bank! . . .

THE UNCLE. They are afraid of my sister. I will go and see. (He calls.) Sister! Sister! Is that you? . . . There is no one there.

THE DAUGHTER. I am sure that someone has come into the garden. You will see.

THE UNCLE. But she would answer me!

THE GRANDFATHER. Are not the nightingales beginning to sing again, Ursula?

THE DAUGHTER. I cannot hear a single one anywhere.

THE GRANDFATHER. And yet there is no noise.

THE FATHER. There is a stillness of death.

THE GRANDFATHER. It must be some stranger who frightens them, for if it were someone from the house, they would not be silent.

THE UNCLE. Are you going to talk about nightingales now?

THE GRANDFATHER. Are all the windows open, Ursula?

THE DAUGHTER. The glass door is open, grandfather.

THE GRANDFATHER. It seems to me that the cold is coming into the room.

THE DAUGHTER. There is a little wind in the garden, grandfather, and the rose leaves are falling.

THE FATHER. Well then, shut the door. It is late.

THE DAUGHTER. Yes, father— I cannot shut the door.

THE TWO OTHER DAUGHTERS. We cannot shut it.

THE GRANDFATHER. Why, what is the matter with the door, my children?

THE UNCLE. You need not say that in such an extraordinary voice. I will go and help them.

THE ELDEST DAUGHTER. We cannot quite shut it all the way.

THE UNCLE. It is because of the damp. Let us all lean on it together. There must be something in the way.

THE FATHER. The carpenter will fix it tomorrow.

THE GRANDFATHER. Is the carpenter coming tomorrow?

THE DAUGHTER. Yes, grandfather; he is coming to do some work in the cellar.

THE GRANDFATHER. He will make a noise in the house!

THE DAUGHTER. I will tell him to work quietly. (Suddenly the sound is heard of a scythe being sharpened outside.)

THE GRANDFATHER (with a shudder). Oh!

THE UNCLE. What is that?

THE DAUGHTER. I don't exactly know; I think it is the gardener. I cannot quite see; he is in the shadow of the house.

THE FATHER. It is the gardener going to mow.

THE UNCLE. He mows at night?

THE FATHER. Is not tomorrow Sunday? Yes—I noticed that the grass was very long around the house.

THE GRANDFATHER. It seems to me that his scythe makes a good deal of noise. . . .

THE DAUGHTER. He is mowing around the house.

THE GRANDFATHER. Can you see him, Ursula?

THE DAUGHTER. No, grandfather. He is in the dark.

THE GRANDFATHER. I am afraid he will wake up my daughter.

THE UNCLE. We can hardly hear him.

THE GRANDFATHER. It sounds to me as if he were mowing inside the house.

THE UNCLE. The sick one will not hear it; there is no danger.

THE FATHER. It seems to me that the lamp is not burning well tonight.

THE UNCLE. It needs oil.

THE FATHER. I saw it oiled this morning. It has been burning badly ever since the window was shut.

THE UNCLE. I think the chimney is dirty.

THE FATHER. It will burn better soon.

THE DAUGHTER. Grandfather is sleeping. He has not slept for three nights.

THE FATHER. He has been worried a lot.

THE UNCLE. He always worries too much. At times he will not listen to reason.

THE FATHER. It is quite excusable at his age.

THE UNCLE. God knows what we shall be like at his age!

THE FATHER. He is almost eighty.

THE UNCLE. Then he has a right to be queer.

THE FATHER. He is like all blind people.

THE UNCLE. They meditate a little too much.

THE FATHER. They have too much time to spare.

THE UNCLE. They don't have anything else to do.

THE FATHER. And besides, they have no fun.

THE UNCLE. It must be terrible.

THE FATHER. Apparently you get used to it.

THE UNCLE. I cannot imagine it.

THE FATHER. They are certainly to be pitied.

THE UNCLE. Not to know where you are, not to know where you have come from, not to know where you are going, not to be able to tell noon from midnight, or summer from winter—and always the darkness, the darkness! I would rather not live. Is it absolutely incurable?

THE FATHER. Apparently.

THE UNCLE. But he is not completely blind?

THE FATHER. He can make out strong lights.

THE UNCLE. We must take care of our poor eyes.

THE FATHER. He often has strange ideas.

THE UNCLE. There are times when he is not a bit funny.

THE FATHER. He says absolutely everything he thinks.

THE UNCLE. But he was not always like this?

THE FATHER. Certainly not. Once he was as normal as we are; he never said a thing out of the way. It is true that Ursula encourages him a little too much; she answers all his questions. . . .

THE UNCLE. It would be better not to answer them. It's not a favor to him. *(Ten o'clock strikes.)*

THE GRANDFATHER *(waking up)*. Am I facing the glass door?

THE DAUGHTER. You have had a good sleep, grandfather?

THE GRANDFATHER. Am I facing the glass door?

THE DAUGHTER. Yes, grandfather.

THE GRANDFATHER. There is no one at the glass door?

THE DAUGHTER. No, grandfather, I do not see any one.

THE GRANDFATHER. I thought someone was waiting. No one has come?

THE DAUGHTER. No one, grandfather.

THE GRANDFATHER (to the UNCLE and FATHER). And your sister has not come?

THE UNCLE. It is too late; she will not come now. It is not nice of her.

THE FATHER. I'm beginning to worry about her. (A noise, as of someone coming into the house.)

THE UNCLE. She is here! Did you hear?

THE FATHER. Yes; someone has come in through the basement.

THE UNCLE. It must be our sister. I recognized her step.

THE GRANDFATHER. I heard slow footsteps.

THE FATHER. She came in very quietly.

THE UNCLE. She knows there is a sick person here.

THE GRANDFATHER. I don't hear anything now.

THE UNCLE. She will come up at once; they will tell her we are here.

THE FATHER. I am glad she has come.

THE UNCLE. I was sure she would come tonight.

THE GRANDFATHER. She is slow in coming up.

THE UNCLE. However, it must be she.

THE FATHER. We are not expecting any other visitors.

THE GRANDFATHER. I cannot hear any noise in the basement.

THE FATHER. I will call the maid. We shall see what's going on. (He pulls a bell-rope.)

THE GRANDFATHER. I can hear a noise on the stairs already.

THE FATHER. It is the maid coming up.

THE GRANDFATHER. It seems to me that she is not alone.

THE FATHER. She is coming up slowly. . . .

THE GRANDFATHER. I hear your sister's step!

THE FATHER. I can only hear the maid.

THE GRANDFATHER. It is your sister! It is your sister!

(There is a knock at the little door.)

THE UNCLE. She is knocking at the door of the back stairs.

THE FATHER. I will go and open it myself because that little door makes too much noise. We use it only when we want to come up without being seen. (He partly opens the little door; the MAID remains outside in the opening.) Where are you?

THE MAID. Here, sir.

THE GRANDFATHER. Your sister is at the door?

THE UNCLE. I can only see the maid.

THE FATHER. It is only the maid. (To the MAID.) Who came into the house?

THE MAID. Came into the house?

THE FATHER. Yes, some one came in just now?

THE MAID. No one came in, sir.

THE GRANDFATHER. Who is sighing like that?

THE UNCLE. It is the maid; she is out of breath.

THE GRANDFATHER. Is she crying?

THE UNCLE. No. Why should she be crying?

THE FATHER (to the MAID). No one came in just now?

THE MAID. No, sir.

THE FATHER. But we heard the door open!

THE MAID. It was I, shutting the door.

THE FATHER. It was open?

THE MAID. Yes, sir.

THE FATHER. Why was it open at this time of night?

THE MAID. I do not know, sir. I had shut it.

THE FATHER. Then who opened it?

THE MAID. I do not know, sir. Someone must have gone out after me, sir. . . .

THE FATHER. You must be careful. But don't push the door; you know what a noise it makes!

THE MAID. But sir, I am not touching the door.

THE FATHER. You are too! You are pushing as if you were trying to get into the room!

THE MAID. But sir, I am three steps away from the door!

THE FATHER. Don't talk so loud.

THE GRANDFATHER. Are they putting out the light?

THE ELDEST DAUGHTER. No, grandfather.

THE GRANDFATHER. It seems to me it has suddenly grown dark.

THE FATHER (to the MAID). You can go down again now; but do not make any more noise on the stairs.

THE MAID. I did not make any noise.

THE FATHER. I tell you that you did make a noise. Go down quietly; you might wake your mistress. And if anyone comes, say that we are not in.

THE UNCLE. Yes; say that we are not in.

THE GRANDFATHER (trembling). You must not say that!

THE FATHER. . . . Except to my sister and the doctor.

THE UNCLE. When will the doctor come?

THE FATHER. He cannot come before midnight. (He shuts the door. A clock is heard striking eleven.)

THE GRANDFATHER. She has come in?

THE FATHER. Who?

THE GRANDFATHER. The maid.

THE FATHER. No, she has gone downstairs.

THE GRANDFATHER. I thought she was sitting at the table.

THE UNCLE. The maid?

THE GRANDFATHER. Yes.

THE UNCLE. That is all we need!

THE GRANDFATHER. No one has come into the room?

THE FATHER. No, no one has come in.

THE GRANDFATHER. And your sister is not here?

THE UNCLE. Our sister has not come.

THE GRANDFATHER. You are trying to deceive me!

THE UNCLE. Deceive you?

THE GRANDFATHER. Ursula, tell me the truth, for the love of God!

THE ELDEST DAUGHTER. Grandfather! Grandfather! What is the matter with you?

THE GRANDFATHER. Something has happened! I am sure my daughter is worse!

THE UNCLE. Are you dreaming?

THE GRANDFATHER. You do not want to tell me! . . . I can see that there is something . . .

THE UNCLE. In that case you can see better than we can.

THE GRANDFATHER. Ursula, tell me the truth!

THE DAUGHTER. But we have told you the truth, grandfather!

THE GRANDFATHER. You are not speaking in your usual voice.

THE FATHER. That is because you frighten her.

THE GRANDFATHER. Your voice is changed too.

THE FATHER. You are going crazy! (He and the UNCLE make signs to each other to show that the GRANDFATHER has lost his reason.)

THE GRANDFATHER. I can hear clearly that you are afraid.

THE FATHER. But what should we be afraid of?

THE GRANDFATHER. Why do you want to deceive me?

THE UNCLE. Who is thinking of deceiving you?

THE GRANDFATHER. Why have you put out the light?

THE UNCLE. But the light is not out; it is as bright as it was before.

THE DAUGHTER. It seems to me that the lamp has dimmed.

THE FATHER. I see as well as ever.

THE GRANDFATHER. I have millstones on my eyes! Tell me, girls, what is going on here! Tell me, for the love of God, you who can see! I am here, all alone, in darkness without end! I do not know who sits down alongside of me! I do not know what is happening two feet from me! . . . Why were you talking under your breath just now?

THE FATHER. No one was talking under his breath.

THE GRANDFATHER. You were talking softly, near the door.

THE FATHER. You heard all I said.

THE GRANDFATHER. You brought some one into the room?

THE FATHER. But I tell you no one has come in!

THE GRANDFATHER. Is it your sister or a priest? You should not try to deceive me—Ursula, who came in?

THE DAUGHTER. No one, grandfather.

THE GRANDFATHER. You should not try to deceive me. I know what I know! How many of us are there here?

THE DAUGHTER. There are six of us around the table, grandfather.

THE GRANDFATHER. You are all around the table?

THE DAUGHTER. Yes, grandfather.

THE GRANDFATHER. You are there, Paul?

THE FATHER. Yes.

THE GRANDFATHER. You are there, Oliver?

THE UNCLE. Of course, of course I am here, in my usual place. That's not alarming, is it?

THE GRANDFATHER. You are there, Genevieve?

ONE OF THE DAUGHTERS. Yes, grandfather.

THE GRANDFATHER. You are there, Gertrude?

ANOTHER DAUGHTER. Yes, grandfather.

THE GRANDFATHER. You are there, Ursula?

THE ELDEST DAUGHTER. Yes, grandfather, next to you.

THE GRANDFATHER. And who is sitting there?

THE DAUGHTER. Where do you mean, grandfather? There is no one.

THE GRANDFATHER. There, there—in the midst of us!

THE DAUGHTER. But there is no one, grandfather!

THE FATHER. We tell you there is no one!

THE GRANDFATHER. But you don't see—any of you!

THE UNCLE. Look, are you joking?

THE GRANDFATHER. I do not want to joke, I assure you.

THE UNCLE. Then trust those who can see.

THE GRANDFATHER (undecidedly). I thought there was someone . . . I believe I shall not live much longer. . . .

THE UNCLE. Why should we deceive you? What use would there be in that?

THE FATHER. We should certainly tell you the truth.

THE UNCLE. What would be the good of deceiving each other?

THE FATHER. You would not be long in finding it out.

THE GRANDFATHER (trying to rise). I should like to break through this darkness! . . .

THE FATHER. Where do you want to go?

THE GRANDFATHER. Over there. . . .

THE FATHER. Don't worry so much. . . .

THE UNCLE. You are strange tonight.

THE GRANDFATHER. It is all of you who seem strange to me!

THE FATHER. What are you looking for? . . .

THE GRANDFATHER. I do not know what is the matter!

THE ELDEST DAUGHTER. Grandfather! Grandfather! What do you want, grandfather!

THE GRANDFATHER. Give me your little hands, my children.

THE THREE DAUGHTERS. Yes, grandfather.

THE GRANDFATHER. Why are you all three of you trembling, my children?

THE ELDEST DAUGHTER. We are hardly trembling at all, grandfather.

THE GRANDFATHER. I believe you are all three quite pale.

THE ELDEST DAUGHTER. It is late, grandfather, and we are tired.

THE FATHER. You must go to bed, and grandfather himself would do well to take a little rest.

THE GRANDFATHER. I could not sleep tonight!

THE UNCLE. We will wait for the doctor.

THE GRANDFATHER. Prepare me for the truth.

THE UNCLE. But there is no truth!

THE GRANDFATHER. Then I do not know what there is!

THE UNCLE. I tell you there is nothing at all!

THE GRANDFATHER. I want to see my poor daughter!

THE FATHER. But you know quite well that is impossible; she must not be wakened unnecessarily.

THE UNCLE. You will see her tomorrow.

THE GRANDFATHER. You can't hear a sound in her room.

THE UNCLE. I would be worried if I heard any sound.

THE GRANDFATHER. It is a long time since I saw my daughter! . . . I took her hands yesterday evening, but I did not see her! . . . I do not know what has become of her. . . . I do not know how she is. . . . I do not know what her face is like anymore. . . . She must have changed these past weeks! . . . I felt her little cheek bones under my hands. . . . There is nothing but the darkness between her and me, and the rest of you! . . . I cannot go on living like this. . . . This is not living! . . . You sit there, all of you, looking with open eyes at my dead eyes, and not one of you has pity! . . . I do not know what is the matter with me. . . . No one says what ought to be said. . . . And everything is terrifying when you dream about it. . . . But why aren't you talking?

THE UNCLE. What should we say, since you will not believe us?

THE GRANDFATHER. You are afraid of betraying yourselves!

THE FATHER. Come now, be reasonable!

THE GRANDFATHER. You have been hiding something from me for a long time! . . . Something has happened in the house. . . . But I am beginning to understand now. . . . I have been deceived for too long! You think that I will never know anything? There are moments when I am less blind than you, do you understand? . . . Haven't I heard you whispering—for days and days—as if you were in the house of someone who had been hanged? I dare not say what I know tonight. . . . But I will know the truth! . . . I will wait for you to tell me the truth; but I have known it for a long time, in spite of you! And now, I know that you are all more pale than the dead!

THE THREE DAUGHTERS. Grandfather! Grandfather! What is wrong with you, grandfather?

THE GRANDFATHER. I am not talking about you, my girls. No, I am not talking about you. . . . I know quite well you would tell me the truth—if they were not around you! . . . And besides, I am sure that they are deceiving you as well. . . . You will see, children—you will see! . . . Don't I hear all three of you sobbing?

THE FATHER. Is my wife really in danger?

THE GRANDFATHER. It is no good trying to deceive me any more; it is too late now, and I know the truth better than you! . . .

THE UNCLE. But really, now, we are not blind!

THE FATHER. Would you like to go into your daughter's room? There is a misunderstanding here that must end. Would you like to?

THE GRANDFATHER (suddenly undecided). No, no, not now . . . not yet . . .

THE UNCLE. You see, you are not reasonable.

THE GRANDFATHER. One never knows all that a man has been unable to say in his life! . . . Who made that noise?

THE ELDEST DAUGHTER. It is the lamp flickering, grandfather.

THE GRANDFATHER. It seems to be very unsteady . . . very unsteady . . .

THE DAUGHTER. It is the cold wind troubling it. . . .

THE UNCLE. There is no cold wind, the windows are closed.

THE DAUGHTER. I think it is going out.

THE FATHER. There is no more oil.

THE DAUGHTER. It has gone completely out.

THE FATHER. We cannot stay in the dark like this.

THE UNCLE. Why not? I am used to it already.

THE FATHER. There is a light in my wife's room.

THE UNCLE. We will get it later, after the doctor has come.

THE FATHER. We can really see enough here; there is light from outside.

THE GRANDFATHER. Is it light outside?

THE FATHER. Lighter than here.

THE UNCLE. For my part, I would just as soon talk in the dark.

THE FATHER. So would I. *(Silence.)*

THE GRANDFATHER. It seems to me the clock makes a great deal of noise! . . .

THE ELDEST DAUGHTER. That is because we are not talking any more, grandfather.

THE GRANDFATHER. But why are you all quiet?

THE UNCLE. What do you want us to talk about? You are not acting right to-night.

THE GRANDFATHER. Is it very dark in this room?

THE UNCLE. It is not very light. *(Silence.)*

THE GRANDFATHER. I do not feel well, Ursula; open the window a little.

THE FATHER. Yes, daughter; open the window a little. I need a little air myself. *(THE DAUGHTER opens the window.)*

THE UNCLE. I really believe we have stayed inside too long.

THE GRANDFATHER. Is the window open?

THE DAUGHTER. Yes, grandfather, it is wide open.

THE GRANDFATHER. You would not think so; there is not a sound from outside.

THE DAUGHTER. No, grandfather; there is not the slightest sound.

THE FATHER. The silence is extraordinary.

THE DAUGHTER. You could hear an angel walking.

THE UNCLE. That is why I do not like the country.

THE GRANDFATHER. I wish I could hear a little noise. What time is it, Ursula?

THE DAUGHTER. Almost midnight, grandfather. *(THE UNCLE begins to pace up and down the room.)*

THE GRANDFATHER. Who is walking around us like that?

THE UNCLE. It is I! It is I! Don't be afraid. I have to walk around a little. *(Silence.)*—But I am going to sit down again. I cannot see where I am going. *(Silence.)*

THE GRANDFATHER. I wish I were some place else!

THE DAUGHTER. Where would you like to go, grandfather?

THE GRANDFATHER. I do not know—into another room, no matter where! no matter where!

THE FATHER. Where could we go?

THE UNCLE. It is too late to go anywhere else. *(Silence. They are sitting, motionless, around the table.)*

THE GRANDFATHER. What do I hear, Ursula?

THE DAUGHTER. Nothing, grandfather; it is the leaves falling. Yes, it is the leaves falling on the terrace.

THE GRANDFATHER. Go and close the window, Ursula.

THE DAUGHTER. Yes, grandfather. *(She closes the window, comes back, and sits down.)*

THE GRANDFATHER. I am cold. *(Silence. THE THREE DAUGHTERS kiss each other.)* What do I hear now?

THE FATHER. It is the three sisters kissing each other.

THE UNCLE. It seems to me they are very pale tonight. *(Silence.)*

THE GRANDFATHER. What do I hear now?

THE DAUGHTER. Nothing, grandfather; it is the clasping of my hands. *(Silence.)*

THE GRANDFATHER. And that? . . .

THE DAUGHTER. I do not know, grandfather. . . . perhaps my sisters are trembling a little? . . .

THE GRANDFATHER. I am afraid, too, my children. *(A ray of moonlight enters through a corner of the stained glass and throws strange gleams here and there in the room. Midnight sounds, and at the last stroke a vague sound is heard, as of some one getting up hurriedly.)*

THE GRANDFATHER *(trembling with unusual dread)*. Who got up?

THE UNCLE. No one got up!

THE FATHER. I did not get up!

THE THREE DAUGHTERS. Nor I! Nor I! Nor I!

THE GRANDFATHER. Someone got up from the table!

THE UNCLE. Light the lamp! . . . *(Suddenly a cry of fear is heard from the child's room, on the right; this cry continues with increasing terror until the end of the scene.)*

THE FATHER. Listen! The baby!

THE UNCLE. He has never cried before!

THE FATHER. Let us go and see!

THE UNCLE. The light! The light! *(At this moment, rapid and heavy steps are heard in the room on the left. Then, a deathly silence. They listen in mute terror, until the door of the room opens slowly. Its light spurts into the room where they are sitting, and the* SISTER OF MERCY *in her black garments appears on the threshold, and bows as she makes the sign of the cross, to announce the wife's death. They understand, and after a moment of hesitation and fear, silently enter the room of the deceased. At the threshold the* UNCLE *courteously steps aside to let the three girls pass. The blind man, left alone, gets up and gropes his way excitedly around the table in the darkness.)*

THE GRANDFATHER. Where are you going? Where are you going? They have left me all alone!

CURTAIN

Development

INTERPRETATION

1. This play involves four important symbols which can be related as pairs: the visitor ("our sister") who does not appear and the intruder who does; the light of the candle and the blindness of the grandfather. Discuss the meaning of these four symbols, and explain the irony which is represented by each pair.

2. *(a)* Cite some of the unexplainable events which occur during the play. *(b)* What two contrasting attitudes toward these events and toward the woman's illness are expressed within the family group? *(c)* Which characters express them? *(d)* Which attitude commands your greater sympathy and respect? Why?

3. *(a)* In what sense does the baby's cry align the child with its grandfather? *(b)* The grandfather's last words (and the last words of the play) are "They have left me all alone." Explain this statement literally and symbolically. *(c)* Is the grandfather aware of his daughter's death at this point? Discuss.

TECHNIQUE

1. Try to imagine this play as it would appear on the stage. *(a)* How do you visualize the stage setting? *(b)* How would you costume the characters? Would the grandfather be costumed differently from the others? If so, in what way? *(c)* What sound effects would be necessary? *(d)* Would you "represent" the intruder by any device? Discuss.

2. Read part of the dialogue from *The Intruder* aloud. *(a)* Characterize its tone. *(b)* How does this tone affect your sympathy for the characters? *(c)* How does it affect your feelings about the action of the play?

3. In his critical writing, Edgar Allan Poe lays great emphasis on ". . . the immensely important effect derivable from unity of impression. . . ." *(a)* What aspects of *The Intruder* make it a particularly good example of a work with "unity of impression"? *(b)* If you were directing *The Intruder*, what "unity of impression" would you try to convey to the audience?

EXTENSIONS

1. It has often been argued that modern man covers up the fact of death and refuses to acknowledge it as an inevitable part of life. Do you think this is true? Discuss, citing examples.

Lament for Ignacio Sanchez Mejias[1]

FEDERICO GARCÍA LORCA / Spain / (1898–1936)

translated from the Spanish by Stephen Spender and J. L. Gili

1.

COGIDA[2] AND DEATH

At five in the afternoon.
It was exactly five in the afternoon.
A boy brought the white sheet
at five in the afternoon.
5 A frail of lime[3] ready prepared
at five in the afternoon.
The rest was death, and death alone
at five in the afternoon.

The wind carried away the cottonwool[4]
10 *at five in the afternoon.*
And the oxide scattered crystal and
     nickel[5]
at five in the afternoon.
Now the dove and the leopard wrestle
at five in the afternoon.
15 And a thigh with a desolate horn
at five in the afternoon.
The bass-string struck up
at five in the afternoon.
Arsenic bells and smoke
20 *at five in the afternoon.*
Groups of silence in the corners
at five in the afternoon.
And the bull alone with a high heart!
At five in the afternoon.
25 When the sweat of snow was coming
at five in the afternoon,
when the bull ring was covered in iodine
at five in the afternoon,
death laid eggs in the wound
30 *at five in the afternoon.*
At five in the afternoon.
Exactly at five o'clock in the afternoon.

A coffin on wheels is his bed
at five in the afternoon.
Bones and flutes resound in his ears   35
at five in the afternoon.
Now the bull was bellowing through his
     forehead
at five in the afternoon.
The room was iridescent with agony
at five in the afternoon.   40
In the distance the gangrene now comes
at five in the afternoon.
Horn of the lily through green groins
at five in the afternoon.
The wounds were burning like suns   45
at five in the afternoon,
and the crowd was breaking the windows
at five in the afternoon.
At five in the afternoon.
Ah, that fatal five in the afternoon!   50
It was five by all the clocks!
It was five in the shade of the afternoon!

1. *Ignacio Sanchez Mejias* (ēg nä′ sē ō sän ches′ me hē′ äs), a good friend and fellow-poet of Lorca's (as well as a bullfighter). He was killed in the bull-ring in 1934. 2. *Cogida* (kō hē′ dä), Spanish word for *goring*. 3. *frail of lime*. Lime is used to disinfect the body. A frail is a bucket or basket. 4. *cottonwool*, the material used to dress the wounds. 5. *the oxide scattered crystal and nickel*. This probably refers to the action of the lime.

2.
THE SPILLED BLOOD

I will not see it!

Tell the moon to come
55 for I do not want to see the blood
of Ignacio on the sand.

I will not see it!

The moon wide open.
Horse of still clouds,
60 and the grey bull ring of dreams
with willows in the barreras.[6]

I will not see it!

Let my memory kindle!
Warn the jasmines
65 of such minute whiteness!

I will not see it!

The cow of the ancient world[7]
passed her sad tongue
over a snout of blood
70 spilled on the sand,
and the bulls of Guisando,[8]
partly death and partly stone,
bellowed like two centuries
sated with treading the earth.
75 No.
I do not want to see it!
I will not see it!

Ignacio goes up the tiers
with all his death on his shoulders.
80 He sought for the dawn
but the dawn was no more.
He seeks for his confident profile
and the dream bewilders him.
He sought for his beautiful body
85 and encountered his opened blood.
I will not see it!
I do not want to hear it spurt
each time with less strength:
that spurt that illuminates
90 the tiers of seats, and spills
over the corduroy and the leather

of a thirsty multitude.
Who shouts that I should come near!
Do not ask me to see it!

His eyes did not close   95
when he saw the horns near,
but the terrible mothers
lifted their heads.
And across the ranches,
an air of secret voices rose,   100
shouting to celestial bulls,
herdsmen of pale mist.
There was no prince in Seville
who could compare with him,
nor sword like his sword   105
nor heart so true.
Like a river of lions
was his marvelous strength,
and like a marble torso
his firm drawn moderation.   110
The air of Andalusian Rome
gilded his head
where his smile was a spikenard[9]
of wit and intelligence.
What a great torero[10] in the ring!   115
What a good peasant in the sierra![11]
How gentle with the sheaves!
How hard with the spurs!
How tender with the dew!
How dazzling in the fiesta!   120
How tremendous with the final
banderillas[12] of darkness!

But now he sleeps without end.
Now the moss and the grass
open with sure fingers   125
the flower of his skull.
And now his blood comes out singing;
singing along marshes and meadows,

---

6. *barreras* (bä rer′äs), wooden barrier or fence around the inside of the bullring; also, the first row of seats. 7. *cow of the ancient world*, probably a reference to the Greek myth of Europa, the celestial cow who licked the world into its shape. 8. *bulls of Guisando* (gē sän′ dō). Guisando is a town in the Avila province of central Spain. 9. *spikenard*, a fragrant ointment. 10. *torero* (tə rer′ ō), bullfighter. 11. *sierra* (sē er′ ə), a mountain range with an irregular outline. 12. *banderillas*, barbed darts used to enrage the bull.

sliding on frozen horns,
130 faltering soulless in the mist,
stumbling over a thousand hoofs
like a long, dark, sad tongue,
to form a pool of agony
close to the starry Guadalquivir.
135 Oh, white wall of Spain!
Oh, black bull of sorrow!
Oh, hard blood of Ignacio!
Oh, nightingale of his veins!
No.
140 I will not see it!
No chalice can contain it,
no swallows can drink it,
no frost of light can cool it,
nor song nor deluge of white lilies,
145 no glass can cover it with silver.
No.
I will not see it!

3.
THE LAID OUT BODY

Stone is a forehead where dreams grieve
without curving waters and frozen
    cypresses.
150 Stone is a shoulder on which to bear
    Time
with trees formed of tears and ribbons
    and planets.

I have seen grey showers move towards
    the waves
raising their tender riddled arms,
to avoid being caught by the lying stone
155 which loosens their limbs without
    soaking the blood.

For stone gathers seed and clouds,
skeleton larks and wolves of penumbra:
but yields not sounds nor crystals nor
    fire,
only bull rings and bull rings and more
    bull rings without walls.

160 Now, Ignacio the well born lies on the
    stone.
All is finished. What is happening?
    Contemplate his face:
death has covered him with pale sulphur

and has placed on him the head of a
    dark minotaur.

All is finished. The rain penetrates his
    mouth.
The air, as if mad, leaves his sunken   165
    chest,
and Love, soaked through with tears of
    snow,
warms itself on the peak of the herd.

What are they saying? A stenching
    silence settles down.
We are here with a body laid out which
    fades away,
with a pure shape which had   170
    nightingales
and we see it being filled with
    depthless holes.

Who creases the shroud? What he
    says is not true!
Nobody sings here, nobody weeps in the
    corner,
nobody pricks the spurs, nor terrifies
    the serpent.
Here I want nothing else but the   175
    round eyes
to see this body without a chance of rest.

Here I want to see those men of hard
    voice.
Those that break horses and dominate
    rivers;
those men of sonorous skeleton who
    sing
with a mouth full of sun and flint.   180

Here I want to see them. Before the
    stone.
Before this body with broken reins.
I want to know from them the way
    out
for this captain strapped down by
    death.

I want them to show me a lament like a   185
    river
which will have sweet mists and deep
    shores,

to take the body of Ignacio where it
    loses itself
without hearing the double panting of
    the bulls.

Loses itself in the round bull ring of
    the moon
190 which feigns in its youth a sad quiet
    bull:
loses itself in the night without song
    of fishes
and in the white thicket of frozen
    smoke.

I don't want them to cover his
    face with handkerchiefs
that he may get used to the death he
    carries.
195 Go, Ignacio: feel not the hot bellowing.
Sleep, fly, rest: even the sea dies!

4.

ABSENT SOUL

The bull does not know you, nor the fig
    tree,
nor the horses, nor the ants in your own
    house.
The child and the afternoon do not
    know you
200 because you have died for ever.

The back of the stone does not know you,
nor the black satin in which you crumble.
Your silent memory does not know you
because you have died for ever.

205 The autumn will come with small white
    snails,
misty grapes and with clustered hills,
but no one will look into your eyes
because you have died for ever.

Because you have died for ever,
210 like all the dead of the Earth,
like all the dead who are forgotten
in a heap of lifeless dogs.

Nobody knows you. No. But I sing of you.
For posterity I sing of your profile and
    grace.

Of the signal maturity of your   215
    understanding.
Of your appetite for death and the taste
    of its mouth.
Of the sadness of your once valiant
    gaiety.
It will be a long time, if ever, before
    here is born
an Andalusian so true, so rich in
    adventure.
I sing of his elegance with words that   220
    groan,
and I remember a sad breeze through
    the olive trees.

Development

1. (a) Summarize the time-sequence, relative to the death of Ignacio, represented in the four parts of the poem. (b) At what point in the poem do you think he actually dies? Discuss.

2. (a) Describe the setting which opens the poem. (b) When does it change, and to what? (c) What is the "coffin on wheels" (page 519, line 33)? (d) How does the setting change again in Parts 2, 3, and 4?

3. Read the first part of the poem without the repeated refrain, "at five in the afternoon." (a) Describe the difference this omission makes to the impact of this section. (b) What type of sound is suggested by the repetition of the phrase?

4. (a) What are the poet's feelings about his friend's death in Part 1 of the poem? Consider both what is said and the tone in which it is said. (b) How have these feelings changed by Part 2? (c) How do they change again in Parts 3 and 4? (d) To what extent do these emotional changes accurately reflect the pattern of feelings we would expect to see in one who has suffered the loss of a close friend? Discuss.

5. (a) What is unusual in the following image from Part 2 of the poem: "Ignacio

goes up the tiers/with all his death on his shoulders" (page 520, lines 78-79)? *(b)* How does the image reflect the general attitude toward Ignacio's death expressed in the poem?

6. *(a)* What does the stone described in the beginning of Part 3 actually refer to? *(b)* What does it appear to symbolize? *(c)* What do you think the "grey showers" (line 152) symbolize? *(d)* Trace the recurrence of these symbols through Part 3. *(e)* How do you interpret the conflict between them?

7. *(a)* According to the poet, what is the attitude of the world toward Ignacio's death after he has been buried? *(b)* Does the poet share this attitude? Explain.

8. A critic has suggested that the bullfight in the poem represents the ancient ritual of sacrifice to the gods:

In such a context, Lorca placed the death of his friend. Ignacio fell by the horns of the bull in the final act of a meaningless ritual that is intimately associated with the human race's ancient need for sacrifice in order to purify itself. Ignacio's death is that of a hero.[1]

(a) Explain what is meant by "the human race's ancient need" to purify itself by offering sacrifice. *(b)* Can a bullfight fulfill this need? Discuss. *(c)* Why, according to the critic, is Ignacio a hero? Do you agree?

9. It has been said that a person truly stricken with grief could not summon up the discipline it takes to write a good elegy; therefore an elegy is always an "insincere" poem. Do you agree or disagree with this opinion?

1. Reprinted from VICTORIOUS EXPRESSION: STUDY OF FOUR CONTEMPORARY SPANISH POETS: UNAMUNO, MACHADO, JIMENEZ, AND LORCA by Howard T. Young. Copyright © 1964, by University of Wisconsin Press.

Comparison

1. Ignacio Sanchez becomes, in García Lorca's poem, a model of heroic death. Compare and contrast the character of Ignacio portrayed in this poem with the character of Iacob in "The End of Iacob Onisia." Is Iacob's death in any sense heroic? Discuss.

2. *(a)* Explain the following statement: Ignacio Sanchez Mejias is eulogized, in part, because the bullfighter's view of death is the opposite of that expressed by the Uncle in Maeterlinck's *The Intruder*. *(b)* Do you agree or disagree with the preceding statement? Discuss.

3. In Part 2 of the García Lorca poem, the narrator, like the Father and Uncle in *The Intruder*, refuses to admit the death of one he loves. Compare the reasons for this refusal in the poem and in the play.

4. Discuss the differences in the view of death expressed in *The Intruder* and in "Lament for Ignacio Sanchez Mejias" as reflected in the symbol of death found in each selection: the silent visitor and the bull.

5. *(a)* Of the selections in this group on death, which one gives us the most intimate portrayal of the person who dies? *(b)* Which selection moves furthest from the person who dies? *(c)* Explain how each of the following elements affects this question of distance: genre, point of view, theme.

6. The idea of the death-wish is frequently implied in literature, especially modern literature. The death-wish is an often unconscious desire to give up the difficulties of life and die. Do you find evidence of this concept in any of the selections included in this unit? Discuss.

KAO 3 by Tomio Kinoshita. Owned by artist, Japan.

The Seeker

FOREVERMORE / S. Y. AGNON / ISRAEL

THE CIRCULAR RUINS / JORGE LUIS BORGES / ARGENTINA

AUTUMN MOUNTAIN / AKUTAGAWA RYŪNOSUKÉ / JAPAN

Forevermore

S. Y. AGNON / Israel

(1888–1970)

translated from the Hebrew by Joel Blocker

For twenty years Adiel Amzeh worked on his history of the great city of Gumlidata,[1] the pride of mighty nations until it was reduced to dust and ashes by the Gothic hordes,[2] and its people enslaved.

After he had gathered all his researches together, examined and tested them, sorted, edited, and arranged them, he decided that his work was finally ready for publication and he sat down and wrote the book he had planned for so many years. He took the book and made the rounds of the publishers but without success. He looked about for patrons and benefactors but had no luck. During all the years he had been occupied with his research he had not taken the trouble to ingratiate himself with the learned men of the universities—nor with their wives and daughters—and now when he came to them seeking a favor, their eyes shone with such cold anger that their glasses seemed to warp. "Who are you, sir?" they said to him. "We've never seen you before." Amzeh shrugged his shoulders and went away disappointed and dejected. He understood that in order to be recognized he would have to become friendly with them and he had no idea of how to go about it. Many years of painstaking research had made him a slave to his work from dawn till night, neglectful of all worldly cares. When he left his bed in the morning, his feet would carry him to the desk, his hands would pick up pen and paper, and his eyes, if not pursuing some obscure vision, would plunge into a book or into maps and sketches of the city and its great battles; and when he lay down to sleep he would go over his notebooks again, sometimes consciously, sometimes hardly realizing what he was doing. Years passed and his book re-

1. *Gumlidata,* a city of Agnon's invention, replete with a cryptic assembly of gods and customs. 2. *Gothic hordes,* the Germanic tribes which migrated into southern Europe between the third and fifth centuries A.D. and hastened the dissolution of the Roman Empire.

mained unpublished. You know, a scholar who is unable to publish his work often benefits from the delay, since he can re-examine his assumptions and correct his errors, testing those hypotheses that may seem far from historical reality and truth.

Finally, when he had despaired of ever seeing the results of his work in print, his luck took a turn for the better. Gebhard Goldenthal, the richest man in the city, informed him that he would publish the book. How did it happen that the name of a humble scholar had reached the ear of this famous rich man? And why would such an eminent personage want to publish a work which was sure to bring no profit? Some said he felt so uneasy about his great wealth that he had decided to become a patron of learning in order to salve his conscience. He followed closely the world of scholarship and somehow had heard the story of Adiel Amzeh's book. According to another explanation, Gebhard Goldenthal secretly believed that his ancestors were among the unhappy people who were driven out of Gumlidata, that they had belonged to the city's aristocracy and that one of them had been an army general, the head of the palace guard. Of course, this was obviously untrue since Gumlidata was destroyed during the first wave of the Gothic invasions when the whole civilized world was turned upside down. No person can say with any certainty that he is a descendant of the exiles of Gumlidata. But whatever the reason, Gebhard Goldenthal was ready to publish Adiel Amzeh's book, even though printing this kind of work would involve many extra expenses. Several colored maps were necessary, requiring many expensive inks: one for a general view of the city, another for its temples, a third for each of its gods—Gomesh, Gush, Gutz, Guach, and Guz; one for the founding mothers of the city, one for its apostates, another for Gomed the Great, one for Gichur and Amul—the twin pillars of prayer—and one each for all the remaining holy men, the priests and priestesses, not to mention the dogs and all the saints —for each and every one a different color, to denote position and function. Add to all these the Goths and their allies, their carts and wagons, their weapons and battle defenses, and you can see how much money was needed to print such a work. Nevertheless, Gebhard Goldenthal was ready to publish the book and make it a fine volume with beautiful printing and good paper, carefully detailed maps, expensive binding—perfect in every respect. His staff had already consulted with illustrators, engravers, and printers, and all that remained was for the author and publisher to meet, for in all his business affairs Gebhard Goldenthal would allow his staff to take care of the preliminaries, but the final arrangements had to be conducted between the client and the head of the business himself. If the client was unknown, he would be invited to Goldenthal's office; if the man was recognized in his field, he might be invited for a cup of tea to Goldenthal's home; and if he was important, he would be invited for dinner. Adiel Amzeh, who was more than a nobody but not well-known enough to be considered important, was invited by the rich man for a cup of tea.

So it was that one day Adiel Amzeh received an invitation for afternoon tea at the home of Gebhard Goldenthal. He was asked to be prompt and come at the designated hour since Mr. Goldenthal was soon leaving for abroad and was pressed for time.

An author who for years has searched without avail for a publisher is not likely to be late for an appointment with the one he has finally found. Almost before he put down his publisher's invitation, he took out his best suit of clothes—untouched since the day he received his doctor's degree—shook it out and pressed it. He hurried back and forth from his manuscript to the bathroom, from his bath to a shop where he bought a new tie, and from the shop back home to look over his book again. By morning of the day of his appointment, he had made all his preparations for his visit to the publisher. Never in his life had he experienced such a day as this. Adiel Amzeh, who for the sake of a city's destruction had put aside all personal affairs, who cared nothing for clothes or any human vanity, was utterly changed. He had become like most celebrated learned men who neglect their work for the sake of the honor they receive from others who know nothing of learning and scholarship. He sat and stared at his manuscript, rose and inspected himself in the mirror, glanced at his watch, examined his clothes, and rehearsed his gestures. This is the regimen of all who wish to meet with a rich man. You must preen yourself and be careful of your demeanor and graces: the rich, even those who honor learning, prefer to honor it when it comes wrapped in a pleasing mantle. Yet that same love of learning which had used up so much of his energy and strength, furrowing his brow and bowing his shoulders, had touched his face with a special kind of radiance that one doesn't find except among those who are truly devoted to seeking wisdom. It's a pity Goldenthal never actually set eyes upon him; had he done so he might have realized that a pleasant and happy face can be shaped from things other than money. But you see, my friends, for the sake of a little moralizing, I have gone and given away the ending at the very beginning of my story.

Well, Amzeh sat for a while, then got up, sat down again, rose again—all the time thinking of the future when the printer would take up his manuscript and transform it into attractive pages; he thought of how he would correct proofs, add and delete, omit and include certain passages; of how the printer does his work and how his book would finally be published and received. Sitting there

dreaming he might have missed the appointed hour, except that all the years he had devoted to his work had sharpened him in his external affairs as well. When the moment came for him to leave for his appointment, he jumped up from his chair, picked up his house key, and made ready to leave and lock the door behind him. He stared at himself in the mirror once more and glanced about his home, astonished that his house had not changed as he had. There ought to have been some transformation, he thought, for this would have been only just for a man who was about to undergo a blessed metamorphosis.

At that moment he heard the sound of footsteps and suddenly became alarmed. Perhaps Mr. Goldenthal had to leave before the appointed time and someone was coming to tell him the interview had been postponed. Amzeh stood transfixed and could hardly catch his breath; his reason was gone, only his senses functioned. His entire body seemed to become one big ear. As he listened intently to the footsteps, he realized that he was hearing the slow shuffling of an old woman. In a moment, his powers of reason returned and he understood that a gentleman like Goldenthal would not send an old woman to deliver a note canceling their appointment. When the sound of the old woman's footsteps came closer, he recognized them as those of a nurse who visited him once each year in order to collect journals and illustrated magazines to take to the inmates of the lepers' hospital where she worked. It was difficult for Amzeh to put the old woman off by telling her he was busy and asking that she come the following year; he had high regard for this nurse who devoted her entire life to those whose existence was a living death. But it was equally hard for him to tarry on her account, for if he was delayed, with Mr. Goldenthal about to go abroad and no one knowing when he would return, then the publication of his book would also be postponed. I should mention another factor as well, which might seem unimportant but perhaps was decisive. To a man whose home is his whole universe, every unnecessary article in the house can cause annoyance. So it was with our scholar. When his mind was occupied with Gumlidata and he strolled through its ruins carrying on long conversations with the priests and holy men of the temple, he would occasionally raise his eyes and notice a pile of dusty old magazines. Now that the old woman had come, here was an opportunity to get rid of them; if he didn't act now, they would accumulate and gather dust for another year.

At the very moment when he was deciding what to do, whether to get rid of the superfluous volumes or to devote all his efforts to his own book, the old woman knocked on the door. He opened it and greeted her. The old woman understood immediately that he was worried and preoccupied, like a man uncertain whether to take an affirmative or negative course. "I see, Herr Doctor," she said, "that I have come at an inconvenient time. I'll leave and go about my business."

He was silent for a moment and didn't answer her. When she finally turned to go, he realized how tired the old woman must be from her long walk. After all, the lepers' home was far from the city, and she had to come on foot. She was unable to travel by autobus for fear that if recognized she would be thrown off—most people are still terrified by the sight of someone who works with lepers.

"I'm sorry," Amzeh said to her as she was about to go, "but I can't take care of you the way I would like. I have been invited to afternoon tea by Gebhard Goldenthal, the famous industrialist whose name you have probably heard." (As a matter of fact, forty years previously Gebhard Goldenthal had courted the nurse and wanted to marry her, but she refused him because she had already given her heart to God's maimed, the poor prisoners of the lepers' home.) "I have a very important matter to discuss with Mr. Goldenthal," Adiel Amzeh went on. "I'll be back in an hour or so. Please sit down until I return, and later I'll fill your basket with books and journals and pamphlets and anything else I have about —they take up so much room here I can hardly breathe."

"I would like to sit here and wait for you, Herr Doctor," the old woman answered, "but I can't leave my good people for more than a short while. They are used to me and I am used to them, and when I'm away from them I miss them as much as they miss me. They are used to receiving all their needs from me. I'll go now, Herr Doctor, and if God grants me life and peace, I'll come back next year."

But Amzeh was unable to let her go away like that, without an explanation of why he was in such a hurry. Without thinking about how little time he had, he began to explain: "Perhaps you have noticed my appearance today. For many years you have been coming to visit me and you have always found me with slippers on my feet and a cap on my head, unshaven, my collar open, my hair disheveled. Today I'm dressed in a good suit and wearing shoes and a hat and a nice tie. The reason for the change is simple: for twenty years I have worked on a book and it is finally ready for publication. Mr. Gebhard Goldenthal has decided to publish it, and I'm now going to see him. He's waiting for me and for my book."

A flush came over the old woman's face. "You mustn't delay a moment, Herr Doctor, hurry, hurry, don't wait, an hour like this doesn't come every day, don't put off even a minute what you have waited for for many years. It is good that you found Mr. Goldenthal. He's an honest man. He keeps his promises. But I'm not a very good friend, intruding on you at a time like this. I remember when I began to serve in the lepers' hospital, the rooms were full of dust and broken beds and chairs, the roof was caved in, the walls tottering and moldy. If he hadn't given us money to put the place together again, to buy new beds and equipment and make all the necessary repairs, it would have been impossible to get along there."

After the old woman had recounted all of Gebhard Goldenthal's good deeds, she let out a deep sigh. "Are you unhappy?" Adiel Amzeh asked her. "Unhappy?" she replied with a shy smile. "I've never been unhappy." He was quiet for a moment. "You are unique, Nurse Eden, you are the only one in the world who can make such a declaration," he said.

The old woman blushed with confusion. "I really should correct what I just said, Herr Doctor. I have had great unhappiness, but not of my own making." Her face turned scarlet and she lapsed into silence.

"You stopped right in the middle of what you were saying, Nurse Adeh," Amzeh said, "and perhaps at the crucial point. I'm certain it would be worthwhile to hear."

"Worthwhile?" the old woman cried, stammering in her effort to speak quickly. "How do we know what is worthwhile and what isn't? I'm an old woman whose grave is waiting for her—let me boast once that I told the whole truth. I flattered myself falsely when I said that I've never been unhappy. On the contrary, I haven't known a day without sorrow, a sorrow greater than that of my good people who suffer more than any other creatures in the world. For the merciful God who inflicts suffering on man provides him with the strength to withstand his woes; but if one is healthy and without physical disability, then he has no special allotment of strength, and when he looks on those who suffer and on their pain he is chastened and has nothing with which to withstand his sorrow. And especially someone like myself, who has to look after the suffering ones. I'm always

afraid that I won't fulfill my obligations, that I don't devote enough of my time to the good people. Even if I leave them for a moment, their suffering does not leave me. . . . But I'm talking too much. I've forgotten that you are in a hurry. Now I'll be going. I hope, Herr Doctor, that your business will bring you a full life and peace. Only pity the poor people who must see me return empty-handed, without any books."

"Why pity them?" he asked, facing her. "Have they finished all the books? They've read them all?"

"They've read them hundreds of times," answered the old woman.

"What kind of books do they have?"

"Oh, I can give you the names of all of them."

"All of them? Surely you exaggerate."

"No, there aren't very many. I've been there so many years, every article and every book is familiar to me."

The old woman then recited the name of each book in the hospital library. "Not many, not very many at all," Amzeh said after she had finished. "I can imagine how happy they must be to receive a new book. But," he went on, jokingly, "I'm sure you have forgotten one or two, and perhaps they were the best books of the lot. For that's the way we are—we always forget the most important thing. Isn't that so, Nurse Adeh?"

The old woman smiled. "I have no love of dialectics. But I must say for truth's sake that there isn't a book in our library that I haven't mentioned—except for one, which is hardly worth discussing, since it isn't read any more."

"Why isn't it read any more?"

"Why? Because it has decayed with age, and on account of the tears."

"On account of the tears?"

"Because of the tears, yes, because of the tears that every reader of the book shed on its pages after reading the awful tales it contains."

"What are these terrible stories?"

"I don't know what they are," the old

woman answered. "Whatever I know I've told you already. It's an old, worn-out book, written on parchment. They say it was written more than a thousand years ago. Had I known you would ask, I would have made inquiries. There are still old men in the hospital who can tell the story, which I remember many years ago the old men before them used to tell with tears—the same story that is in the book. But they say that even then, years ago, the old men already had difficulty in reading the book because its pages were torn and the words blurred. The manuscript is a heap of moldy, decayed matter. There have been many requests to burn it. In my time one of the caretakers was all set to destroy it, but I asked him to return it. I told him that a book which had found shelter with us mustn't be treated like a dog. I believe, Herr Doctor, that a piece of work done by an artist gives joy to the creator as long as it endures."

"Tell me, Nurse Adeh," Amzeh said, mulling over the old woman's words, "perhaps you have heard something about the contents of the book. What do your old men say about it? I'm sure if they say anything at all, they must know more."

"I've heard that all its pages are of parchment," the old woman answered. "As far as what is written in it, I've heard that it contains the history of a city which was destroyed and disappeared from the face of the earth."

"A city which had been destroyed and disappeared from the world!" Amzeh repeated excitedly. "Please tell me, Nurse Eden, perhaps you have heard the name of the city?"

"Yes, I have heard the name. The name of the city is Gumlidata, yes, Gumlidata is the name."

"What? What? What?" Amzeh stammered, his tongue caught in his mouth. "Have . . . have . . . you heard the name correctly . . . ? Gum . . . Gum . . . Gumli . . . lidata . . . you said. Please, my good

nurse, tell me again, what is the name of the city you mentioned? Guml . . . ."

She repeated what she had said. "Gumlidata is the name of the city, and the book is an account of its history."

Adiel Amzeh grasped a table in front of him, leaning forward so that he would not collapse and fall. The old woman noticed his sudden paling and moved to help him. "What is the trouble, Herr Doctor," she said staring at him, "are you ill? Is it your heart?"

He straightened up and pulled himself together. "It's nothing, my good nurse," he began with a smile, "there's nothing wrong with me. On the contrary, you have given me new life. Let me tell you about it. For twenty years I have devoted myself to the history of this same city. There isn't a piece of paper which mentions the city's name that I haven't read. If I were king, I could build the city anew, just as it was before its destruction. If you want, I'll tell you about the historical trips I have taken. I have walked in the city's markets, strolled in its streets and alleys, seen its palaces and temples. Oh, my good nurse, what headaches I've suffered from the walks I've taken there. And I know how it was destroyed, who took part in the destruction, the name of each and every tribe that helped reduce it to ruins, how many were killed by the sword, how many died of starvation and thirst, and how many perished from the plague that followed the war. I know everything except one detail—from which side Gediton's brigades entered the city, whether from the side of the great bridge which was called the Bridge of Valor, or whether they entered secretly by way of the Valley of Aphardat, that is, the Valley of the Cranes . . . the plural of crane in the language of Gumlidata is *aphardat;* the word does not mean ravens or chestnut trees or overshoes as some linguists believe. In point of fact, 'raven' in the language of Gumlidata is *eldag* and in the plural *elgadata,* since when the letters 'd' and 'g' come together in the plural they reverse their order. I don't know the words for chestnut trees or overshoes in the language of Gumlidata. I really don't know what they are."

Suddenly his expression changed, his voice dropped, his lips twisted, and he let out a hoarse, stuttering laugh. His knees began to shake and he pinched his mouth. "I'm surprised at you, Nurse Adeh," he said, "after all, you are an intelligent woman. You should be more careful about what you say. How can you believe something which doesn't make any sense. How can you say that your hospital possesses a book containing the history of Gumlidata. Gumlidata was destroyed in the days of the first Gothic invasions. And you say that a book from these ancient times has come down to our day, and the old people in the hospital have read it. Now really, my dear nurse, how can you reconcile this kind of nonsense with simple reality? How could a book like this ever get to the hospital . . . to the hospital which you, my dear nurse, serve so well. . . . How? How? Pardon me, my dear Adinah, if I tell you that this is a very doubtful story. You have heard a silly old folk tale and it has enchanted you with its romance. Or perhaps you have confused Gumlidata with . . . with . . . I don't know with what city you might have confused Gumlidata. What did you hear about this manuscript? How did it get to the hospital? You have made me curious, my dear lady, very curious for more information. I feel just like a psychoanalyst. Aren't you surprised at me, the author of a book myself, being so curious about someone else's book? It's not enough that my house is filled with books, I must go looking for others. Let me tell you, just between us, all these books in my cabinet are not there for reading, they're there for effect. And if you want, I'll tell you the real reason: self-preservation. People see the books and start talking about them, and I don't have to discuss my own work with them. Please tell me,

though, how did this history of Gumlidata ever get to your hospital?"

"I haven't read the book," answered the nurse Adeh Eden, "and when it was taken out of the reading room some time ago I forgot it. I don't devote much time to books generally. When I come to your house for books, it's not for myself, of course, but for the sake of my good people, in order to ease their suffering. Sometimes books can do that. As for the parchment pages, I remember how surprised I was when I first saw them about forty years ago—like most nurses, I had to know everything about every article I saw where I worked. An old man noticed that the volume of parchment interested me and he told me what he had heard about the book. I still remember a little of what he said. If old age hasn't confused my memory, I'll try to pass on his story. May I sit down and tell you what I heard?"

Amzeh was suddenly embarrassed. "My God!" he cried out in confusion. "How could I let you stand all this time! Sit down, do sit down . . . here, on this chair. Not that one, this chair over here . . . it is the most comfortable one in my house. Please sit down and tell me your story."

The old woman sat down in the chair that he brought her, gathered up the folds of her dress, clasped her hands together, and, taking a deep breath, began. "As far as I can remember, this is the story. After the Gothic hordes had conquered the great city of Gumlidata and reduced its strength to dust, they found the tyrant ruler of the city, Count Gifayon Glaskinon Gitra'al, of the house of Giara'al, just as he was about to flee. He moaned and wept and pleaded for his life, asking that he be made a slave to their nation and their king, Alaric.[3] The Goths allowed him to live, and carried him off with them as a slave. He had with him a history which contained stories

---

3. *Alaric* (al′ ər ik), the leader of the Visigoths in their campaigns through Greece and Italy which culminated in the sack of Rome in 410 A.D.

of the city's might and valor, stories that used to be read before the time of Alaric the King. On the way he fell sick, and the Goths left him for dead and went on. He wandered about in the fields until some lepers, who were following the soldiers for scraps of food and clothing, came upon him. They took pity on him, released him from his chains, and nursed him until he regained his health. He soon realized who his saviors were and began to groan and curse, declaring that death was better than life with the lepers. For in those days a leper was looked upon as a dead man and anyone who came in contact with an untouchable was himself considered to be infected. They tried to comfort him by saying that if he went away he might fall into the hands of the Goths and their allies who would surely kill him, or else he might be waylaid by roving packs of wild beasts who would surely eat him alive; but if he stayed with them he would be saved from the punishments of both men and beasts and have food to sustain him. They took him to their camp and gave him a bundle of straw to carry, so that if he were approached by a healthy man he might warn him away by shaking the straw, and they hung a small cup about his neck, for merciful people would sometimes throw scraps of food to the sick.

"He lived with them for some time, eating what they ate and drinking what they drank. He saw how well they treated him and began to repay them in kind. On long winter nights he would read to them from his book, entertaining them with stories of the great city of Gumlidata and tales of his ancestors, the tyrant counts who governed over Gumlidata and its dependencies. In time, both the Count and his benefactors died. No trace remained of them except the book. Men live and die, but their instruments remain and live on. The Count's friends died, but their place was taken by a new generation. They discovered the book and read it from cover to cover, joining their tears to those of the first generation. After many generations the world began to change and people began to realize how great was the suffering of the lepers, how difficult and terrible their ordeal. Not only was their sickness a great tribulation, but they were forced to live in forests and deserts and wander about in search of food. And there were times during the hard winter days when they had no sustenance and were unable to beg for food and they simply died of starvation. Eventually, benevolent groups were formed and a shelter established for the lepers, where they were brought together and their needs taken care of. Herr Doctor, I doubt whether there is anyone else in the world who knows more than I have told you about these sheets of parchment. But you want to leave. I hope you aren't late for your appointment."

"No, I'm not late for my appointment," answered Adiel Amzeh. "In fact, this is only the beginning of my appointment. Take a little more time, sit a little while longer, and we'll fill our hands with books and take them to the good people. Sit where you are, Nurse, sit a while and forget about my book. My book is used to waiting." Amzeh went over to the cabinets lining his walls and began to take books down. When he had accumulated a large pile, he tied them up in packages. He took down more books, muttering: "They'll enjoy them, they'll enjoy these books." Several times he repeated the process, searching and ransacking his shelves, whispering and muttering all the time, "What shall I give? What shall I give?" If the old woman had not stayed his hand, he would have taken all his books from their shelves and given them to her.

"You take a bundle and I'll take a bundle," he said when he had finished, "and we'll deliver them to your patients. As for Mr. . . . as for Mr. what's-his-name . . . . Mr. Goldenthal, Gebhard Goldenthal, who is waiting for me to come, well,

I'm sure he will find something else to occupy himself with. And now, my dear Adeh Eden, let's hurry so that we arrive before the sun sets, and you will open the gate for me and take me to see the book—the book of which you have spoken. What's the matter, Nurse? Why do you make such a face? Don't you think they'll allow me to enter? We'll swear that I'm going to visit my mother, and if they don't let me in I'll lie down on the steps of the hospital and won't move an inch until they say I can enter. Are you unhappy? Are you sorry about something? If it's because of me, don't be sorry. This is the most glorious day of my life, sweeter than any day I have ever lived, and what you have told me is sweeter than anything I have ever heard since . . . since . . . I'm really confused now, I don't know since when. Look, look, it's already going down. I mean the sun, the sun. The sun is more beautiful when it sets than when it rises. For twenty years a man must be hidden in the sun's shadow in order to be able to utter such a simple piece of wisdom."

They went out of the city, the two of them walking together, Amzeh in long strides, the old woman with short steps. He chattered as he walked; she managed every so often to bring forth a word which sounded more like a sigh. Everyone who passed by and recognized her stepped aside, and she avoided them as well; she knew these people were afraid of her and was careful not to arouse any unnecessary terror. But Adiel Amzeh was not conscious of the passers-by avoiding them as they went along. He turned to his companion suddenly. "Do you remember whether I locked the door?" he asked. He put down his package and saw that the key was still in his hand. "I'm carrying the key with the package and am not conscious of what I'm doing," he said with a laugh. "It's because of the heaviness of the burden I have to bear." For a minute he was silent. Then he cried out, "My God!" with a mixture

of impatience and reproach, for at the edge of his consciousness he saw himself reading the book of Gumlidata in the hospital and the faded words on the parchment prevented him from progressing quickly. Because of this book, too, he had forgotten his own book which he had worked on for twenty years, and he had forgotten Mr. Goldenthal who had agreed to publish it. After about an hour's walk, they arrived at the lepers' hospital.

I don't know through which gate they entered or how much time it took before he was granted admittance. And I can't describe the condition of the book itself, which was so covered with pus that even the lepers felt a loathing for it. I don't know all the details and have no love for suppositions. Let me put aside the doubtful and come back to what is certain.

Amzeh came to the house of the untouchables and after much argument he finally was allowed to enter. He went in and they tied him in an antiseptic apron which reached from his neck to his feet. They took the book out of the chest it was stored in, and gave it to him with a warning not to touch it. Amzeh stared at it until his eyes seemed to occupy half his face. He looked at it for a long time, then jumped up quickly to open it. They took hold of him and told him to wait. He was fitted with a pair of white gloves which they carefully tied so they would not fall off. Then they warned him again not to touch the book unless his hands were protected with gloves. They told him that only a simple-minded man would neglect such a warning. I don't know whether he heard them or not. This I do know: his eyes grew so large they seemed to cover his entire face—and half his neck as well. When they saw that he had somewhat regained his composure, they left, providing him with a place in the hospital garden among the trees which are known as the "Trees of Eden." Adiel Amzeh sat there and painstakingly read every letter, every word, column, and page which the book contained, the caretaker standing by his side and turning the pages as he progressed. For they were still afraid he was so excited that he would not exercise the necessary restraint. The book had been touched by the hands of many untouchables, and it seemed almost as if it were not written on parchment, but on the skin of a leper, and not ink but pus had been used to inscribe the words.

What more can I say? After he had carefully gone over every sentence in the book, he found the answer to the riddle that had troubled him for many years: how Gumlidata had been conquered, from which side of the city the first bands of the Goths had entered. For Gumlidata had been surrounded by a solid wall of stone and protected on all sides by natural fortifications. And so within a few short hours Amzeh solved the problem that had caused him so much trouble during his years of exhaustive research. For your sake, my friends, and for the sake of the whole House of Israel, let me tell you the story the dead words told our scholar. I'll try to summarize what was written there at great length.

The book of parchment told the story of one of the Hun women, a young girl named Geldag or Eldag, who one day left the camp of the Huns, the allies of the Goths, and rode about on a wild ass. She reached the cisterns behind the city of Gumlidata where she was caught and brought to the city. The servants of the tyrant, the old Count Gifayon Glaskinon Gitra'al of the house of Giara'al, grandfather of the young Count Gifayon Glaskinon Gitra'al Giara'al, noticed her and brought her for a gift to their master. She was horrified by the old man and his city, disgusted by his groaning and drooling, his narrow bed and his strange manners, and nauseated by the smell of the city and its sacrificial altars. She tried to flee at once, but was caught and returned to the Count. The same thing happened three or four times; each time she was caught. Finally, she saw that escape was impossible and she sat brooding how to gain revenge on her captors.

At about the same time the girl was held captive, the Goths, with Gaditon the Brave at their head, rose up and waged war with Gumlidata. The city's inhabitants held the Goths in great terror, for they knew that every place the barbarians conquered they slaughtered and burned, and if Gumlidata was vanquished, their future was annihilation. The tyrant Count saw that his city was cut off from all help, and he fell into a deep, sorrowful melancholy. Had it not been for Eldag, the Hun girl, who had changed her ways and begun to show him a love and devotion he had known with no other woman, he probably would have died of his sorrow before the Goths had a chance to hang him.

When the court guards saw that Eldag had changed her attitude toward the Count, they ceased watching her as carefully as before. Eldag took advantage of the guards' carelessness and began to take long walks through the city, wandering about everywhere. She even visited the city wall near the Valley of the Cranes, which most people avoided for fear that it might collapse. Years before, an earthquake had struck the city and shaken the wall in several places. The citizens of Gumlidata were careful not to bother Eldag, for they knew that only the power of her charms had saved their king from melancholy. So enamored of the girl was their king that he had his tailors make her a mantle as a gift, a kind of priestly garment normally worn by a queen, woven with bands of calves' eyes arranged in the shape of the Valley of the Cranes.

One day Eldag remained in the king's garden, playing with her wild ass among the tall trees. This ass was one of many animals in the garden, each of which had suckled at a woman's breast. For there was a strange custom in Gumlidata.

If a woman conceived and it was not known who the father was, her relatives waited until she gave birth and then took the infant and brought it to these animals to be suckled. They looked for an animal that had recently given birth, and left the infant to be weaned, taking the animal's young to the human mother for suckling. If they could not find the young of a tame animal, they brought her the young of a wild one. They were most careful about the children of the noblewomen, *Givyatans* in their language, for if a noblewoman had given birth and the father was unknown, the infant was killed and the young of an animal was brought to the mother, so that her noble blood would not be mixed with the blood of the common people.

So Eldag played with her pet in the garden among the tall trees. She was quite unafraid of animals, having spent most of her life with them: her father, Gichul the Clown, was the owner of a dancing bear. A young ass saw them and began snorting and hee-hawing, as if in reproach. Eldag heard the young animal's cries. "An ass always sounds like an ass," she said with a laugh, "even if it has been suckled by a duchess. What is it you want? Do you want this mantle which covers my heart? Come and I will wrap round your neck an ornament more beautiful than any that has been worn by your noble wet-nurse." The young ass heard her and came close. She took her mantle from her bosom and tied it about the animal's throat, and made him bow his head as if in thanks, as she had seen Gothic noblemen do when they received gifts.

Suddenly the girl was overwhelmed with a deep longing for her home, her family, and her people. She was filled with a burning rage and her anger turned against the ass who had reminded her of her former happiness. She was angry at the ass because he was more faithful than she was: even after she had placed the gift around his neck, the ass con-

tinued to groan. She grabbed hold of him by the ears in order to strike him. The calves' eyes which had been woven into the mantle in the shape of the Valley of Cranes shone before her. Her heart began to beat wildly. She tried to gain control of herself so that she would not cry out and give away her plan. She forced herself to smile and dragged the ass to the city wall near the Valley of Cranes; there, she found the place which had collapsed during the earthquake and had not been completely repaired. She broke through the opening and pushed the ass with the mantle around his neck outside. And Eldag was happy, for she knew that if the Goths saw the ass, they would understand he had been sent as a sign that they should enter the city through the Valley of Cranes. She controlled her joy and returned to the old Count, assuming a happy countenance for him, his court, and his city. So charmed was the population by Eldag's grace and beauty that they forgot about the Gothic soldiers who were besieging their city.

The ass went out of the city and reached a nearby forest. His nose sniffed the odors of trees and flowers and he began to snort loudly like a wild ass who has returned to his home. The noise was heard by some Gothic soldiers. They were surprised to see the ass with the mantle around his neck, for they had never seen an animal adorned like this. They brought the animal to Gaditon, their general. Gaditon the Brave saw the mantle. "Is there a place known as the Valley of the Cranes?" he asked his soldiers. "Is there one of our people in Gumlidata?" Gichul the Clown was brought to the general, and he told him that his daughter had disappeared. He saw the ass and the strange ornament it wore, and he knew that it was his daughter's work. The Goths sent soldiers to inspect the wall near the Valley of Cranes, and when they saw the place through which Eldag had sent the ass, the Goths entered the city. They set the city on fire, killing everyone in their path: old and young, infant and aged, male and female. Not a man or woman was left alive except Eldag, the Hun girl, who was released from her bondage, and the grandson of the old Count who was made a slave. . . .

All this was written on the last page of the book as a kind of epilogue by the author. And when Adiel Amzeh read the story, his eyes shed many tears. How great is the true writer, he thought, who does not abandon his work even when the sword of death hangs over his neck, who writes with his very blood what his eyes have seen!

Adiel Amzeh read many other things in the book. There were pages which supported some of his theories, and there were other pages which completely contradicted what he had previously thought. It seems he had relied too much on earlier scholars, even though he realized that much of what they wrote was confused. Adiel Amzeh remained at the hospital throughout the summer reading the book. When the days grew colder and the land was covered with frost, he had to stop working outside. He took a room at the hospital and had a heater brought in. He sat there studying the text, joining letter to letter and word to word until he could read whole passages without trouble. And if he discovered something unusual he would read the passage aloud to the patients in the great hall. "My friends and brothers," he would say, "listen while I read to you." And he would read to them about the people of the great city of Gumlidata, who had been a mighty nation, full of pride and valor, until the Gothic hordes conquered them and reduced the city to dust and ashes. He would tell them about Gomesh and Gutz and Gush and Guach, the gods of Gumlidata, and about its apostates, its great temples, its priests—each one named according to its function. And sometimes Adiel Amzeh would tell them about his new theories. He had thought out many new hypotheses and some of them

he had noted on the parchment book. But his book never reached the hands of the living, for it was forbidden to remove any article or letter or book from the lepers' house. Nevertheless, in some way or other, some of his new ideas became known to his colleagues. Many times, when Adeh Eden had brought from his house the scientific journals which he received regularly, he would read his ideas in articles signed by others. He was shocked that something which he had worked on so long and hard was now published under another scholar's signature. "If this kind of thing can happen,"—he would ask himself, "then why do I work? I ought to be satisfied with what the others say."

Yet learning bestows a special blessing on those who are not put off so easily. Yes, Adiel Amzeh would ask himself for what and for whom he was working. But the Goddess of Wisdom herself would take hold of him and whisper: "Sit, my love, sit and do not leave me." So he would sit and discover new things which had been unknown to all the learned men of the ages until he came and revealed them. And since there were many things and learning is endless and there is much to discover and investigate and understand, he did not put his work aside and did not leave the hospital and he remained there forevermore.

THE END

Development

INTERPRETATION

1. Describe your impressions of Adiel Amzeh which result from Agnon's descriptions of: *(a)* Adiel's first encounter with the publishers; *(b)* Adiel's preparations for his meeting with Gebhard Goldenthal; *(c)* his annoyance at having unnecessary books around; and *(d)* his reactions as Nurse Adeh Eden begins to unfold her story.

2. *(a)* What is similar about the role Gebhard Goldenthal once played in the life of Nurse Adeh Eden and now plays in the life of Adiel Amzeh? *(b)* What common quality might have prompted both Adiel and Nurse Eden to react to Goldenthal as they did?

3. The book in the lepers' colony telling the history of Gumlidata is stained with the tears of generations, yet Nurse Eden has preserved it because she feels ". . . a piece of work done by an artist gives joy to the creator as long as it endures" (page 531, column 1, lines 22-24). The idea of joy and suffering existing together is paradoxical. *(a)* In what other ways is this paradox embodied in "Forevermore"? *(b)* What do you think Agnon is implying? Discuss.

4. What do you feel is the importance of the summarized account of the fall of Gumlidata to the story of Adiel Amzeh?

5. *(a)* What does Adiel Amzeh come to doubt near the end of "Forevermore"? *(b)* What is the assurance that the Goddess of Wisdom brings him? *(c)* Do you think that it is important that Adiel Amzeh's book is ever published? Discuss.

TECHNIQUE

1. Agnon, as the narrator of "Forevermore," occasionally turns aside from his story to make direct comments to you, his reader. Do you feel this technique has any advantages over a strictly detached and impersonal narrative? Why or why not?

2. Much of the information Agnon has given us about Gumlidata seems part of a great though unsolved puzzle. Have the many obscure elements in "Forevermore" worked to enliven or deaden your interest? Discuss.

EXTENSIONS

1. In a moment of sudden enlightenment, Adiel Amzeh says: "The sun is more beautiful when it sets than when it rises. For twenty years a man must be hidden in the sun's shadow in order to be able to utter such a simple piece of wisdom" (page 534, column 1, lines 23-27). Since the "twenty years . . . hidden in the sun's shadow" would include all the time Adiel has been researching his book, the implication seems to be that there is a difference between scholarship and wisdom. What do you think that difference is? Explain.

2. Suppose that a member of Adiel Amzeh's family, having learned of the events in "Forevermore," was trying by some legal maneuver to have Adiel removed from the lepers' colony, by force if necessary. This person has told you that he is taking said action "for Adiel's own good." *(a)* Would you sanction his action or oppose it? *(b)* What arguments might you use to support your view?

3. Adiel Amzeh seems far removed from Nurse Adeh Eden in terms of involvement with and service to one's fellowmen. Do you think that one would be justified in saying that Nurse Eden's dedication to the sufferers of the lepers' colony has a greater value than Adiel Amzeh's dedication to the history of Gumlidata? Why or why not?

The Circular Ruins

JORGE LUIS BORGES [1] / Argentina
(1899–   )
translated from the Spanish by James E. Irby

And if he left off dreaming about you . . .
—*Through the Looking Glass, IV.*[2]

No one saw him disembark in the unanimous night, no one saw the bamboo canoe sink into the sacred mud, but in a few days there was no one who did not know that the taciturn man came from the South and that his home had been one of those numberless villages upstream in the deeply cleft side of the mountain, where the Zend language[3] has not been contaminated by Greek and where leprosy is infrequent. What is certain is that the gray man kissed the mud, climbed up the bank without pushing aside (probably, without feeling) the blades which were lacerating his flesh, and crawled, nauseated and bloodstained, up to the circular enclosure crowned with a stone tiger or horse, which sometimes was the color of flame and now was that of ashes. This circle was a temple which had been devoured by ancient fires, profaned by the miasmal jungle, and whose god no longer received the homage of men. The stranger stretched himself out beneath the pedestal. He was awakened by the sun high overhead. He was not astonished to find that his wounds had healed; he closed his pallid eyes and slept, not through weakness of flesh but through determination of will. He knew that this temple was the place required for his invincible intent; he knew that the incessant trees had not succeeded in strangling the ruins of another propitious temple downstream which had once belonged to gods now burned and dead; he knew that his immediate obligation was to dream. Toward midnight he was awakened by the inconsolable

1. *Jorge Luis Borges* (hôr′ hā lü ēs′ bôr′ hes).
2. *Through the Looking Glass, IV*, a reference to the book by Lewis Carroll, a sequel to his *Alice's Adventures in Wonderland*. In Chapter IV, Alice, in the company of the identical schoolboy twins Tweedledum and Tweedledee, comes upon the Red King, who is sleeping under a tree. The context in which the quoted line appears is as follows:
"He's dreaming now," said Tweedledee: "and what do you think he's dreaming about?"
Alice said, "Nobody can guess that."
"Why, about *you!*" Tweedledee exclaimed, clapping his hands triumphantly. "And if he left off dreaming about you, where do you suppose you'd be?"
"Where I am now, of course," said Alice.
"Not you!" Tweedledee retorted contemptuously. "You'd be nowhere. Why, you're only a sort of thing in his dream!"
3. *Zend language*, the language of the Zend-Avesta, the sacred scriptures of the seventh-century B.C. Persian teacher, Zarathustra. He is more widely known as Zoroaster, the Greek transliteration of the name. The followers of Zoroaster's teachings are still numerous in parts of Asia.

shriek of a bird. Tracks of bare feet, some figs and a jug warned him that the men of the region had been spying respectfully on his sleep, soliciting his protection or afraid of his magic. He felt a chill of fear, and sought out a sepulchral niche in the dilapidated wall where he concealed himself among unfamiliar leaves.

The purpose which guided him was not impossible, though supernatural. He wanted to dream a man; he wanted to dream him in minute entirety and impose him on reality. This magic project had exhausted the entire expanse of his mind; if some one had asked him his name or to relate some event of his former life, he would not have been able to give an answer. This uninhabited, ruined temple suited him, for it contained a minimum of visible world; the proximity of the workmen also suited him, for they took it upon themselves to provide for his frugal needs. The rice and fruit they brought him were nourishment enough for his body, which was consecrated to the sole task of sleeping and dreaming.

At first, his dreams were chaotic; then in a short while they became dialectic in nature. The stranger dreamed that he was in the center of a circular amphitheater which was more or less the burnt temple; clouds of taciturn students filled the tiers of seats; the faces of the farthest ones hung at a distance of many centuries and as high as the stars, but their features were completely precise. The man lectured his pupils on anatomy, cosmography, and magic: the faces listened anxiously and tried to answer understandingly, as if they guessed the importance of that examination which would redeem one of them from his condition of empty illusion and interpolate him into the real world. Asleep or awake, the man thought over the answers of his phantoms, did not allow himself to be deceived by impostors, and in certain perplexities he sensed a growing intelligence. He was seeking a soul worthy of participating in the universe.

After nine or ten nights he understood with a certain bitterness that he could expect nothing from those pupils who accepted his doctrine passively, but that he could expect something from those who occasionally dared to oppose him. The former group, although worthy of love and affection, could not ascend to the level of individuals; the latter preexisted to a slightly greater degree. One afternoon (now afternoons were also given over to sleep, now he was only awake for a couple of hours at daybreak) he dismissed the vast illusory student body for good and kept only one pupil. He was a taciturn, sallow boy, at times intractable, and whose sharp features resembled those of his dreamer. The brusque elimination of his fellow students did not disconcert him for long; after a few private lessons, his progress was enough to astound the teacher. Nevertheless, a catastrophe took place. One day, the man emerged from his sleep as if from a viscous desert, looked at the useless afternoon light which he immediately confused with the dawn, and understood that he had not dreamed. All that night and all day long, the intolerable lucidity of insomnia fell upon him. He tried exploring the forest, to lose his strength; among the hemlock he barely succeeded in experiencing several short snatchs of sleep, veined with fleeting, rudimentary visions that were useless. He tried to assemble the student body but scarcely had he articulated a few brief words of exhortation when it became deformed and was then erased. In his almost perpetual vigil, tears of anger burned his old eyes.

He understood that modeling the incoherent and vertiginous matter of which dreams are composed was the most difficult task that a man could undertake, even though he should penetrate all the enigmas of a superior and inferior order; much more difficult than weaving a rope out of sand or coining the faceless wind. He swore he would forget the enormous hallucination which had thrown him off at first, and he sought another method of work. Before putting it into execution, he spent a month recovering his strength, which had been squandered by his delirium. He abandoned all premeditation of dreaming and almost immediately succeeded in sleeping a reasonable part of each day. The few times that he had dreams during this period, he paid no attention to them. Before resuming his task, he waited until the moon's disk was perfect. Then, in the afternoon, he purified himself in the waters of the river, worshiped the planetary gods, pronounced the prescribed syllables of a mighty name, and went to sleep. He dreamed almost immediately, with his heart throbbing.

He dreamed that it was warm, secret, about the size of a clenched fist, and of a garnet color within the penumbra of a human body as yet without face or sex; during fourteen lucid nights he dreamt of it with meticulous love. Every night he perceived it more clearly. He did not touch it; he only permitted himself to witness it, to observe it, and occasionally to rectify it with a glance. He perceived it and lived it from all angles and distances. On the fourteenth night he lightly touched the pulmonary artery with his index finger, then the whole heart, outside and inside. He was satisfied with the examination. He deliberately did not dream for a night; he then took up the heart again, invoked the name of a planet, and undertook the vision of another of the principle organs. Within a year he had come to the skeleton and the eyelids. The innumerable hair was perhaps the most difficult task. He dreamed an entire man—a young man, but who did not sit up or talk, who was unable to open his eyes. Night after night, the man dreamt him asleep.

In the Gnostic cosmogonies, demiurges fashion a red Adam who cannot stand[4]; as clumsy, crude and elemental as this Adam of dust was the Adam of dreams forged by the wizard's nights. One afternoon, the man almost destroyed his entire work, but then changed his mind. (It would have been better had he destroyed it.) When he had exhausted all supplications to the deities of the earth, he threw himself at the feet of the effigy which was perhaps a tiger or perhaps a colt and implored its unknown help. That evening, at twilight, he dreamt of the statue. He dreamt it was alive, tremulous: it was not an atrocious bastard of a tiger and a colt, but at the same time these two fiery creatures and also a bull, a rose, and a storm. This multiple god revealed to him that his earthly name was Fire, and that in this circular temple (and in others like it) people had once made sacrifices to him and worshiped him, and that he would magically animate the dreamed phantom, in such a way that all creatures, except Fire itself and the dreamer, would believe it to be a man of flesh and blood. He commanded that once this man had been instructed in all the rites, he should be sent to the other ruined temple whose pyramids were still standing downstream, so that some voice would glorify him in that deserted edifice. In the dream of the man that dreamed, the dreamed one awoke.

The wizard carried out the orders he had been given. He devoted a certain length of time (which finally proved to

4. *In the Gnostic cosmogonies, demiurges fashion a red Adam who cannot stand.* A cosmogony is a theory or story which explains the origin of the universe. Gnosticism was a religious cult, mixing Persian, Syrian, Egyptian, and Greek influences, which flourished in the first centuries A.D. In the Gnostic myth of man's creation, the demiurge was a minor deity who had trespassed against one of the seven supreme deities and was thus banished from their circle. He roamed the universe and, through either arrogance or ignorance, took himself to be the supreme being. As such, he fashioned out of clay a man in his own image. He had not, however, the power to give life to his model. At the critical moment in his project, the seven supreme deities intervened and completed the creation of man, in the hope that man would recognize through knowledge (from the Greek, *gnosis*) the true nature of the universe.

be two years) to instructing him in the mysteries of the universe and the cult of fire. Secretly, he was pained at the idea of being separated from him. On the pretext of pedagogical necessity, each day he increased the number of hours dedicated to dreaming. He also remade the right shoulder, which was somewhat defective. At times, he was disturbed by the impression that all this had already happened. . . . In general, his days were happy; when he closed his eyes, he thought: *Now I will be with my son.* Or, more rarely: *The son I have engendered is waiting for me and will not exist if I do not go to him.*

Gradually, he began accustoming him to reality. Once he ordered him to place a flag on a faraway peak. The next day the flag was fluttering on the peak. He tried other analogous experiments, each time more audacious. With a certain bitterness, he understood that his son was ready to be born—and perhaps impatient. That night he kissed him for the first time and sent him off to the other temple whose remains were turning white downstream, across many miles of inextricable jungle and marshes. Before doing this (and so that his son should never know that he was a phantom, so that he should think himself a man like any other) he destroyed in him all memory of his years of apprenticeship.

His victory and peace became blurred with boredom. In the twilight times of dusk and dawn, he would prostrate himself before the stone figure, perhaps imagining his unreal son carrying out identical rites in other circular ruins downstream; at night he no longer dreamed, or dreamed as any man does. His perceptions of the sounds and forms of the universe became somewhat pallid: his absent son was being nourished by these diminutions of his soul. The purpose of his life had been fulfilled; the man remained in a kind of ecstasy. After a certain time, which some chroniclers prefer to compute in years and others in decades, two oarsmen awoke him at midnight; he could not see their faces, but they spoke to him of a charmed man in a temple of the North, capable of walking on fire without burning himself. The wizard suddenly remembered the words of the god. He remembered that of all the creatures that people the earth, Fire was the only one who knew his son to be a phantom. This memory, which at first calmed him, ended by tormenting him. He feared lest his son should meditate on this abnormal privilege and by some means find out he was a mere simulacrum. Not to be a man, to be a projection of another man's dreams—what an incomparable humiliation, what madness! Any father is interested in the sons he has procreated (or permitted) out of the mere confusion of happiness; it was natural that the wizard should fear for the future of that son whom he had thought out entrail by entrail, feature by feature, in a thousand and one secret nights.

His misgivings ended abruptly, but not without certain forewarnings. First (after a long drought) a remote cloud, as light as a bird, appeared on a hill; then, toward the South, the sky took on the rose color of leopard's gums; then came clouds of smoke which rusted the metal of the nights; afterwards came the panic-stricken flight of wild animals. For what had happened many centuries before was repeating itself. The ruins of the sanctuary of the god of Fire was destroyed by fire. In a dawn without birds, the wizard saw the concentric fire licking the walls. For a moment, he thought of taking refuge in the water, but then he understood that death was coming to crown his old age and absolve him from his labors. He walked toward the sheets of flame. They did not bite his flesh, they caressed him and flooded him without heat or combustion. With relief, with humiliation, with terror, he understood that he also was an illusion, that someone else was dreaming him.

THE END

Development

INTERPRETATION

Imagine that you are the ultimate dreamer whose consciousness has created and maintained the seemingly infinite progression of dream-wizards and their progeny which Borges has described in this story. While witnessing the events of "The Circular Ruins" you are asked the following questions. Be as imaginative as you like in your answers, which should develop and expand the myth Borges has created. Bear in mind, though, that even the most esoteric myths have a logical, if fanciful, basis.

1. Why is the wizard not astonished by the miraculous way his wounds have healed?

2. Why are the peasants solicitous to this old man camping in the ruins?

3. Why doesn't the wizard think it strange that he cannot remember any of his former life?

4. Why does the wizard choose to lecture on anatomy, cosmography, and magic?

5. Is the wizard right in thinking that argumentative students have more fiber? Explain.

6. Why does the wizard fail in creating a man through lecture and discussion?

7. Why does the wizard's second project of organic creation seem to work better than his first?

8. Would it really have been better if the wizard had destroyed his Adam of dreams? Explain.

9. What is the nature of the spirit which appears to the wizard as fire?

10. Why does the wizard linger so long over his son's lessons?

11. Why does the wizard feel his purpose in life has been fulfilled?

12. Why is the sanctuary periodically destroyed by fire?

13. Would the wizard have welcomed death more than the knowledge of his true nature? Explain.

TECHNIQUE

1. Do you feel Borges was wise in choosing a very primitive setting for a story as intellectually sophisticated as "The Circular Ruins"? Why or why not?

2. Using the style of "The Circular Ruins" as your criterion, what reasons might you offer to explain why Borges has never written anything longer than a short story.

EXTENSIONS

1. What elements can you find in the relationship of the wizard to his son that have a relevance to real family situations?

2. The wizard's problems in creating a son suggest some of the difficulties authors have in creating convincing fictional characters. Try to equate these problems. What pitfalls or limitations might an author face if he, like the wizard, relied solely upon either (a) dialogue or (b) physical description in creating his characters?

3. In the Gnosticism from which Borges has borrowed, every man is a seeker of knowledge as the key to truth. If twentieth-century man, like Borges' wizard, directs that search within himself, do you think that he will find that truth is, indeed, both circular and illusory? Discuss.

Autumn Mountain

AKUTAGAWA RYŪNOSUKÉ[1] / Japan
(1892–1927)
translated from the Japanese by Ivan Morris

And speaking of Ta Ch'ih,[2] have you ever seen his Autumn Mountain painting?"

One evening, Wang Shih-ku,[3] who was visiting his friend Yün Nan-t'ien,[4] asked this question.

"No, I have never seen it. And you?"

Ta Ch'ih, together with Mei-tao-jen and Huang-hao-shan-ch'iao, had been one of the great painters of the Mongol dynasty.[5] As Yün Nan-t'ien replied, there passed before his eyes images of the artist's famous works, the Sandy Shore painting and the Joyful Spring picture scroll.

"Well, strange to say," said Wang Shih-ku, "I'm really not sure whether or not I have seen it. In fact. . . ."

"You don't know whether you have seen it or you haven't?" said Yün Nan-t'ien, looking curiously at his guest. "Do you mean that you've seen an imitation?"

"No, not an imitation, I saw the original. And it is not I alone who have seen it. The great critics Yen-k'o and Lien-chou[6] both became involved with the Autumn Mountain."

Wang Shih-ku sipped his tea and smiled thoughtfully. "Would it bore you to hear about it?"

"Quite the contrary," said Yün Nan-

t'ien, bowing his head politely. He stirred the flame in the copper lamp.

At that time (began Wang Shih-ku) the old master Yüan Tsai was still alive. One evening while he was discussing paintings with Yen-k'o, he asked him whether he had ever seen Ta Ch'ih's Autumn Mountain. As you know, Yen-k'o made a veritable religion of Ta Ch'ih's painting and was certainly not likely to have missed any of his works. But he had never set eyes on this Autumn Mountain.

"No, I haven't seen it," he answered shamefacedly, "and I've never even heard of its existence."

"In that case," said Yüan Tsai, "please don't miss the first opportunity you have of seeing it. As a work of art it's on an

"Autumn Mountain" by Akutagawa Ryūnosuké, translated by Ivan Morris from MODERN JAPANESE STORIES. Reprinted by permission of Charles E. Tuttle Co., Inc.
1. *Akutagawa Ryūnosuké* (ä kü′ tä gä′ wä ryü-nô′ sü ke′). 2. *Ta Ch'ih* (tä chē′). 3. *Wang Shih-ku* (vang shē′ kü). 4. *Yün Nan-t'ien* (yün nän′-tyēn). 5. *the Mongol dynasty.* The Mongol dynasty is usually dated from the crowning of Kublai Khan in 1260 as head of the Mongol Empire, which had been built by Ghenghis Khan between 1206-1227. The last ruler of the dynasty died in 1368. 6. *Yen-k'o* (yen′ kō) *and Lien-chou* (lin′ chou).

even higher level than his Summer Mountain or Wandering Storm. In fact, I'm not sure that it isn't the finest of all Ta Ch'ih's paintings."

"Is it really such a masterpiece? Then I must do my best to see it. May I ask who owns this painting?"

"It's in the house of a Mr. Chang[7] in the County of Jun. If you ever have occasion to visit the Chin-shan Temple, you should call on him and see the picture. Allow me to give you a letter of introduction."

As soon as Yen-k'o received Yüan Tsai's letter, he made plans to set out for the County of Jun. A house which harbored so precious a painting as this would, he thought, be bound to have other great works of different periods. Yen-k'o was quite giddy with anticipation as he started out.

When he reached the County of Jun, however, he was surprised to find that Mr. Chang's house, though imposing in structure, was dilapidated. Ivy was coiled about the walls, and in the garden grass and weeds grew rank. As the old man approached, chickens, ducks, and other barnyard fowl looked up, as if surprised to see any stranger enter here. For a moment he could not help doubting Yüan Tsai's words and wondering how a masterpiece of Ta Ch'ih's could possibly have found its way into such a house. Upon a servant's answering his knock, he handed over the letter, explaining that he had come from far in the hope of seeing the Autumn Mountain.

He was led almost immediately into the great hall. Here again, though the divans and tables of red sandalwood stood in perfect order, a moldy smell hung over everything and an atmosphere of desolation had settled even on the tiles. The owner of the house, who now appeared, was an unhealthy-looking man; but he had a pleasant air about him and his pale face and delicate hands bore signs of nobility. Yen-k'o, after briefly introducing himself, lost no time in telling his host how grateful he would be if he might be shown the famous Ta Ch'ih painting. There was an urgency in the master's words, as if he feared that were he not to see the great painting at once, it might somehow vanish like a mist.

Mr. Chang assented without hesitation and had the painting hung on the bare wall of the great hall.[8]

"This," he said, "is the Autumn Mountain to which you refer."

At the first glance Yen-k'o let out a gasp of admiration. The dominant color was a dark green. From one end to the other a river ran its twisting course; bridges crossed the river at various places and along its banks were little hamlets. Dominating it all rose the main peak of the mountain range, before which floated peaceful wisps of autumn cloud. The mountain and its neighboring hills were fresh green, as if newly washed by rain, and there was an uncanny beauty in the red leaves of the bushes and thickets scattered along their slopes. This was no ordinary painting, but one in which both design and color had reached an apex of perfection. It was a work of art instinct with the classical sense of beauty.

"Well, what do you think of it? Does it please you?" said Mr. Chang, peering at Yen-k'o with a smile.

"Oh, it is truly of godlike quality!" cried Yen-k'o, while he stared at the picture in awe. "Yüan Tsai's lavish praise was more than merited. Compared to this painting, everything I have seen until now seems second-rate."

"Really? You find it such a masterpiece?"

Yen-k'o could not help turning a surprised look at his host. "Can you doubt it?"

"Oh no, it isn't that I have any doubts,"

7. *Chang* (cheng). 8. *Mr. Chang assented without hesitation and had the painting hung on the bare wall of the great hall.* The painting of the *Autumn Mountain* is a scroll and as such is protected in storage when not on display.

said Mr. Chang, and he blushed with confusion like a schoolboy. Looking almost timidly at the painting, he continued: "The fact is that each time I look at this picture I have the feeling that I am dreaming, though my eyes are wide open. I cannot help feeling that it is I alone who see its beauty, which is somehow too intense for this world of ours. What you just said brought back these strange feelings."

But Yen-k'o was not much impressed by his host's evident attempt at self-vindication. His attention was absorbed by the painting, and Mr. Chang's speech seemed to him merely designed to hide a deficiency in critical judgment.

Soon after, Yen-k'o left the desolate house.

As the weeks passed, the vivid image of the Autumn Mountain remained fresh in Yen-k'o's mind (continued Wang Shih-ku after accepting another cup of tea). Now that he had seen Ta Ch'ih's masterpiece, he felt ready to give up anything whatsoever to possess it. Inveterate collector that he was, he knew that not one of the great works that hung in his own house—not even Li Ying-ch'iu's Floating Snowflakes, for which he had paid five hundred taels of silver[9]—could stand comparison with that transcendent Autumn Mountain.

While still sojourning in the County of Jun, he sent an agent to the Chang house to negotiate for the sale of the painting. Despite repeated overtures, he was unable to persuade Mr. Chang to enter into any arrangement. On each occasion that pallid gentleman would reply that while he deeply appreciated the master's admiration of the Autumn Mountain and while he would be quite willing to lend the painting, he must ask to be excused from actually parting with it.

These refusals only served to strengthen the impetuous Yen-k'o's resolve. "One day," he promised himself, "that great picture will hang in my own hall." Con-fident of the eventual outcome, he finally resigned himself to returning home and temporarily abandoning the Autumn Mountain.

About a year later, in the course of a further visit to the County of Jun, he tried calling once more at the house of Mr. Chang. Nothing had changed: the ivy was still coiled in disorder about the walls and fences, and the garden was covered with weeds. But when the servant answered his knock, Yen-k'o was told that Chang was not in residence. The old man asked if he might have another look at the Autumn Mountain despite the owner's absence, but his importunacy was of no avail: the servant repeated that he had no authority to admit anyone until his master returned. As Yen-k'o persisted, the man finally shut the door in his face. Overcome with chagrin, Yen-k'o had to leave the house and the great painting that lay somewhere in one of the dilapidated rooms.

Wang Shih-ku paused for a moment.

"All that I have related so far," he said, "I heard from the master Yen-k'o himself."

"But tell me," said Yün Nan-t'ien, stroking his white beard, "did Yen-k'o ever really see the Autumn Mountain?"

"He said that he saw it. Whether or not he did, I cannot know for certain. Let me tell you the sequel, and then you can judge for yourself."

Wang Shih-ku continued his story with a concentrated air, and now he was no longer sipping his tea.

When Yen-k'o told me all this (said Wang Shih-ku) almost fifty years had passed since his visits to the County of Jun. The master Yüan Tsai was long since dead and Mr. Chang's large house

9. *five hundred taels of silver.* A tael is a Chinese coin equal to the current value of its weight in pure silver.

had already passed into the hands of two successive generations of his family. There was no telling where the Autumn Mountain might be—nor if the best parts of the scroll might not have suffered hopeless deterioration. In the course of our talk old Yen-k'o described that mysterious painting so vividly that I was almost convinced I could see it before my eyes. It was not the details that had impressed the master but the indefinable beauty of the picture as a whole. Through the words of Yen-k'o, that beauty had entered into my heart as well as his.

It happened that, about a month after my meeting with Yen-k'o, I had myself to make a journey to the southern provinces, including the County of Jun. When I mentioned this to the old man, he suggested that I go and see if I could not find the Autumn Mountain. "If that painting ever comes to light again," he said, "it will indeed be a great day for the world of art."

Needless to say, by this time I also was anxious to see the painting, but my journey was crowded and it soon became clear that I would not find time to visit Mr. Chang's house. Meanwhile, however, I happened to hear a report that the Autumn Mountain had come into the hands of a certain nobleman by the name of Wang. Having learned of the painting, Mr. Wang had despatched a messenger with greetings to Chang's grandson. The latter was said to have sent back with the messenger not only the ancient family documents and the great ceremonial cauldron which had been in the family for countless generations, but also a painting which fitted the description of Ta Ch'ih's Autumn Mountain. Delighted with these gifts, Mr. Wang had arranged a great banquet for Chang's grandson, at which he had placed the young man in the seat of honor and regaled him with the choicest delicacies, gay music, and lovely girls; in addition he had given him one thousand pieces of gold.

On hearing this report I almost leaped with joy. Despite the vicissitudes of half a century, it seemed that the Autumn Mountain was still safe! Not only that, but it actually had come within my range. Taking along only the barest necessities, I set out at once to see the painting.

I still vividly remember the day. It was a clear, calm afternoon in early summer and the peonies were proudly in bloom in Mr. Wang's garden. On meeting Mr. Wang, my face broke into a smile of delight even before I had completed my ceremonial bow. "To think that the Autumn Mountain is in this very house!" I cried. "Yen-k'o spent all those years in vain attempts to see it again—and now I am to satisfy my own ambition without the slightest effort. . . ."

"You come at an auspicious time," replied Mr. Wang. "It happens that today I am expecting Yen-k'o himself, as well as the great critic Lien-chou. Please come inside, and since you are the first to arrive you shall be the first to see the painting."

Mr. Wang at once gave instructions for the Autumn Mountain to be hung on the wall. And then it all leaped forth before my eyes: the little villages on the river, the flocks of white clouds floating over the valley, the green of the towering mountain ranges which extended into the distance like a succession of folding screens—the whole world, in fact, that Ta Ch'ih had created, a world far more wonderful than our own. My heart seemed to beat faster as I gazed intently at the scroll on the wall.

These clouds and mists and hills and valleys were unmistakably the work of Ta Ch'ih. Who but Ta Ch'ih could carry the art of drawing to such perfection that every brush-stroke became a thing alive? Who but he could produce colors of such depth and richness, and at the same time hide all mechanical trace of brush and paint? And yet . . . and yet I felt at once that this was not the same painting that Yen-k'o had seen once long ago. No, no, a magnificent painting it surely was, yet just as surely not the unique painting which he had described with such religious awe!

Mr. Wang and his entourage had gathered around me and were watching my expression, so I hastened to express my enthusiasm. Naturally I did not want him to doubt the authenticity of his picture, yet it was clear that my words of praise failed to satisfy him. Just then Yen-k'o himself was announced—he who had first spoken to me of this Autumn Mountain. As the old man bowed to Mr. Wang, I could sense the excitement inside him, but no sooner had his eyes settled on the scroll than a cloud seemed to pass before his face.

"What do you think of it, Master?" asked Mr. Wang, who had been carefully observing him. "We have just heard the teacher Wang Shih-ku's enthusiastic praise, but . . ."

"Oh, you are, sir, a very fortunate man to have acquired this painting," answered Yen-k'o promptly. "Its presence in your house will add luster to all your other treasures."

Yen-k'o's courteous words only seemed to deepen Mr. Wang's anxiety; he, like me, must have heard in them a note of insincerity. I think we were all a bit relieved when Lien-chou, the famous critic, made his appearance at this juncture. After bowing to us, he turned to the scroll and stood looking at it silently, chewing his long mustaches.

"This, apparently, is the same painting that the master Yen-k'o last saw half a century ago," Mr. Wang explained to him. "Now I would much like to hear your opinion of the work. Your candid opinion," Mr. Wang added, forcing a smile.

Lien-chou sighed and continued to look· at the picture. Then he took a deep breath and, turning to Mr. Wang, said: "This, sir, is probably Ta Ch'ih's greatest work. Just see how the artist has shaded those clouds. What power there was in his brush! Note also the color of his trees. And then that distant peak which brings the whole composition to life." As he spoke, Lien-chou pointed to various outstanding features of the painting, and needless to say, a look of relief, then of delight, spread over Mr. Wang's face.

Meanwhile I secretly exchanged glances with Yen-k'o. "Master," I whispered, "is that the real Autumn Mountain?" Almost imperceptibly the old man shook his head, and there was a twinkle in his eyes.

"It's all like a dream," he murmured. "I really can't help wondering if that Mr. Chang wasn't some sort of hobgoblin."

"So that is the story of the Autumn Mountain," said Wang Shih-ku after a pause, and took a sip of his tea. "Later on it appears that Mr. Wang made all sorts of exhaustive enquiries. He visited Mr. Chang, but when he mentioned to him the Autumn Mountain, the young man denied all knowledge of any other version. So one cannot tell if that Autumn Mountain which Yen-k'o saw all those years ago is not even now hidden away somewhere. Or perhaps the whole thing was just a case of faulty memory on an old man's part. It would seem unlikely, though, that Yen-k'o's story about visiting Mr. Chang's house to see the Autumn Mountain was not based on solid fact."

"Well, in any case the image of that strange painting is no doubt engraved forever on Yen-k'o's mind. And on yours too."

"Yes," said Wang Shih-ku, "I still see the dark green of the mountain rock, as Yen-k'o described it all those years ago. I can see the red leaves of the bushes as if the painting were before my eyes this very moment."

"So even if it never existed, there is not really much cause for regret!"

The two men laughed and clapped their hands with delight.

THE END

Development

INTERPRETATION

1. *(a)* What about Mr. Chang and his home is incongruous with Yen-k'o's expectations? *(b)* What is prophetic in Mr. Chang's comments about the *Autumn Mountain*? *(c)* Do you think that Yen-k'o's frustrated attempts to purchase and view the *Autumn Mountain* influenced his recollection of the painting? Explain.

2. *(a)* What kindles Wang Shih-ku's desire to see the *Autumn Mountain*? *(b)* What is significant about Wang Shih-ku's observation: "Yen-k'o spent all those years in vain attempts to see it again—and now I am to satisfy my ambition without the slightest effort"?

3. *(a)* What is different about the attitudes and circumstances of Mr. Chang and Mr. Wang? *(b)* In what way might these differences have influenced the final viewing of the painting by Wang Shih-ku and Yen-k'o?

4. Although Wang Shih-ku and Yen-k'o respond to Mr. Wang's inquiries with considerable reserve, Lien-chou, "the famous critic," praises the *Autumn Mountain* unconditionally. To what do you attribute this discrepancy? Explain.

5. Imagine that you are also visiting at the house of Yün Nan-t'ien and that you have been listening to Wang Shih-ku's story of the *Autumn Mountain*. At the moment Wang Shih-ku and Yün Nan-t'ien are laughing and clapping their hands with delight, a fourth guest enters and asks you the cause of their merriment. How would you sum up the situation without repeating the story Wang Shih-ku has already told?

TECHNIQUE

1. If someone were to comment that Wang Shih-ku was a master in the art of storytelling, would you agree with his view or challenge it? Give specific examples from the story to support your argument.

2. *(a)* Without looking back at the story, try to describe Ta Ch'ih's painting of the *Autumn Mountain*. *(b)* Do you feel that your success or failure in answering part *(a)* reflects upon Akutagawa's ability as a writer? Explain.

EXTENSIONS

1. The philosophers and sages of the East have for millenniums used parables as a way of initiating the unenlightened into the wisdom of their teachings. *(a)* What idea or philosophy might one teach using the story "Autumn Mountain" as a parable? *(b)* Do you think parables are more effective than straight exposition in communicating an abstract concept? Why or why not?

2. The *Autumn Mountain* painting is described as depicting a beauty "which is somehow too intense for this world of ours." *(a)* Does the idea of beauty imply impermanence, or can something be eternally beautiful? Explain. *(b)* Can art capture a beauty that is in the world, or only hope to convey an impression of it? Discuss.

3. Suppose that you have found "Autumn Mountain" dull and confusing. Also suppose that twenty years from today you happen to reread the story and are delighted by it. *(a)* What reasons might you give for the discrepancy in your reactions? *(b)* Given this possibility, upon what criteria can we legitimately evaluate art?

Comparison

1. Suppose that you are trying to explain the meaning of the word *irony* to a class of students unfamiliar with literary terminology. What common elements could you isolate from the selections in this group to exemplify what you mean by *ironic*?

2. Nurse Adeh Eden seems somewhat out of place among the characters in these selections. *(a)* In what ways is she different from the wizard, Adiel Amzeh, and Wang Shih-ku? *(b)* Do you feel that Nurse Eden could also be considered a seeker? Explain.

3. "Forevermore" and "The Circular Ruins" are both somewhat obscure stories. If they were to appear in a section of a book to which you were writing an introduction, with what attitudes might you suggest that the reader approach them?

4. In "The Circular Ruins" and "Autumn Mountain" Borges and Akutagawa have played with the often insubstantial line between illusion and reality. How might you introduce this conflict into a story with a contemporary setting? Explain your strategy.

5. *(a)* What is distinctly different about the narrative styles of the three selections in this group? *(b)* In what ways does each reflect the author's attitude toward his characters? *(c)* Which narrative form did you find most effective? Why?

6. The idea of seeking implies the idea of eventually finding or arriving, of being satisfied or fulfilled. *(a)* Do you feel that the wizard, Adiel Amzeh, and Wang Shih-ku, at the end of their respective stories, have reached a state of accomplishment? Why or why not? *(b)* What differences can you find between the seekers portrayed in this group and the stereotyped images of the "man of action" or the American "go-getter"?

BIOGRAPHIES OF AUTHORS

PETER ABRAHAMS (1919 –   )

In an essay entitled "The Blacks" Peter Abrahams speaks of "that dark unhappy land which yet compelled my love." Although it has been some years since the author lived there, it is from Africa that he draws his subject matter. As a child who grew up in the black ghettos of Johannesburg, Abrahams had experienced the endless struggle against poverty and the treachery of apartheid, both frequent topics of his fiction.

After graduating from college in 1938, Abrahams worked as a teacher and later as a magazine editor; his dream, though, was to go to England. He traveled around the world for two years as a ship's stoker and finally came to England, where he began writing in earnest. South Africa is the scene of his five novels, numerous short works, and of his autobiography, *Tell Freedom.* Abrahams now lives in Jamaica and continues to write of Africa and its people.

AESOP (620? – 560? B.C.)

It is not known for certain whether the man Aesop ever really lived, although references to him do exist in the works of Plutarch and Aristotle. The most prevalent theory is that he was a Phrygian slave who was freed and who traveled about the country telling his fables. A statue, supposedly of Aesop, in the Villa Albani in Paris, depicts him as an ugly dwarf, but this too is a matter of controversy.

The fables themselves were drawn from folktales, many of them centuries old. As we know them, they were related by the Greek writer Valerius Babrius, who probably lived during the second century B.C.

S. Y. AGNON (1888–1970)

In 1966 S. Y. Agnon became the first Israeli author to receive the Nobel Prize for Literature. Agnon had migrated to Palestine in 1908 from his native home in Galicia, which is now part of Poland. As the Zionist movement in Europe brought more Jews to Palestine in the 1930's and '40's, Agnon began to fear that the modern ways of the new immigrants would displace the older Hebraic traditions. His stories from that period often involve a conflict between what is authentic and what is only ephemeral. Agnon reconciled himself to the necessary influx when Israel became a nation in 1948, although he himself continued to live by the old customs. Even the award of the Nobel Prize brought little change to Agnon's life, except that outside his modest home in Jerusalem the Israeli government posted a sign which warned: "Quiet! Agnon Is Writing."

ILSE AICHINGER (1921 –   )

Ilse Aichinger, novelist and dramatist, was awarded the Austrian state prize for literature in 1953. Her short stories are found in *The Bound Man and Other Stories.* Like Franz Kafka, her first literary model, the author portrays the ambiguity of human existence. Man, as presented by Ilse Aichinger, is truly a "bound man" —shackled and alienated.

Ilse Aichinger is married to the German poet Gunther Eich and lives in southwest Germany.

AKUTAGAWA RYŪNOSUKÉ (1892 – 1927)

Akutagawa was attending Tokyo University in 1915 when his short story "Rashomon," published in a student magazine, brought him to the attention of Japan's authors and critics. Inspired by this recognition, Akutagawa devoted his life to writing and completed over 150 short stories, many of them ancient tales reconstructed with the ironies of twentieth-century insight. From his youth, Akutagawa suffered from a nature that seemed little suited for the world. In 1927 he committed suicide, moved by what he enigmatically described as a "vague uneasiness."

JERZY ANDRZEJEWSKI (1909 –   )

Jerzy Andrzejewski was in the forefront of contemporary Polish fiction shortly before the Second World War. His first novel, *Harmony of the Heart,* claimed the Young Writers' Prize from the Academy of Polish Literature in 1938. During the German occupation, Andrzejewski was sought out as an arbiter in matters touching upon Poland's unwritten patriotic code. These wartime experiences form the core of the collection of tales entitled *Night,* which was published in 1946.

Andrzejewski was proclaimed an adherent of Socialist Realism for chronicling the rise of Polish Communism in his next novel, *Ashes and Diamonds,* which earned a Polish state prize in 1948. In practice, though, Andrzejewski's work escaped the rigidity of the Party line by his balanced portrayal of the strengths and weaknesses of Poland's Communist visionaries.

Andrzejewski resigned from the Communist Party in 1957 to underline his protest against censorship in Poland. His two subsequent novels, *Darkness Covers the Earth,* published in 1957 and translated into English under the title *The Inquisitors,* and *Gates of Paradise,* published in 1960, probe contemporary ideas and conflicts through the use of historical situation and metaphor.

FERNANDO ARRABAL (1932 –   )

Arrabal grew up when Spain was under a military dictatorship; as a result, a hatred of tyranny became the basis for much of his writing. His heroes tend to be naive little men unable to cope with the overwhelming and mysterious demands of their society. But they remain optimistic and, consequently, they are laughable. Arrabal has also come under the influence of several famous men: the writers Samuel Beckett, Franz Kafka, Lewis Carroll, and the comedian W. C. Fields. Each expresses some facet of the comic, the fanciful, and the absurd, all of which are important to Arrabal's work.

Despite his Spanish origin, Arrabal writes in French. He is now living in Paris with his wife Luce, who is a professor at the Sorbonne.

BIBHUTI BHUSAN BANDYOPADHYAY (1893 – 1950)

Bandyopadhyay, the son of a *kathak,* or village storyteller, spent most of his adult life as a schoolteacher in Calcutta. The author's ability to depict the simple, sometimes harsh lives of Indian villagers is evident in "The Trellis," which he considered one of his finest works. The story was eventually expanded into a novel entitled *Pather Panchali.* Bandyopadhyay became internationally known when this novel was made into the motion picture, "Song of the Road."

HERMAN JOACHIM BANG (1857 – 1912)

Herman Bang's childhood in Denmark was marked by family tragedy and extreme personal difficulty. This resulted in an unhappy and unstable life which finally ended in suicide when Bang was fifty-five.

The writer's personal problems are reflected in the various short stories he wrote about isolated, miserable people who somehow cannot manage to live normally productive lives. "Irene Holm" is an example of such a story. Critics say that these short works are superior to Bang's novels, which tend to be wordy and overdone.

Bang, who enjoyed his greatest popularity during the 1890's, was a strong influence on many young Danish novelists.

GEO BOGZA (1908 –   )

Although he began his career writing surrealistic verse, Geo Bogza has earned his literary reputation as a master in the art of writing nonfiction feature articles. He wrote these as a member of the Rumanian People's Republic Academy; and most of them pay tribute to the achievements of the working class of Rumanian people.

His published collections of articles include: *Years of Resistance* (1953), *Geographical Survey* (1953), and *Contemporary Pages* (1957).

HEINRICH BÖLL (1917 –   )

Heinrich Böll's early manhood was ended by service in the German infantry during World War II. He fought on several fronts, was wounded, captured, and finally repatriated.

In some of his works Böll combines a compassion for the plight of the common man in postwar Germany with an indictment of the emerging materialistic society. In other works, he writes of the evils of war and of racial persecution under the Nazi regime.

Among his works translated into English are *Acquainted with the Night* (1954), *Billiards at Half-past Nine* (1961), and *The Clown* (1965). In 1972 Böll received a Nobel Prize for his role in the postwar "renewal of German literature."

JORGE LUIS BORGES (1899 –   )

Although born in Buenos Aires, Jorge Luis Borges is lineally and intellectually as European as he is South American. Borges finished his education in Geneva, Switzerland, during the years of the First World War before his return to Argentina in 1921. In Buenos Aires, Borges became the chief exponent of *ultraism,* a Spanish movement which emulated in poetry the experimentalism of the surrealist painters.

The political upheavals in South America and Europe during the 1930's drove Borges unconditionally into himself. He began writing short stories haunted by ironies, paradoxes, and intricate metaphysical involutions.

Although today nearly blind, Borges, a relentless scholar, continues his researches into the arcane literatures, histories, and philosophies of the world. His stories are currently available in two English translations entitled *Labyrinths* and *Ficciones.*

ALBERT CAMUS (1913 – 1960)

Albert Camus was trusted by even his most severe critics; his life seemed to give currency to every word he wrote. He was born in Algeria shortly before his father died in World War I. His mother moved their family into the city of Algiers, where she worked as a domestic servant. He knew the poverty of the dispossessed, yet it never embittered him; rather, he exulted in his freedom to roam Algiers and bask in the sun of his Mediterranean homeland.

Camus won a scholarship to the University of Algiers, where he studied philosophy while working as actor, director, and playwright for his own theater company. After graduating he took a job as a reporter and wrote enough on his own to publish a volume of essays, *The Wrong Side and the Right Side,* in 1937, and another, *Nuptials,* the following year. When, in 1942, Camus left Algiers for a newspaper job in Nazi-occupied Paris, he was carrying with him the manuscripts for three of his major works: a novel, *The Stranger*; an essay, *The Myth of Sisyphus;* and a play, *Caligula.* The novel was published that year, while Camus became the editor of *Combat,* the underground paper of the French Resistance. When France was liberated in 1944, Camus was a national hero, both as a writer and a patriot.

Camus' immediate recognition can be partly attributed to the relevance of his thought for the post-World War II generation. He rejected any attempt to justify the indifference of history and fate, yet he stood implacably against the defeatism which, he felt, undermined the twentieth century. In its place he offered courage that was not self-deceptive, revolt that was not destructive, and joy that was not an escape—all characteristics embodied in Dr. Rieux, the protagonist of Camus' novel, *The Plague,* published in 1947.

Camus was awarded the Nobel Prize for Literature in 1957, at the age of forty-four. He had completed the rough draft for a large novel when, after the Christmas holidays of 1960, some friends dropped by unexpectedly to drive him back to Paris. Camus died instantly when their car hurtled into a tree.

KAREL ČAPEK (1890–1938)

Karel Čapek was born in Male Svatonovice in northeast Bohemia (since 1949 a part of the Czechoslovak state). He studied in Prague, Paris, and Berlin, receiving a doctorate in philosophy from the University of Prague in 1917. His doctoral dissertation dealt with the concept of pragmatism, which implies a practical, activist view of life. After graduation, he did indeed begin to live such a life—publishing stories, reporting, stage managing at a Czech theater, and finding time to support various liberal and democratic causes.

Čapek's plays established him as the chief writer for the Czech national theater. Most of these plays involve some social criticism, and they are frequently experimental in technique. His brother Josef often collaborated with him, supplying futuristic, expressionistic designs to uphold and intensify Karel's language and ideas.

Although Čapek is known primarily for his dramatic works, he experimented with a variety of forms: satirical fancies, fables, a mystery, a prose trilogy wherein one story is told from three different points of view, and a novel, *War with the Newts.*

Čapek's best-known play, *R.U.R.,* concerns a future world where robots are manufactured to do all of man's mechanized labor. The robots (a word, incidentally, coined by Čapek) rebel against their human masters and destroy them. However, at the end of the play they recognize the need to develop souls, the lack of which had destroyed mankind.

Čapek died of a heart attack on Christmas Day (1938) just as parts of the German army entered Prague prior to World War II.

CARLO CASSOLA (1917–   )

Carlo Cassola lived in Rome until the age of twenty-three. During World War II he was an active participant in the Italian Resistance, which inspired him to write politically oriented fiction. At present Cassola is teaching history and philosophy in the small Italian town of Grosseto. He prefers to remain apart from the literary life of the cities.

Besides his fictional works, Cassola has written and published a diary of a trip to China and collaborated on a study of the Tuscan miners. In 1960 his novel *La ragazza di Bube* [*Bebo's Girl*] was awarded the *Premio Strega,* an important Italian literary award.

ANTON CHEKHOV (1860 – 1904)

Anton Chekhov once described his early life by saying, "There was no childhood in my childhood." Born into a family just recently released from serfdom, he had to work long hours in his father's store and was beaten at the slightest provocation. When he was sixteen, his family fled from the town of Taganrog to Moscow to escape debtor's prison, and he was left to shift for himself.

Chekhov began writing slight and amusing stories to help pay his way through medical school at the University of Moscow. These early stories are generally brief, amusing sketches with little depth. His later works show an increasing concern for the ills of man and of society, but an undertow of the early humor always remains, for Chekhov especially disliked sentimentality and preachiness. These works—especially the major plays—attempt to depict the tragedy that lies behind much of everyday living.

Since Chekhov's writing attempts only to depict—and not to interpret—it was confusing to many of his contemporaries. Leo Tolstoy admitted his own confusion, and yet could still perceive Chekhov's genius. He said: "I have as yet no clear picture of Chekhov's plays. But it is possible that in the future, perhaps a hundred years hence, people will be amazed at what they find in Chekhov about the inner workings of the human soul."

KAY CICELLIS (1926 –   )

Kay Cicellis was born of Greek parentage in Marseilles, France. When the author was nine she moved with her family to Athens. Although she learned Greek as a child, all of her work has been written in English. Four of her books have been published in London and Germany as well as in the United States. In 1960 she published *The Way to Colonus,* three long stories based on ancient Greek myths, of which "The Exile" is one. Of this story, Kay Cicellis writes, "'The Exile' was to me the most interesting of the three stories because there are far more conflicts in it, and because from the start Philoctetes is not a hero; it is one of the few ancient plays in which there is no hero."

Besides short stories and novels, she has also had articles and stories published in *Harper's Bazaar, Mademoiselle, Paris Review,* and *London Magazine.*

EURIPIDES (485 – 406? B.C.)

Euripides wrote eighty-eight plays during his lifetime, thirteen of which are extant; but he received only four prizes in the Athenian drama contests. This surprising lack of recognition reflects Euripides' lifelong quarrel with the society of Athens. His talent was recognized, but his views—political, religious, and even aesthetic—were considered unacceptable.

Although he was compared by his contemporaries to the other two giants of Greek theater, Aeschylus and Sophocles, Euripides differed from his two forerunners in his refusal to accept either the traditional structure or concept of Greek drama. Instead of constructing his plays as means for religious instruction and edification, he used them as vehicles for attacking the corruptions which he hated most: superstition, social injustice, the subjection of women, and Athenian aggression under the guise of democracy (the last two are especially evident in *Medea*).

This change in purpose implied some rather drastic changes in technique as well: use of the chorus was strictly limited —perhaps in an attempt to get his audiences to see and think for themselves; use of music was complicated and embellished; long epilogues and prologues were introduced; the number of actors was increased; and, generally speaking, all "classic restraint" was discarded in favor of adventure, suspense, and psychological probing.

It is little wonder that Euripides eventually became the most highly imitated and influential of all the Greek playwrights; added to the excellence of the plays themselves is the charm always conveyed by the rebel and the innovator. Euripides died at the age of seventy-eight while enduring voluntary exile in Macedonia.

GUSTAVE FLAUBERT (1821–1880)

Gustave Flaubert was born in Rouen, France, the son of a doctor. He left Rouen to study law in Paris, but his contact with the literary figures in the city, including the great French romantic writer Victor Hugo, proved to be more stimulating to him than a legal career. While still in his twenties, Flaubert began work on three novels, among them *Madame Bovary*, which took him five years to complete.

From the very beginning Flaubert's writing showed a doctor's eye for detail and a scorn for sentimentality. Some critics trace these qualities, in part, to his childhood exposure to illness and death. He detested sloppiness in thought, as well as in writing, and thus soon came to oppose what he regarded as the extreme romanticism of Hugo and his followers. Language, Flaubert once wrote to a friend, should be "as rhythmical as verse and as precise as science." This statement summarizes the nature of Flaubert's masterful style. He sought to make his readers see reality in all of its trivia and sorrow, and yet to make the experience of seeing poetic and beautiful.

FEDERICO GARCÍA LORCA (1899–1936)

Despite his reputation as a "primitive" poet, García Lorca was born of well-to-do parents, and he received a good education in law and literature at the University of Granada. His father was a wealthy farmer, and his mother, to whom he was devoted, was a gifted concert pianist.

García Lorca's primitivism was therefore a matter of conscious choice rather than of environment. He loved the folk poetry of his country, and he was fascinated with its Gypsy life. A trip to New York in 1929 increased this fascination, for he saw much in New York's Harlem to remind him of the Gypsies of Spain.

García Lorca was established as a poet by the year 1927 through the success of his *Book of Poems and Songs*. After returning to Spain from America, he began writing and directing plays. These plays show the same primitive, violent, and richly metaphorical quality as do his poems. Although he wrote both comedy and tragedy, the latter are considered quite superior. Many critics have remarked especially on the great insight which García Lorca has into his female characters, so that the more successful plays concern women as much or more than men. These include *Yerma, Blood Wedding,* and *The House of Bernardo Alba.*

García Lorca was brutally executed in Spain by the adherents of Franco in 1936, an act which did much to lose Franco's government the sympathy of the rest of the world.

JOÃO GUIMARÃES ROSA (1908–1967)

Guimarães Rosa was born and raised in the Brazilian backlands, or *sertao,* which is the setting for most of his stories. He was for some years a doctor in this region, and thus came to know the inhabitants very well.

He began his writing career at the age of twenty-eight with the publication of a group of poems sponsored by the Brazilian Academy of Letters. He soon turned from poetry to prose. *Sagarma,* his first collection of stories, was published in 1946 and brought him wide acclaim. His last collection, from which "The Third Bank of the River" was taken, bears the ironic title *First Stories*. The title refers to a marked change in style evident in this collection. These tales have a fanciful, almost mystic, quality which is a new element in Guimarães Rosa's fiction.

WOLFGANG HILDESHEIMER (1916–   )

Wolfgang Hildesheimer has quite a varied biography. He was born in Germany, attended high school in England until he was seventeen, then he traveled to Palestine, where he spent three years learning cabinetry. Next he returned to Germany, apprenticed himself to a theatrical set builder, then left for London in 1937 to work in the theater, while studying painting and graphic design. When World War II began Hildesheimer was made an officer in the British Intelligence and stationed in Palestine, where he doubled as an art critic while exhibiting his paintings in Jerusalem and Tel Aviv.

Hildesheimer was back in London when the war ended. He immediately went to Nuremberg, the site of the post-war trials for Nazi war criminals, and worked there as an interpreter until 1949. Since then he has divided his time between painting and writing at his home in Poschiavo, Switzerland.

HENRIK IBSEN (1828–1906)

Ibsen, whose first love was medicine, did not enter the theater until 1851, when he accepted a job as a stage manager. In 1857 he advanced to Director of the Norwegian Theater in Christiania (now Oslo); these two positions taught him the practical aspects of drama. As a playwright, Ibsen pioneered by introducing realistic themes, usually concerned with social characterizations rather than plot, and by writing natural dialogue.

Peer Gynt, one of his first successful plays, draws heavily upon Norwegian folklore for its background. *A Doll's House, Hedda Gabler,* and *The Wild Duck* are among his most widely read plays; they deal, to a large extent, with the problems of the individual in society. In later life Ibsen grew concerned with the role of the artist in the world and several of his last plays, among them *The Master Builder,* deal with this theme.

EUGENE IONESCO (1912–   )

Eugene Ionesco has always written. One of his childhood stories depicted a tea party at which the young guests began by volleying their biscuits, then their cups and saucers, next the tables and chairs, and finally their parents, who were ejected through the window.

Though born in Rumania, Ionesco spent most of his youth in France, where he earned an advanced degree in French literature. He returned to Rumania in 1936 to teach at the University of Bucharest. While there he witnessed the terrorism of the Iron Guard, a fascist group that often transformed the sanest of men into fanatics. Ionesco fled to Paris in 1939, where he has since resided as a French citizen.

Ionesco's first attempt at playwriting was inspired by a dramatized lesson book from which he was learning English. The characters in the lessons continually repeated the most obvious but incongruous truisms. This struck Ionesco as a metaphor for the senseless repetition in the lives of people who lack interior direction. The resulting play, entitled *The Bald Soprano,* was first performed in 1950 to an unenthusiastic public. But Ionesco was intrigued by the unique immediacy of the theater and continued to write.

In 1956 a revival of Ionesco's *The Chairs,* then five years old, suddenly struck French critics as the work of a master. By 1961 Ionesco's other most popular plays, *The Lesson, The Killer* (adapted from his short story, "The Photograph of the Colonel"), *Amedee,* and *The Rhinoceros,* were produced and acclaimed throughout the world.

FRANZ KAFKA (1883–1924)

Franz Kafka knew isolation well: as a Jew he was segregated from European society; as a skeptic he was estranged from his religious heritage; as one of the German-speaking minority under the predominantly Slavic Austro-Hungarian monarchy, he had no national identity; and as the frail but only surviving son of a domineering father, he was obsessed by a feeling of inferiority he could neither master nor escape.

Kafka studied law in his native Prague and took a job in a government insurance agency. At the prompting of his friend Max Brod, he published a few short stories but wrote nothing major before he was twenty-nine. In that year Kafka began a courtship which brought into conflict all the disparities of his personality. When it ended, chaotically, five years later, Kafka had completed the majority of his short stories, including "The Metamorphosis," and the larger part of his novel, *The Trial.* He had also contracted tuberculosis, which forced him to spend much of his remaining seven years in sanatoriums.

Little of Kafka's work was published during his lifetime and, on his deathbed, Kafka instructed Max Brod to destroy the rest, including his large though uncompleted novel, *The Castle.* Brod refused, and most of Kafka's work was published by 1931.

ALEXANDER KIELLAND (1849–1906)

In his schooling in his native town of Stavanger, Norway, and particularly at the University of Christiania (now Oslo), Alexander Kielland became acquainted with the problems of modern liberal Europe. Much of Kielland's work reveals his dissatisfaction with the restrictions and deficiencies of society.

Kielland's first collection of short stories, published in 1879, made him known throughout Scandinavia. The clergy, who in Kielland's opinion used religion for unethical purposes, were his main target in the novel, *Garman and Worse,* published in 1880. In the same year the author published a second collection of short stories in which his social criticism was sharper than ever. Ironically enough, Kielland was elected mayor of his native town, and, in 1902, prefect of a local district, thus becoming one of the officials he had so bitterly criticized.

MARIA KONOPNICKA (1842–1910)

On her sixtieth birthday the Polish government awarded Maria Konopnicka a lifetime subsidy as Poland's greatest poetess, although twelve years earlier she had been expelled from Poland for engaging in subversive activities. This turnabout reflects the tumultuous era in which Konopnicka lived. As a feminist, patriot, and stubborn social critic, Konopnicka was forced to live for periods in France, Switzerland, and Italy as the Polish government underwent frequent purges.

In or out of exile, Konopnicka recorded

her experience of common oppression and injustice. It is primarily for her short stories of social impact that Konopnicka is remembered outside of Poland. She brought a psychological perspective to her rustic subject matter and utilized the particular to magnify the faults of the whole.

KUME MASAO (1891 – 1952)

Kume Masao, novelist, poet, and playwright, was born in Nagano, Japan. While a student at Tokyo University, he earned a favorable reputation with his first play titled *Brothers of the Ranch*. After graduating he founded, together with others, a literary magazine titled *New Current Thoughts*. He frequently wrote haiku poetry under the pen name of Santei. Among his better known novels are *A Memorandum of a Student Appearing for his Entrance Examination, Defeated, Cold Fire*, and *Golden Snowslip*.

PÄR LAGERKVIST (1891 – 1974)

Life was colored with the somber hue of homespun frugality in the Swedish province where Pär Lagerkvist was born. Like Ibsen's folk hero Peer Gynt, Lagerkvist longed to experience the greater world. In 1913 he took up residence in Paris, where he was soon to witness the carnage of World War I. When a collection of Lagerkvist's poetry appeared in 1916 it was entitled *Anguish* and was described by a critic as "one long cry of despair over the bestiality of man."

By the 1930's Lagerkvist was recognized as an uncompromising enemy of totalitarianism in all its social and political forms. The anti-hero of his novel *The Dwarf*, published in 1944, displays a Machiavellian capacity for evil that stunts by comparison the deeds of "The Children's Campaign." When Lagerkvist received the Nobel Prize for Literature in 1951 he had published thirty-five books in various genres. The dedication of the award read, in part: "for the artistic power and deep-rooted independence he demonstrates . . . . in seeking an answer to the eternal questions of humanity."

SELMA LAGERLÖF (1858 – 1940)

Selma Lagerlöf, the first woman to win the Nobel Prize for Literature (1909), grew up in the region of Marbacka, Varmland, in Sweden. Since she was lame as a child, she studied at home, with the intention of becoming a schoolteacher. She pursued this career only briefly, however, for the publication of her first novel (*Gosta Berling's Saga*, 1894) induced her to become a writer instead.

This novel, which won her the Nobel Prize, makes considerable use of legendary material as a backdrop for the adventures of its romantic hero. Gosta Berling is an impulsive and idealistic adventurer who becomes involved in various misfortunes before winning a beautiful countess as his bride. Through her influence his ideals are given a more orderly direction; and as befitting a legendary romance, they live happily ever after.

Like *Gosta Berling's Saga,* the short story "The Outlaws" has the remote and timeless quality of legend which characterizes Lagerlöf's works as a whole. It is from a collection of stories published in 1894 called *Missing Links*. A number of other books followed, including *The Miracles of Antichrist* (1897), *The Queens of Kungahälla* (1917), *Tales of a Manor* (1922), *The Ring of the Lowenskolds* (1925), and *Memories of My Childhood* (1930).

Miss Lagerlöf died in 1940 at her childhood home in Varmland, which she had repurchased with the money she received as part of the Nobel Prize. Although greatly admired and respected in her homeland, her work has had surprisingly little influence on the national literature of Sweden.

MAURICE MAETERLINCK (1862–1949)

Maeterlinck was born and educated in Belgium. After completing his education at the Jesuit College of Sainte-Barbe, he moved to Paris. There he became involved with the Symbolist movement, which emphasized personal emotional response as the proper subject of art. His first works, a group of poems called *Hot Houses* and a play *The Princess Maleine,* were published in 1899. The latter received such great acclaim that it won Maeterlinck the title "The Belgian Shakespeare."

Other successes followed. His two best-knows plays are *Pelléas and Mélisande,* which was made into an opera by Debussy, and the fantasy, *The Blue Bird,* which at the present time is being filmed in the Soviet Union with Soviet technicians and an American cast, as a cooperative effort between the USSR and the United States.

Maeterlinck is a noted essayist as well as a playwright. While at his estate in Belgium he turned out a charming series based on his observations as a beekeeper. *The Life of the Bees* illustrates that the writer, judged "mystical" by many literary critics, could be quite scientific when he wished to be.

Maeterlinck received the Nobel Prize for Literature in 1911, and was offered election to the French Academy in 1937. He refused the latter honor, however, as it would have required him to become a French citizen.

THOMAS MANN (1875–1955)

Thomas Mann was born in Lübeck, Germany. In 1929 he was awarded the Nobel Prize for Literature. His first novel, *Buddenbrooks,* published in 1901, demonstrated his superb talents as a storyteller. Among his principal works are *The Magic Mountain* (1924), which is considered not only a masterpiece but a major contribution to world literature; *Doctor Faustus,* a postwar novel; and *Joseph and His Brothers,* a series of four novels.

Prior to the Nazi takeover in Germany, Mann had believed that an artist should concern himself with spiritual matters and remain aloof from politics. Once the Nazis were in power, he changed his stance and became actively involved in politics as a defender of the free, creative life. The Nazi regime burnt his books and deprived him of his German citizenship.

In 1938 Mann moved to the United States, but settled in Switzerland after World War II; there he died with the satisfaction of knowing his works had again found favor in his native country.

GUY DE MAUPASSANT (1850–1893)

Maupassant's childhood and youth were spent in Normandy, in northern France, the province which was to become a common setting for his short stories and novels. The author spent ten years studying under Gustave Flaubert, a close friend of the Maupassant family. From Flaubert, Maupassant learned the value of precision, conciseness, and accurate detail in his writing. "Ball of Fat," Maupassant's first published short story, was a great success. His literary activity lasted only about ten years (1880–1890), during which he wrote six novels and over three hundred short stories.

The atmosphere of Maupassant's works is usually somber and pessimistic. His characters are frequently mean, greedy, and vain men and women who are portrayed without moralizing. The peasants of Normandy, the Franco-Prussian War, and the petty bureaucrats of the French civil service were favorite subjects of Maupassant as well as those most familiar to him. In 1884 Maupassant began to suffer from nervous troubles, obsessions, and hallucinations. After attempting to commit suicide twice, he was committed to a private asylum where he died in 1893.

MOLIÈRE (JEAN BAPTISTE POQUELIN) (1622–1673)

Molière was born of a prosperous Parisian family. In his youth he studied law, but his attraction to the theater led him to abandon law to form a theatrical company. Life in the company (called L'Illustre Theatre) was both exciting and difficult for him. Financial problems resulted in three stays in debtors' prison, and his satirical plays were continually in danger of misunderstanding and censorship.

Being a practical and diplomatic man, Molière did his best to counteract these difficulties by courting the favor of royalty. As director of a second theatrical company (the first one folded in 1644), he won the patronage of King Louis XIV. But in spite of this, he still had to face considerable opposition to *Tartuffe* and to a play called *Don Juan* on the grounds that they were offensive to religion.

All of Molière's plays reveal a rational mind and an unfailing sense of humor—directed at times even at himself. Two of his plays, *The School for Wives* and *The School for Husbands*, reflect Molière's own life in their theme of an aging husband married to a young wife (Molière married nineteen-year-old Armand Bejart when he was forty). His laughter is never malicious; it is aimed at human foibles grown excessive to the point of being ridiculous. This is evident from the titles of some of his best-known works: *The Romantic Ladies* (1659), *The Misanthrope* (1666), *The Miser* (1668), *The Bourgeois Gentleman* (1670), *The Hypochondriac* (1673).

Apart from his skill as a comic playwright, Molière was also known as a fine comic actor, and as a gentleman whom women found very attractive.

ALBERTO MORAVIA (1907–   )

Alberto Moravia, the son of an established Roman architect, was destined for a strict, formal education. But at the age of nine he contracted tuberculosis and spent the next eight years of his life in various European sanatoriums. Left to educate himself, Moravia read extensively, following his own inclinations, and often completed a novel a day. At sixteen he began work on a novel of his own and continued rewriting it when he was released from sanatorium life the next year. The book, a saga of middle-class corruption entitled *The Time of Indifference,* was published when Moravia was twenty and earned unrivaled popular acclaim in Italy.

By his mid-twenties Moravia was an established writer. He traveled extensively, living for periods in Paris, London, Peking, New York, and Athens. A number of Moravia's books were suppressed by Italy's Fascist dictator, Benito Mussolini. When the Germans invaded Italy in 1943, Moravia and a number of other Italian writers had to hide in the mountains.

After the war, Moravia's work was widely translated, bringing him international recognition. To date, he has completed ten novels, five volumes of short stories, a play, and a collection of essays. When an interviewer recently asked Moravia if he found himself writing less as he grew older, he replied, laconically, that he could not foresee a time when he would have nothing to say.

OVID (43 B.C.–17 or 18 A.D.)

Publius Ovidius Naso was born at Sulmo, northeast of Rome. Although he was offered a seat in the Senate, Ovid chose a career in literature. Most of his works depict the lives of rich and fashionable Romans during the last half of the reign of Augustus Caesar. Because of controversy provoked by some of his writings, Ovid was banished in 8 A.D. to the half-barbaric town of Tomi where, in spite of his many pleas for pardon, he remained until his death.

The author's greatest work was the fifteen books of *Metamorphoses*, a panorama of Greek mythology, recounting miraculous transformations ranging from the change of chaos to cosmos in the world to the tale of Julius Caesar's metamorphosis into a star. Ovid's work is characterized by its smoothness and variety of expression and description.

BENITO PÉREZ GALDÓS (1843 – 1920)

Pérez Galdós has been called the father of the modern Spanish novel. His output of nationally oriented fiction was prodigious: between 1870 and 1918 he completed seventy-seven novels and twenty-one plays, among them forty-six volumes of *National Episodes*. These *Episodes* were Pérez Galdós' attempt to re-create in fiction the history of nineteenth-century Spain. He became blind in 1912, however, so that the project had to be abandoned.

Most of Pérez Galdós' other novels deal with political and ethical themes. Some of his plays are dramatized versions of these novels, but none are considered as excellent as the narrative fiction. After 1897 Pérez Galdós was himself directly involved in Spanish politics (he entered Congress as a reform delegate), but his failing sight forced him to give up politics also.

Pérez Galdós has been praised for his accurate portrayal of the Spanish national spirit. Where his contemporaries were content to write of their own local areas, he saw and expressed Spain as a totality.

CEZAR PETRESCU (1892 – 1961)

Cezar Petrescu has made a valuable contribution to the development of the contemporary Rumanian novel: his work presents a broad picture of Rumanian society of the first half of the twentieth century. Petrescu began his career as a publicist and short-story writer. His published works include numerous articles printed in newspapers and reviews. Before his death, Petrescu was preparing to write a cycle of seven novels analyzing Rumanian society in the nineteenth century. Tolstoy, Balzac, Zola, and the Rumanian Mihail Sadoveanu were his literary models.

HEINZ PIONTEK (1925 –   )

Heinz Piontek has been living in West Germany since the war and at present resides in Munich. Besides his volumes of poetry, Piontek has published both short stories and criticism. *Die Furt,* his first group of poems, appeared in 1952 and was incorporated into a second book in 1956.

LUIGI PIRANDELLO (1867 – 1936)

Luigi Pirandello was born in Sicily when it was still a violent and primitive country. A candid and sensitive boy, Pirandello was appalled by the special privileges given the upper classes to which he belonged. He came to abhor the sham and hypocrisy he observed around him, a feeling that is clearly reflected in much of his writing.

In 1888 he left his native country to enroll in the German University of Bonn; while there he published several collections of verse. The novelist Luigi Capuana persuaded Pirandello to give up poetry for prose, and in 1893 he published his first book of stories.

In 1894 Pirandello married a girl of his father's choosing, Antonietta Portulano. After a period of time during which the family suffered severe financial reversals, Pirandello's wife became insane. Through the many years of her illness, which took the form of unreasoning jealousy,

Pirandello lived with her and cared for her; and in the midst of this personal grief he continued to write.

In his early stages as an author Pirandello showed an interest in regionalism, particularly in re-creating the manners and customs of his native Sicily. As he developed, the use of local color, while remaining a part of his writing, became secondary to introspective analysis. He frequently directed attention to the realities that lie beneath appearance. The works of his later period are deeply concerned with death, insanity, and jealousy —themes drawn from his own tormented life.

Though Pirandello tried his hand at most types of literature, it was as a playwright that he gained a lasting reputation. The most noted works of Pirandello include *Six Characters in Search of an Author* and *Henry IV* sometimes called the first play "of the absurd." The mood of the absurd drama is anticipated in other works such as *Right You Are If You Think You Are, Each in His Own Way,* and *The Man with the Flower in His Mouth.*

Pirandello was awarded the Nobel Prize for Literature in 1934.

SALVATORE QUASIMODO (1901 – 1968)

Salvatore Quasimodo was relatively unknown outside of Italy when he was awarded the Nobel Prize for Literature in 1959. Although born in rural Sicily, Quasimodo early decided upon a technical career and went to Rome to complete his studies in engineering. For the next ten years he traveled throughout Italy, working on various projects for the Italian government, while devoting his extra hours to poetry.

The experience of World War II radically transformed Quasimodo. The pure, serene, detached mood of his early work was supplanted by a total engagement in crisis and struggle, set in language that was direct and concrete. It was this later work, dedicated to the theorem that the ultimate concern of poetry is reality, that brought Quasimodo recognition from the Nobel Academy and from the world.

JEAN-PAUL SARTRE (1905–1980)

Jean-Paul Sartre spent his formative years in the Paris home of his maternal grandfather, Professor Charles Schweitzer, a bookish, bourgeois patriarch, half-scholar and half-buffoon. Looking back on this time, Sartre once wrote, "Docile by virtue of circumstance, by taste, and by custom, I came to rebellion later only because I carried submission to an extreme."

In 1938 Sartre was a professor of philosophy when the publication of his first two fictional works, "The Wall" and *Nausea,* catapulted him into the avant-garde of French letters. He spent the war years spearheading the underground Resistance Movement in France, about which he later wrote: "Every instant we lived the full meaning of that banal little phrase, 'All men are mortal.' The choice that each of us made of his life and his being was a genuine choice because it could have been expressed in the form, 'Rather death than . . . .'"

This was the most intensely productive period of Sartre's career. He wrote his two most famous plays, *The Flies* and *No Exit,* completed the first novel, *The Age of Reason,* in a proposed tetralogy called *Roads to Freedom,* and published his seven-hundred-page philosophical tome, *Being and Nothingness,* which relates man's condition to the basic tenet of existentialism: that there is no innate human nature, but only man, vulnerable, conscious, existing, and continually redefining himself in action.

Sartre had written only plays and essays

since 1949, concentrating since 1960 upon completing his autobiography. In 1964 he politely declined the Nobel Prize for Literature, fearing, with appropriate irony, that it might transform him into an institution. On his 70th birthday he declared his writing career over; he was nearly blind.

IGNAZIO SILONE (1900–1978)

Ignazio Silone (pseudonym for Secondo Tranquilli) was born in the little Italian town of Pescina dei Marsi, Abruzzi. At an early age he became involved in the peasants' resistance to the inroads of Fascism, and has remained actively concerned with the ethical and political problems of which he writes. As a result of his anti-Fascist activities, Mussolini exiled him from Italy after the march on Rome in 1922. Silone returned in 1925, however, a militant Communist and anti-Fascist; and although he eventually came to renounce Communism (a change clearly reflected in his novels), he continued to work for social and political reforms.

All of Silone's novels express his concern for mankind and his humanitarian ideals. These novels include: *Fontamara* (1930), *Bread and Wine* (1937), *The Seed Beneath the Snow* (1940), and *A Handful of Blackberries,* which is particularly critical of the Communist system.

LEO TOLSTOY (1828–1910)

Leo Tolstoy's journals testify to the ferment of a life which was, outwardly, lavished with good fortune. Born into the Russian aristocracy, heir to a wealthy estate, heroic in battle, celebrated in literature, father of a large and thriving family, favored with good health and a long life, Tolstoy was, nevertheless, cease-lessly tormented by what he deemed the inadequacy of his goals and achievements.

As a young count, Tolstoy dedicated himself to the betterment of the peasants on his estate; but his youthful idealism was continually dissipated by sprees of compulsive gambling in the Russian capital. In 1851 he despaired of making progress against familiar temptations and rode off to join his brother in the army of the Caucasus.

While an officer in the artillery, Tolstoy witnessed the bloody seige of Sevastopol during the Crimean War (1855 – 1856). He recorded his impressions in a series of articles published under the title *Sevastopol Sketches*. The critical acclaim afforded these pieces drew Tolstoy from the military into the circle of St. Petersburg literati. Soon tiring of their intellectual niceties, Tolstoy again sought refuge with the peasants on his beloved estate.

His marriage in 1862 brought Tolstoy, for a time, the simple productive family life he craved. It enabled him to devote six years, 1863 – 1869, to the research and writing of his romantic epic *War and Peace*. But literary success and the growth of his family drew Tolstoy back into the aristocratic society he alternately embraced and reviled. This ambivalent attitude was a major theme in his next novel, *Anna Karenina,* written in the years 1873 – 1877.

Tolstoy underwent a profound spiritual crisis in 1879 which he recorded in his *Confession.* He resolved to follow a code of fundamental Christianity rooted in the simplicity of peasant life. Yet he found himself, as always, quick to point the way but slow to follow. The anguish he felt over this failure adds vigor to the best literature of his later years: *The Death of Ivan Ilyitch* (1886), *The Kreutzer Sonata* (1891), and *Resurrection* (1899).

One night, at the age of eighty-two, dressed in peasant clothes, Tolstoy fled from the privileged life on his estate which, he felt, made hypocrisy of all his ideals. A few days later he died at a remote railway station, in search of a peace which remained forever distant.

GIOVANNI VERGA (1840–1922)

Giovanni Verga wrote fashionable and popular novels for over fifteen years, but it was not until he turned back to his native Sicily and found subject matter in the lives of the peasants he had known as a youth that he produced his greatest works. Verga became a master of realism, vividly expressing the style and customs of the Sicilian peasants. Much of his writing is concerned with the unrelieved struggles of daily life in which man is the inevitable victim of circumstances.

"Cavalleria Rusticana," Verga's tale of passion and violence, was dramatized in 1884 and was later used as the libretto for the Mascagni opera of the same name. Verga's greatest fame came from *The House by the Medlar Tree,* a novel of Sicilian fishermen continually defeated in their struggle for existence.

ANDREI VOZNESENSKY (1933–   )

Andrei Voznesensky is considered one of the pioneers in the effort to free Russian poetry from the strictures placed on it during the Stalin era. Voznesensky was born in Moscow, where he now lives with his wife, Zoya, an author and literary critic. As a boy, Voznesensky enjoyed reading and writing verse, some of which he mailed to Boris Pasternak, whose poetry had already taken firm root in the boy's mind.

Because his early interests also included painting and drawing, he enrolled in the Moscow Architectural Institute in 1951. Upon graduating from the Institute, he became an architect and poet simultaneously.

The first published poems of Voznesensky appeared in 1958 in *Literary Gazette,* an organ of the Union of Soviet Writers. His first two books, *Mosaic* and *Parabola,* were published in 1960. His next book to be published was *I Write As I Love,* 1962, followed by *The Three Cornered Pear,* composed after a brief tour of the United States. "To B. Akhmadulina" reflects Voznesensky's concern with the poet as a man of special calling.

In discussing the role of the poet, Voznesensky has said, ". . . When a man writes he feels his prophetic mission in the world. The task of the Russian poet today is to look deep inside man."

YEVGENY YEVTUSHENKO (1933–   )

Yevgeny Yevtushenko is one of the most widely publicized Russian writers of the last decade. He was born into an era of Russian history characterized by the repressions and political purges of Joseph Stalin. He came of age on the streets of Moscow when all of Russia was impoverished by World War II. In 1949 Yevtushenko, at the age of sixteen, had quit school and was hopeful of a career playing professional soccer, when a poem of his was published on the sports page of a Moscow newspaper. Insignificant though the event seemed, it brought Yevtushenko the help and encouragement of older Russian intellectuals. In 1953, when Russia underwent a cultural thaw after the death of Stalin, Yevtushenko emerged in his poetry as a spokesman for the liberal ideals of Russia's youth.

During the 1960's Yevtushenko traveled extensively outside of Russia. It was on a tour of the United States that Yevtushenko visited Alaska, the setting of his "Cemetery of Whales." Yevtushenko's unguarded candor with the press during this period brought him political animosity both in and outside of Russia, but the integrity of his poetry earned him friendship beyond ideological bounds.

GLOSSARY OF LITERARY TERMS

Words in italics indicate other entries listed in the Glossary. They are italicized only the first time they appear within an entry.

ABSURD, a term used by modern existential writers to describe what they consider to be the meaninglessness of life in today's world: an absurd world is one which is without absolutes, such as virtue and justice, and which confers no dignity on the state of being human. (See *existentialism*.)

ACT, one of the major divisions of a play; it usually marks a stage in the development of the *action*. In the ancient Greek and Roman plays, the action could generally be divided into five stages of dramatic development: *exposition*, complication, *climax*, falling action, and *catastrophe* or *denouement*. The actual division of a play into five acts, which came later, was an attempt to formally indicate this basic *structure*. Modern playwrights, however, have come to divide their plays according to their own unique structure rather than attempting to follow this abstract pattern.

ACTION, the happenings in a work of fiction.

ADAPTATION, the redoing of a literary work to fit another *genre* or audience. For example, many novels, such as *War and Peace,* have been adapted for the movies; Chaucer's *Canterbury Tales* has been adapted for the reading of children.

ALLEGORY, a narrative in which characters, *action,* and sometimes *setting* represent abstract concepts or moral qualities to form a consistent pattern of meaning. These representations are unlike *symbols* in that they involve one-to-one relationships rather than complex and multileveled ones.

ALLUSION, a brief, often indirect, reference to a well-known person, event, story, or work of art. An allusion is used to evoke associations which enrich the meaning of the passage in which it occurs.

AMBIGUITY, the expression of an idea in such a way that more than one meaning is suggested. When ambiguity is deliberate and effective, it enriches the meaning of the passage in which it occurs; when it is accidental or ineffective, the meaning is simply blurred.

ANACHRONISM, the error of placing something out of its proper time period, for example, the appearance of a telephone in a play set during the eighteenth century.

ANALOGY, a comparison made between two, frequently dissimilar, items or situations in order to provide insight into the nature of one or both of them.

ANTAGONIST, a character who stands directly opposed to the *protagonist*. He is often the villain.

ANTI-HERO, a kind of *protagonist* frequently found in modern, existential literature. He lacks the conventionally heroic qualities of nobility, courage, and dedication to a cause; he is frequently an outsider who passively observes the futile lives of those about him. (See *hero, romantic hero*.)

ARCHETYPE, an image, story-pattern, or character type which recurs frequently enough in literature to be recognizable and to evoke strong, often unconscious, associations in the reader. For example, many of the character types in fairy tales are archetypal: the wicked witch, the enchanted prince, the sleeping beauty, and the fairy godmother are all widely dispersed throughout the literature, and turn up again, in slightly different forms, in adult fiction.

ATMOSPHERE, the prevailing emotional aura of a literary work; for example, it may be fanciful, bleak, violent, gay. This is achieved in part by the handling of *setting;* but character, *dialogue,* and *action* also contribute to it.

BALLAD, a type of verse which has been passed on in the oral tradition. Ballads were originally designed to be sung. They usually tell a story in a terse, simple style which employs a great deal of *dialogue* and uses repetition for stress and impact. (See *literary ballad*.)

BLANK VERSE, unrhymed iambic pentameter, ten-syllable lines with five unstressed syllables alternating with five stressed syllables. An unstressed syllable begins the line.

CATASTROPHE, the ending of a *tragedy*, where the *conflict* is resolved and the actions resulting from the *climax* are completed. *Denouement* is a synonym for *catastrophe*, but the former is a more general term that can be applied to plays other than tragedies.

CATHARSIS, a word used by Aristotle in his *Poetics* to describe the desired effect of *tragedy*, the "purgation" of the emotions of pity and fear; that is, in feeling pity and fear for the *tragic hero*, the viewer's own emotional tensions are released and temporarily resolved.

CHARACTERIZATION, the *techniques* used by an author in portraying his characters. These include: (1) direct description, (2) the character's speech, (3) the depiction of the character's actions, (4) the depiction of the character's emotions and thoughts. The extent to which any one of these techniques is used depends largely on the *genre* and *point of view* of the work and on the *style* of the author.

CHORUS, a group of actors, speaking in unison, whose purpose is to comment on the *action* of the play, thereby aiding the audience in interpreting this *action*. The device originated with Greek drama, but it has also been employed by some modern playwrights, such as T. S. Eliot. Where a chorus is not employed, it is common for one or more individual characters in a play to take over this "choric function."

CLASSICAL TRAGEDY, the tragedies of ancient Greece and Rome; those dealing with Greek and Roman subjects; and those written according to the "rules" of tragic drama derived from Aristotle. Such classically constructed plays enjoyed a great revival in the seventeenth and eighteenth centuries. (See *drama*, *tragedy*.)

CLIMAX. As a term of dramatic structure, this refers to the decisive point in a play, where the *action* changes course and begins to resolve itself. The word is also used to describe the point of highest emotional intensity in a play. The two climaxes—technical and emotional—do not always coincide. (See *act*.)

COMEDY, a play with a happy ending written to amuse the audience. It has generally been thought that comic writing appeals more to the intellect while *tragedy* appeals more to the emotions. As a result, the comic mode has often been used to "instruct" the audience about the follies of certain social conventions and human foibles. In tragedy, one is supposedly too caught up in the fate of the *hero* to be able to view his state objectively. Thus, what one learns from tragic writing is intuitive rather than rational. (See *satire*.)

CONFLICT, the struggle that grows out of the interplay between two opposing forces, a central element in most *plots*. The four basic kinds of conflict are (1) a man against another man, (2) a man against nature, (3) a man against society, (4) two elements within a man struggling for mastery.

CONNOTATION, the emotional associations surrounding a word, as opposed to its strict, dictionary meaning. (See *denotation*, *diction*.)

CRITICISM, the analysis of works of literature for the purpose of understanding and evaluating them. Criticism need not always involve a judgment, however; it is sometimes confined to *explication*. (See *explication*.)

DENOTATION, the strict dictionary meaning of a word as opposed to its emotional associations. (See *connotation*, *diction*.)

DENOUEMENT. See *act*, *catastrophe*.

DIALOGUE, the conversation between two or more people represented in a literary work. Dialogue can serve many purposes, among them (1) *characterization* (of those speaking and spoken of), (2) *exposition*, (3) the creation of *mood*, (4) the advancement of *plot*, (5) the development of a *theme*, (6) a commentary on the *action*.

DICTION, the particular choice of words made in a literary work. The best choice always considers both the connotative and the denotative meanings of a word, and how these are relevant to the context. Level or type of usage is another important consideration in a writer's choice of diction. Although the four traditional levels—formal, informal, colloquial, and slang—have blurred considerably in recent times, it is still true that various kinds of language remain appropriate to particular speakers, audiences, and *topics*. The writer must be aware of all these factors in order to choose his words as effectively as possible. (See *style*.)

DRAMA, a story told by means of characters speaking *dialogue*. Drama first developed out of the religious ceremonies of the ancient Greeks—*comedy* from the rites of fertility, and *tragedy* from the rites dealing with life and death. (See *comedy, tragedy*.)

DRAMATIC IRONY. See *irony*.

DRAMATIC POINT OF VIEW. See *point of view*.

ELEGY, generally, a traditional poetic form that treats of death, or some other grave topic, in a formal, philosophical way. In its Greek and Latin origins, the elegy dealt with a variety of subjects and was distinguished primarily by the use of a particular *meter*.

EPIGRAM, a short, pointed or witty saying; a short poem ending in a witty or clever turn of thought.

EPISODE, an incident in the course of a *plot* which has a unity of its own. It is sometimes used to describe a story occurring within a story, which does nothing to advance the action of the latter.

EXISTENTIALISM, a term used to describe a trend in modern thinking, which is frequently evident in modern literature. The existentialist stresses man's free will in a universe he sees as without meaning or values, but he insists on man's responsibility to make his own meaning and to assert his own values. However, even though man is seen as morally responsible, his position as a moral being is *absurd*, because his commitment is gratuitous and without any ultimate reward. The existentialist distrusts the traditional ways of determining right from wrong—systems of philosophy, organized religion, social convention—because he regards these as petrified forms which falsify an intensely complicated real world. Some important literary figures often considered existential are: Jean-Paul Sartre, Albert Camus, Eugene Ionesco, Franz Kafka, and Fernando Arrabal. (See *absurd, theater of the absurd*.)

EXPLICATION, the explanation of a literary text derived from close reading and careful internal analysis. (See *criticism*.)

EXPOSITION, the beginning of a work of fiction, wherein the author sets the *atmosphere* and *tone*, and provides the reader with the information he will need in order to understand the unfolding of the *plot*.

EXTENDED METAPHOR, a comparison that is used throughout an entire work, or a large portion of it. (See *figurative language*.)

FABLE, a brief tale, in which the characters are often animals, told to point out a *moral* truth.

FANTASY, a work which takes place in an unreal world, concerns incredible characters, or employs physical and scientific principles not yet discovered. It may be used for its own sake as a source of amusement, or it may be a *technique* employed for some other end, for example, to express a comment on society (as in *satire*).

FARCE, a type of *comedy* which depends for its effect on outlandish situations rather than on witty *dialogue, plot,* and character.

FICTION, writing drawn from the imagination of a writer rather than from actual fact.

FIGURATIVE LANGUAGE, a writer's use of words in such a way as to attempt to restore vitality and freshness to them. He achieves this by departing from their common, dulled meanings to gain renewed meaning through imaginative transformations. These transformations are classified as the various *figures of speech:* for example, a *metaphor* or *simile* equates two unlike things; a *personification* changes the nature of ("humanizes") a thing; a hyperbole can either exalt or diminish something through exaggeration. Figures of speech which depend on an actual change in the meaning of a word are called tropes (e.g., *metaphor*).

FIGURE OF SPEECH. See *figurative language*.

FLASHBACK, an interlude in the unfolding of a *plot* that shows something that occurred prior to the story.

FOIL, a character whose main function is to contrast with and therefore set off another character. (See *characterization*.)

FORESHADOWING, a hint given to the reader of what is to come. Foreshadowing helps to sustain interest by providing suspense.

FRAME-STORY, a story which encloses another story as a "frame."

FREE VERSE, a type of poetry which differs from conventional verse forms in being "free" from a fixed pattern of *meter* (the regular occurrence of stressed and unstressed syllables) and rhyme. However, the writer of free verse is not totally free: he must attempt to achieve significant rhythmic effects which support the meaning of his words by exploiting all of the sound possibilities of language. These include *syntax* and *tempo* as well as meter and rhyme, which he uses deliberately rather than consistently. Successful poems in free verse, while they do not have regular meter, do have *rhythm,* a looser kind of patterning based on repetition, regular recurrence of pauses, and *parallel* grammatical structure among groups of lines in the poem.

FUNCTIONAL, a term applied to elements in a work which are effectively related to other elements or to the unity of the work as a whole.

GENRE, a form or type of literary work. For example, the *novel,* the short story, and the poem are all genres. The term is a very loose one, however, so that subheadings under these three would themselves also be called genres, e.g., the picaresque novel, the tale, the epic poem.

HERO, the chief male character in an imaginative work. Since in popular use the word also connotes a person with certain noble qualities, the more neutral term *protagonist* is preferred.

HEROINE, the chief female character in an imaginative work, the female *protagonist.* (See *hero.*)

IMAGERY, the sensory details in a literary work. They provide vividness and immediacy; and they tend to evoke in the reader a complex of emotional suggestions which abstract language does not. Some critics feel that a study of recurring images (for example, images of decay in *Hamlet*) can provide great insight into a literary work and unearth meanings of which even the author was unaware. Although figures of speech are sometimes images, the term *image* includes literal details as well as figurative ones. (See *figurative language.*)

IRONY, a term used to describe any situation where two meanings or interpretations are at odds. In *verbal irony* the actual meaning of a statement is different, often opposite, from what the statement literally says, for example, to describe a dull book as "fascinating." Obviously, tone of voice is a great aid in conveying and understanding verbal irony; and one who employs the device in writing must attempt to compensate for the absence of tone of voice. *Irony of situation* refers to an occurrence which is contrary to what is expected or appropriate. It can have either tragic or comic implications, depending on the seriousness of the consequences. For example, a singer with laryngitis may be comic; a singer with throat cancer is certainly tragic; but both are ironic. The term *dramatic irony* describes a situation where one or more characters in a literary work (generally a play) are unaware of a significant fact known by the audience or reader.

IRONY OF SITUATION. See *irony.*

LITERARY BALLAD, a *ballad* with a known author who has used this traditional form deliberately in order to achieve the feeling of folk art. (See *ballad.*)

LOCAL COLOR, writing which intends primarily to portray the speech, customs, and *setting* of a particular geographical region.

MELODRAMA, a play with a sensational *plot* and stereotyped "good" and "bad" characters, which depends for its effect on the stock emotional responses of the audience.

METAPHOR. See *figurative language.*

METER, the patterns of stressed and unstressed syllables used in poetry. (See *free verse.*)

MICROCOSM, literally, "little world," an object or a situation which reflects, in miniature, a pattern implicit in the world as a whole.

MONOLOGUE, an extended speech given by one speaker.

MOOD, the prevailing emotional aura of a literary work. (See *atmosphere.*)

MORAL, the lesson taught in a work such as a *fable*. A moral differs from a *theme* in that the former suggests that the reader act in a certain way; a theme may be simply a *topic* or a general attitude involved in a work of literature.

MOTIF, a character, incident, or idea that recurs frequently in various works or in various parts of the same work. The term comes from its use in music and art, where it is also used to refer to recurring elements.

MOTIVATION, the portrayal of circumstances

and aspects of personality which make a character's actions and reactions appear believable or inevitable to the reader.

MYTH, a traditional anonymous tale, connected with a people's folk beliefs, which attempts to express some interpretation of an element of the natural world. Although traditional myths are nonliterary, many modern writers, who see myths as expressions of profound truths, have self-consciously employed these primitive materials to express their own perceptions of the modern world. T. S. Eliot's *The Waste Land* is a good example of a modern writer's use of myth. (See *archetype*.)

NARRATOR, the teller of a story, usually either an anonymous voice used by the author, or a character in the story itself. When this teller appears unaware of certain obvious implications of the tale he is telling, he is called a naive narrator. (See *point of view*.)

NATURALISM, a type of writing that depicts events as rigidly determined by the forces of heredity and environment. The world described tends to be a bleak and hopeless place.

NOVEL, a long work of prose fiction dealing with characters, situations, and *settings* that imitate those of real life.

NOVELLA, a brief tale, especially the early tales of French and Italian writers. These early novellas were a popular source of plot material for later English writers, and they are considered to be the form which engendered the later *novel*. The term *novella* is also used as a synonym for *novelette*, or short novel.

OBJECTIVE, self-effacing, approached without personal bias or comment. An objective writer is one who attempts to show what happens without any attempt at interpretation. (See *point of view*.)

OMNISCIENT POINT OF VIEW. See *point of view*.

ONE-DIMENSIONAL CHARACTER, a "flat" character, often comic, who is intended to represent a single trait of personality, for example, jealousy, frivolity, greed. (See *characterization*.)

PARABLE, a brief fictional work which concretely illustrates an abstract idea; for example, Christ's parable of the prodigal son. It differs from a *fable* in that the characters in it are generally people rather than

animals; and it differs from an *allegory* in that its characters do not necessarily represent abstract qualities. (See *allegory, fable*.)

PARADOX, a statement that seems to be self-contradictory but which is actually true, for example, "birth is the beginning of death."

PARALLEL, a likeness, usually in pattern or structure (of a sentence, character, situation, etc.).

PARALLELISM, the arrrangement of the parts of some grammatical unit (phrase, clause, sentence, paragraph) so that it reflects in form and idea a coordinate unit. For example, the sentence, "I came, I saw, I conquered" consists of three *parallel* independent clauses.

PATHOS, the quality of literature which evokes pity. (See *Medea,* Interpretation question 4, page 125.)

PERSONIFICATION, the representation of ideas, animals, or objects as human beings, by endowing them with human qualities. (See *figurative language*.)

PLOT, a series of happenings in a work of fiction that progress from a *conflict* of opposing forces to a settlement of the conflict. (See *act*.)

POINT OF VIEW, the relation assumed between the teller of a story and the characters in it. The teller, or *narrator,* may himself be a character; or he may be a remote and anonymous voice to be identified, more or less, with the author. A writer who describes, in the third person, both the thoughts and the actions of his characters is said to use the *omniscient point of view;* one who describes only what can be seen, like a newspaper reporter, is said to use the *dramatic point of view*. A narrator's attitude toward his subject is also capable of much variation: it can range from one of apparent indifference to one of extreme conviction and feeling. When a narrator appears to have some bias regarding his subject, it becomes especially important to determine whether he and the author are to be regarded as the same person. (See *narrator, objective, tone*.)

PROP, short for *property*, any kind of movable piece used in staging a play.

PROPAGANDA, writing which directly advocates a certain doctrine as the solution to some social or political problem.

PROTAGONIST, the leading character in a work of fiction. (See *hero*.)

PROTEST LITERATURE, works of fiction designed primarily to expose the unfairness, inefficiency, or immorality of some social or political situation; propaganda. Since it must be *topical*, protest literature often loses its relevance as time passes.

REALISM, the tendency in certain works of literature to stress the limitations that everyday living imposes on humanity, and to show how these limitations affect the nature of life. In this sense, realistic fiction itself must involve a distortion of the world in order to emphasize one aspect of it. "Pure" realism, in the sense of a photographic copy of the world, has never proved to make good fiction.

RHYTHM, the patterns found in both poetry and prose produced by a recurrence of types of sentence structure, sounds, images, *themes*, and feelings.

ROMANTIC HERO, the traditional hero-figure who possesses great courage, a strong sense of dedication, and other admirable qualities. Although often a rebel (e.g., Robin Hood), he is clearly on the side of good and invites our unqualified admiration. (See *hero, anti-hero*.)

ROMANTICISM, a tendency opposite that of *realism* in that it stresses man's glory and freedom rather than his limitations. Generally speaking, romantic writers take an optimistic view of individuals; they prefer to stress the past over the present, and to dwell on the exciting, the exotic, and the beautiful.

SATIRE, the *technique* which employs wit to ridicule a subject, usually some social institution or human foible. The satirist's intention, however, is not simply to deride, but to inspire reform. (See *comedy*.)

SCENE, in *drama*, a division of an *act* which may indicate (1) a stage in the *action*, (2) a shift in place, (3) a change in the number of actors on the stage. However, the criteria for determining scenic division remains very loose. In the *novel*, the term is used to refer to a portion of the book which the writer has constructed as a scene in drama, first describing the *setting* and the characters, and then presenting their conversation and actions.

SETTING, the literal place and time in which the *action* of a work of fiction occurs, as opposed to the emotional aura evoked by the work. (See *atmosphere, mood*.)

SIMILE. See *figurative language*.

STAGE DIRECTION, a dramatist's written direction as to how scenes are to be set, how lines are to be spoken, and how his play is to be produced. The number of lines devoted to such directions can range from none at all to a number exceeding that of the *dialogue*.

STANZA, a division of a poem consisting of two or more lines. Generally, each stanza will be the same length and take the same metrical form and rhyme scheme. However, some poems include stanzas of varying lengths and forms.

STREAM OF CONSCIOUSNESS, the depiction of a character's flow of thought without any apparent attempt at clarification. (See *point of view*.)

STRUCTURE, the pattern, outline, or "blueprint" which underlies a finished work of literature. In the *drama*, for example, the traditional five-part division is an aid to determining a play's structure (see *act*). An analysis of structure is an important aspect of *explicating* and understanding a work of fiction.

STYLE, the distinctive handling of language by a given author, involving the specific choices he makes with regard to *diction, syntax, figurative language*, etc. These choices are determined by a combination of the author's personality and the idea he wishes to express with the possibilities offered him by the language he is using. (See *diction, tone*, Comparative question 4 in The Group, page 445.)

SURREALISM, the literary *technique* of presenting dreamlike sequences to express some truth about the unconscious.

SYMBOLISM, the use, in literature, of objects, characters, and situations which represent something beyond themselves. Symbols differ from *images* in that they suggest another level of meaning beyond the literal "picture" evoked by an image. Some symbols suggest the same meaning to almost all readers who share a common tradition, for example, the heart as a symbol for love; others derive much of their meaning from the context of the work in which they appear. Especially with this latter type, the real meaning of a symbol becomes a complex problem, which is sometimes capable of a number of possible solutions.

SYNTAX, sentence structure.

TECHNIQUE, the craftsmanship used by an author to give his work form and meaning. Also, a specific literary device, such as *symbolism* or *satire,* may be referred to as a technique.

TEMPO, rate of movement, speed.

TEXTURE, those elements which make up the details of a work of literature (for example, *images, motifs,* the writer's use of *diction* and *syntax*) apart from its basic *structure.*

THEATER OF THE ABSURD, a movement in twentieth-century drama which seeks to depict the unsettled state of modern man through the use of various experimental *techniques.* These include eccentric *settings* evoking a sense of madness, distorted language, and seemingly aimless plot structure. The value of the movement is a point of controversy, some critics affirming that the plays it engenders are too chaotic to be meaningful. Others defend the plays as accurate reflections of man's present chaotic state—his loss of a firm set of values and a sense of identity. Writers associated with the movement include Eugene Ionesco, Jean Cocteau, Franz Kafka, Samuel Beckett, and Luigi Pirandello. (See *absurd, existentialism.*)

THEME, a central idea developed in a work of fiction.

TONE, the attitude and feelings of an author expressed in a given work, as these may be inferred from what he says and how he says it. Since the written language cannot express tone in the sense of tone of voice, the author must rely instead on such things as word choice and arrangement to convey just that impression which he wishes to convey. Many of these choices are a natural result of the writer's personality and *style;* but others may be very deliberate and the result of considerable revision. (See *diction, style.*)

TOPIC, a subject that people think, talk, and write about.

TOPICAL FICTION, fiction which concerns a subject which is popular at the time it is written. Topical fiction thus frequently loses its appeal when its subject is no longer popular. (See *propaganda, protest literature.*)

TRAGEDY, a *drama* in which the *protagonist* (tragic hero) suffers disaster but in so doing attains heroic stature. The concept of tragic drama and the tragic hero necessarily alter with the values and tastes of the age in which the drama is written. However, almost any tragedy can be illuminated by viewing it in terms of the original Greek concept described by Aristotle: an *action* involving a noble man who, because of some "tragic flaw," makes a wrong decision which leads to an unhappy *catastrophe.* The experience, although disastrous, deepens the hero's insight into his own nature and destiny, and effects a *catharsis* in the audience. In the Middle Ages the term *tragedy* was broadened to include any fictional account of a man's fall from high to low fortune. During the Renaissance tragic drama became less rigidly constructed and formal in *tone:* scenes of comic relief and elements of sensationalism were introduced. Although classic formalism had a revival during the eighteenth century, this century also began to produce "domestic" tragedies about middle-class people, a trend which has continued and expanded. Contemporary tragedy frequently depicts middle- and low-class *heroes* and *heroines* thwarted by the twentieth-century counterparts of the Greek concept of destiny—heredity, environment, and various types of social oppression. (See *act, catharsis, catastrophe, classical tragedy, drama.*)

TRAGIC HERO. See *tragedy.*

VERBAL IRONY. See *irony.*

PRONUNCIATION KEY

The pronunciation of each word is shown just after the word, in this way: **ab bre vi ate** (ə brē/vē āt). The letters and signs used are pronounced as in the words below. The mark / is placed after a syllable with primary or heavy accent, as in the example above. The mark / after a syllable shows a secondary or lighter accent, as in **ab bre vi a tion** (ə brē/vē ā shən).

Some words, taken from foreign languages, are spoken with sounds that do not otherwise occur in English. Symbols for these sounds are given in the key as "foreign sounds."

a	hat, cap	o	hot, rock	ə represents:
ā	age, face	ō	open, go	a in about
ä	father, far	ô	order, all	e in taken
		oi	oil, voice	i in pencil
b	bad, rob	ou	house, out	o in lemon
ch	child, much			u in circus
d	did, red			

		p	paper, cup
e	let, best	r	run, try
ē	equal, be	s	say, yes
ėr	term, learn	sh	she, rush
		t	tell, it
		th	thin, both
f	fat, if	ŦH	then, smooth
g	go, bag		
h	he, how		

		u	cup, butter
i	it, pin	ù	full, put
ī	ice, five	ü	rule, move

j	jam, enjoy		
k	kind, seek	v	very, save
l	land, coal	w	will, woman
m	me, am	y	young, yet
n	no, in	z	zero, breeze
ng	long, bring	zh	measure, seizure

foreign sounds

Y as in French *du*. Pronounce (ē) with the lips rounded as for (ü).

à as in French *ami*. Pronounce (ä) with the lips spread and held tense.

œ as in French *peu*. Pronounce (ā) with the lips rounded as for (ō).

N as in French *bon*. The N is not pronounced, but shows that the vowel before it is nasal.

H as in German *ach*. Pronounce (k) without closing the breath passage.

The pronunciation key is from the *Thorndike-Barnhart Advanced Dictionary*, copyright 1974 by Scott, Foresman and Company.

INDEX OF AUTHORS AND TITLES

INDEX OF TRANSLATORS